McGraw-Hill

ELECTRICAL AND ELECTRONIC ENGINEERING SERIES

FREDERICK EMMONS TERMAN, *Consulting Editor*

ANTENNAS

McGraw-Hill
ELECTRICAL AND ELECTRONIC
ENGINEERING SERIES

FREDERICK EMMONS TERMAN, *Consulting Editor*

ANTENNAS

43

By
JOHN D. KRAUS, Ph.D.

PROFESSOR OF ELECTRICAL ENGINEERING
THE OHIO STATE UNIVERSITY

FIRST EDITION

NEW YORK   TORONTO   LONDON
McGRAW-HILL BOOK COMPANY, INC.
1950

ANTENNAS

86474

PREFACE

It is the purpose of this book to present the basic theory of antennas with emphasis on their engineering applications. An effort has been made to give a unified treatment of antennas from the electromagnetic theory point of view while keeping in mind the aspects of engineering importance.

. The principles given are basic and are applied to antennas for all frequencies. The first four chapters deal with the fundamental theory of point sources and of the antenna as an aperture. These are followed by three chapters on linear, loop, and helical antennas in that order. The theories of the biconical antenna and of the cylindrical antenna are then discussed. The self and mutual impedance of antennas and the theory of arrays of linear antennas are taken up in the next chapters, and these are followed by chapters on reflector-type antennas, slot, horn, complementary, lens, long wire antennas, and many other types. The final chapter describes methods and techniques of antenna measurements and includes a discussion of wave polarization. The Appendix has a number of useful tables for reference.

Antennas form the dominant theme of the book, and other subjects are placed in a subordinate position. For example, transmission lines are not considered per se but are discussed in connection with impedance measurements and matching arrangements for antennas.

The book is an outgrowth of lectures given in recent years by the author in a course on antennas at The Ohio State University. The material is suitable for use at about senior or first-year graduate level and is more than sufficient in amount for a one-semester course, allowing considerable latitude as to the subjects treated. Problem sets are given at the end of each chapter. As preparation for the course on antennas, it is desirable that the student have a knowledge of elementary electromagnetic theory, transmission lines and wave guides, and vector analysis.

"Antennas" has been written to serve not only as a textbook but also, it is hoped, as a reference book for the practicing engineer and scientist. As an aid to those seeking additional information on a particular subject, the book is well documented with footnote references. Some of the material in the book is published here for the first time. This refers particularly to portions of the treatments on point sources and on helical antennas.

v

An aim throughout the book has been to approach a new subject gradually. For example, wherever possible, simple special cases are considered first, and then with these as background the general case is developed.

The rationalized mks system of units is employed. This system, which is rapidly coming into almost universal use, has many practical advantages. A very complete table of units in this system is included in the Appendix.

Although great care has been exercised, some errors in the text or figures will inevitably occur. Anyone finding them would do me a great service to call them to my attention so that they can be corrected in subsequent printings.

I wish to express my appreciation to many of my associates and students for helpful suggestions. In particular I greatly appreciate the comments and criticisms of Professor John N. Cooper, of the Department of Physics, and of Professors Victor H. Rumsey and Sidney Bertram, of the Department of Electrical Engineering, at The Ohio State University.

JOHN D. KRAUS

COLUMBUS, OHIO
August, 1950

CONTENTS

CONTENTS

CHAPTER 1

INTRODUCTION

1-1. Definitions. A radio *antenna*[1] may be defined as the structure associated with the region of transition between a guided wave and a free-space wave, or vice versa.

In connection with this definition it is also useful to consider what is meant by transmission line and by resonator. A *transmission line* is a device for transmitting or guiding radio-frequency energy from one point to another. Usually it is desirable to transmit the energy with a minimum of attenuation, heat and radiation losses being as small as possible. This means that while the energy is being conveyed from one point to another it is confined within the transmission line or to the vicinity of the line. Thus, the wave transmitted along the line is one-dimensional in that it does not spread out into space but follows along the line. From this general point of view the term transmission line includes not only coaxial and two-wire transmission lines but also hollow pipes, or *wave guides.*

A generator connected to an infinite, lossless transmission line produces a uniform traveling wave along the line. If the line is short-circuited, a standing wave appears because of interference between the incident and reflected waves. A standing wave has associated with it local concentrations of energy. If the reflected wave is equal to the incident wave, we have a pure standing wave. The energy concentrations in such a wave oscillate from entirely electric to entirely magnetic energy and back twice per cycle. Such energy behavior is characteristic of a resonant circuit, or *resonator.* (Although the term resonator, in its most general sense, may be applied to any device with standing waves, the term is usually reserved for devices with stored energy concentrations that are large compared with the inflow or outflow of energy.[2] When there are no internal con-

---

[1] In its zoological sense, an antenna is the feeler, or organ of touch, of an insect. According to usage in the United States the plural of "insect antenna" is "antennae," but the plural of "radio antenna" is "antennas." However, the usage in England makes no distinction, the plural of both "insect antenna" and "radio antenna" being "antennae."

[2] The ratio of the energy stored to that lost per cycle is proportional to the Q, or sharpness of resonance of the resonator.

1

ductors, as in a short-circuited section of wave guide, the device is called a *cavity resonator*.

As illustrations of these definitions, consider Fig. 1-1. A generator or

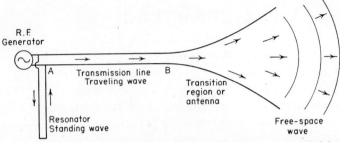

FIG. 1-1. The antenna is a region of transition between a wave guided by a transmission line and a free-space wave.

transmitter is connected to a two-wire transmission line AB. Assuming that the line is properly matched, it carries a single outward-traveling wave and behaves as a pure transmission line. At A there is a short-circuited section of line connected in parallel. This line has a standing wave and acts as a resonator or resonant line. Beyond B the transmission line spreads out gradually until the separation between conductors is many wavelengths. In this region the wave guided by the transmission line is radiated into a free-space wave. This region of the line acts as an antenna.

Let the transmission line now be connected to a dipole antenna as in

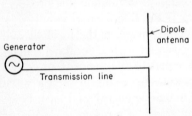

FIG. 1-2. Dipole antenna.

Fig. 1-2. The dipole acts as an antenna because it launches a free-space wave. However, it may also be regarded as a section of terminated transmission line (see Sec. 1-2). In addition, it exhibits many of the characteristics of a resonator, since energy reflected from the ends of the dipole gives rise to a standing wave on the antenna. Thus, a single device, in this case the dipole, exhibits simultaneously properties characteristic of an antenna, a transmission line, and a resonator.

The energy radiated by antennas oscillates at radio frequencies. The associated free-space waves range in wavelength from thousands of meters at the long-wave extreme to fractions of a centimeter at the short-wave extreme. The relation of radio waves to lengths in general is illustrated by the length chart of Fig. 1-3. Short radio waves and long infrared waves overlap into a twilight zone that may be regarded as belonging to both.

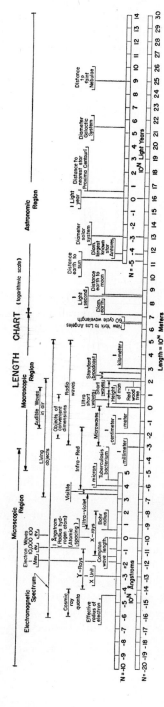

FIG. 1-3. Length chart. The main scale gives lengths in meters, the length being expressed by the exponent N where the length in meters equals 10^N. Thus, $N = \log_{10}$ (length). For example, 1 light-second $= 3 \times 10^8$ meters so that for this length, $N = \log_{10} 3 + 8 = 8.48$. Two auxiliary scales give lengths also in angstrom units and in light-years.

1-2. The Antenna as a Terminated Transmission Line.[1] According to

this analogy the space around an antenna may be separated into two regions: one next to the antenna known as the "antenna region" and one outside known as the "outer region." The boundary between the two regions is a sphere whose center is at the middle of the antenna and whose surface passes across the ends of the antenna. The relation of this "boundary sphere" to a symmetrical, biconical ½-wavelength antenna is shown in Fig. 1-4.

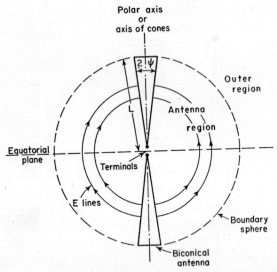

FIG. 1-4. Schelkunoff's biconical antenna with boundary sphere.

The wave caused by a very brief voltage pulse applied to the terminals travels outward with the electric field, or E lines, forming concentric circles as shown in Fig. 1-4. The magnetic field, or H lines, are normal to the E lines and are concentric with the axis of the cones. The field has no radial component. It is strictly transverse (TEM).[2] It is said that these fields belong to the principal, or zero-order, mode.

After a time $t = L/c$, where L equals the length of one cone and c equals the velocity of light, the pulse field reaches the boundary sphere. At the end of the cones there is an abrupt discontinuity, while at the equator there is none. Hence, there is a large reflection at the end of the cones, and little energy is radiated in this direction. On the other hand, at the

---

[1] S. A. Schelkunoff, "Electromagnetic Waves," D. Van Nostrand Company, Inc., New York, 1943, Chap. 11.

[2] TEM = Transverse Electro Magnetic.

equator the energy continues into the outer region without reflection, and radiation is a maximum in this direction.

The energy flow around a $\frac{1}{2}$-wavelength cylindrical dipole antenna is similar. This is indicated by the arrows in Fig. 1-5a. Most of the energy

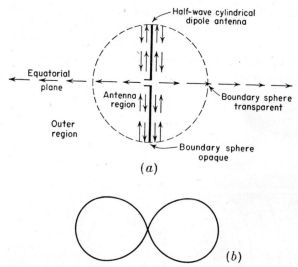

(a)

(b)

FIG. 1-5. Energy flow near a dipole antenna (a) and radiation field pattern (b).

guided from the terminals close to the antenna is reflected at the ends as though the boundary sphere were opaque. Energy traveling out in the equatorial plane, however, continues on into the outer region as though the boundary sphere were transparent. This explanation accounts in a qualitative way for the field pattern of the $\frac{1}{2}$-wavelength dipole shown in Fig. 1-5b.

The E lines of principal-mode fields must end on conductors and, hence, cannot exist in free space. The waves which can exist and propagate in free space are higher mode forms in which the E lines form closed loops. The principal-mode wave is called a zero-order wave, and higher order waves are of order 1 and greater. The configuration of the E lines of a first-order wave in the outer region is illustrated in Fig. 1-6. This wave has been radiated from a short dipole antenna. The wave started on the antenna as a principal-mode wave, has passed through the boundary sphere, and has been transformed.[1] The field has a radial component

[1]Some first-order mode is also present inside the antenna boundary sphere as a reflected wave. This and higher order modes may exist both inside and outside of the boundary sphere in such a way that there is continuity of the fields at the boundary sphere.

which is largest near the polar axis. At the equatorial plane the radial component is zero, and the E lines at this plane travel through the boundary sphere without change. Since the radial components of the field attenuate more rapidly than the transverse components, the radial field becomes negligible in comparison with the transverse field at a large distance from the antenna. Although the field at a large distance from the antenna is of a higher order type, the measurable components are only of the transverse type. To suggest the fact that the radial field components are weak and become negligible at large distances, the E lines in the polar region in Fig. 1-6 are dashed.

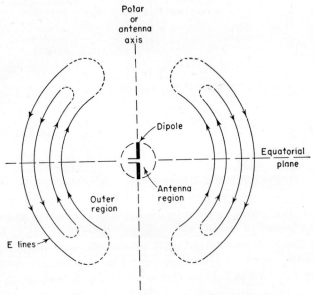

FIG. 1-6. Field configuration near dipole antenna.

The distinction between the fields at a large distance and those nearer to the antenna may be emphasized by subdividing the outer region into two regions, the one near the antenna called the "near field," or Fresnel region, and the one at a large distance called the "far field," or Fraunhofer region. The boundary between the two may be arbitrarily taken to be at a radius $R = 2L^2/\lambda$ as shown in Fig. 1-7. In the Fraunhofer region the measurable field components are transverse, and the shape of the field pattern is independent of the radius at which it is taken, while in the Fresnel region the radial field may be appreciable and the shape of the field pattern is, in general, a function of the radius.

Returning now to a further consideration of the biconical antenna, this type is particularly convenient in the transmission-line analogy because it has a constant characteristic impedance Z_0 given by

$$Z_0 = 120 \ln \cot \frac{\psi}{2} \qquad (1\text{-}1)^*$$

where ψ = one-half of the cone angle (see Fig. 1-4)

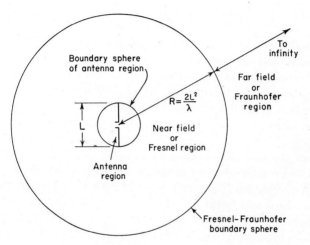

FIG. 1-7.   Antenna region, Fresnel region, and Fraunhofer region.

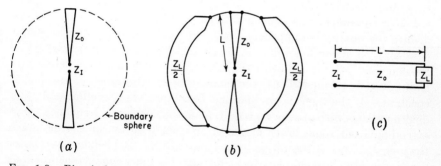

FIG. 1-8.   Biconical antenna with boundary sphere (a) and as a terminated transmission line (b) and (c).

According to Schelkunoff's theory the boundary sphere (Fig. 1-8a) may be replaced by an equivalent load impedance Z_L connected between the ends of the cones by zero impedance leads as suggested in the schematic

* This relation is derived in Chap. 8.

at (b). The effect of the end caps is here neglected. The equivalent transmission-line circuit is shown in Fig. 1-8c. If Z_L can be determined, the input impedance Z_I may be obtained by ordinary transmission-line relations for a line of characteristic impedance Z_0 and length L terminated in an impedance Z_L. Thus, the antenna has been replaced by an equivalent transmission line, the antenna acting as a matching section, or transformer, between the terminals and space. Based on this analogy, the general definition of an antenna in Sec. 1-1 may be specialized to the following: An antenna is a transformer (or matching section) between a two-terminal input and space or, in the receiving case, is a transformer between space and the terminals.

The reflected wave in the antenna region gives rise to standing waves and energy storage in this region. It is as though the boundary sphere forms a spherical shell resonator that reflects effectively in polar zones but not at all in the equatorial zone. In a $\frac{1}{2}$-wavelength dipole antenna the energy is stored at one instant of time in the electric field mainly near the ends of the antenna, while $\frac{1}{4}$ cycle later the energy is stored in the magnetic field mainly near the center of the antenna, or maximum current region. If the biconical antenna is made very thin, the reflection at the ends is increased and the stored energy in the antenna region is relatively large. However, the reflection at the ends of a biconical antenna of wide cone angle is less so that the stored energy is smaller. Thus, this antenna is less frequency-sensitive[1] than the thin one and is better suited for wide-band applications. It also follows that a thick cylindrical dipole is less frequency-sensitive than a thin dipole.

1-3. Shape-impedance Considerations.[2] It is possible in many cases to deduce the qualitative impedance behavior of an antenna from its shape. This may be illustrated with the aid of Fig. 1-9. At (a) a coaxial transmission line is flared out with the ratio of the conductor diameters D/d maintained constant. Thus, the characteristic impedance of the line is constant. If the taper is gradual and D is large where the line ends, this device radiates with little or no reflection on the line over a frequency range extending from some lower or cutoff frequency to an indefinitely high frequency. This is the ultimate in band width. By bending the outer conductor into a ground plane as at (b) with the inner conductor formed as shown, the band width is nearly as wide as for the type at (a).[3] Modifying

---

[1] Q is smaller.

[2] Chap. 1 by Andrew Alford, "Very High Frequency Techniques," by Radio Research Laboratory Staff, McGraw-Hill Book Company, Inc., New York, 1947.

[3] The wide-band characteristics of an antenna of the general appearance of (b) have been discussed by N. E. Lindenblad, Antennas and Transmission Lines at the Empire State Television Station, *Communications*, **21**, 10–14, 24–26, April, 1941.

this antenna to the conical type at (c) or cylindrical type at (d) further reduces the band width. The band width is still narrower for the thin stub antenna at (e) which represents an extreme to which the modification may be carried. If the type at (a) is regarded as the basic form, the thin type at (e) is the most degenerate form.

As we depart more from the basic type, the discontinuity in the line becomes more abrupt at what eventually becomes the junction of the ground plane and transmission line. This discontinuity is caused by the change in the ratio D/d and results in some energy being reflected back

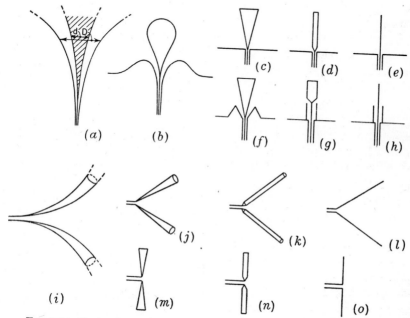

FIG. 1-9.   Derivation of thin wire antennas from basic broad-band types.

into the line. The discontinuity at the end of the antenna also becomes greater as the antenna becomes thinner. At some frequency the two reflections may compensate, but the band width of compensation is narrow. Antennas with large and abrupt discontinuities have large reflections and act as reflectionless transformers or matching-sections only over narrow frequency bands where the reflections cancel. Antennas with discontinuities that are small and gradual have small reflections and are, in general, relatively reflectionless transformers over wide frequency bands.

The antenna types at (f), (g), and (h), in Fig. 1-9 are similar to those shown above them except that the ground plane is modified into a sleeve.

In a similar way to that discussed for the coaxial types, the thin wire V antenna at (l) and the thin dipole at (o) may be derived by successive steps from a balanced two-wire transmission line with a constant characteristic impedance that is gradually flared out as suggested at (i). The types tend to be of progressively narrower band width as we proceed from left to right in the figure.

CHAPTER 2

POINT SOURCES

2-1. Introduction. Let us consider an antenna contained within a volume of radius b as in Fig. 2-1a. Confining our attention only to the far field of the antenna, we may make observations of the fields along an observation circle of large radius R. At this distance the measurable fields are entirely transverse, and the power flow, or Poynting vector, is entirely radial. It is convenient in many analyses to assume that the fields of the antenna are everywhere of this type. In fact, we may assume, by extrapolating inward along the radii of the circle, that the waves

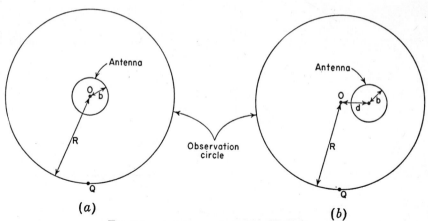

FIG. 2-1. Antenna and observation circle.

originate at a fictitious volumeless emitter, or *point source*, at the center O of the observation circle. The actual field variation near the antenna, or "near field," is ignored, and we describe the source of the waves only in terms of the "far field" it produces. Provided that our observations are made at a sufficient distance, any antenna, regardless of its size or complexity, can be represented in this way by a single point source.

Instead of making field measurements around the observation circle with the antenna fixed, the equivalent effect may be obtained by making the measurements at a fixed point Q on the circle and rotating the antenna

11

around the center O. This is usually the more convenient procedure if the antenna is small.

In Fig. 2-1a the center O of the antenna coincides with the center of the observation circle. If the center of the antenna is displaced from O, even to the extent that O lies outside the antenna as in Fig. 2-1b, the distance d between the two centers has a negligible effect on the field pattern at the observation circle provided $R \gg d$, $R \gg b$, and $R \gg \lambda$.

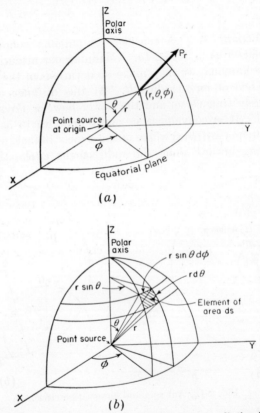

(a)

(b)

Fig. 2-2. Spherical coordinates for a point source of radiation in free space.

However, the phase patterns[1] will generally differ depending on d. If $d = 0$, the phase shift around the observation circle is usually a minimum. As d is increased, the observed phase shift becomes larger.

A complete description of the far field of a source requires a knowledge of the electric field as a function of both space and time. For many purposes, however, such a complete knowledge is not necessary. It may

[1] Phase variation around the observation circle.

be sufficient to specify merely the variation with angle of the power density[1] from the antenna. In this case the vector nature of the field is disregarded, and the radiation is treated as a scalar quantity. This is done in Sec. 2-2. The vector nature of the field is recognized in the discussion on the magnitude of the field components in Sec. 2-16. A complete description of an elliptically polarized field, for example, requires that the variation of the field components be known as a function of time. This may be conveniently accomplished by specifying one or two phase angles. Although the cases considered as examples in this chapter are hypothetical, they could be approximated by actual antennas.

/ 2-2. Power Patterns. Let a transmitting antenna in free space be represented by a point-source radiator located at the origin of the coordinates in Fig. 2-2. The radiated energy streams from the source in radial lines. The time rate of energy flow per unit area is the *Poynting vector*, or *power density*. The Poynting vector of a point source has only a radial component P_r with no components in either the θ or the ϕ directions ($P_\theta = P_\phi = O$). Thus, the magnitude of the Poynting vector, or power density, is equal to the radial component ($|\mathbf{P}| = P_r$).

A source that radiates energy uniformly in all directions is an *isotropic source*. For such a source the radial component P_r of the Poynting vector is independent of θ and ϕ. A graph of P_r at a constant radius as a function of either θ or ϕ is a Poynting-vector, or power-density, pattern but is usually called a *power pattern*. Referring to Fig. 2-2a, consider P_r

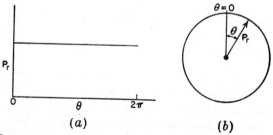

(a)　　　　　　　　　　　　　　　　　(b)

FIG. 2-3. (a) Rectangular power pattern of isotropic source. (b) Polar power pattern of isotropic source.

as a function of θ in the y-z plane ($\phi = \pm 90°$). The power pattern for the isotropic source is a straight line on a rectangular graph as shown in Fig. 2-3a or a circle on a polar graph as shown in Fig. 2-3b. In the polar graph the magnitude of the Poynting vector P_r is proportional to the length of the radius vector. The three-dimensional power pattern for an isotropic source is a sphere of which the circle of Fig. 2-3b is a cross section.

[1] Power per unit area.

Although the isotropic source is convenient in theory, it is not a physically realizable type. Even the simplest antennas have directional properties, that is, they radiate more energy in some directions than in others. In contrast to the isotropic source, they might be called *anisotropic* sources. As an example, the power pattern of such a source is shown in Fig. 2-4a.

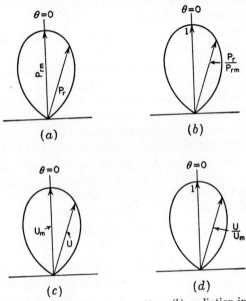

FIG. 2-4. Power pattern (a), relative power pattern (b), radiation-intensity pattern (c), and relative radiation-intensity pattern (d) for the same directional or anisotropic source. All patterns have the same shape. The relative power and radiation-intensity patterns (b and d) also have the same magnitude and, hence, are identical.

If P_r is expressed in watts per square meter, the graph is an *absolute power pattern*. On the other hand, if P_r is expressed in terms of its value in some reference direction, the graph is a *relative power pattern*. It is customary to take the reference direction as that in which P_r is a maximum. Thus, the radius vector for a relative power pattern is P_r/P_{rm} where P_{rm} is the maximum value of P_r. The maximum value of the relative power pattern is unity as shown in Fig. 2-4b. A pattern with a maximum of unity is also called a *normalized pattern*.

2-3. A Power Theorem[1] and its Application to an Isotropic Source. If the Poynting vector is known at all points on a sphere of radius r from a

[1] This theorem is a special case of a more general relation for the complex power flow through any closed surface as given by

$$W' = \tfrac{1}{2} \iint (\mathbf{E} \times \mathbf{H}^*) \cdot d\mathbf{s} \qquad (2-1)$$

where W' is the total complex power flow and $\mathbf{E}$ and $\mathbf{H}^*$ are complex vectors representing point source in a lossless medium, *the total power radiated by the source is the integral over the surface of the sphere of the radial component P_r of the average Poynting vector.* Thus,

$$W = \iint \mathbf{P} \cdot d\mathbf{s} = \iint P_r \, ds \tag{2-3}$$

where W = power radiated, watts

$\quad P_r$ = radial component of average Poynting vector, watts per square meter

$\quad ds$ = infinitesimal element of area of sphere (see Fig. 2-2b)

$\quad\quad = r^2 \sin \theta \, d\theta \, d\phi$

For an isotropic source P_r is independent of θ and ϕ. Thus (2-3) becomes

$$W = P_r \iint ds \tag{2-4}$$

The integral is equal to the area of the sphere so that

$$W = P_r 4\pi r^2 \tag{2-5}$$

or

$$P_r = \frac{W}{4\pi r^2} \tag{2-6}$$

Equation (2-6) states that the magnitude of the Poynting vector varies inversely as the square of the distance from a point-source radiator. This is a statement of the well-known inverse-square law for the variation of power per unit area as a function of the distance from a point source. P_r is in watts per square meter if W is in watts and r in meters.

2-4. Radiation Intensity. Multiplying the power density P_r by the square of the radius r at which it is measured, we obtain the *power per unit solid angle* or *radiation intensity U*. Thus,

$$r^2 P_r = U = \text{radiation intensity} \tag{2-7}$$

Whereas the power density P_r is expressed in watts per square meter, the radiation intensity U is expressed in watts per unit solid angle (watts per square radian or steradian).[1] The radiation intensity is independent of the radius.

---

the electric and magnetic fields, $\mathbf{H}^*$ being the complex conjugate of $\mathbf{H}$. The average Poynting vector is

$$\mathbf{P} = \tfrac{1}{2} \text{Re} \, (\mathbf{E} \times \mathbf{H}^*) \tag{2-2}$$

Now the power flow in the far field is entirely real; hence, taking the real part of (2-1) and substituting (2-2), we obtain the special case of (2-3).

[1] Dimensionally, U is simply power since radians are dimensionless. Numerically, U is equal to P_r at unit radius.

Substituting (2-7) into (2-3), the power theorem assumes the form

$$W = \iint U \sin\theta \, d\theta \, d\phi = \iint U \, d\Omega \qquad (2\text{-}8)$$

where $d\Omega = \sin\theta \, d\theta \, d\phi$ = element of solid angle

Thus, the power theorem may be restated as follows. *The total power radiated is given by the integral of the radiation intensity U over a solid angle of 4π.* A pattern of U as a function of angle is a radiation-intensity pattern as shown by Fig. 2-4c. The maximum radiation intensity U_m is in the direction $\theta = 0$. A relative radiation-intensity pattern is given by U/U_m and has a maximum value of unity as shown by Fig. 2-4d. Relative power and radiation-intensity patterns are identical. Hence, for brevity both will often be referred to as power patterns.

Applying (2-8) to an isotropic source gives

$$W = 4\pi U_0 \qquad (2\text{-}9a)$$

where U_0 = power per square radian

Equation (2-9a) may also be expressed as[1]

$$W = 41{,}253 \, U_0^0 \qquad (2\text{-}9b)$$

where U_0^0 = power per square degree

Equations (2-9a) and (2-9b) also apply for a nonisotropic source provided that U_0 is the *average* power per square radian and U_0^0 the *average* power per square degree.

2-5. Source with Hemisphere Power Pattern. As further illustrations of the power theorems, let us apply (2-8) to a number of sources with different types of assumed power patterns. Consider, for example, a source with a power or radiation-intensity pattern which is a hemisphere. That is, the power per unit solid angle, or radiation intensity, U equals a constant U_m in the upper hemisphere ($0 \le \theta \le \pi/2$ and $0 \le \phi \le 2\pi$) and is zero in the lower hemisphere. This is illustrated by the three-dimensional or space power pattern of Fig. 2-5a and the two-dimensional power pattern of Fig. 2-5b. Then the total power radiated is the radiation intensity integrated over a hemisphere, or

$$W = \iint U \, d\Omega = \int_0^{2\pi} \int_0^{\pi/2} U_m \sin\theta \, d\theta \, d\phi = 2\pi U_m \qquad (2\text{-}10)$$

Assuming that the total power W radiated by the hemispheric source is the same as the total power radiated by an isotropic source taken as a reference, (2-10) and (2-9a) can be equated, yielding,

$$2\pi U_m = 4\pi U_0 \qquad (2\text{-}11)$$

[1] 4π square radians (steradians) = $4\pi \times 57.3^2$ square degrees = 41,253 square degrees.

or

$$\frac{U_m}{U_0} = 2 = \text{directivity} \qquad (2\text{-}12)$$

The ratio of U_m to U_0 in (2-12) is called the *directivity* of the hemispheric source. The directivity of a source is equal to the ratio of its maximum radiation intensity to its average radiation intensity. Or the directivity of a source may be stated as the ratio of its maximum radiation intensity to the radiation intensity of an isotropic source radiating the same total power.[1] By (2-12), the directivity of the hemispheric source is 2. That is to say, the power per unit solid angle U_m in one hemisphere from the hemispheric source is twice the power per unit solid angle U_0 from an isotropic source radiating the same total power. This we would expect, since a power W radiated uniformly over one hemisphere will give twice the power per unit solid angle as when radiated uniformly over both

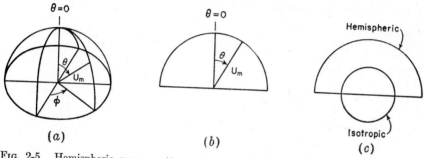

FIG. 2-5. Hemispheric power patterns, (a) and (b), and comparison with isotropic pattern (c).

hemispheres. The power patterns of a hemispheric source and an isotropic source are compared in Fig. 2-5c for the same power radiated by both.

2-6. Source With Unidirectional Cosine Power Pattern. Let us consider next a source with a cosine radiation-intensity pattern, that is,

$$U = U_m \cos \theta \qquad (2\text{-}13)$$

where U_m = maximum radiation intensity
The radiation intensity U has a value only in the upper hemisphere $(0 \leq \theta \leq \pi/2$ and $0 \leq \phi \leq 2\pi)$ and is zero in the lower hemisphere. The radiation intensity is a maximum at $\theta = 0$. The pattern is shown in

[1] One can also compare the power W' radiated by the source to the power W'' that must be radiated by an isotropic source to give the same radiation intensity. Then $U_0 = U_m$, and the directivity is given by $D = W''/W'$. For instance in the above case (Sec. 2-5), $W'' = 4\pi U_0$ and $W' = 2\pi U_m$. For $U_0 = U_m$, the directivity $D = W''/W' = 2$.

Fig. 2-6. The space pattern is a figure of revolution of this circle around the polar axis.

To find the total power radiated by the cosine source, we apply (2-8) and integrate only over the upper hemisphere. Thus

$$W = \int_0^{2\pi} \int_0^{\pi/2} U_m \cos\theta \sin\theta \, d\theta \, d\phi = \pi U_m \qquad (2\text{-}14)$$

If the power radiated by the unidirectional cosine source is the same as for an isotropic source, then (2-14) and (2-9a) may be set equal, yielding

$$\pi U_m = 4\pi U_0$$

or

$$\text{Directivity} = \frac{U_m}{U_0} = 4 \qquad (2\text{-}15)$$

Thus, the maximum radiation intensity U_m of the unidirectional cosine source (in the direction $\theta = 0$) is four times the radiation intensity U_0

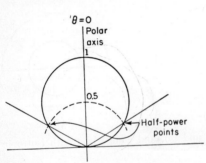

Fig. 2-6. Unidirectional cosine power pattern.

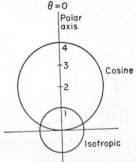

Fig. 2-7. Power patterns of unidirectional cosine source compared with isotropic source for same power radiated by both.

from an isotropic source radiating the same total power. The power patterns for the two sources are compared in Fig. 2-7 for the same total power radiated by each.

2-7. Source with Bidirectional Cosine Power Pattern. Let us assume that the source has a cosine pattern as in the preceding example but that the radiation intensity has a value in both hemispheres, instead of only in the upper one. The pattern is then as indicated by Fig. 2-8. It follows that W is twice its value for the unidirectional cosine power pattern, and hence the directivity is 2 instead of 4.

2-8. Source with Sine (Doughnut) Power Pattern. Consider next a source having a radiation-intensity pattern given by

$$U = U_m \sin \theta \qquad (2\text{-}16)$$

The pattern is shown in Fig. 2-9. The space pattern is a figure of revolution of this pattern around the polar axis and has the form of a doughnut. Applying (2-8), the total power radiated is

$$W = U_m \int_0^{2\pi} \int_0^\pi \sin^2 \theta \, d\theta \, d\phi = \pi^2 U_m \qquad (2\text{-}17)$$

If the power radiated by this source is the same as for an isotropic source taken as reference, we have

$$\pi^2 U_m = 4\pi U_0 \qquad (2\text{-}18)$$

and

$$\text{Directivity} = \frac{U_m}{U_0} = \frac{4}{\pi} = 1.27 \qquad (2\text{-}19)$$

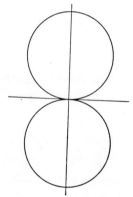

FIG. 2-8.   Bidirectional cosine power pattern.

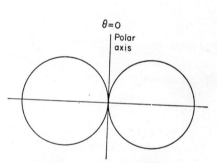

FIG. 2-9.   Sine power pattern.

2-9. Source with Sine-squared (Doughnut) Power Pattern.

Next consider a source with a sine squared radiation-intensity or power pattern. The radiation-intensity pattern is given by

$$U = U_m \sin^2 \theta \qquad (2\text{-}20)$$

The power pattern is shown in Fig. 2-10. This type of pattern is of considerable interest because it is the pattern produced by a short dipole coincident with the polar axis in Fig. 2-10. Applying (2-8), the total power radiated is

$$W = U_m \int_0^{2\pi} \int_0^\pi \sin^3 \theta \, d\theta \, d\phi = \frac{8}{3} \pi U_m \qquad (2\text{-}21)$$

If W is the same as for the isotropic source,

$$\tfrac{8}{3} U_m = 4\pi U_0$$

and

$$\text{Directivity} = \frac{U_m}{U_0} = \frac{3}{2} = 1.5 \tag{2-22}$$

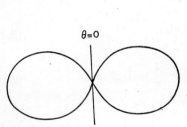

FIG. 2-10.   Sine squared power pattern.   FIG. 2-11.   Unidirectional cosine squared power pattern.

2-10. Source with Unidirectional Cosine Squared Power Pattern. Let us consider next the case of a source with a unidirectional cosine squared radiation-intensity pattern as given by

$$U = U_m \cos^2 \theta \tag{2-23}$$

with the radiation intensity having a value only in the upper hemisphere. The pattern is shown in Fig. 2-11. The three-dimensional or space pattern is a figure of revolution of this pattern around the polar axis and has the form of a prolate spheroid (football shape). The total power radiated is

$$W = U_m \int_0^{2\pi} \int_0^{\pi/2} \cos^2 \theta \sin \theta \, d\theta \, d\phi = \frac{2}{3} \pi U_m \tag{2-24}$$

If W is the same as radiated by an isotropic source,

$$\tfrac{2}{3}\pi U_m = 4\pi U_0$$

and

$$\text{Directivity} = \frac{U_m}{U_0} = 6 \tag{2-25}$$

Thus, the maximum power per unit solid angle (at $\theta = 0$) from the source with the cosine squared power pattern is six times the power per unit solid angle from an isotropic source radiating the same power.

2-11. Source with Unidirectional Cosine^n Power Pattern. A more general case for a unidirectional radiation-intensity pattern which is symmetrical around the polar axis is given by

$$U = U_m \cos^n \theta \tag{2-26}$$

where n is any real number. In Fig. 2-12, relative radiation-intensity or

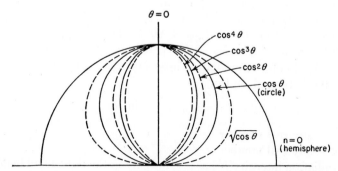

Fig. 2-12. Unidirectional $\cos^n \theta$ power patterns for various values of n.

power patterns plotted to the same maximum value are shown for the cases where $n = 0, \frac{1}{2}, 1, 2, 3,$ and 4. The case for $n = 0$ is the same as the source with the hemispheric power pattern discussed in Sec. 2-5. The cases for $n = 1$ and $n = 2$ were treated in Secs. 2-6 and 2-10. When $n = \frac{1}{2}$,

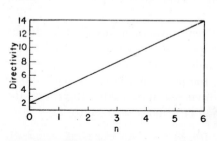

Fig. 2-13. Directivity vs. n for unidirectional sources with $\cos^n \theta$ power patterns.

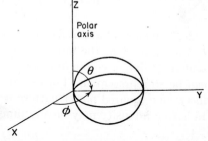

Fig. 2-14. Unidirectional source radiating maximum power in the direction $\theta = 90°, \phi = 90°,$ or y axis.

3, and 4, the directivity is 3, 8, and 10, respectively.[1] These calculations are left to the reader as an exercise. A graph of the directivity of a unidirectional source as a function of n is presented in Fig. 2-13.

[1] It may be shown that the directivity of sources with power patterns of the type given by (2-26) can be reduced to the simple expression, directivity $= 2(n + 1)$. The proof is left to the reader as an exercise.

2-12. Source with Unidirectional Power Pattern That Is Not Symmetrical.

All the patterns considered thus far have been symmetrical around the polar axis. That is, the space pattern could be constructed as a figure of revolution about the polar axis. Let us now consider a more general case in which the pattern is unidirectional but is unsymmetrical around its major axis. In discussing this type of pattern it will be convenient to shift the direction of the major axis or direction of maximum radiation from the polar axis ($\theta = 0$) to a direction in the equatorial plane as shown in Fig. 2-14 ($\theta = 90°$, $\phi = 90°$). The $\theta = 90°$ plane coincides with the x-y plane and the $\phi = 90°$ plane with the y-z plane. A rather general expression for the radiation intensity with its maximum at $\theta = 90°$ and $\phi = 90°$ is then given by

$$U = U_m \sin^n \theta \sin^m \phi \qquad (2\text{-}27)$$

where n = any real number
m = any real number
and the radiation intensity U has a value only in the right-hand hemisphere (Fig. 2-14) ($0 \leq \theta \leq \pi$; $0 \leq \phi \leq \pi$). When $m = n$, (2-27) becomes the equation for a symmetrical power pattern of the same form as considered in Sec. 11. When m and n are not the same (2-27) represents the general case in which the pattern has different shapes in the $\theta = 90°$ and $\phi = 90°$ planes. The total power radiated in this general case is

$$W = U_m \int_0^\pi \int_0^\pi \sin^{n+1} \theta \sin^m \phi \, d\theta \, d\phi \qquad (2\text{-}28)$$

2-13. General Case of Source with Power Pattern of Any Shape.

In the preceding sections the radiation-intensity or power patterns are all represented by sine or cosine functions of angle. Some actual antenna patterns can be so represented. For example, the power pattern of a short dipole has a sine squared power pattern as discussed in Sec. 2-9. In general the radiation intensity may be any function of θ and ϕ as given by

$$U = U_a f(\theta, \phi) \qquad (2\text{-}29)$$

where U_a = a constant
To find the total power radiated, U is substituted into (2-8), that is,

$$W = \iint U_a f(\theta, \phi) \sin \theta \, d\theta \, d\phi \qquad (2\text{-}30)$$

If this expression cannot be integrated analytically, W may be obtained by a graphical integration (see Prob. 2-5), or approximately by selecting n and m in (2-28) to give a sine-function power pattern which approximates the actual pattern.

The mathematical expression for the power pattern may be unknown, but the pattern may be measurable. In measuring patterns which have a maximum in the y direction, it is customary to take two patterns, one as a function of ϕ in the $\theta = 90°$ plane and the other as a function of θ in the $\phi = 90°$ plane. From these patterns the space pattern may be estimated and W calculated by graphical integration, or values of n and m in (2-28) may be selected to give integrable sine functions which approximate the measured patterns. By assuming that the same power is radiated by an isotropic source, the directivity may be obtained as in the preceding sections. Another very simple but approximate method for obtaining the directivity is discussed on page 25.

2-14. Directivity. The concept of directivity, treated above in some special cases, may be extended to several more general expressions which will now be developed.

In Sec. 2-5 directivity was defined as the ratio of U_m to U_0 where U_m is the maximum radiation intensity or watts per square radian from the source under consideration and U_0 is the radiation intensity from an isotropic source radiating the same power (or U_0 is the *average* radiation intensity from the source under consideration). Thus,

$$D = \frac{U_m}{U_0} = \frac{\text{maximum radiation intensity}}{\text{average radiation intensity}} \tag{2-31}$$

where $D =$ directivity
Multiplying numerator and denominator of (2-31) by 4π gives

$$D = \frac{4\pi U_m}{4\pi U_0} = \frac{4\pi U_m}{W} = \frac{4\pi \, (\text{maximum radiation intensity})}{\text{total power radiated}} \tag{2-32}$$

Let us now develop a more general expression for the directivity. Let the radiation-intensity pattern be expressed as in (2-29) by

$$U = U_a f(\theta, \phi) \tag{2-33}$$

and its maximum value by

$$U_m = U_a f(\theta, \phi)_{\max} \tag{2-34}$$

where $U_a =$ a constant
For the special case where

$$f(\theta, \phi)_{\max} = 1 \tag{2-35}$$

then $U_m = U_a$ and (2-33) can be written

$$U = U_m f(\theta, \phi) \tag{2-36}$$

The average radiation intensity is

$$U_0 = \frac{W}{4\pi} = \frac{\iint U_a\, f(\theta, \phi)\, d\Omega}{4\pi} \tag{2-37}$$

where W = total power radiated

$d\Omega = \sin \theta\, d\theta\, d\phi$ = element of solid angle

The directivity D is then given by

$$D = \frac{U_m}{U_0} = \frac{U_a\, f(\theta, \phi)_{max}}{\dfrac{\iint U_a\, f(\theta, \phi)\, d\Omega}{4\pi}} = \frac{4\pi\, f(\theta, \phi)_{max}}{\iint f(\theta, \phi)\, d\Omega} \tag{2-38}$$

Equation (2-38) can be reexpressed as

$$D = \frac{4\pi}{\dfrac{\iint f(\theta, \phi)\, d\Omega}{f(\theta, \phi)_{max}}} = \frac{4\pi}{B} \tag{2-39}$$

where B is defined as the *beam area*. It is given by[1]

$$B = \frac{\iint f(\theta, \phi)\, d\Omega}{f(\theta, \phi)_{max}} \tag{2-40}$$

From (2-31) and (2-39)

$$D = \frac{U_m}{U_0} = \frac{4\pi}{B} \tag{2-41}$$

and

$$4\pi U_0 = U_m B \tag{2-42}$$

Since $U_0 = W/4\pi$,

$$W = U_m B \tag{2-43}$$

where W = total power radiated

Therefore, *the beam area B is the solid angle through which all the power radiated would stream if the power per unit solid angle equaled the maximum value U_m over the beam area.*

[1]Note that $f(\theta, \phi)/f(\theta, \phi)_{max}$ is the relative (normalized) total power pattern. Thus, (2-40) may also be written

$$B = \iint \frac{f(\theta, \phi)}{f(\theta, \phi)_{max}} \sin \theta\, d\theta\, d\phi$$

The integration may be done analytically or graphically, or it may be done approximately by (2-44). Graphical integration procedures for a special case are discussed in Prob. 2-5. If the total far-field pattern is given it should be noted that the relative total power pattern in (2-40) is equal to the *square* of the relative total field pattern [see Eq. (2-58c)].

From (2-42)

$$B = \frac{4\pi U_0}{U_m} \text{ square radians} = 41{,}253 \frac{U_0}{U_m} \text{ square degrees} \qquad (2\text{-}43a)$$

Consider the unidirectional power pattern shown in Fig. 2-15.- The pattern is a figure of revolution around the y axis. The included angle θ' of the corresponding beam area is also shown. If the power per unit solid angle over the beam area were equal to the maximum value U_m of the directional source, the power through the beam area would equal that radiated by the source.

From this it is only a step to a very simple approximate method of calculating the directivity for a single lobed pattern, based on an estimate of the beam area from the half-power beam widths of the patterns in two planes at right angles. Thus, suppose that θ_1 is the beam width between half-power points in one plane and ϕ_1 is the width in a plane at right angles. Then, approximately

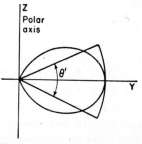

$$B \simeq \theta_1 \phi_1 \qquad (2\text{-}44)$$

Substituting (2-44) in (2-41) gives

$$D = \frac{4\pi}{\theta_1 \phi_1} \qquad (2\text{-}45)$$

FIG. 2-15. Unidirectional power pattern in cross section with included angle θ' of the beam area. The space patterns are figures of revolution around the y axis.

where θ_1 and ϕ_1 are the half-power beam widths expressed in radians. Equation (2-45) may also be expressed as

$$D = \frac{41{,}253}{\theta_1^0 \phi_1^0} \qquad (2\text{-}46)$$

where θ_1^0 and ϕ_1^0 are the half-power beam widths in degrees.[1]

[1] For the special case of a doughnut-type pattern (as in Secs. 2-8 and 2-9) Eq. (2-45) reduces to $D = 4\pi/2\pi\theta_1 = 2/\theta_1$, or $D = 114.6/\theta_1°$. A somewhat better approximation for doughnut patterns is given by $D = 1/[\sin(\theta_1/2)]$. When θ_1 is small the two approximations are equivalent.

For the special case of a bidirectional pattern with two identical lobes, as in Fig. 2-8, it is to be noted that the directivity is half that obtained on the basis of a single lobe.

If (2-45) or (2-46) is applied to a unidirectional beam type of pattern with minor lobes, these lobes are neglected and the calculated directivity is usually too high. To improve the accuracy, (2-46) may be multiplied by a correction factor. The value of this factor (usually between 0.6 and 1.0) depends in each case on the characteristics of the pattern but may be relatively constant for patterns of a certain class of antennas.

As an illustration let us find the directivity of the source of Sec. 2-6 by this method. This source has a unidirectional cosine power pattern given by $U = U_m \cos \theta$ and an exact value of directivity of 4. The half-power beam widths are 120°. Thus

$$D = \frac{41,253}{\theta_1^0 \phi_1^0} = \frac{41,253}{120^2} = 2.87$$

This approximate value is about 35 per cent in error.

As another illustration, consider a source with a unidirectional power pattern given by $U = U_m \cos^3 \theta$ which has an exact directivity of 8. The half-power beam widths are 75.2°, and

$$D = \frac{41,253}{75.2^2} = 7.3$$

which is about 10 per cent in error.

2-15. Gain. The definition of directivity in the preceding section is based entirely on the shape of the radiated power pattern. The power input and antenna efficiency are not involved. A quantity called *gain* will now be introduced which does involve the antenna efficiency. The gain[1] G of an antenna is defined as

$$G = \frac{\text{maximum radiation intensity}}{\substack{\text{maximum radiation intensity from a} \\ \text{reference antenna with same power input}}} \qquad (2\text{-}47)$$

Any type of antenna may be taken as the reference. Often the reference is a linear $\frac{1}{2}$-wavelength antenna. Gain includes the effect of losses both in the antenna under consideration (subject antenna) and in the reference antenna.

It will be convenient in some of the following discussion to assume that the reference antenna is an isotropic source of 100 per cent efficiency. The gain so defined for the subject antenna is called the *gain with respect to an isotropic source* and is designated G_0. Thus,

$$G_0 = \frac{\text{maximum radiation intensity from subject antenna}}{\substack{\text{radiation intensity from (lossless) isotropic} \\ \text{source with same power input}}} \qquad (2\text{-}48)$$

Let the maximum radiation intensity from the subject antenna be U'_m. Let this be related to the value of the maximum radiation intensity U_m

---

[1] The gain G as here defined is sometimes called *power gain*. This quantity is equal to the square of the *gain in field intensity* G_f. Thus, if E_1 is the maximum electric field intensity from the antenna at a large distance R and E_0 is the maximum electric field intensity from the reference antenna with the same power input at the same distance R, then the power gain G is given by $G = (E_1/E_0)^2 = G_f^2$.

for a 100 per cent efficient subject antenna by a *radiation efficiency factor k*. Thus,

$$U'_m = kU_m \qquad (2\text{-}49)$$

where $0 \leq k \leq 1$

Therefore, (2-48) may be written

$$G_0 = \frac{U'_m}{U_0} = \frac{kU_m}{U_0} \qquad (2\text{-}50)$$

where U_0 is the radiation intensity from a lossless isotropic source with the same power input. If W is the power input, $U_0 = W/4\pi$. But the ratio U_m/U_0 is by (2-31) the directivity D so that (2-50) becomes

$$G_0 = kD \qquad (2\text{-}51)$$

Thus, the gain of an antenna over a lossless isotropic source equals the directivity if the antenna is 100 per cent efficient ($k = 1$) but is less than the directivity if any losses are present in the antenna ($k < 1$).

The directivity D and gain G_0 imply the maximum values for an antenna. The directivity or gain in a direction for which the radiation intensity U is not a maximum may be designated by specifying the angle ϕ at which it is measured or, in general, by the symbol $D(\theta, \phi)$ or $G_0(\theta, \phi)$. That is,

$$D(\theta, \phi) = \frac{U}{U_m} D \qquad (2\text{-}52a)$$

and

$$G_0(\theta, \phi) = \frac{U}{U_m} G_0 \qquad (2\text{-}52b)$$

where U = radiation intensity in the direction (θ, ϕ)

U_m = maximum radiation intensity

Both directivity and gain may be expressed as a decibel ratio by taking 10 times the logarithm to the base 10. That is,

$$\text{Db directivity} = 10 \log_{10} D \qquad (2\text{-}53a)$$

$$\text{Db gain} = 10 \log_{10} G \qquad (2\text{-}53b)$$

Since the *power gain* G is equal to the square of the *gain in field intensity* G_f, we also have

$$\text{Db gain} = 20 \log_{10} G_f \qquad (2\text{-}53c)$$

Thus, *db gain* is the same, whether based on power gain or gain in field intensity.

2-16. Field Patterns. The discussion in the preceding sections of this chapter has been based on considerations of power. This has afforded a

ANTENNAS

simplicity of analysis, since the power flow from a point source has only a radial component which can be considered as a scalar quantity. To describe the field of a point source more completely, let us consider the electric field intensity,[1] or **E** vector of the field, which is usually called simply the *electric field*, or **E**.

Since the Poynting vector around a point source is everywhere radial, it follows that the electric field is entirely transverse, having only E_θ and E_ϕ components. The relation of the radial component P_r of the Poynting vector and the electric field components is illustrated by the spherical coordinate diagram of Fig. 2-16. The conditions characterizing the far field are then:

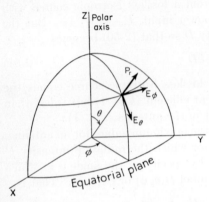

1. Poynting vector radial (P_r component only)
2. Electric field transverse (E_θ and E_ϕ components only)

The Poynting vector and the electric field at a point of the far field are related in the same manner as they are in a plane wave, since, if r is sufficiently large, a small section of the spherical wave front may be considered as a plane.

FIG. 2-16. Relation of the Poynting vector and the electric field components of the far field.

The relation between the average Poynting vector and the electric field at a point of the far field is

$$P_r = \frac{1}{2}\frac{E^2}{Z_0} \qquad (2\text{-}54)$$

where Z_0 = intrinsic impedance of free space* and

$$E = \sqrt{E_\theta^2 + E_\phi^2} \qquad (2\text{-}55)$$

where E = total electric field intensity
E_θ = amplitude of θ component
E_ϕ = amplitude of ϕ component
The field may be elliptically, linearly, or circularly polarized.

---

[1] We could equally well use the magnetic field intensity, or **H** vector. However, in the far field the magnitude of the magnetic field is related to the electric field by the intrinsic impedance Z of the medium ($H = E/Z$). The two fields at each point are in time phase and in space quadrature. Since the magnetic field can be obtained from the electric, we shall, for simplicity, consider only the electric field patterns.

* Z_0 is a pure resistance (= 377 ohms).

A pattern showing the variation of the electric field intensity at a constant radius r as a function of angle (θ, ϕ) is called a *field pattern*. In presenting information concerning the far field of an antenna, it is customary to give the field patterns for the two components, E_θ and E_ϕ, of the electric field since the total electric field E can be obtained from the components by (2-55), but the components cannot be obtained from a knowledge of only E.

When the field intensity is expressed in volts per meter, it is an *absolute field pattern*.[1] On the other hand, if the field intensity is expressed in units relative to its value in some reference direction, it is a *relative field pattern*. The reference direction is usually taken in the direction of maximum field intensity. The relative pattern of the E_θ component is then given by

$$\frac{E_\theta}{E_{\theta m}} \qquad (2\text{-}56)$$

and the relative pattern of the E_ϕ component is given by

$$\frac{E_\phi}{E_{\phi m}} \qquad (2\text{-}57)$$

where $E_{\theta m}$ = maximum value of E_θ
$\qquad E_{\phi m}$ = maximum value of E_ϕ

The magnitudes of both the electric field components, E_θ and E_ϕ, of the far field vary inversely as the distance from the source. However, they may be different functions, F_1 and F_2, of the angular coordinates, θ and ϕ. Thus, in general,

$$E_\theta = \frac{1}{r} F_1(\theta, \phi) \qquad (2\text{-}58a)$$

$$E_\phi = \frac{1}{r} F_2(\theta, \phi) \qquad (2\text{-}58b)$$

Since $P_{rm} = E_m^2/2Z$, where E_m is the maximum value of E, it follows on dividing this into (2-54) that the relative total power pattern is equal to the square of the relative total field pattern. Thus,

$$\frac{P_r}{P_{rm}} = \frac{U}{U_m} = \left(\frac{E}{E_m}\right)^2 \qquad (2\text{-}58c)$$

Example 1. Consider first the case of an antenna whose far field has only an E_ϕ component in the equatorial plane, the E_θ component being zero in this plane.

---

[1] The magnitude depends on the radius, varying inversely as the distance, $(E \propto 1/r)$.

Suppose that the relative equatorial-plane pattern of the E_ϕ component (that is, E_ϕ as a function of ϕ for $\theta = 90°$) is given by

$$\frac{E_\phi}{E_{\phi m}} = \cos \phi \qquad (2\text{-}59a)$$

This pattern is illustrated by Fig. 2-17a.[1] The length of the radius vector in the diagram is proportional to E_ϕ. A pattern of this form could be produced by a short dipole coincident with the y axis.

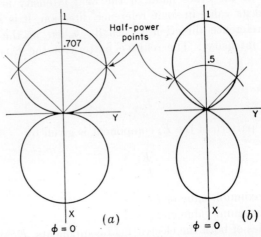

Fig. 2-17. Relative E_ϕ pattern of Example 1 at (a) with relative power pattern at (b).

The relative power pattern in the equatorial plane is equal to the square of the relative field pattern. Thus

$$\frac{P_r}{P_{rm}} = \frac{U}{U_m} = \left(\frac{E_\phi}{E_{\phi m}}\right)^2 \qquad (2\text{-}59b)$$

and substituting (2-59a) into (2-59b) we have

$$\frac{P_r}{P_{rm}} = \cos^2 \phi$$

This pattern is illustrated in Fig. 2-17b.

Example 2. Consider next the case of an antenna with a far field that has only an E_θ component in the equatorial plane, the E_ϕ component being zero in this plane.

---

[1] Another method of presenting the variation of field with respect to ϕ and θ is by contours of constant absolute or relative field intensity on a spherical surface, or the contours may be mapped on a flat projection of the spherical surface.

A graph showing contours of constant field intensity is commonly used to show the coverage of broadcasting stations in a horizontal plane. Here the contours are functions of one angle ϕ and of distance r.

Assume that the relative equatorial-plane pattern of the E_θ component (that is, E_θ as a function of ϕ for $\theta = 90°$) for this antenna is given by

$$\frac{E_\theta}{E_{\theta m}} = \sin \phi \qquad (2\text{-}60)$$

This pattern is illustrated by Fig. 2-18a and could be produced by a small loop antenna, the axis of the loop coincident with the x axis.

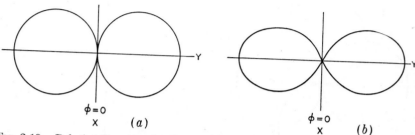

FIG. 2-18.   Relative E_θ pattern of Example 2 at (a) with relative power pattern at (b)

The relative power pattern in the equatorial plane is

$$\frac{P_r}{P_{rm}} = \sin^2 \phi$$

This pattern is shown by Fig. 2-18b.

Example 3. Let us consider finally an antenna whose far field has both E_θ and E_ϕ components in the equatorial plane ($\theta = 90°$). Suppose that this antenna is a composite of the two antennas we have just considered in Examples 1 and 2 and that equal power is radiated by each antenna. It then follows that at a radius r from the composite antenna, $E_{\theta m} = E_{\phi m}$. The individual patterns for the E_θ and E_ϕ components as given by (2-60) and (2-59a) may then be shown to the same scale by one diagram as in Fig. 2-19a. The relative pattern of the total field E is

$$\frac{E}{E_m} = \sqrt{\sin^2 \phi + \cos^2 \phi} = 1$$

which is a circle as indicated by the dashed line in Fig. 2-19a.

For this antenna, we may speak of two types of power patterns. One type shows the power variation for one component of the electric field. Thus, the power in the E_θ component of the field is as shown by Fig. 2-18b and the power in the E_ϕ component by Fig. 2-17b. The second type of power pattern shows the variation of the total power. This is proportional to the square of the total electric field intensity. Accordingly, the relative total power pattern for the composite antenna is

$$\frac{P_r}{P_{rm}} = \left(\frac{E}{E_m}\right)^2 = 1$$

The relative pattern in the equatorial plane for the total power is, therefore, a circle of radius unity as illustrated by Fig. 2-19b.

We note in Fig. 2-19*b* that at $\phi = 45°$ the magnitudes of the two field components, E_θ and E_ϕ, are equal. Depending on the time phase between E_θ and E_ϕ, the field in this direction could be plane, elliptically or circularly polarized. To determine the type of polarization requires that the phase angle between E_θ and E_ϕ be known. This is discussed in the next section.

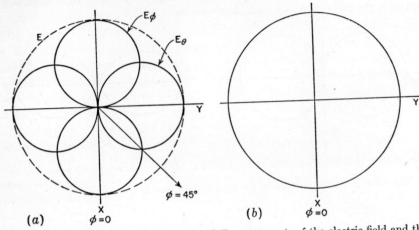

FIG. 2-19.   (*a*) Relative patterns of E_θ and E_ϕ components of the electric field and the total field E for antenna of Example 3.   (*b*) Relative total power pattern.

2-17. Phase Patterns. Assuming that the field varies harmonically with time and that the frequency is known, the far field in all directions from a source may be completely specified by a knowledge of the following four quantities:[1]

1. Amplitude of the polar component E_θ of the electric field as a function of r, θ, and ϕ
2. Amplitude of the azimuthal component E_ϕ of the electric field as a function of r, θ, and ϕ
3. Phase lag δ of E_ϕ behind E_θ as a function of θ and ϕ
4. Phase lag η of a field component behind its value at a reference point as a function of r, θ, and ϕ

Since we regard the field of a point source as a far field everywhere, the above four quantities can be considered as those required for a complete knowledge of the field of a point source.

---

[1] In general, for the near or far field, six quantities are required. These are E_θ, E_ϕ, δ, and η each as a function of r, θ, ϕ and in addition the amplitude of the radial component of the electric field E_r and its phase lag behind E_θ both as a function of r, θ, ϕ. Since $E_r = 0$ in the far field, only four quantities are needed to describe completely the field in the Fraunhofer region.

If the amplitudes of the field components are known at a particular radius, from a point source in free space, their amplitude at all distances is known from the inverse-distance law. Thus, it is usually sufficient to specify E_θ and E_ϕ as a function only of θ and ϕ as, for example, by a set of field patterns.

As shown in the preceding sections, the amplitudes of the field components give us directly or indirectly a knowledge of the peak and effective values of the total field and Poynting vector. However, if both field components have a value, the polarization is indeterminate without a knowledge of the phase angle δ between the field components. Focusing our attention on one field component, the phase angle η with respect to the phase at some reference point is a function of the radius and may also be a function of θ and ϕ. A knowledge of η as a function of θ and ϕ is essential when the fields of two or more point sources are to be added.

We now proceed to a discussion of the phase angles, δ and η, and of phase patterns for showing their variation. Let us consider three examples.

Example 1. Consider first a point source that radiates uniformly in the equatorial plane and has only an E_ϕ component of the electric field. Then at a distance r from the source, the instantaneous field $E_{\phi i}$ in the equatorial plane is

$$E_{\phi i} = \frac{\sqrt{2} E_\phi}{r} \sin (\omega t - \beta r) \qquad (2\text{-}61)$$

where E_ϕ = rms value of ϕ component of electric field intensity at unit radius from
   the source
 $\omega = 2\pi f$
 $\beta = 2\pi/\lambda$

The relation given by (2-61) is the equation for the field of a spherical wave traveling radially outward from the source. The equation gives the *instantaneous* value of the field as a function of time and distance. The amplitude or peak value of the field is $\sqrt{2} E_\phi/r$. The amplitude is independent of space angle (θ and ϕ) but varies inversely with the distance r. The variation of the instantaneous field with distance for this example is illustrated by the upper graph in Fig. 2-20 in which the amplitude is taken as unity at a distance r. When $r = 0$, the variation of the instantaneous field varies as $\sin \omega t$. It is often convenient to take this variation as a reference for the phase, designating it as the phase of the generator or source. The fact that the amplitude at $r = 0$ is infinite need not detract from using the phase at $r = 0$ as a reference. The phase at a distance r is then retarded behind that at the source by the angle βr. A *phase retardation* or lag of E_ϕ with respect to a reference point will, in general, be designated as η. In the present case the reference point is the source;[1] hence

$$\eta = \beta r = \frac{2\pi r}{\lambda} \qquad \text{radians} \qquad (2\text{-}62)$$

[1] If the phase is referred to some point at a distance r_1 from the source, then (2-61) becomes $E_{\phi i} = (\sqrt{2} E_\phi/r) \sin (\omega t - \beta d)$, where $d = r - r_1$.

Thus, the phase lag η increases linearly with the distance r from the source. This is illustrated by the chart of phase lag vs. distance in Fig. 2-20.

The phase lag η in this example is assumed to be independent of ϕ. To demonstrate experimentally that η depends on r but is independent of ϕ, the arrangement shown at the lower left in Fig. 2-20 could be used. The outputs of two probes or small antennas are combined in a receiver. With both probes at or very near the same point, the receiver output is reduced to a minimum by adjusting the length of one of the probe cables. The voltages from the probes at the receiver are then in

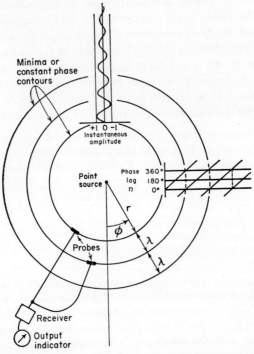

FIG. 2-20. Illustration for Example 1. Phase of E_ϕ of point source radiating uniformly in ϕ plane is a function of r but is independent of ϕ. Phase lag η increases linearly with distance r.

phase opposition. With one probe fixed in position, the other is then moved in such a way as to maintain a minimum output. The locus of points for minimum output constitutes a contour of constant phase. For the point source under consideration, each contour is a circle of constant radius with a separation of 1 wavelength between contours. The radius of the contours is then given by $r_1 \pm n\lambda$, where r_1 is the radius to the reference probe, and n is any integer.

Example 2. Consider next the case of a point source that has only an E_ϕ component and that radiates nonuniformly in the equatorial or ϕ plane. The instantaneous value in the equatorial plane is

$$E_{\phi i} = \frac{\sqrt{2}E_{\phi m}}{r} \cos \phi \sin (\omega t - \beta r) \qquad (2\text{-}63)$$

where $E_{\phi m}$ = rms value of E_ϕ component at unit radius in the direction of maximum field intensity

Let a point at unit radius and in the direction $\phi = 0$ be taken as the reference for phase. Then at this radius,

$$E_{\phi i} = \sqrt{2}E_{\phi m} \cos \phi \sin \omega t \qquad (2\text{-}64)$$

Setting $\sin \omega t = 1$, the relative field pattern of the E_ϕ component as a function of ϕ is, therefore,

$$E_\phi = \cos \phi \qquad (2\text{-}65)$$

as illustrated in Fig. 2-21a. A pattern of this type could be obtained by a short dipole coincident with the y axis at the origin. The phase lag η as a function of ϕ

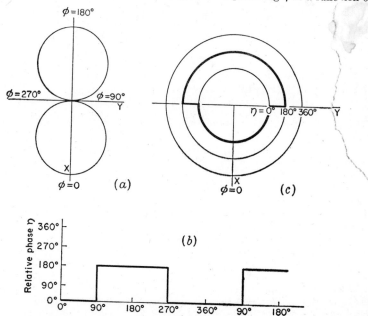

FIG. 2-21. Illustration for Example 2. Field pattern is shown at (a), the phase pattern in rectangular coordinates at (b), and in polar coordinates at (c).

is a step function as shown in the rectangular graph of Fig. 2-21b and in the polar graph of Fig. 2-21c. The variation shown is at a constant radius with the phase in the direction $\phi = 0$ as a reference. We note that η has an apparent discontinuity of 180° as ϕ passes through 90° and 270° since at these angles $\cos \phi$ changes sign while passing through zero magnitude. The phase angle η is accordingly a continuous, linear function of r but a discontinuous, step function of ϕ. To demonstrate this variation experimentally, the two-probe arrangement described in Example 1 may be used. In practice, attenuators, not shown, would be desirable in the probe leads to equalize the probe outputs. Referring to Fig. 2-22, if both fixed and movable probes are in the lower quadrants (1 and 4), a set of constant or equiphase circles is obtained with a radial separation of 1 wavelength. If one probe is fixed in quadrant 1 while the upper quadrants are explored with the movable probe, a set of equiphase circles is obtained which have a radial separation of 1 wavelength but are displaced radially from the set in the lower quadrants by $\frac{1}{2}$ wavelength. Thus, the constant phase contours have an apparent discontinuity at the y axis, as shown in Fig. 2-22.

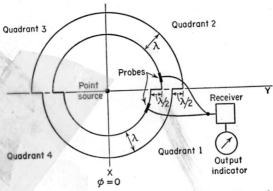

FIG. 2-22.   Constant phase contours for source of Example 2.

The phase of the field of any linear antenna coincident with the y axis exhibits this discontinuity at the y axis.[1]

Example 3. Consider lastly a point source which radiates a field with both E_θ and E_ϕ components in the equatorial plane, the instantaneous values being given by

$$E_{\theta i} = \frac{\sqrt{2}E_{\theta m}}{r} \sin \phi \sin (\omega t - \beta r) \qquad (2\text{-}66)$$

and

$$E_{\phi i} = \frac{\sqrt{2}E_{\phi m}}{r} \cos \phi \sin \left(\omega t - \beta r - \frac{\pi}{2}\right) \qquad (2\text{-}67)$$

Referring to Fig. 2-23, a field of the form of the E_θ component in the equatorial plane could be produced by a small loop at the origin oriented parallel to the y-z plane. A field of the form of the E_ϕ component in the equatorial plane could be produced by a short dipole at the origin coincident with the y axis. Let a point at

[1] It is to be noted that this phase change is actually a characteristic of the method of measurement, since by a second method no phase change may be observed between the upper and lower hemispheres. In the second method the probe is moved from the upper to the lower hemisphere along a circular path in the x-z plane at a constant radius from the source. However, for a linear antenna the second method is trivial since it is equivalent to rotating the antenna on its own axis with the probe at a fixed position.

unit radius in the first quadrant be taken as the reference for phase. Assuming that loop and dipole radiate equal power,

$$E_{\theta m} = E_{\phi m} \qquad (2\text{-}68)$$

Then at unit radius the relative patterns as a function of ϕ and t are given by

$$E_{\theta i} = \sin \phi \sin \omega t \qquad (2\text{-}69)$$

and

$$E_{\phi i} = \cos \phi \sin \left(\omega t - \frac{\pi}{2} \right)$$
$$= -\cos \phi \cos \omega t \qquad (2\text{-}70)$$

The relative field patterns in the equatorial plane are shown in Fig. 2-23. The field components are in phase quadrature ($\delta = \pi/2$). In quadrants 1 and 3, E_ϕ lags E_θ by 90°, while in quadrants 2 and 4, E_ϕ leads E_θ by 90°. The phase patterns in the equatorial plane for E_θ and E_ϕ are shown in polar form by Fig. 2-24 and in rectangular form by Fig. 2-25a.

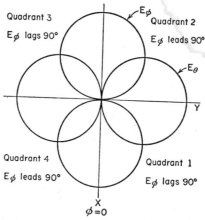

FIG. 2-23.   Field patterns for source of Example 3.

Since E_θ, E_ϕ, and δ are known, the polarization ellipses may be determined.

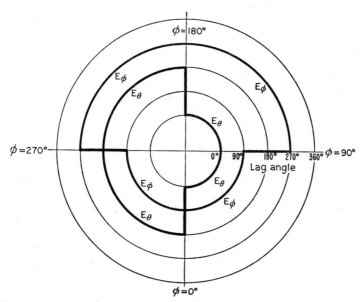

FIG. 2-24.   Phase lag as a function of ϕ for field components of source of Example 3.

These polarization ellipses (see Secs. 15-10 to 15-17) for different directions in the equatorial plane are shown in Fig. 2-25b. It is to be noted that in quadrants 1 and 3, where E_ϕ lags E_θ, the **E** vector rotates counterclockwise, while in quadrants 2 and 4, where E_ϕ leads E_θ, the rotation is clockwise.

At four angles the polarization is circular, **E** rotating counterclockwise at $\phi = 45°$ and 225° and rotating clockwise at $\phi = 135°$ and 315°. The polarization is linear at four angles, being horizontally polarized at 0° and 180° and vertically polarized at 90° and 270°. At all other angles the polarization is elliptical.

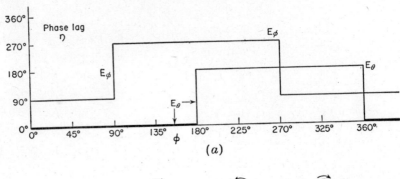

Fig. 2-25. Phase patterns in rectangular coordinates for source of Example 3 at (a) with polarization ellipses for every 22.5° interval of ϕ at (b).

2-18. General Equation for the Field of a Point Source. Both components of the far field of a point source in free space vary inversely with the distance. Therefore, in general, the two electric field components may be expressed as

$$E_\theta = \frac{E_{\theta m}}{r} f_1(\theta, \phi) \qquad (2\text{-}71)$$

and

$$E_\phi = \frac{E_{\phi m}}{r} f_2(\theta, \phi) \qquad (2\text{-}72)$$

where $E_{\theta m}$ = rms value of E_θ component at unit radius in the direction of maximum field

$E_{\phi m}$ = rms value of E_ϕ component at unit radius in the direction of maximum field

f_1 and f_2 are, in general, different functions of θ and ϕ but of maximum value unity

The instantaneous values of the field components vary harmonically with time and are given by (2-71) and (2-72) multiplied, in general, by different functions of the time. Thus, for the instantaneous field components

$$E_{\theta i} = \frac{\sqrt{2}E_{\theta m}}{r} f_1(\theta, \phi) \sin(\omega t - \eta) \tag{2-73}$$

and

$$E_{\phi i} = \frac{\sqrt{2}E_{\phi m}}{r} f_2(\theta, \phi) \sin(\omega t - \eta - \delta) \tag{2-74}$$

where $\eta = \beta(r - r_1) + f_3(\theta, \phi)$
$\quad \delta = f_4(\theta, \phi)$
$\quad r$ = radius to field point (r, θ, ϕ)
$\quad r_1$ = radius of point to which phase is referred
$\quad f_3$ and f_4 are, in general, different functions of θ and ϕ

The instantaneous value of the total electric field at a point (r, θ, ϕ) due to a point source is the vector sum of the instantaneous values of the two components. That is,

$$\mathbf{E}_i = \mathbf{a}_\theta E_{\theta i} + \mathbf{a}_\phi E_{\phi i} \tag{2-75}$$

where $\mathbf{a}_\theta$ = unit vector in θ direction
$\quad \mathbf{a}_\phi$ = unit vector in ϕ direction

Substituting (2-73) and (2-74) into (2-75) then gives a general equation for the electric field of a point source at any point (r, θ, ϕ) as follows:

$$\mathbf{E}_i = \mathbf{a}_\theta \frac{\sqrt{2}E_{\theta m}}{r} f_1(\theta, \phi) \sin(\omega t - \eta)$$

$$+ \mathbf{a}_\phi \frac{\sqrt{2}E_{\phi m}}{r} f_2(\theta, \phi) \sin(\omega t - \eta - \delta) \tag{2-76}$$

In this equation the instantaneous total electric field vector $\mathbf{E}_i$ is a function of both space and time, thus

$$\mathbf{E}_i = f(r, \theta, \phi, t) \tag{2-77}$$

The far field is entirely specified by (2-76). When f_1 and f_2 are complicated expressions, it is often convenient to describe $\mathbf{E}_i$ by means of graphs for the four quantities E_θ, E_ϕ, η, and δ, as has been discussed. It is assumed that the field varies harmonically with time and that the frequency is known.

PROBLEMS

2-1. *a.* Calculate the exact directivity for three unidirectional sources having the following power patterns:

$$U = U_m \sin \theta \sin^2 \phi$$
$$U = U_m \sin \theta \sin^3 \phi$$
$$U = U_m \sin^2 \theta \sin^3 \phi$$

U has a value only for $0 \leq \theta \leq \pi$ and $0 \leq \phi \leq \pi$ and is zero elsewhere.

b. Calculate the approximate directivity from the product of the half-power beam widths for each of the sources.

c. Tabulate the results for comparison.

2-2. Show that the directivity for a source with a unidirectional power pattern given by $U = U_m \cos^n \theta$ can be expressed as $D = 2(n + 1)$. U has a value only for $0 \leq \theta \leq \pi/2$ and $0 \leq \phi \leq 2\pi$ and is zero elsewhere.

2-3. The earth receives from the sun 2.2 gram calories/min/cm^2.

a. What is the corresponding Poynting vector in watts per square meter?

b. What is the power output of the sun, assuming that it is an isotropic source?

c. What is the rms field intensity at the earth due to the sun's radiation, assuming all the sun's energy is at a single frequency?

Note: 1 watt = 14.3 gm cal/min.

Distance earth to sun = 149×10^6 kilometers.

2-4. Prove the following theorem: If the minor lobes of a radiation pattern remain constant as the beam width of the main lobe approaches zero, then the directivity of the antenna approaches a constant value as the beam width of the main lobe approaches zero.

2-5. *a.* Calculate by graphical integration the directivity of a source with a unidirectional power pattern given by $U = \cos \theta$. Compare this directivity value with the exact value. U has a value only for $0 \leq \theta \leq \pi/2$ and $0 \leq \phi \leq 2\pi$ and is zero elsewhere.

b. Repeat for a unidirectional power pattern given by $U = \cos^2 \theta$.

c. Repeat for a unidirectional power pattern given by $U = \cos^3 \theta$.

Note that the directivity in each case is given by $D = 2/(\int_0^{\pi/2} U \sin \theta \, d\theta)$. To evaluate the integral graphically lay off 0 to $\pi/2$ (0° to 90°) as abscissa and 0 to 1 as ordinate on rectangular graph paper. The value of the integral is then the ratio of the area a under the curve $U \sin \theta$ to the total area A of the rectangle (0 to $\pi/2$ by 0 to 1), both in the same arbitrary units, multiplied by $\pi/2$. That is, $\int_0^{\pi/2} U \sin \theta \, d\theta = (a/A)(\pi/2)$. The evaluation of the area a may be done by square counting or by dividing the area into vertical strips and taking the area of any strip as the product of its base width and average ordinate.

CHAPTER 3

THE ANTENNA AS AN APERTURE

3-1. Introduction. In this chapter an antenna will be regarded as possessing an aperture or equivalent area over which it extracts energy from a passing radio wave.[1]

The concept of aperture is most simply introduced by considering a receiving antenna. Suppose that the receiving antenna is an electromagnetic horn immersed in the field of a plane wave as suggested in Fig. 3-1. Let the Poynting vector, or power density, of the plane wave

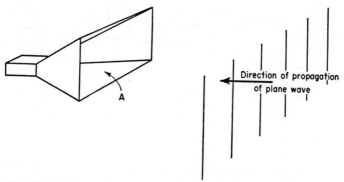

Fig. 3-1. Plane wave incident on electromagnetic horn of mouth aperture A.

be P watts/meter^2 and the area of the mouth of the horn be A meters^2. If the horn were able to extract all the power from the wave over its entire area A, then the total power W absorbed from the wave would be

$$W = PA \qquad \text{watts} \tag{3-1}$$

[1] J. C. Slater, "Microwave Transmission," McGraw-Hill Book Company, Inc., New York, 1942, p. 235.

Chap. 10 by Kraus, Clark, Barkofsky, and Stavis, "Very High Frequency Techniques," by Radio Research Laboratory staff, McGraw-Hill Book Company, Inc., New York, 1947, pp. 225–228.

H. T. Friis, A Note on a Simple Transmission Formula, *Proc. I.R.E.*, **34**, 254–256, May, 1946.

Thus, the electromagnetic horn may be regarded as an aperture, the total power it extracts from a passing wave being proportional to the aperture or area of its mouth.*

It will be convenient to distinguish between several types of apertures, namely, effective aperture, scattering aperture, loss aperture, collecting aperture, and physical aperture. These different types of apertures are defined and discussed in the following sections.

In the following discussion in this chapter, it is assumed, unless otherwise stated, that the antenna has the same polarization as the incident wave and is oriented for maximum response.

3-2. Effective Aperture. Consider any type of collector or receiving antenna which is situated in the field of a passing electromagnetic wave as suggested in Fig. 3-2a. The antenna collects power from the wave and

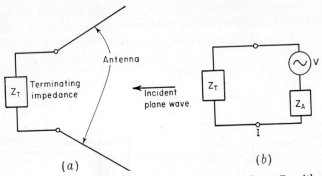

FIG. 3-2. Schematic diagram of antenna terminated in impedance Z_T with plane wave incident on antenna (a) and equivalent circuit (b).

delivers it to the terminating or load impedance Z_T connected to its terminals. The Poynting vector, or power density of the wave, is P watts/meter^2. Referring to the equivalent circuit of Fig. 3-2b, the antenna may be replaced by an equivalent or Thévenin generator having an equivalent voltage V and internal or equivalent antenna impedance Z_A. The voltage V is induced by the passing wave and produces a current I through the terminating impedance Z_T given by

$$I = \frac{V}{Z_T + Z_A} \tag{3-2}$$

where I and V are rms or effective values.

* Actual electromagnetic horns have effective apertures which are smaller than the physical area of the mouth, being usually 0.5 to 0.7 of this value.

In general, the antenna and terminating impedances are complex, thus

$$Z_T = R_T + jX_T \tag{3-3}$$

and

$$Z_A = R_A + jX_A \tag{3-4}$$

The antenna resistance may be divided into two parts, a radiation resistance R_r and a loss resistance R_L, that is,

$$R_A = R_r + R_L \tag{3-5}$$

Let the power delivered by the antenna to the terminating impedance be W. Then

$$W = I^2 R_T \tag{3-6}$$

From (3-2), (3-3), and (3-4) the current magnitude

$$I = \frac{V}{\sqrt{(R_r + R_L + R_T)^2 + (X_A + X_T)^2}} \tag{3-7}$$

Substituting (3-7) into (3-6) gives

$$W = \frac{V^2 R_T}{(R_r + R_L + R_T)^2 + (X_A + X_T)^2} \tag{3-8}$$

The ratio of the power W in the terminating impedance to the power density of the incident wave will be defined as the effective aperture A_e.
Thus,

$$\text{Effective aperture} = \frac{W}{P} = A_e \tag{3-9}$$

If W is in watts and P in watts per square meter, then A_e is in square meters. If P is in watts per square wavelength, then A_e is in square wavelengths, which is often a convenient unit of measurement for apertures.

Substituting (3-8) into (3-9) gives the effective aperture in terms of the incident power density, the induced voltage, and the antenna and terminating impedances, that is,

$$A_e = \frac{V^2 R_T}{P[(R_r + R_L + R_T)^2 + (X_A + X_T)^2]} \tag{3-10}$$

Unless otherwise specified, it is assumed that V is the induced voltage when the antenna is oriented for maximum response and the incident wave has the same polarization as the antenna. As shown by (3-10), the effective aperture takes into account antenna losses, as given by R_L, and any mismatch between the antenna and its terminating impedance.[1]

Let us now consider the special case where the terminating impedance is the complex conjugate of the antenna impedance so that maximum power is transferred. It will also be assumed that the antenna losses are zero ($R_L = 0$ and therefore $R_A = R_r$). Thus,

$$X_T = -X_A \tag{3-12}$$

and

$$R_T = R_r \tag{3-13}$$

Introducing the conditions for maximum power transfer as given by (3-12) and (3-13) into (3-8) results in the largest possible power W' in the terminating impedance as follows:

$$W' = \frac{V^2 R_T}{4R_T^2} = \frac{V^2}{4R_T} = \frac{V^2}{4R_r} \tag{3-14}$$

The power W' is delivered to the terminating impedance under conditions of maximum power transfer and zero antenna losses.

The ratio of this power to the power density of the incident wave is

[1] It is sometimes convenient to express the induced voltage V in terms of the incident field intensity E and an *effective height* h of the antenna. That is

$$V = hE$$

where V is in volts if h is in meters and E in volts per meter (or h may be in wavelengths and E in volts per wavelength). The effective height and the effective aperture are related as may be shown in the following way. In (3-10) $P = E^2/Z$, where Z is the intrinsic impedance of the medium ($Z = \sqrt{\mu/\epsilon}$). Thus, on solving (3-10) for V we have,

$$V = \sqrt{\frac{A_e[(R_r + R_L + R_T)^2 + (X_A + X_T)^2]}{R_T Z}} E$$

so that the effective height is given by

$$h = \sqrt{\frac{A_e[(R_r + R_L + R_T)^2 + (X_A + X_T)^2]}{R_T Z}} E$$

Under the conditions considered in the next paragraphs of the text for the maximum effective aperture A_{em}, the expression for the effective height reduces to

$$h = 2\sqrt{\frac{A_{em}R_r}{Z}} \quad \text{or} \quad A_{em} = \frac{h^2 Z}{4R_r} \tag{3-11}$$

As an example, for a thin linear $\frac{1}{2}$-wavelength antenna $A_{em} = 0.13$ square wavelength and $R_r = 73$ ohms. Now $Z = 377$ ohms for free space, so that for the $\frac{1}{2}$-wavelength antenna the effective height $h = 0.32$ wavelength.

the *maximum effective aperture*[1] A_{em}. That is,

$$\text{Maximum effective aperture} = \frac{W'}{P} = A_{em} \qquad (3\text{-}15)$$

Substituting (3-14) in (3-15) yields an expression for the maximum effective aperture in terms of the incident power density, the induced voltage, and the antenna radiation resistance, as follows:

$$A_{em} = \frac{V^2}{4PR_r} \qquad (3\text{-}16)$$

The ratio of the effective aperture to the maximum effective aperture is called the *effectiveness ratio* α. That is,

$$\text{Effectiveness ratio} = \alpha = \frac{A_e}{A_{em}} \quad \text{(dimensionless)} \qquad (3\text{-}17)$$

The effectiveness ratio may assume values between zero and 1 ($0 \leq \alpha \leq 1$). A perfectly matched, 100 per cent efficient antenna has an effectiveness ratio of unity.

Ordinarily the terminating impedance is not located physically at the antenna terminals as suggested in Fig. 3-2. Rather, it is in a receiver which is connected to the antenna by a length of transmission line. In this case Z_T is the equivalent impedance which appears across the antenna terminals. If the transmission line is lossless, the power delivered to the receiver is the same as that delivered to the equivalent terminating impedance Z_T. If the transmission line has attenuation, the power delivered to the receiver is less than that delivered to the equivalent terminating impedance by the amount lost in the line.

3-3. Scattering Aperture. In the preceding section we discussed the effective area from which power is absorbed. Referring to Fig. 3-2b, the voltage induced in the antenna produces a current through both the antenna impedance Z_A and the terminal or load impedance Z_T. The power W absorbed by the terminal impedance is, as we have seen, the square of this current times the real part of the load impedance. Thus, as given in (3-6), $W = I^2 R_T$. Let us now inquire into the power appearing in the antenna impedance Z_A. The real part of this impedance R_A has two parts, the radiation resistance R_r and the loss resistance R_L ($R_A = R_r + R_L$). Therefore, some of the power which is received will be dissipated as heat in the antenna as given by

$$W = I^2 R_L \qquad (3\text{-}18)$$

---

[1] The "maximum effective aperture," as here defined, is equivalent to the "effective area" of an antenna based on its directivity as defined by the Institute of Radio Engineers' (IRE) Standards.

The remainder is "dissipated" in the radiation resistance, in other words, is reradiated from the antenna. The reradiated power is

$$W'' = I^2 R_r \tag{3-19}$$

This reradiated or scattered power is analogous to the power that is dissipated in a generator in order that power be delivered to a load. Under conditions of maximum power transfer, as much power is dissipated in the generator as is delivered to the load.

The reradiated power may be related to a *scattering aperture* or scattering cross section. This aperture A_s may be defined as the ratio of the reradiated power to the power density of the incident wave. Thus

$$A_s = \text{scattering aperture} = \frac{W''}{P} \tag{3-20}$$

where

$$W'' = I^2 R_r = \frac{V^2 R_r}{(R_r + R_L + R_T)^2 + (X_A + X_T)^2} \tag{3-21}$$

If the antenna loss resistance $R_L = 0$, and $R_T = R_r$ and $X_A = -X_T$ for maximum power transfer, then

$$A_s = \frac{V^2}{4PR_r} \tag{3-22}$$

or the scattering aperture equals the maximum effective aperture, that is,

$$A_s = A_{em} \tag{3-23}$$

Thus, under conditions for which maximum power is delivered to the terminal impedance, an equal power is reradiated from the receiving antenna.

The ratio of the scattering aperture to the effective aperture will be called the *scattering ratio* β, that is,

$$\text{Scattering ratio} = \frac{A_s}{A_e} = \beta \quad \text{(dimensionless)} \tag{3-24}$$

The scattering ratio may assume values between zero and infinity $(0 \leq \beta \leq \infty)$.

For conditions of maximum power transfer and zero antenna losses, the scattering ratio is unity. If the terminal resistance is increased, both the scattering aperture and the effective aperture decrease, but the scattering aperture decreases more rapidly so that the scattering ratio becomes smaller. By increasing the terminal resistance, the ratio of the scattered to absorbed power can be made as small as we please, although by so doing the absorbed power is also reduced (see Fig. 3-3).

On the other hand, it may be that we should like to make the reradiation as large as possible. This might be the case, for example, if the antenna is not connected to a receiver but is used as a so-called parasitic antenna whose function is to reradiate the power received from a nearby transmitting antenna. The field reradiated by the parasitic antenna interferes with the field from the transmitting antenna so as to produce the desired directional pattern. Depending on the phase of the current in the parasitic antenna, it may act either as a director or as a reflector. To make the reradiated power a maximum, the terminal impedance should be zero and

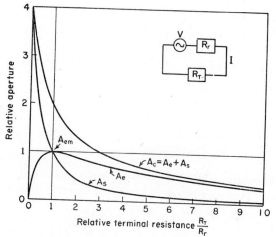

FIG. 3-3. Variation of effective aperture A_e, scattering aperture A_s, and collecting aperture A_c as a function of the relative terminal resistance R_T/R_r of a small antenna. It is assumed that $R_L = X_A = X_T = 0$.

the antenna should also be resonant, that is, $R_T = X_T = X_A = 0$. We also assume $R_L = 0$. Then from (3-21) the reradiated power is

$$W'' = \frac{V^2}{R_r} \qquad (3\text{-}25)$$

and the maximum scattering aperture becomes

$$A_{sm} = \frac{V^2}{PR_r} \qquad (3\text{-}26)$$

or

$$A_{sm} = 4A_{em} \qquad (3\text{-}27)$$

The maximum cross section of an antenna as a scatterer of energy is thus four times as great as its maximum effective aperture as an absorber of energy.

The relation between A_s and A_e as a function of the relative terminal

resistance R_T/R_r is shown in Fig. 3-3. In this graph it is assumed that
$R_L = X_A = X_T = 0$.

The reradiated or scattered field of an absorbing antenna may be considered as interfering with the incident field so that a shadow is cast behind the antenna as illustrated in Fig. 3-4. The shadow will not be so sharply defined as suggested in Fig. 3-4, but a decrease in the field intensity or a partial shadow must be present.

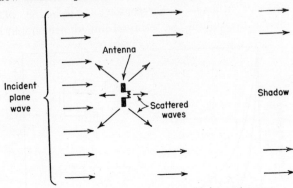

FIG. 3-4. Shadow cast by a receiving antenna.

3-4. Loss Aperture. If R_L is not zero, some power is dissipated as heat in the antenna. This may be related to a *loss aperture* A_L which is given by

$$A_L = \frac{I^2 R_L}{P} = \frac{V^2 R_L}{P[(R_r + R_L + R_T)^2 + (X_A + X_T)^2]} \qquad (3\text{-}28)$$

3-5. Collecting Aperture.[1] Three types of apertures have now been discussed: effective, scattering, and loss. These three apertures are related to three ways in which power collected by the antenna may be converted: into heat in the terminal resistance (effective aperture); into heat in the antenna (loss aperture); or into reradiated power (scattering aperture). By conservation of energy the total power collected is the sum of these three powers. Thus, adding these three apertures together yields what will be called the *collecting aperture* as given by

$$A_c = \frac{V^2(R_r + R_L + R_T)}{P[(R_r + R_L + R_T)^2 + (X_A + X_T)^2]} = A_s + A_L + A_e \qquad (3\text{-}29)$$

The variation of A_c with R_T/R_r for the case of $A_L = 0$ is shown in Fig. 3-3.

3-6. Physical Aperture. It is often convenient to speak of a fifth type of aperture called the physical aperture A_p. This aperture is a measure of

---

[1] Collecting aperture as here defined is different from that given in "Very High Frequency Techniques," by Radio Research Laboratory staff, McGraw-Hill Book Company, Inc., New York, 1947, p. 227. Collecting aperture as defined in that reference is what we have here called the maximum effective aperture.

the physical size of the antenna. The manner in which it is defined is entirely arbitrary. For example, it may be defined as the physical cross section (in square meters or square wavelengths) perpendicular to the direction of propagation of the incident wave with the antenna oriented for maximum response. This is a practical definition in the case of many antennas. For example, the physical aperture of an electromagnetic horn is the area of its mouth, while the physical aperture of a linear cylindrical dipole is the cross-sectional area of the dipole. However, in the case of a short stub antenna mounted on a very large ground plane, the simple definition given above is of questionable significance owing to the importance of the currents on the ground plane. Thus, the physical aperture has a simple, definite meaning only for some antennas. On the other hand, the effective aperture has a definite, simply defined value for all antennas.

The ratio of the maximum effective aperture to the physical aperture will be called the *absorption ratio* γ, that is,

$$\text{Absorption ratio} = \frac{A_{em}}{A_p} = \gamma \qquad \text{(dimensionless)} \qquad (3\text{-}30)$$

The absorption ratio may assume values between zero and infinity $(0 \leq \gamma \leq \infty)$.

3-7. Maximum Effective Aperture of a Short Dipole.

In this section the maximum effective aperture of a short dipole with uniform current will be calculated. Let the dipole have a length l which is short compared with the wavelength ($l \ll \lambda$). Let it be coincident with the y axis at the origin as shown in Fig. 3-5, with a plane wave traveling in the negative x direction incident on the dipole. The wave is assumed to be linearly polarized with E in the y direction. The current on the dipole is assumed constant and in the same phase over its entire length, and the terminating resistance R_T is assumed equal to the dipole radiation resistance R_r. The antenna loss resistance R_L is assumed equal to zero.

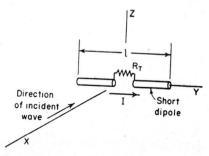

FIG. 3-5. Short dipole with uniform current induced by incident wave.

The maximum effective aperture of an antenna is given by (3-16) as

$$A_{em} = \frac{V^2}{4PR_r} \qquad (3\text{-}31)$$

where the effective value of the induced voltage V is here given by the product of the effective electric field intensity at the dipole and its length,[1] that is,

$$V = El \tag{3-32}$$

The radiation resistance R_r of a short dipole of length l with uniform current will be shown later to be given by

$$R_r = \frac{80\pi^2 l^2}{\lambda^2} \tag{3-33}$$

where $\lambda =$ wavelength

The power density, or Poynting vector, of the incident wave at the dipole is related to the field intensity by

$$P = \frac{E^2}{Z} \tag{3-34}$$

where $Z =$ intrinsic impedance of the medium

In the present case, the medium is free space so that $Z = 120\pi$ ohms. Now substituting (3-32), (3-33), and (3-34) into (3-31), we obtain for the maximum effective aperture of a short dipole

$$A_{em} = \frac{120\pi E^2 l^2 \lambda^2}{320\pi^2 E^2 l^2} = \frac{3}{8\pi} \lambda^2 = 0.119\, \lambda^2 \tag{3-35}$$

Equation (3-35) indicates that the maximum effective aperture of a short dipole is somewhat more than 1/10 square wavelength and is independent of the length of the dipole provided only that it is small ($l \ll \lambda$). The maximum effective aperture neglects the effect of any losses, which probably would be considerable for an actual short dipole antenna. If we assume that the terminating impedance is matched to the antenna impedance but that the antenna has a loss resistance equal to its radiation resistance, the effective aperture from (3-10) is one-half the maximum effective aperture obtained in (3-35).

3-8. Maximum Effective Aperture of a Linear $\frac{1}{2}$-Wavelength Antenna. As a further illustration, the maximum effective aperture of a linear $\frac{1}{2}$-wavelength antenna will be calculated. It is assumed that the current has a sinusoidal distribution and is in phase along the entire length of the antenna. It is further assumed that $R_L = 0$. Referring to Fig. 3-6a, the current I at any point y is then

$$I = I_0 \cos \frac{2\pi y}{\lambda} \tag{3-36}$$

A plane wave incident on the antenna is traveling in the negative x direction. The wave is linearly polarized with E in the y direction. The

---

[1] The effective height h of the short dipole with uniform current is equal to its length l.

equivalent circuit is shown in Fig. 3-6b. The antenna has been replaced by an equivalent or Thévenin generator. The infinitesimal voltage dV of this generator due to the voltage induced by the incident wave in an infinitesimal element of length dy of the antenna is

$$dV = E \, dy \, \cos \frac{2\pi y}{\lambda} \tag{3-37}$$

It is assumed that the infinitesimal induced voltage is proportional to the current at the infinitesimal element as given by the current distribution (3-36).

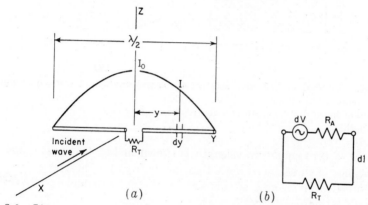

Fig. 3-6. Linear $\frac{1}{2}$-wavelength antenna in field of electromagnetic wave (a) and equivalent circuit (b).

The total induced voltage V is given by integrating (3-37) over the length of the antenna. This may be written as

$$V = 2 \int_0^{\lambda/4} E \, \cos \frac{2\pi y}{\lambda} \, dy \tag{3-38}$$

Performing the integration in (3-38) we have

$$V = \frac{E\lambda}{\pi} \tag{3-39}$$

The value of the radiation resistance R_r of the linear $\frac{1}{2}$-wavelength antenna will be taken as 73 ohms.[1] The terminating resistance R_T is assumed equal to R_r. The power density at the antenna is as given by (3-34). Substituting (3-39), (3-34), and $R_r = 73$ into (3-16), we obtain, for the maximum effective aperture of a linear $\frac{1}{2}$-wavelength antenna,

$$A_{em} = \frac{120\pi E^2 \lambda^2}{4\pi^2 E^2 73} = \frac{30}{73\pi} \lambda^2 = 0.13 \, \lambda^2 \tag{3-40}$$

[1] The derivation of this value is given in Chap. 5.

Comparing (3-40) with (3-35), the maximum effective aperture of the linear $\frac{1}{2}$-wavelength antenna is about 10 per cent greater than that of the short dipole.

The maximum effective aperture of the $\frac{1}{2}$-wavelength antenna is approximately the same as an area $\frac{1}{2}$ by $\frac{1}{4}$ wavelength on a side, as illustrated in Fig. 3-7a. This area is $\frac{1}{8}$ square wavelength. An elliptically shaped

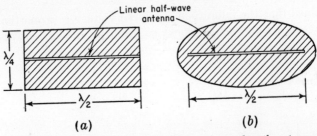

Fig. 3-7. (a) Maximum effective aperture of linear $\frac{1}{2}$-wavelength antenna is approximately represented by rectangle $\frac{1}{2}$ by $\frac{1}{4}$ wavelength on a side. (b) Maximum effective aperture of linear $\frac{1}{2}$-wavelength antenna represented by elliptical area of 0.13 square wavelength.

aperture of 0.13 square wavelength is shown in Fig. 3-7b. The physical significance of these apertures is that power from the incident plane wave is absorbed over an area of this size by the antenna and is delivered to the terminating resistance.

A typical thin $\frac{1}{2}$-wavelength antenna may have a conductor diameter of 1/400 wavelength, so that its physical aperture is only 1/800 square wavelength. For such an antenna the maximum effective aperture of 0.13 square wavelength is about 100 times larger.

3-9. Relation of Aperture to Directivity and Gain. In Chap. 2 the concept of directivity was developed for a point source of radiation or transmitting antenna. By reciprocity, the shape of the radiation pattern of a transmitting antenna is identical with its pattern when it is a receiving antenna (see Sec. 10-2). Thus, the concept of directivity, which is based on pattern shape, can be extended to receiving antennas, the directivity being the same for both transmission and reception.

The aperture of receiving antennas has been discussed in the preceding sections. It follows that if the directivity of a receiving antenna is increased, its maximum effective aperture is increased in direct proportion. Therefore, the maximum effective apertures of two antennas, A_{em1} and A_{em2}, are in the same proportion as the directivities of the two antennas D_1 and D_2. That is,

$$\frac{D_1}{D_2} = \frac{A_{em1}}{A_{em2}} \tag{3-41}$$

In Chap. 2 the gain of a transmitting antenna with respect to a lossless isotropic source was shown to be equal to the directivity times the antenna efficiency. If the definition of gain is now extended to include both losses, as expressed by the efficiency factor k and the effect of impedance mismatch, we may replace k in (2-51) by the effectiveness ratio α; then

$$G_0 = \alpha D \qquad \qquad (3\text{-}42)$$

where G_0 is the gain of a transmitting or receiving antenna with respect to a lossless isotropic antenna. The isotropic antenna is assumed to be terminated for maximum power transfer, but the antenna under consideration may or may not be. If the antenna is terminated for maximum power transfer, $\alpha = k$ and (3-42) reduces to (2-51).

Let us now compare the gain of two antennas, G_{01} and G_{02}. If the directivities of these antennas are D_1 and D_2 and their effectiveness ratios, α_1 and α_2, respectively, we have from (3-41)

$$\frac{G_{01}}{G_{02}} = \frac{\alpha_1 D_1}{\alpha_2 D_2} = \frac{\alpha_1 A_{em1}}{\alpha_2 A_{em2}} \qquad (3\text{-}43)$$

By (3-17) the product of the maximum effective aperture and the effectiveness ratio is the effective aperture. Therefore, (3-43) becomes

$$\frac{G_{01}}{G_{02}} = \frac{A_{e1}}{A_{e2}} \qquad (3\text{-}44)$$

where A_{e1} and A_{e2} are the effective apertures of antennas 1 and 2.

3-10. Maximum Effective Aperture of an Isotropic Source. The maximum effective aperture of an isotropic source will now be derived. The directivity of an isotropic source is unity. If antenna 1 is an isotropic source, then, in (3-41), $D_1 = 1$ and

$$A_{em1} = \frac{A_{em2}}{D_2} \qquad (3\text{-}45)$$

Equation (3-45) states that the maximum effective aperture of an isotropic antenna (antenna 1) is equal to the ratio of the maximum effective aperture to the directivity of *any* antenna (antenna 2). We have already calculated the maximum effective aperture and directivity for a short dipole antenna. These are $(3/8\pi)\lambda^2$ and $3/2$, respectively. Introducing these values into (3-45) gives

$$A_{em1} = \frac{3 \times 2 \lambda^2}{3 \times 8\pi} = \frac{\lambda^2}{4\pi} = 0.079 \lambda^2 \qquad (3\text{-}46)$$

Substituting (3-46) in (3-45), we obtain the relation that the directivity of any antenna is equal to its maximum effective aperture, divided by the maximum effective aperture of an isotropic antenna. That is, the directivity of any antenna is equal to $4\pi/\lambda^2$ times its maximum effective aperture in square wavelengths. Thus,

$$D = \frac{4\pi}{\lambda^2} A_{em} \tag{3-47}$$

3-11. Maximum Effective Aperture and Directivity of Isotropic, Short Dipole, and $\frac{1}{2}$-Wavelength Antennas. The maximum effective aperture of a linear $\frac{1}{2}$-wavelength antenna was calculated in Sec. 3-8 as 0.13 square wavelength. The directivity of the $\frac{1}{2}$-wavelength antenna can now be calculated from (3-47) as

$$D = 4\pi \frac{30}{73\pi} = 1.64 \tag{3-48}$$

The maximum effective aperture and directivity of isotropic, short dipole, and $\frac{1}{2}$-wavelength antennas have now been calculated. The values are summarized in Table 3-1.

TABLE 3-1

Antenna	Maximum effective aperture, λ^2	Directivity	Db directivity*
Isotropic................	$\dfrac{1}{4\pi} = 0.079$	1	0
Short dipole.............	$\dfrac{3}{8\pi} = 0.119$	1.5	1.76
Linear $\frac{1}{2}$-wavelength.......	$\dfrac{30}{73\pi} = 0.13$	1.64	2.14

* Db directivity $= 10 \log_{10} D$.

3-12. Friis Transmission Formula. As a further illustration of the utility of the aperture concept, it will be applied to the derivation of a simple free-space transmission formula which has been presented by H. T. Friis.[1]

Referring to Fig. 3-8, an isotropic, 100 per cent efficient[2] point source radiates a power W_t. At a distance r in free space, the power density is

[1] A Note on a Simple Transmission Formula, *Proc. I.R.E.*, **34**, 254–256, May, 1946.
[2] Power radiated equals power input.

$$P = \frac{W_t}{4\pi r^2} \tag{3-49}$$

The power W_r delivered to the equivalent impedance appearing across the antenna terminals is

$$W_r = A_{er}P = \frac{W_t A_{er}}{4\pi r^2} \tag{3-50}$$

where A_{er} is the effective aperture of the receiving antenna. If the source is not isotropic but has a directivity D_t, (3-50) becomes

$$\frac{W_r}{W_t} = \frac{A_{er}D_t}{4\pi r^2} \tag{3-51}$$

From (3-47) we have

$$D_t = \frac{4\pi}{\lambda^2} A_{emt} \tag{3-52}$$

where A_{emt} is the maximum effective aperture of the source or transmitting antenna. The concept of aperture, originally developed for receiving antennas, is here extended to transmitting antennas, the aperture

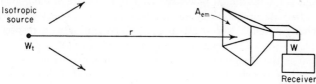

FIG. 3-8.   Free-space transmission circuit consisting of isotropic source and receiving horn of maximum effective aperture A_{em}.

of a transmitting antenna being equal to its aperture when used as a receiving antenna. Introducing (3-52) into (3-51) gives the Friis transmission formula,[1]

$$\frac{W_r}{W_t} = \frac{A_{er}A_{emt}}{\lambda^2 r^2} \tag{3-53}$$

This formula may be made more general by replacing the maximum effective aperture of the source by its effective aperture A_{et}. Then we have

$$\frac{W_r}{W_t} = \frac{A_{er}A_{et}}{\lambda^2 r^2} \tag{3-54}$$

The ratio W_r/W_t in (3-54) may be called a *power transfer ratio*. It expresses the fraction of the power input to a transmitting antenna

[1] In the formula as given by Friis both apertures are maximum effective apertures.

which is picked up and delivered to the terminals of a receiving antenna at a distance r in free space. The power-transfer ratio is expressed by (3-54) in terms of the effective apertures of the transmitting and receiving antennas, their separation, and the wavelength. Equation (3-54) is a far-field relation and hence will not apply if r is too small compared with the size of the antenna. However, the error is less than a few per cent if

$$r \geq \frac{2d^2}{\lambda} \qquad (3\text{-}55)$$

where d is the maximum linear dimension of either antenna. The formula is also restricted to free-space circuits. If transmission is via a direct path *and* a simple ground reflection, the power transfer ratio may lie between the extremes of four times the value given by (3-54) and zero, depending on whether the direct and reflected waves reinforce or cancel at the receiving location.

PROBLEMS

3-1. What is the maximum effective aperture of a microwave antenna with a directivity of 900?

3-2. What is the maximum power received at a distance of 0.5 kilometer over a free-space 1,000-Mc circuit consisting of a transmitting antenna with a 25-db gain and a receiving antenna with a 20-db gain? The gain is with respect to a lossless isotropic source. The transmitting antenna input is 150 watts.

3-3. What is the maximum effective aperture (approximately) for a beam antenna having half-power widths of 30° and 35° in perpendicular planes intersecting in the beam axis? Minor lobes are small and can be neglected.

CHAPTER 4

ARRAYS OF POINT SOURCES

4-1. Introduction.[1] In Chap. 2 an antenna was considered as a single point source. In Chap. 3 an antenna was treated as an aperture. In this chapter we return again to the point-source concept, however, extending it to a consideration of arrays of point sources. This approach is of great value since the pattern of any antenna can be regarded as produced by an array of point sources. Much of the discussion will concern arrays of isotropic point sources which may represent many different kinds of antennas. Arrays of nonisotropic but similar point sources are also treated, leading to the principle of pattern multiplication. From arrays of discrete point sources we proceed to continuous arrays of point sources and Huygens' principle.

4-2. Arrays of Two Isotropic Point Sources. Let us introduce the subject of arrays of point sources by considering the simplest situation, namely, that of two isotropic point sources. As illustrations, five cases involving two isotropic point sources will be discussed.

Case 1. Two Isotropic Point Sources of Same Amplitude and Phase. The first case we shall analyze is that of two isotropic point sources having equal amplitudes and oscillating in the same phase. Let the two point sources, 1 and 2, be separated by a distance d and located symmetrically with respect to the origin of the coordinates as shown in Fig. 4-1a. The angle ϕ is measured counterclockwise from the positive x axis. The origin of the coordinates is taken as the reference for phase. Then at a distant point in the direction ϕ the field from source 1 is retarded by $\frac{1}{2}d_r \cos \phi$, while the field from source 2 is advanced by $\frac{1}{2}d_r \cos \phi$, where d_r is the distance between the sources expressed in radians. That is,

$$d_r = \frac{2\pi d}{\lambda}$$

---

[1] In calculating patterns much labor may be saved in evaluating trigonometric functions by expressing the argument of the function in *turns* instead of in *radians* or *degrees*. Those not already familiar with this timesaving technique may refer to the discussion in the Appendix on "Radians, degrees, and turns." A table of trigonometric functions of arguments expressed in turns is also included in the Appendix.

The total field at a large distance r in the direction ϕ is then

$$E = E_0 e^{-i\frac{\psi}{2}} + E_0 e^{+i\frac{\psi}{2}} \tag{4-1}$$

where $\psi = d_r \cos \phi$ and the amplitude of the field components at the distance r is given by E_0.

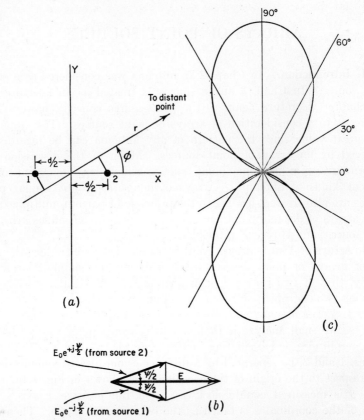

(a)

(b)

(c)

FIG. 4-1. (a) Relation to coordinate system of two isotropic point sources separated by a distance d. (b) Vector addition of the fields from two isotropic points sources of equal amplitude and same phase located as in (a). (c) Field pattern of two isotropic point sources of equal amplitude and same phase located as in (a) for the case where the separation d is $\frac{1}{2}$ wavelength.

The first term in (4-1) is the component of the field due to source 1 and the second term the component due to source 2. Equation (4-1) may be rewritten

$$E = 2E_0 \frac{e^{+i\frac{\psi}{2}} + e^{-i\frac{\psi}{2}}}{2} \tag{4-2}$$

which by a trigonometric identity is

$$E = 2E_0 \cos \frac{\psi}{2} = 2E_0 \cos \left(\frac{d_r}{2} \cos \phi \right) \qquad (4\text{-}3)$$

This result may also be obtained with the aid of the vector diagram shown in Fig. 4-1b, from which (4-3) follows directly. We note in Fig. 4-1b that the phase of the total field E does not change as a function of ψ. To normalize (4-3), that is, make its maximum value unity, set $2E_0 = 1$. Suppose further that d is $\frac{1}{2}$ wavelength. Then $d_r = \pi$. Introducing these conditions into (4-3) gives

$$E = \cos \left(\frac{\pi}{2} \cos \phi \right) \qquad (4\text{-}4)$$

The field pattern of E vs. ϕ as expressed by (4-4) is presented in Fig. 4-1c. The pattern is a bidirectional figure of eight with maxima along the y axis. The space pattern is doughnut-shaped, being a figure of revolution of this pattern around the x axis.

The same pattern can also be obtained by locating source 1 at the origin of the coordinates and source 2 at a distance d along the positive x axis as indicated in Fig. 4-2a. Taking now the field from source 1 as reference, the field from source 2 in the direction ϕ is advanced by $d_r \cos \phi$. Thus, the total field E at a large distance r is the vector sum of the fields from the two sources as given by

$$E = E_0 + E_0 e^{+i\psi} \qquad (4\text{-}5)$$

where $\psi = d_r \cos \phi$

The relation of these fields is indicated by the vector diagram of Fig. 4-2b. From the vector diagram it is apparent that the magnitude of the total field can be expressed

$$E = 2E_0 \cos \frac{\psi}{2} = 2E_0 \cos \frac{d_r \cos \phi}{2} \qquad (4\text{-}6)$$

as obtained before in (4-3). The phase of the total field E is, however, not constant in this case but is $\psi/2$. This may also be shown by rewriting (4-5) as

$$E = E_0(1 + e^{i\psi}) = 2E_0 e^{i\frac{\psi}{2}} \left(\frac{e^{i\frac{\psi}{2}} + e^{-i\frac{\psi}{2}}}{2} \right) = 2E_0 e^{i\frac{\psi}{2}} \cos \frac{\psi}{2} \qquad (4\text{-}7)$$

Normalizing by setting $2E_0 = 1$, (4-7) becomes

$$E = e^{i\frac{\psi}{2}} \cos \frac{\psi}{2} = \cos \frac{\psi}{2} \bigg/ \!\!\underline{\frac{\psi}{2}} \qquad (4\text{-}8)$$

In (4-8) the cosine factor gives the amplitude variation of E, and the exponential or angle factor gives the phase variation *with respect to source 1* as the reference. The phase variation for the case of $\frac{1}{2}$-wavelength spacing ($d_r = \pi$) is shown by the dashed line in Fig. 4-2c. Here the phase angle with respect to the phase of source 1 is given by $\psi/2 = (\pi/2) \cos \phi$.

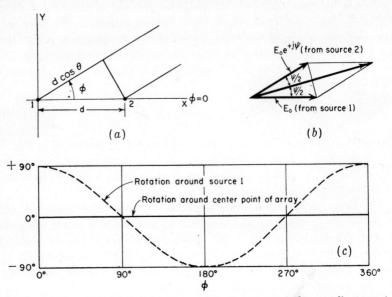

(a)   (b)

(c)

Fig. 4-2. (a) Two isotropic point sources with the origin of the coordinate system coincident with one of the sources. (b) Vector addition of the fields from two isotropic point sources of equal amplitude and same phase located as in (a). (c) Phase of total field as a function of ϕ for two isotropic point sources of same amplitude and phase spaced $\frac{1}{2}$ wavelength apart. The phase change is zero when referred to the center point of the array but is $\psi/2$ as shown by the dashed curve when referred to source 1.

The magnitude variation for this case has already been presented in Fig. 4-1c. When the phase is referred to the point midway between the sources (Fig. 4-1a), there is no phase change around the array as shown by the solid line in Fig. 4-2c. Thus, an observer at a fixed distance observes no phase change when the array is rotated (with respect to ϕ) around its mid-point, but a phase change (dashed curve of Fig. 4-2c) is observed if the array is rotated with source 1 as the center of rotation.

Case 2. Two Isotropic Point Sources of Same Amplitude But Opposite Phase. This case is identical with the one we have just considered except that the two sources are in opposite phase instead of in the same phase. Let the sources be located as in Fig. 4-1a. Then the total field in the direction ϕ at a large distance r is given by

$$E = E_0 e^{+i\frac{\psi}{2}} - E_0 e^{-i\frac{\psi}{2}} \tag{4-9}$$

from which

$$E = 2jE_0 \sin \frac{\psi}{2} = 2jE_0 \sin \left(\frac{d_r}{2} \cos \phi \right) \qquad (4\text{-}10)$$

Whereas in Case 1 Eq. (4-3) involves the cosine of $\psi/2$, (4-10) for Case 2 involves the sine. Equation (4-10) also includes an operator j, indicating that the phase reversal of one of the sources in Case 2 results in a 90° phase shift of the total field as compared with the total field for

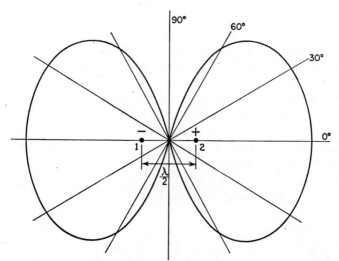

FIG. 4-3.   Relative field pattern for two isotropic point sources of the same amplitude but opposite phase, spaced $\frac{1}{2}$ wavelength apart.

Case 1.   This is unimportant here. Thus, putting $2jE_0 = 1$ and considering the special case of $d = \lambda/2$, (4-10) becomes

$$E = \sin \left(\frac{\pi}{2} \cos \Phi \right) \qquad (4\text{-}11)$$

The directions ϕ_m of maximum field are obtained by setting the argument of (4-11) equal to $\pm(2k + 1)\pi/2$. Thus,

$$\frac{\pi}{2} \cos \phi_m = \pm(2k + 1) \frac{\pi}{2} \qquad (4\text{-}11a)$$

where $k = 0, 1, 2, 3. \ldots$ For $k = 0$, $\cos \phi_m = \pm 1$ and $\phi_m = 0°$ and 180°. The null directions ϕ_0 are given by

$$\frac{\pi}{2} \cos \phi_0 = \pm k\pi \qquad (4\text{-}11b)$$

For $k = 0$, $\phi_0 = \pm 90°$.

The half-power directions are given by

$$\frac{\pi}{2} \cos \phi = \pm(2k + 1) \frac{\pi}{4} \tag{4-11c}$$

For $k = 0$, $\phi = \pm 60°$, $\pm 120°$.

The field pattern given by (4-11) is shown in Fig. 4-3. The pattern is a relatively fat figure of eight with the maximum field in the same direction as the line joining the sources (x axis). The space pattern is a figure of revolution of this pattern around the x axis. The two sources, in this case, may be described as a simple type of "end-fire" array. In contrast to this pattern, the in-phase point sources produce a pattern with the maximum field normal to the line joining the sources, as shown in Fig. 4-1c. The two sources for this case may be described as a simple "broadside" type of array.

Case 3. *Two Isotropic Point Sources of the Same Amplitude and in Phase Quadrature.* Let the two point sources be located as in Fig. 4-1a. Taking the origin of the coordinates as the reference for phase, let source 1 be retarded by 45° and source 2 advanced by 45°. Then the total field in the direction ϕ at a large distance r is given by

$$E = E_0 e^{+i\left(\frac{d_r \cos \phi}{2} + \frac{\pi}{4}\right)} + E_0 e^{-i\left(\frac{d_r \cos \phi}{2} + \frac{\pi}{4}\right)} \tag{4-12}$$

From (4-12) we obtain

$$E = 2E_0 \cos \left(\frac{\pi}{4} + \frac{d_r}{2} \cos \phi\right) \tag{4-13}$$

Letting $2E_0 = 1$ and $d = \lambda/2$, (4-13) becomes

$$E = \cos \left(\frac{\pi}{4} + \frac{\pi}{2} \cos \phi\right) \tag{4-14}$$

The field pattern given by (4-14) is presented in Fig. 4-4. The space pattern is a figure of revolution of this pattern around the x axis. Most of the radiation is in the second and third quadrants. It is interesting to note that the field in the direction $\phi = 0°$ is the same as in the direction $\phi = 180°$. The directions ϕ_m of maximum field are obtained by setting the argument of (4-14) equal to $k\pi$, where $k = 0, 1, 2, 3. \ldots$ In this way we obtain

$$\frac{\pi}{4} + \frac{\pi}{2} \cos \phi_m = k\pi \tag{4-15}$$

For $k = 0$,

$$\frac{\pi}{2} \cos \phi_m = -\frac{\pi}{4} \tag{4-16}$$

and

$$\phi_m = 120° \text{ and } 240° \tag{4-17}$$

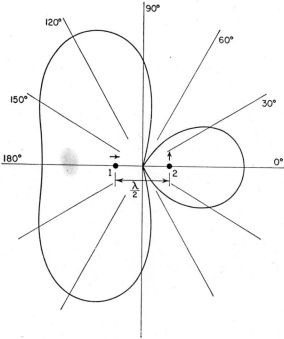

FIG. 4-4. Relative field pattern of two isotropic point sources of same amplitude and in phase quadrature for a spacing of $\frac{1}{2}$ wavelength. The source to the right leads that to the left by 90°.

If the spacing between the sources is reduced to $\frac{1}{4}$ wavelength, (4-13) becomes

$$E = \cos\left(\frac{\pi}{4} + \frac{\pi}{4} \cos \phi\right) \tag{4-18}$$

The field pattern for this case is illustrated by Fig. 4-5a. It is a cardioid-shaped, unidirectional pattern with maximum field in the negative x direction. The space pattern is a figure of revolution of this pattern around the x axis.

A simple method of checking the direction of maximum field is illustrated by Fig. 4-5b. Source 2 leads source 1 by 90° as indicated by the vectors in the top diagram. By the time the field from source 2 has arrived at source 1, the phase of source 1 has advanced 90° so that the fields add in the $-x$ direction as shown in the middle diagram. On the other hand, by the time the field from source 1 arrives at source 2, the phase of source 2 has advanced 90° so that the two fields are in phase opposition, and, therefore, the total field in the $+x$ direction is zero as shown in the bottom diagram.

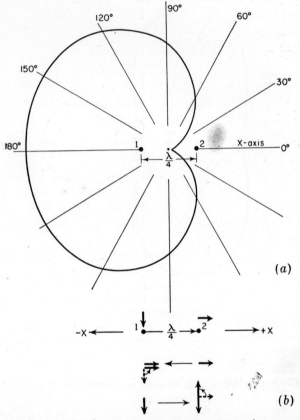

(a)

(b)

FIG. 4-5. (a) Relative field pattern of two isotropic sources of same amplitude and in phase quadrature for a spacing of $\frac{1}{4}$ wavelength. Source 2 leads source 1 by 90°. (b) Vector diagrams illustrating field reinforcement in $-x$ direction and field cancellation in $+x$ direction.

Case 4. General Case of Two Isotropic Point Sources of Equal Amplitude and Any Phase Difference. Proceeding now to a more general situation, let us consider the case of two isotropic point sources of equal amplitude but of any phase difference δ. The total phase difference ψ between the fields from source 2 and source 1 at a distant point in the direction ϕ (see Fig. 4-2a) is then

$$\psi = d_r \cos \phi + \delta \qquad (4\text{-}19)$$

Taking source 1 as the reference for phase, the positive sign in (4-19) indicates that source 2 is advanced in phase by the angle δ. A minus sign would be used to indicate a phase retardation. If, instead of referring the phase to source 1, it is referred to the center point of the array, the phase of the field from source 1 at a distant point is given by $-\psi/2$ and that from source 2 by $+\psi/2$. The total field is then

$$E = E_0(e^{i\frac{\psi}{2}} + e^{-i\frac{\psi}{2}}) = 2E_0 \cos\frac{\psi}{2} \qquad (4\text{-}20)$$

Normalizing (4-20), we have the general expression for the field pattern of two isotropic sources of equal amplitude and arbitrary phase,

$$E = \cos\frac{\psi}{2} \qquad (4\text{-}21)$$

where ψ is given by (4-19). The three cases we have discussed are obviously special cases of (4-21). Thus, Cases 1, 2, and 3 are obtained from (4-21) when $\delta = 0°$, 180°, and 90°, respectively.

Case 5. Most General Case of Two Isotropic Point Sources of Unequal Amplitude and Any Phase Difference. A still more general situation, involving two isotropic point sources, exists when the amplitudes are unequal and the phase difference is arbitrary. Let the sources be situated as in Fig. 4-6a with source 1 at the origin. Assume that the source 1

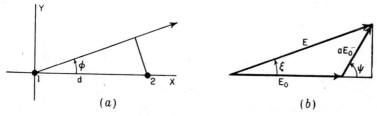

(a) (b)

Fig. 4-6. (a) Two isotropic point sources of unequal amplitude and arbitrary phase with respect to coordinate system. (b) Vector addition of fields from unequal sources arranged as in (a). The amplitude of source 2 is assumed to be smaller than that of source 1 by the factor a.

has the larger amplitude and that its field at a large distance r has an amplitude of E_0. Let the field from source 2 be of amplitude aE_0 ($0 \leq a \leq 1$) at the distance r. Then, referring to Fig. 4-6b, the magnitude and phase angle of the total field E is given by

$$E = E_0\sqrt{(1 + a\cos\psi)^2 + a^2\sin^2\psi} \ \bigg/ \arctan\frac{a\sin\psi}{1 + a\cos\psi} \qquad (4\text{-}22)$$

where $\psi = d_r \cos \phi + \delta$ and the phase angle ($\angle$) is referred to source 1. This is the phase angle ξ shown in Fig. 4-6b.

4-3. Nonisotropic But Similar Point Sources and the Principle of Pattern Multiplication. The cases considered in the preceding section all involve *isotropic* point sources. These cases can readily be extended to a more general situation in which the sources are *nonisotropic but similar*.

The word *similar* is here used to indicate that the variation with absolute angle ϕ of both the amplitude and phase of the field is the same.[1] The maximum amplitudes of the individual sources may be unequal. If, however, they are also equal, the sources are not only similar but are *identical*.

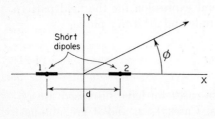

FIG. 4-7. Two nonisotropic sources with respect to coordinate system.

As an example, let us reconsider Case 4 of Sec. 4-2 in which the sources are identical, with the modification that both sources 1 and 2 have field patterns given by

$$E_0 = E_0' \sin \phi \qquad (4\text{-}23)$$

Patterns of this type might be produced by short dipoles oriented parallel to the x axis as suggested by Fig. 4-7. Substituting (4-23) in (4-20) and normalizing by setting $2E_0' = 1$ gives the field pattern of the array as

$$E = \sin \phi \cos \frac{\psi}{2} \qquad (4\text{-}24)$$

where $\psi = d_r \cos \phi + \delta$

This result is the same as obtained by multiplying the pattern of the individual source ($\sin \phi$) by the pattern of two isotropic point sources ($\cos \psi/2$).

If the similar but unequal point sources of Case 5 (Sec. 4-2) each has a pattern as given by (4-23), the total normalized pattern is

$$E = \sin \phi \ \sqrt{(1 + a \cos \psi)^2 + a^2 \sin^2 \psi} \qquad (4\text{-}25)$$

Here again the result is the same as that obtained by multiplying the pattern of the individual source by the pattern of an array of isotropic point sources.

These are examples illustrating the *principle of pattern multiplication*, which may be expressed as follows: The field pattern of an array of nonisotropic but similar point sources is the product of the pattern of the

[1] The patterns not only must be of the same shape but also must be oriented in the same direction to be called "similar."

individual source and the pattern of an array of isotropic point sources, having the same locations, relative amplitudes, and phases as the non-isotropic point sources. This principle may be applied to arrays of any number of sources provided only that they are similar. The individual nonisotropic source or antenna may be of finite size but can be considered as a point source situated at the point in the antenna to which phase is referred. This point is said to be the "phase center."

The above discussion of pattern multiplication has been concerned only with the field pattern or magnitude of the field. If the field of the non-isotropic source and the array of isotropic sources vary in phase with space angle, that is, have a phase pattern which is not a constant, the statement of the principle of pattern multiplication may be extended to include this more general case as follows: *The total field pattern of an array of non-isotropic but similar sources is the product of the individual source pattern and the pattern of an array of isotropic point sources each located at the phase center of the individual source and having the same relative amplitude and phase, while the total phase pattern is the sum of the phase patterns of the individual source and the array of isotropic point sources.* The total phase pattern is referred to the phase center of the array. In symbols, the total field E is then

$$E = \underbrace{f(\theta, \phi)\, F(\theta, \phi)}_{\text{Field pattern}} \underbrace{\big/ f_p(\theta, \phi) + F_p(\theta, \phi)}_{\text{Phase pattern}} \qquad (4\text{-}26)$$

where $f(\theta, \phi)$ = field pattern of individual source

$f_p(\theta, \phi)$ = phase pattern of individual source

$F(\theta, \phi)$ = field pattern of array of isotropic sources

$F_p(\theta, \phi)$ = phase pattern of array of isotropic sources

The patterns are expressed in (4-26) as a function of both polar angles to indicate that the principle of pattern multiplication applies to space patterns as well as to the two-dimensional cases we have been considering.

To illustrate the principle, let us apply it to two special modifications of Case 1 (Sec. 4-2).

Example 1. Assume two identical point sources separated by a distance d, each source having the field pattern given by (4-23) as might be obtained by two short dipoles arranged as in Fig. 4-7. Let $d = \lambda/2$ and the phase angle $\delta = 0$. Then the total field pattern is

$$E = \sin \phi\, \cos \left(\frac{\pi}{2} \cos \phi \right) \qquad (4\text{-}27)$$

This pattern is illustrated by Fig. 4-8c as the product of the individual source pattern $(\sin \phi)$ shown at (a) and the array pattern $\{\cos [(\pi/2) \cos \phi]\}$ as shown at (b). The pattern is sharper than it was in Case 1 (Sec. 4-2) for the isotropic sources. In this instance, the maximum field of the individual source is in the direction $\phi = 90°$, which coincides with the direction of the maximum field for the array of two isotropic sources.

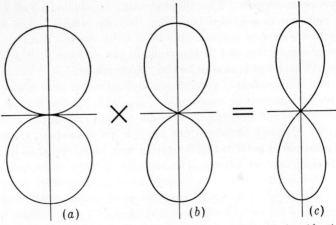

(a)   (b)   (c)

Fig. 4-8. Example of pattern multiplication. Two nonisotropic but identical point sources of same amplitude and phase, spaced $\frac{1}{2}$ wavelength apart, and arranged as in Fig. 4-7, produce the pattern shown at (c). The individual source has the pattern shown at (a), which, when multiplied by the pattern of an array of two isotropic point sources (of the same amplitude and phase) as shown at (b), yields the total array pattern of (c).

Example 2. Let us consider next the situation in which $d = \lambda/2$ and $\delta = 0$ as in Example 1 but with individual source patterns given by

$$E_0 = E_0' \cos \phi \qquad (4\text{-}28)$$

This type of pattern might be produced by short dipoles oriented parallel to the y axis as in Fig. 4-9. Here the maximum field of the individual source is in the direction ($\phi = 0$) of a null from the array, while the individual source has a null in the direction ($\phi = 90°$) of the pattern maximum of the array. By the principle of pattern multiplication the total normalized field is

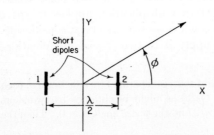

Fig. 4-9. Array of two nonisotropic sources with respect to coordinate system.

$$E = \cos \phi \cos \left(\frac{\pi}{2} \cos \phi \right) \qquad (4\text{-}29)$$

The total array pattern in the x-y plane as given by (4-29) is illustrated in Fig. 4-10c as the product of the individual source pattern ($\cos \phi$) shown at (a) and the array pattern $\{\cos [(\pi/2) \cos \phi]\}$ shown at (b). The total array pattern in the x-y plane has four lobes with nulls at the x and y axes.

The above examples illustrate two applications of the principle of pattern multiplication to arrays in which the source has a simple pattern. However, in the more general case the individual source may represent an antenna of any complexity provided that the amplitude and phase of its field can be expressed as a function of angle, that is to say, provided that the field pattern and the phase pattern with respect to the phase center are known. If only the total field pattern is desired, phase patterns need not be known provided that the individual sources are identical.

If the arrays in the above examples are parts of still larger arrays, the smaller arrays may be regarded as nonisotropic point sources in the larger array, another application of the principle of pattern multiplication yielding the complete pattern. In this way the principle of pattern multiplication can be applied n times to find the patterns of arrays of arrays of arrays.

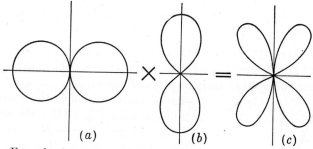

(a) (b) (c)

Fig. 4-10.   Example of pattern multiplication.   Total array pattern (c) as product of pattern (a) of individual nonisotropic source and pattern (b) of array of two isotropic sources.   The pattern (b) for the array of two isotropic sources is identical with that of Fig. 4-8b, but the individual source pattern (a) is rotated through 90° with respect to the one in Fig. 4-8a.

4-4. Example of Pattern Synthesis by Pattern Multiplication. The
principle of pattern multiplication, discussed in the preceding section, is of great value in pattern synthesis. By pattern synthesis is meant the process of finding the source or array of sources which produces a desired pattern. Theoretically an array of isotropic point sources can be found which will produce any arbitrary pattern. This process is not always simple and may yield an array which is difficult or impossible to construct. A simpler, less elegant approach to the problem of antenna synthesis is by the application of pattern multiplication to combinations of practical arrays, the combination which best approximates the desired pattern being arrived at by a trial-and-error process.

To illustrate this application of pattern multiplication, let us consider the following hypothetical problem: A broadcasting station (in the 500- to 1,500-kc frequency band) requires a pattern in the horizontal plane fulfilling the conditions indicated in Fig. 4-11a. The maximum field in-

tensity, with as little variation as possible, is to be radiated in the 90°
sector between northwest and northeast. No nulls in the pattern can
occur in this sector. However, nulls may occur in any direction in the

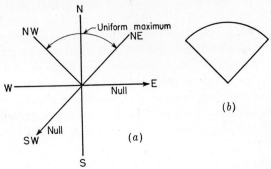

(b)

(a)

Fig. 4-11. (a) Requirements for pattern of broadcast station, and (b) idealized pattern
fulfilling them.

complementary 270° sector, but, as an additional requirement, nulls must
be present in the due east and due southwest directions in order to prevent
interference with other stations in these directions. An idealized sector
shaped pattern fulfilling those requirements
is illustrated in Fig. 4-11b. The antenna producing this pattern is to consist of an array of
four vertical towers. The currents in all
towers are to be equal in magnitude, but the
phase may be adjusted to any relationship.
There is also no restriction on the spacing or
geometrical arrangement of the towers.

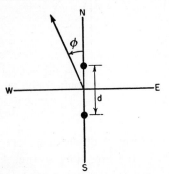

Fig. 4-12. Arrangement of two
isotropic point sources for both
primary and secondary arrays.

Since we are interested only in the horizontal plane pattern, each tower may be considered as an isotropic point source. The
problem then becomes one of finding a space
and phase relation of four isotropic point
sources located in the horizontal plane which
fulfills the above requirements.

The principle of pattern multiplication will be applied to the solution
of this problem by seeking the patterns of two pairs of isotropic sources
which yield the desired pattern when multiplied together. First let us
find a pair of isotropic sources whose pattern fulfills the requirements of
a broad lobe of radiation with maximum north and a null southwest.
This will be called the "primary" pattern.

Two isotropic sources phased as an end-fire array can produce a pattern
with a broader major lobe than when phased as a broadside array (for
example, compare Figs. 4-1c and 4-5). Since a broad lobe to the north

is desired, an end-fire arrangement of two isotropic sources as shown in
Fig. 4-12 will be tried. From a consideration of pattern shapes as a
function of separation and phase,[1] a spacing between $\frac{1}{4}$ and $\frac{3}{8}$ wavelength

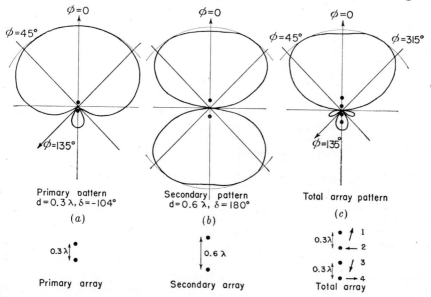

Fig. 4-13. Field patterns of primary and secondary arrays of two isotropic sources
which multiplied together give pattern of total array of four isotropic sources.

appears suitable (see Fig. 11-11). Accordingly, let $d = 0.3\lambda$. Then the
field pattern for the array is

$$E = \cos\frac{\psi}{2} \tag{4-30}$$

where

$$\psi = 0.6\pi \cos\phi + \delta \tag{4-31}$$

For there to be a null in the pattern of (4-30) at $\phi = 135°$ it is necessary
that[2]

$$\psi = (2k + 1)\pi \tag{4-32}$$

where $k = 0, 1, 2, 3 \ldots$

[1] See for example, G. H. Brown, Directional Antennas, *Proc. I.R.E.*, **25**, January,
1937; F. E. Terman, "Radio Engineers' Handbook," McGraw-Hill Book Company,
Inc., New York, 1943, p. 804; C. E. Smith, "Directional Antennas," Cleveland Institute
of Radio Electronics, Cleveland, Ohio, 1946.
[2] The azimuth angle ϕ (Fig. 4-12) is measured counterclockwise (ccw) from the
north. This is consistent with the engineering practice of measuring positive angles
in a counterclockwise sense. However, it should be noted that the *geodetic azimuth angle*
of a point is measured in the opposite, or clockwise (cw), sense from the reference direction, which is sometimes taken as south and sometimes as north.

Equating (4-31) and (4-32) then gives

$$-0.6\pi \frac{1}{\sqrt{2}} + \delta = (2k + 1)\pi \qquad (4\text{-}33)$$

or

$$\delta = (2k + 1)\pi + 0.425\pi \qquad (4\text{-}34)$$

For $k = 0$, $\delta = -104°$. The pattern for this case ($d = 0.3\lambda$ and $\delta = -104°$) is illustrated by Fig. 4-13a.

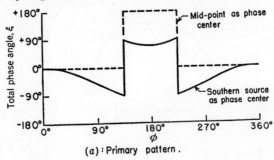

(a): Primary pattern.

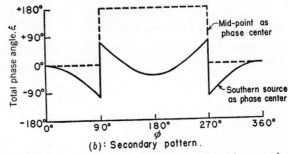

(b): Secondary pattern.

FIG. 4-14. Phase patterns of primary, secondary, and total arrays having the field patterns shown in Fig. 4-13. Phase patterns are given for the phase center at the mid-point of the array and at the southernmost source, the arrangement of the arrays and the phase centers being shown at (d). The phase angle ξ is adjusted to zero at $\phi = 0$ in all cases. Parts (a) and (b) appear above and (c) and (d) on p. 73.

Next, let us find the array of two isotropic point sources which will produce a pattern that fulfills the requirements of a null at $\phi = 270°$ and that also has a broad lobe to the north. This will be called the "secondary" pattern. This pattern multiplied by the primary array pattern will then yield the total array pattern. If the secondary isotropic sources are also arranged as in Fig. 4-12 and have a phase difference of 180°, there is a null at $\phi = 270°$. Let the spacing $d = 0.6\lambda$. Then the secondary pattern is given by (4-30), where

$$\psi = 1.2\pi \cos \phi + \pi \qquad (4\text{-}35)$$

The pattern is illustrated by Fig. 4-13*b*. By the principle of pattern multiplication, the total array pattern is the product of this pattern and the primary array pattern, or

$$E = \cos (54° \cos \phi - 52°) \cos (108° \cos \phi + 90°) \qquad (4\text{-}36)$$

This pattern, which is illustrated by Fig. 4-13*c*, satisfies the pattern requirements. The complete array is obtained by replacing each of the isotropic sources of the secondary pattern by the two-source array pro-

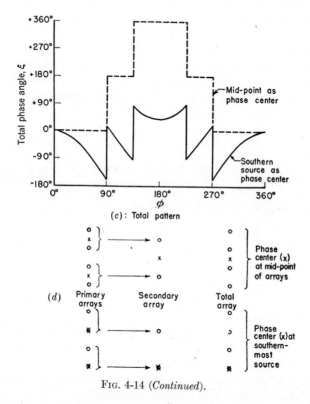

Fig. 4-14 (*Continued*).

ducing the primary pattern. The mid-point of each primary array is its phase center, so that this point is placed at the location of a secondary source. The complete antenna is then a linear array of four isotropic point sources as shown in the lower part of Fig. 4-13, where now each source represents a single vertical tower. All towers carry the same current. The current of tower 2 leads tower 1 and the current of tower 4 leads tower 3 by 104°, while the current in towers 1 and 3 and 2 and 4 are in phase opposition. The relative phase of the current is illustrated by the vectors in the lower part of Fig. 4-13*c*.

The solution obtained is only one of an infinite number of possible solutions involving four towers. It is, however, a satisfactory and practical solution to the problem.

The phase variation ξ around the primary, secondary, and total arrays is shown in Fig. 4-14a, b, and c with the phase center at the center point of each array and also at the southernmost source. The arrangement of the arrays with their phase centers is illustrated in Fig. 4-14d for both cases.

4-5. Nonisotropic and Dissimilar Point Sources. In Sec. 4-3 nonisotropic but similar point sources were discussed, and it was shown that the principle of pattern multiplication could be applied. However, if the sources are dissimilar, this principle is no longer applicable and the fields of the sources must be added at each angle ϕ for which the total field is calculated. Thus, for two dissimilar sources 1 and 2 situated on the x axis with source 1 at the origin and the sources separated by a distance d (same geometry as Fig. 4-6) the total field is in general

$$E = E_1 + E_2 = E_0 \sqrt{[f(\phi) + aF(\phi) \cos \psi]^2 + [aF(\phi) \sin \psi]^2}$$
$$\bigg/ \; f_p(\phi) + \arctan \frac{aF(\phi) \sin \psi}{f(\phi) + aF(\phi) \cos \psi} \qquad (4\text{-}37)$$

where the field from source 1 is taken as

$$E_1 = E_0 \, f(\phi) \; \underline{/ f_p(\phi)} \qquad (4\text{-}38)$$

and from source 2 as

$$E_2 = aE_0 \, F(\phi) \; \underline{/ F_p(\phi) + d_r \cos \phi + \delta} \qquad (4\text{-}39)$$

where E_0 = constant

a = ratio of maximum amplitude of source 2 to source 1 $(0 \leq a \leq 1)$

$\psi = d_r \cos \phi + \delta - f_p(\phi) + F_p(\phi)$, where

δ = relative phase of source 2 with respect to source 1

$f(\phi)$ = relative field pattern of source 1

$f_p(\phi)$ = phase pattern of source 1

$F(\phi)$ = relative field pattern of source 2

$F_p(\phi)$ = phase pattern of source 2

In (4-37) the phase angle $(\angle)$ is referred to the phase of the field from source 1 in some reference direction $(\phi = \phi_0)$.

Rather than perform the calculation of (4-37), it is usually much easier to find the amplitude and phase of the total field by a graphical vector addition of E_1 and E_2. In the special case where the field patterns are identical but the phase patterns are not, $a = 1$, and

$$f(\phi) = F(\phi) \qquad (4\text{-}40)$$

from which

$$E = 2E_0 \, f(\phi) \, \cos\frac{\psi}{2} \Big/\!\underline{\; f_p(\phi) + \frac{\psi}{2} \;} \qquad (4\text{-}41)$$

where phase is again referred to source 1 in some reference direction ϕ_0.

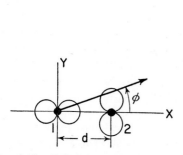

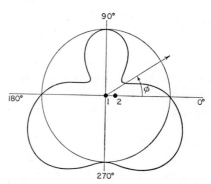

Fig. 4-15. Relation of two nonisotropic dissimilar sources to coordinate system.

Fig. 4-16. Field pattern of array of two nonisotropic dissimilar sources of Fig. 4-15 for $d = \lambda/4$ and $\delta = 90°$.

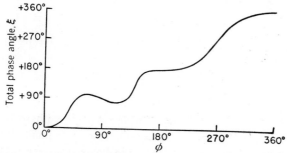

Fig. 4-17. Phase pattern of array having field patterns of Fig. 4-16. The phase angle ξ is with respect to source 1 as phase center.

As an illustration of nonisotropic, dissimilar point sources, let us consider an example in which the field from source 1 is given by

$$E_1 = \cos\phi \,\underline{/0} \qquad (4\text{-}42)$$

and from source 2 by

$$E_2 = \sin\phi \,\underline{/\psi} \qquad (4\text{-}43)$$

where $\psi = d_r \cos\phi + \delta$

The relation of the two sources to the coordinate system and the individual field patterns are shown in Fig. 4-15. Source 1 is located at the origin. The total field E is then the vector sum of E_1 and E_2, or

$$E = \cos \phi + \sin \phi \; \underline{/\psi} \qquad (4\text{-}44)$$

Let us consider the case for $\frac{1}{4}$-wavelength spacing ($d = \lambda/4$) and phase quadrature of the sources ($\delta = \pi/2$). Then

$$\psi = \frac{\pi}{2}(\cos \phi + 1) \qquad (4\text{-}45)$$

The calculation for this case is most easily carried out as a graphical vector addition. The resulting field pattern for the total field E of the array is presented in Fig. 4-16, and the resulting phase pattern for the angle ξ is given in Fig. 4-17. The angle ξ is the phase angle between the total field and the field of source 1 in the direction $\phi = 0$.

4-6. *a. Linear Arrays of n Isotropic Point Sources of Equal Amplitude and Spacing.*[1] Let us now proceed to the case of n isotropic point sources of equal amplitude and spacing arranged as a linear array, as indicated in Fig. 4-18, where n is any positive integer. The total field E at a large distance in the direction ϕ is given by

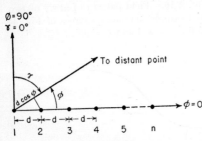

$$E = 1 + e^{j\psi} + e^{2j\psi}$$
$$+ e^{3j\psi} + \cdots + e^{j(n-1)\psi} \qquad (4\text{-}46)$$

where ψ is the total phase difference of the fields from adjacent sources as given by

FIG. 4-18.   Arrangement of linear array of n isotropic point sources.

$$\psi = d_r \cos \phi + \delta \qquad (4\text{-}46a)$$

where δ is the phase difference of adjacent sources. In the case under consideration this phase difference can assume any value. The amplitudes of the fields from the sources are all equal and taken as unity. Source 1 (Fig. 4-18) is the phase center so that the field from source 2 is advanced in phase by ψ; the field from source 3 is advanced by 2ψ, etc.

Equation (4-46) is a geometric series. Each term represents a vector, and the amplitude of the total field E and its phase angle ξ can be obtained by a graphical vector addition as in Fig. 4-19. However, a very simple trigonometric expression for E can be developed as follows:

---

[1] S. A. Schelkunoff, "Electromagnetic Waves," D. Van Nostrand Company, Inc., New York, 1943, p. 342.

   J. A. Stratton, "Electromagnetic Theory," McGraw-Hill Book Company, Inc., New York, 1941, p. 451.

Multiply (4-46) by $e^{i\psi}$, giving

$$Ee^{i\psi} = e^{i\psi} + e^{i2\psi} + e^{i3\psi} + \cdots + e^{in\psi} \qquad (4\text{-}47)$$

Now subtract (4-47) from (4-46), and divide by $1 - e^{i\psi}$, yielding

$$E = \frac{1 - e^{in\psi}}{1 - e^{i\psi}} \qquad (4\text{-}48)$$

Equation (4-48) may be rewritten as

$$E = \frac{e^{i\frac{n\psi}{2}}}{e^{i\frac{\psi}{2}}} \left(\frac{e^{i\frac{n\psi}{2}} - e^{-i\frac{n\psi}{2}}}{e^{i\frac{\psi}{2}} - e^{-i\frac{\psi}{2}}} \right) \qquad (4\text{-}49)$$

from which

$$E = e^{i\xi} \frac{\sin (n\psi/2)}{\sin (\psi/2)} = \frac{\sin (n\psi/2)}{\sin (\psi/2)} \underline{/\xi} \qquad (4\text{-}50)$$

where ξ is referred to the field from source 1. The value of ξ is given by

$$\xi = \frac{n-1}{2} \psi \qquad (4\text{-}50a)$$

If the phase is referred to the center point of the array (4-50) becomes

$$E = \frac{\sin (n\psi/2)}{\sin (\psi/2)} \qquad (4\text{-}51)$$

In this case the phase pattern is a step function as given by the sign of

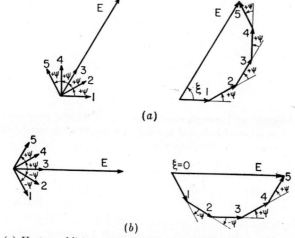

FIG. 4-19. (a) Vector addition of fields at a large distance from linear array of five isotropic point sources of equal amplitude with source 1 as the phase center (reference for phase). (b) Same, but with mid-point of array (source 3) as phase center.

(4-51). The phase of the field is constant wherever E has a value but changes by 180° in directions for which $E = 0$ (null directions) and (4-51) changes sign.

When $\psi = 0$ (4-50) or (4-51) is indeterminate so that for this case E must be obtained as the limit of (4-51) as ψ approaches zero. Thus, for $\psi = 0$ we have the relation that

$$E = n$$

This is the maximum value which E can attain. Hence, the normalized value of the total field for $E_{max} = n$ is

$$E = \frac{1}{n} \frac{\sin (n\psi/2)}{\sin (\psi/2)} \tag{4-52}$$

The field as given by (4-52) will be referred to as the "array factor." Values of the array factor as obtained from (4-52) for various numbers of

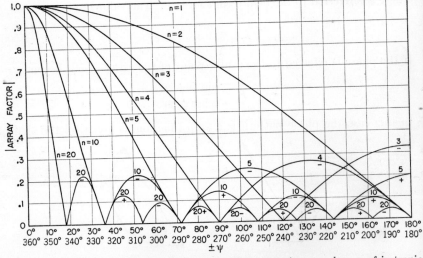

FIG. 4-20. Universal field-pattern chart for arrays of various numbers n of isotropic point sources of equal amplitude and spacing. Charts for all integral values of n from 1 through 24 are included in the Appendix.

sources are presented in Fig. 4-20.[1] If ψ is known as a function of ϕ, then the field pattern can be obtained directly from Fig. 4-20.

We may conclude from the above discussion that the field from the array will be a maximum in any direction ϕ for which $\psi = 0$. Stated in another way, the fields from the sources all arrive at a distant point in the same phase when $\psi = 0$. In special cases, ψ may not be zero for any

---

[1] Universal pattern charts giving the array factor as a function of ψ for all integral values of n from 1 through 24 are included in the Appendix.

value of ϕ, and in this case the field is usually a maximum at the minimum value of ψ.

To illustrate some of the properties of linear arrays equation (4-52) will now be applied to several special cases.

Case 1. *Broadside array (sources in phase).* The first case is a linear array of n isotropic sources of the same amplitude and phase. Therefore, $\delta = 0$, and

$$\psi = d_r \cos \phi \tag{4-53}$$

To make $\psi = 0$ requires that $\phi = (2k + 1)(\pi/2)$, where $k = 0, 1, 2, 3 \ldots$ The field is, therefore, a maximum when

$$\phi = \frac{\pi}{2} \text{ and } \frac{3\pi}{2}$$

That is, the maximum field is in a direction normal to the array. Hence, this condition, which is characterized by in-phase sources ($\delta = 0$), results in a "broadside" type of array.

As an example, the pattern of a broadside array of four in-phase isotropic point sources of equal amplitude is shown in Fig. 4-21a. The spacing between sources is $\frac{1}{2}$ wavelength. The field pattern in rectangular coordinates and the phase patterns for this array are presented in Fig. 4-21b.

The calculation of the field pattern of this or other arrays is facilitated by first calculating and plotting ψ as a function of ϕ. Then by means of this graph and one of the array factor vs. ψ for the appropriate number of sources (as in Fig. 4-20), the array factor E is obtained for any value of ϕ in two steps.

The range of ψ as a function of ϕ for the broadside array of four isotropic sources spaced $\frac{1}{2}$ wavelength is $+180°$ to $-180°$ and back again for a variation of ϕ from $0°$ to $360°$. That is,

ϕ	ψ
0°	180°
90°	0°
180°	−180°
270°	0°
360°	180°

On Fig. 4-20 ψ completes two cycles of values from 180° to 0° and back to 180° for a variation of ϕ from 0° to 360°.

Case 2. *Ordinary end-fire array.* Let us now find the phase angle between adjacent sources that is required to make the field a maximum in the direction of the array ($\phi = 0$). An array of this type may be called an "end-fire" array. For this we substitute the conditions $\psi = 0$ and $\phi = 0$ into (4-46a), from which

$$\delta = -d_r \tag{4-54}$$

Hence, for an end-fire array, the phase between sources is retarded progressively by the same amount as the spacing between sources in radians. Thus, if the spacing is $\frac{1}{4}$ wavelength, source 2 in Fig. 4-18 should lag source 1 by 90°; source 3 should lag source 2 by 90°, etc.

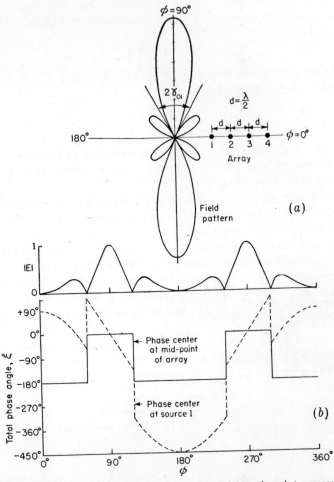

Fig. 4-21. (a) Field pattern of broadside array of four isotropic point sources of same amplitude and phase. The spacing between sources in $\frac{1}{2}$ wavelength. (b) Field pattern in rectangular coordinates and phase patterns of same array with phase center at mid-point and at source 1. The reference direction for phase is taken at $\phi = 90°$.

As an example, the field pattern of an end-fire array of four isotropic point sources is presented in Fig. 4-22a. The spacing between sources is $\frac{1}{2}$ wavelength, and $\delta = -\pi$. The field pattern in rectangular coordinates and the phase patterns are shown in Fig. 4-22b. The same shape of field pattern is obtained in this case if $\delta = +\pi$ since with $d = \lambda/2$ the pattern is bidirectional. However, if the spacing is less than $\lambda/2$, the maximum radiation is in the direction $\phi = 0$ when $\delta = -d_r$ and in the direction $\phi = 180°$ when $\delta = +d_r$.

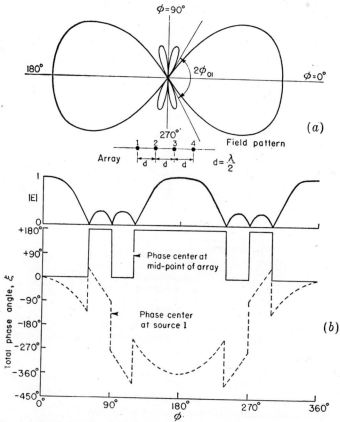

FIG. 4-22. (a) Field pattern of ordinary end-fire array of four isotropic point sources of same amplitude. Spacing is $\frac{1}{2}$ wavelength, and the phase angle $\delta = -\pi$. (b) Field pattern in rectangular coordinates and phase patterns of same array with phase center at mid-point and at source 1. The reference direction for phase is at $\phi = 0$.

Case 3. End-fire array with increased directivity. The situation discussed in Case 2, namely, for $\delta = -d_r$, produces a maximum field in the direction $\phi = 0$ but does not give the maximum directivity. It has been shown by Hansen and Woodyard[1] that a larger directivity is obtained by increasing the phase change between sources so that

$$\delta = -\left(d_r + \frac{\pi}{n}\right) \qquad (4\text{-}55)$$

[1] W. W. Hansen and J. R. Woodyard, A New Principle in Directional Antenna Design, *Proc. I.R.E.*, **26**, March, 1938, 333–345.

This condition will be referred to as the condition for "increased directivity." Thus for the phase difference of the fields at a large distance we have

$$\psi = d_r(\cos\phi - 1) - \frac{\pi}{n} \qquad (4\text{-}56)$$

As an example, the field pattern of an end-fire array of four isotropic point sources for this case is illustrated in Fig. 4-23. The spacing between

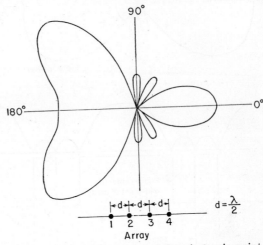

FIG. 4-23. Field pattern of end-fire array of four isotropic point sources of equal amplitude spaced $\frac{1}{2}$ wavelength apart. The phasing is adjusted for increased directivity ($\delta = -\frac{5}{4}\pi$).

sources is $\frac{1}{2}$ wavelength, and therefore $\delta = -(5\pi/4)$. Hence, the conditions are the same as for the array with the pattern of Fig. 4-22, except that the phase difference between sources is increased by $\pi/4$. Comparing the field patterns of Figs. 4-22a and 4-23, it is apparent that the additional phase difference yields a considerably sharper main lobe in the direction $\phi = 0$. However, the back lobes in this case are excessively large because the large value of spacing results in too great a range in ψ.

To realize the directivity increase afforded by the additional phase difference requires that $|\psi|$ be restricted in its range to a value of π/n at $\phi = 0$ and a value in the vicinity of π at $\phi = 180°$. This can be fulfilled if the spacing is reduced. For example, the field pattern of an end-fire array of 10 isotropic point sources of equal amplitude and spaced $\frac{1}{4}$ wavelength is presented in Fig. 4-24a for the phase condition giving increased directivity ($\delta = -0.6\pi$). In contrast to this pattern, one is presented in Fig. 4-24b for the identical antenna with the phasing of an ordinary end-fire array ($\delta = -0.5\pi$). Both patterns are plotted to the same maximum.

The increased directivity is apparent from the greater sharpness of the upper pattern. Integrating the pattern, including the minor lobes, the directivity of the upper pattern is found to be about 19 and of the lower pattern about 11. The beam widths and directivities for the two patterns are compared in Table 4-1.

TABLE 4-1

	Ordinary endfire	Endfire with increased directivity
Beam width between half-power points	68°	37°
Beam width between first nulls........	106°	74°
Directivity........................	11	19

The maximum of the field pattern of Fig. 4-24a occurs at $\phi = 0$ and $\psi = -\pi/n$. In general, any increased directivity end-fire array, with maximum at $\psi = -\pi/n$, has a normalized field pattern given by

$$E = \sin (\pi/2n) \frac{\sin (n\psi/2)}{\sin (\psi/2)} \right\} \quad (4\text{-}56a)$$

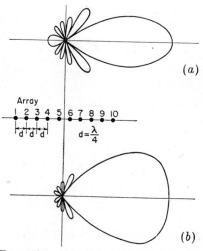

(a)

(b)

FIG. 4-24. Field patterns of end-fire arrays of 10 isotropic point sources of equal amplitude spaced $\frac{1}{4}$ wavelength apart. The pattern at (a) has the phase adjusted for increased directivity ($\delta = -0.6\pi$), while the pattern at (b) has the phasing of an ordinary end-fire array ($\delta = -0.5\,\pi$).

Case 4. Array with maximum field in an arbitrary direction. Let us consider the case of an array with a field pattern having a maximum in some arbitrary direction ϕ_1 not equal to $k\pi/2$ where $k = 0, 1, 2,$ or 3. Then (4-46a) becomes

$$0 = d_r \cos \phi_1 + \delta \quad (4\text{-}57)$$

By specifying the spacing d_r, the required phase difference δ is then determined by (4-57).

As an example suppose that $n = 4$, $d = \lambda/2$ and that we wish to have a maximum field in the direction of $\phi = 60°$. Then $\delta = -\pi/2$, yielding the field pattern shown in Fig. 4-25.

4-6. b. Null Directions for Arrays of n Isotropic Point Sources of Equal Amplitude and Spacing. In this section simple methods are discussed for finding the directions of the pattern nulls of the arrays considered in Sec. 4-6a.

Following the procedure given by Schelkunoff[1], the null directions for an array of n isotropic point sources of equal amplitude and spacing occur when $E = 0$ or, provided that the denominator of (4-48) is not zero, when

$$e^{in\psi} = 1 \qquad (4\text{-}58)$$

Equation (4-58) requires that

$$n\psi = \pm 2K\pi \qquad (4\text{-}59)$$

where $K = 1, 2, 3 \ldots$

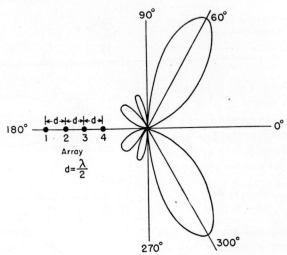

FIG. 4-25. Field pattern of array of four isotropic point sources of equal amplitude with phasing adjusted to give maximum at $\phi = 60°$. The spacing is $\frac{1}{2}$ wavelength.

Equating the value of ψ in (4-59) to its value in (4-46a) gives

$$\psi = d_r \cos \phi_0 + \delta = \pm \frac{2K\pi}{n} \qquad (4\text{-}60)$$

Thus,

$$\phi_0 = \arccos \left[\left(\pm \frac{2K\pi}{n} - \delta \right) \frac{1}{d_r} \right] \qquad (4\text{-}61)$$

where ϕ_0 gives the direction of the pattern nulls. Note that values of K must be excluded for which $K = mn$, where $m = 1, 2, 3, \ldots$ Thus, if $K = mn$, Eq. (4-59) reduces to $\psi = \pm 2m\pi$ and the denominator of (4-48

[1] S. A. Schelkunoff, "Electromagnetic Waves," D. Van Nostrand Company, Inc New York, 1943, p. 343.

S. A. Schelkunoff, "A Mathematical Theory of Arrays," Bell System Tech. J., 2 80–107, January, 1943.

equals zero so that the null condition of (4-58), that the numerator of (4-48) be zero, is insufficient.

In a broadside array $\delta = 0$, so that for this case (4-61) becomes

$$\phi_0 = \arccos\left(\pm\frac{2K\pi}{nd_r}\right) = \arccos\left(\pm\frac{K\lambda}{nd}\right) \qquad (4\text{-}62)$$

As an example, the field pattern of Fig. 4-21 ($n = 4$, $d = \lambda/2$, $\delta = 0$) has the null directions

$$\phi_0 = \arccos\left(\pm\frac{K}{2}\right) \qquad (4\text{-}63)$$

For $K = 1$, $\phi_0 = \pm 60°$ and $\pm 120°$, and for $K = 2$, $\phi_0 = 0°$ and $180°$. These are the six null directions for this array.

If ϕ_0 in (4-60) is replaced by its complementary angle γ_0 (see Fig. 4-18), then (4-62) becomes

$$\gamma_0 = \arcsin\left(\pm\frac{K\lambda}{nd}\right) \qquad (4\text{-}64)$$

If the array is long, so that $n\lambda \gg K\lambda$,

$$\gamma_0 \simeq \pm\frac{K\lambda}{nd} \qquad (4\text{-}65)$$

The first nulls either side of the maximum occur for $K = 1$. These angles will be designated γ_{01}. Thus,

$$\gamma_{01} \simeq \pm\frac{\lambda}{nd} \qquad (4\text{-}66)$$

and the total beam width of the main lobe between first nulls *for a long broadside array* is then

$$2\gamma_{01} \simeq \frac{2\lambda}{nd} \qquad (4\text{-}67)$$

For the field pattern in Fig. 4-21 this width is exactly 60°, while as given by (4-67) it is 1 rad, or 57.3°. This pattern is for an array 2 wavelengths long. The agreement would be better with longer arrays.

Turning next to *end-fire arrays*, the condition for an ordinary end-fire array is that $\delta = -d_r$. Thus, for this case (4-60) becomes

$$\cos\phi_0 - 1 = \pm\frac{2K\pi}{nd_r} \qquad (4\text{-}67a)$$

from which we obtain

$$\frac{\phi_0}{2} = \arcsin\pm\sqrt{\frac{K\pi}{nd_r}} \qquad (4\text{-}67b)$$

or

$$\phi_0 = 2 \arcsin \pm \sqrt{\frac{K\lambda}{2nd}} \tag{4-67c}$$

As an example, the field pattern of Fig. 4-22 ($n = 4$, $d = \lambda/2$, $\delta = -\pi$) has the null directions

$$\phi_0 = 2 \arcsin \pm \sqrt{\frac{K}{2}} \tag{4-67d}$$

For $K = 1$, $\phi_0 = \pm 60°$; for $K = 2$, $\phi_0 = \pm 90°$, etc.

If the array is long, so that $nd \gg K\lambda$, (4-67c) becomes

$$\phi_0 \simeq \pm \sqrt{\frac{2K\lambda}{nd}} \tag{4-68}$$

The first nulls either side of the main lobe occur for $K = 1$. These angles will be designated ϕ_{01}. Thus,

$$\phi_{01} \simeq \pm \sqrt{\frac{2\,\lambda}{nd}} \tag{4-69}$$

and the total beam width of the main lobe between first nulls *for a long ordinary end-fire array* is then,

$$2\phi_{01} \simeq 2\sqrt{\frac{2\,\lambda}{nd}} \tag{4-70}$$

For the field pattern in Fig. 4-22 this width is exactly 120°, while as given by (4-70) it is 2 rad, or 115°.

For end-fire arrays with increased directivity as proposed by Hansen and Woodyard, the condition is that $\delta = -(d_r + \pi/n)$. Thus, for this case (4-60) becomes

$$d_r(\cos \phi_0 - 1) - \frac{\pi}{n} = \pm 2\,\frac{K\pi}{n} \tag{4-71}$$

from which

$$\frac{\phi_0}{2} = \arcsin \pm \sqrt{\frac{\pi}{2nd_r}\,(2K - 1)} \tag{4-72}$$

or

$$\phi_0 = 2 \arcsin \pm \sqrt{\frac{\lambda}{4nd}\,(2K - 1)} \tag{4-73}$$

If the array is long, so that $nd \gg K\lambda$, (4-73) becomes

$$\phi_0 \simeq \pm \sqrt{\frac{\lambda}{nd}\,(2K - 1)} \tag{4-74}$$

The first nulls either side of the main lobe, ϕ_{01}, occur for $K = 1$. Thus,

$$\phi_{01} \simeq \pm \sqrt{\frac{\lambda}{nd}} \tag{4-75}$$

and the total beam width of the main lobe between first nulls *for a long end-fire array with increased directivity* is then

$$2\phi_{01} \simeq 2\sqrt{\frac{\lambda}{nd}} \tag{4-76}$$

This width is $1/\sqrt{2}$, or 71 per cent, of the width of the ordinary end-fire array. As an example, the ordinary end-fire array pattern of Fig. 4-24*b* has a beam width between first nulls of 106°. The width of the pattern in Fig. 4-24*a* for the array with increased directivity is 74°, or 70 per cent as much.

Table 4-2 lists the formulas for null directions and beam widths for the different arrays considered above. The null directions in column 2 apply to arrays of any length. The formulas in the third and fourth columns are approximate and apply only to long arrays.

TABLE 4-2

NULL DIRECTIONS AND BEAM WIDTHS BETWEEN FIRST NULLS
FOR LINEAR ARRAYS OF n ISOTROPIC POINT SOURCES
OF EQUAL AMPLITUDE AND SPACING

(The angles are expressed in radians. To convert to degrees, multiply by 57.3)

Type of array	Null directions (array any length)	Null directions (long array)	Beam width between first nulls (long array)
General case	$\phi_0 = \arccos\left[\left(\dfrac{\pm 2K\pi}{n} - \delta\right)\dfrac{1}{d_r}\right]$		
Broadside	$\gamma_0 = \arcsin\left(\pm\dfrac{K\lambda}{nd}\right)$	$\gamma_0 \simeq \pm\dfrac{K\lambda}{nd}$	$2\gamma_{01} \simeq \dfrac{2\lambda}{nd}$
Ordinary endfire	$\phi_0 = 2\arcsin \pm\sqrt{\dfrac{K\lambda}{2nd}}$	$\phi_0 \simeq \pm\sqrt{\dfrac{2K\lambda}{nd}}$	$2\phi_{01} \simeq 2\sqrt{\dfrac{2\lambda}{nd}}$
Endfire with increased directivity (Hansen and Woodyard)	$\phi_0 = 2\arcsin \pm\sqrt{\dfrac{\lambda}{4nd}(2K-1)}$	$\phi_0 \simeq \pm\sqrt{\dfrac{\lambda}{nd}(2K-1)}$	$2\phi_{01} \simeq 2\sqrt{\dfrac{\lambda}{nd}}$

The formulas in Table 4-2 have been used to calculate the curves presented in Fig. 4-26. These curves show the beam width between first nulls as a function of nd_λ for three types of arrays: broadside, ordinary

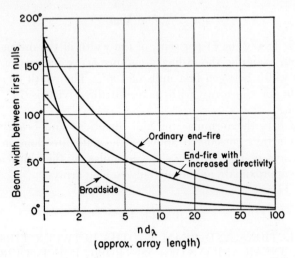

FIG. 4-26.   Beam width between first nulls as a function of nd_λ for arrays of n isotropic point sources of equal amplitude.   For long arrays, nd_λ is approximately equal to the array length.

end-fire, and end-fire with increased directivity.   The quantity nd_λ ($= nd/\lambda$) is approximately equal to the length of the array in wavelengths for long arrays.   The exact value of the array length is $(n - 1) \, d_\lambda$.

The beam width of long broadside arrays is inversely proportional to the array length, whereas the beam width of long end-fire types is inversely proportional to the square root of the array length.   Hence, the beam width in the plane of a long linear broadside array is much smaller than for end-fire types of the same length as shown by Fig. 4-26. It should be noted, however, that the broadside array has a disc-shaped pattern with a narrow beam width in a plane through the array axis but a circular pattern (360° beam width) in the plane normal to

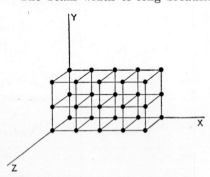

FIG. 4-27.   Volume array of point sources with equal spacing in the three coordinate directions.

the array axis.   On the other hand, the end-fire array has a cigar-shaped pattern with the same beam width in all planes through the array axis.

4-6. *c. Some Remarks on Volume Arrays.* It is interesting to digress at this point to consider the possibilities and limitations of a volume distribution[1] of equally spaced point sources. Suppose we have a space array consisting of linear arrays of n_x, n_y, and n_z sources in the three coordinate directions. For equal spacing in the three coordinate directions, the case where $n_x = 5$, $n_y = 3$, and $n_z = 2$ is illustrated in Fig. 4-27. If the field patterns of the arrays in each coordinate direction are $E_x(\theta, \phi)$, $E_y(\theta, \phi)$, and $E_z(\theta, \phi)$ then by the principle of pattern multiplication the total array factor E_v of a volume distribution of isotropic point sources is

$$E_v(\theta, \phi) = E_x(\theta, \phi)E_y(\theta, \phi)E_z(\theta, \phi) \qquad (4\text{-}77)$$

Suppose that we wish to have maximum radiation in the $+x$ direction. Then the arrays in the y and z directions are broadside arrays while the array in the x direction is an end-fire array. The pattern in the x-y plane E_{xy} depends only on the x and y arrays. Thus,

$$E_{xy} = E_x(\theta, \phi)E_y(\theta, \phi) \qquad (4\text{-}78)$$

The pattern in the x-z plane, E_{xz}, depends only on the x and z arrays, so that

$$E_{xz} = E_x(\theta, \phi)E_z(\theta, \phi) \qquad (4\text{-}79)$$

If in (4-78) $E_y(\theta, \phi)$ is much sharper than $E_x(\theta, \phi)$, then E_{xy} is nearly equal to $E_y(\theta, \phi)$. To have an appreciable effect on E_{xy}, $E_x(\theta, \phi)$ must be approximately as sharp as $E_y(\theta, \phi)$. That is to say, a sharp pattern must be multiplied by a pattern nearly as sharp in order to be made appreciably sharper. Therefore, if the y array is much sharper than the x array, one might as well use only the y array. On the other hand if the x array is much sharper, then one might as well use only the x array. For both to contribute equally it is required that both be equally sharp, or that

$$E_x(\theta, \phi) = E_y(\theta, \phi) \qquad (4\text{-}80)$$

Similar remarks may be made concerning the pattern in the x-z plane as related to the x and z arrays. It follows that, for equal patterns in the x-y and x-z planes, we must make

$$n_y = n_z$$

if the spacing between sources is the same in both arrays. If the y and z arrays are, for example, 10 wavelengths long $[(n_y - 1)d = 10\ \lambda]$, then the x array must be nearly 100 wavelengths long to have much effect on the beam width of the main lobe. However, a small x array may be de-

[1] G. C. Southworth, *Certain Factors Affecting the Gain of Directive Antennas,* *Proc. I.R.E.*, **18**, 1502–1536, September, 1930.

sirable in order to obtain a unidirectional pattern in the x direction. Assuming now that the x array is unidirectional, then any greater length would not produce much effect on the main-lobe beam width unless it is of the order of 100 wavelengths. An x array less than 100 wavelengths long would, nevertheless, have some effect on the directivity because of the change it produces in the minor-lobe pattern. From these considerations it is apparent that broadside-area arrays are generally to be preferred over single linear end-fire types for pencil beams, since they require smaller maximum dimensions. However, for arrays of moderate directivity with dimensions of a few wavelengths or less these remarks do not necessarily apply.

4-6. *d. Directions of Maxima for Arrays of n Isotropic Point Sources of Equal Amplitude and Spacing.* Let us now proceed to a discussion of the methods for locating the positions of the pattern maxima. The major-lobe maximum usually occurs when $\psi = 0$. This is the case for the broadside or ordinary end-fire array. The main lobes of the broadside array are then at $\phi = 90°$ and $270°$, while for the ordinary end fire the main lobe is at $0°$ or $180°$ or both. For the end-fire array with increased directivity the main-lobe maximum occurs at a value of $\psi = \pm\pi/n$ with the main lobe at $0°$ or $180°$. Referring to Fig. 4-24a, the main-lobe maximum (first maximum) for this case occurs at the first maximum of the numerator of (4-51).

The maxima of the minor lobes are situated between the first- and higher-order nulls. It has been pointed out by Schelkunoff that these maxima occur approximately whenever the numerator of (4-51) is a maximum, that is, when

$$\sin \frac{n\psi}{2} = 1 \qquad (4\text{-}81)$$

Referring to Fig. 4-28, we note that the numerator of (4-51) varies as a function of ψ more rapidly than the denominator $\sin(\psi/2)$. This is especially true when n is large. Thus, although the nulls occur exactly where $\sin(n\psi/2) = 0$, the maxima occur approximately where $\sin(n\psi/2) = 1$. This condition requires that

$$\frac{n\psi}{2} = \pm(2K + 1)\frac{\pi}{2} \qquad (4\text{-}82)$$

where $K = 1, 2, 3 \ldots$
Substituting the value of ψ from (4-82) into (4-46a) gives

$$d_r \cos \phi_m + \delta = \frac{\pm(2K + 1)\pi}{n} \qquad (4\text{-}83)$$

Therefore

$$\phi_m \simeq \arccos \left\{ \left[\frac{\pm(2K + 1)\pi}{n} - \delta \right] \frac{1}{d_r} \right\} \tag{4-84}$$

where ϕ_m = direction of the minor-lobe maxima

For a *broadside array*, $\delta = 0$ so that (4-84) becomes

$$\phi_m \simeq \arccos \frac{\pm(2K + 1)\lambda}{2nd} \tag{4-85}$$

As an example, the field pattern of Fig. 4-21 ($n = 4$, $d = \lambda/2$, $\delta = 0$) has the minor-lobe maxima at

$$\phi_m \simeq \arccos \frac{\pm(2K + 1)}{4} \tag{4-86}$$

For $K = 1$, $\phi_m = \pm41.4°$ and $\pm138.6°$. These are the approximate directions for the maxima of the four minor lobes of this pattern.

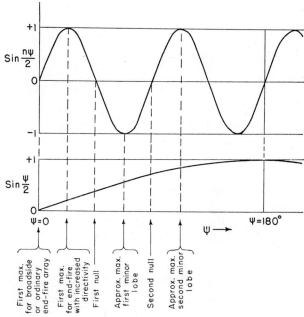

FIG. 4-28.   Graphs of the numerator (sin $n\psi/2$) and denominator (sin $\psi/2$) of the array factor as functions of ψ, showing the values of ψ corresponding to maxima and nulls of a field pattern for the case $n = 8$.

For an *ordinary end-fire array* $\delta = -d_r$ so that (4-84) becomes

$$\phi_m \simeq \arccos \left[\frac{\pm(2K + 1)\lambda}{2nd} + 1 \right] \tag{4-87}$$

while, for an *end-fire array with increased directivity*, $\delta = -(d_r + \pi/n)$ and

$$\phi_m \simeq \arccos \left\{ \frac{\lambda}{2nd} [1 \pm (2K + 1)] + 1 \right\} \tag{4-88}$$

The above formulas for the approximate location of the minor lobe maxima are listed in Table 4-3.

TABLE 4-3

DIRECTIONS OF MINOR-LOBE MAXIMA FOR LINEAR ARRAYS OF n ISOTROPIC POINT SOURCES OF EQUAL AMPLITUDE AND SPACING

Type of array	Directions of minor-lobe maxima
General	$\phi_m \simeq \arccos \left\{ \left[\frac{\pm(2K+1)\pi}{n} - \delta \right] \frac{1}{d_r} \right\}$
Broadside	$\phi_m \simeq \arccos \frac{\pm(2K+1)\lambda}{2nd}$
Ordinary endfire	$\phi_m \simeq \arccos \left[\frac{\pm(2K+1)\lambda}{2nd} + 1 \right]$
Endfire with increased directivity (Hansen and Woodyard)	$\phi_m \simeq \arccos \left\{ \frac{\lambda}{2nd} [1 \pm (2K+1)] + 1 \right\}$

The amplitudes of the field at the minor-lobe maxima are also of interest. It has been shown by Schelkunoff that since the numerator of (4-52) is approximately unity at the maximum of a minor lobe, the relative amplitude of a minor-lobe maximum E_{ML} is given by

$$E_{ML} \simeq \frac{1}{n \sin (\psi/2)} \tag{4-89}$$

Introducing the value of ψ from (4-82) into (4-89) yields

$$E_{ML} \simeq \frac{1}{n \sin [(2K + 1)\pi/2n]} \tag{4-90}$$

When $n \gg K$, that is, for the first few minor lobes of an array of a large number of sources, we have the further approximation

$$E_{ML} \simeq \frac{2}{(2K + 1)\pi} \tag{4-91}$$

Thus, for arrays of a large number of sources the relative amplitude of the first few minor lobes is given by (4-91) for $K = 1, 2, 3$, etc. In a broadside or ordinary end-fire array, the major-lobe maximum is unity so that the relative amplitudes of the maximum and first five minor lobes for arrays of these types and many sources are 1, 0.21, 0.13, 0.09, 0.07, and 0.06. From the curve for $n = 20$ in Fig. 4-20 we have the corresponding relative amplitudes given by 1, 0.22, 0.13, 0.09, 0.07, and 0.06. For an end-fire array with increased directivity the maximum for $\phi = 0$ and $n = 20$ occurs at $\psi = \pi/20 = 9°$. At this value of ψ the array factor is 0.63. Putting the maximum equal to unity then makes the relative amplitudes 1, 0.35, 0.21, 0.14, 0.11, and 0.09. It is interesting to note in (4-90) that the maximum amplitude of the smallest minor lobe occurs for $2K + 1 = n$. Then

$$\sin\left[\frac{(2K + 1)\pi}{2n}\right] = 1 \qquad (4\text{-}92)$$

and

$$E_{ML} \simeq \frac{1}{n} \qquad (4\text{-}93)$$

The condition $2K + 1 = n$ is exactly fulfilled when n is odd for the minor-lobe maximum at $\psi = 180°$ (see Fig. 4-20). When n is even, the condition is approximately fulfilled by the minor lobes nearest $\psi = 180°$. Thus, the maximum amplitude of the smallest minor lobe of the field pattern of any array of n isotropic point sources of equal amplitude and spacing will never be less than $1/n$ of the major-lobe maximum. An exception to this is where the range of ψ ends after a null in the array factor has been passed but before the next maximum has been reached. In this case the maximum of the smallest minor lobe may be arbitrarily small.

4-7. Linear Broadside Arrays with Nonuniform Amplitude Distributions. General Considerations. In the preceding section, our discussion was limited to linear arrays of n isotropic sources of *equal* amplitude. This discussion will now be extended to the more general case where the amplitude distribution may be nonuniform. In introducing this subject, it is instructive to compare field patterns of four types of amplitude distributions, namely, uniform, binomial, edge, and optimum. To be specific, let us consider a linear array of five isotropic point sources with $\frac{1}{2}$ wavelength spacing. If the sources are in phase and all equal in amplitude, we may calculate the pattern as discussed in Sec. 4-6, the result being as shown in Fig. 4-29 by the pattern designated *uniform*. A uniform distribution yields the maximum directivity. The pattern has a half-power beam width of 23°, but the minor lobes are relatively large. The amplitude of the first minor lobe is 24 per cent of the major-lobe maximum (see

Fig. 4-20, $n = 5$). In some applications this minor-lobe amplitude may be undesirably large.

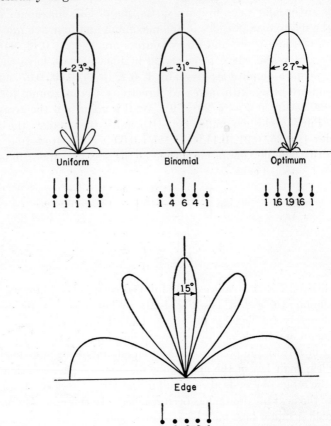

FIG. 4-29. Normalized field patterns of broadside arrays of five isotropic point sources spaced $\frac{1}{2}$ wavelength apart. All sources are in the same phase, but the relative amplitudes have four different distributions: uniform, binomial, optimum, and edge. Only the upper half of the pattern is shown. The relative amplitudes of the five sources are indicated in each case by the array below the pattern, the height of the line at each source being proportional to its amplitude. All patterns are adjusted to the same maximum amplitude.

To reduce the side-lobe level of linear in-phase broadside arrays, John Stone Stone[1] proposed that the sources have amplitudes proportional to the coefficients of a binomial series of the form

$$(a + b)^{n-1} = a^{n-1} + (n-1)a^{n-2}b + \frac{(n-1)(n-2)}{2!} a^{(n-3)}b^2 + \cdots \quad (4\text{-}94)$$

[1] John Stone Stone, U.S. Patents 1,643,323 and 1,715,433.

where n is the number of sources.* Thus, for arrays of three to six sources the relative amplitudes are given by

n	Relative amplitudes
3	1, 2, 1
4	1, 3, 3, 1
5	1, 4, 6, 4, 1
6	1, 5, 10, 10, 5, 1

Applying the binomial distribution to the array of five sources spaced $\frac{1}{2}$ wavelength apart, the sources have the relative amplitudes 1, 4, 6, 4, 1. The resulting pattern, designated *binomial*, is shown in Fig. 4-29. Methods of calculating such patterns are discussed in the next section. The pattern has no minor lobes, but this has been achieved at the expense of an increased beam width (31°). For spacings of $\frac{1}{2}$ wavelength or less between elements, the minor lobes are eliminated by Stone's binomial distribution. However, the increased beam width and the large ratio of current amplitudes required in large arrays are disadvantages.

At the other extreme from the binomial distribution, we might try an edge distribution in which only the end sources of the array are supplied with power, the three central sources being either omitted or inactive. The relative amplitudes of the five-source array are, accordingly, 1, 0, 0, 0, 1. The array has, therefore, degenerated to two sources 2 wavelengths apart and has the field pattern designated as *edge* in Fig. 4-29. The beam width between half-power points of the "main" lobe (normal to the array) is 15°, but "minor" lobes are the same amplitude as the "main" lobe.

Comparing the binomial and edge distributions for the five-source array with $\frac{1}{2}$-wavelength spacing, we have

Type of distribution	$\frac{1}{2}$-power beamwidth	Minor-lobe amplitude (% of major lobe)
Binomial..........................	31°	0
Edge.............................	15°	100

Although for most applications it would be desirable to combine the 15° beam width of the edge distribution with the zero minor-lobe level of the binomial distribution, this combination is not possible. However, if the distribution is between the binomial and the edge type, a compromise between the beam width and the side-lobe level can be made. That is, the side-lobe level will not be zero, but the beam width will be less than

*The coefficients of the binomial series are very simply obtained from Pascal's triangle (see Appendix).

for the binomial distribution. An amplitude distribution of this nature for linear in-phase broadside arrays has been proposed by Dolph[1] which has the further property of optimizing the relation between beam width and side-lobe level. That is, if the side-lobe level is specified, the beam width between first nulls is minimized; or, conversely, if the beam width between first nulls is specified, the side-lobe level is minimized. Dolph's distribution is based on the properties of the Tchebyscheff polynomials and accordingly will be referred to as the Dolph-Tchebyscheff or optimum distribution.

Applying the Dolph-Tchebyscheff distribution to our array of five sources with $\frac{1}{2}$-wavelength spacing, let us specify a side-lobe level 20 db below the main lobe, that is, a minor-lobe amplitude 10 per cent of the main lobe. The relative amplitude distribution for this side-lobe level is 1, 1.6, 1.9, 1.6, 1 and yields the pattern designated *optimum* in Fig. 4-29. Methods of calculating the distribution and pattern are discussed in the next section. The beam width between half-power points is 27°, which is less than for the binomial distribution. Smaller beam widths can be obtained only by raising the side-lobe level. The Dolph-Tchebyscheff distribution includes all distributions between the binomial and the edge. In fact, the binomial and edge distributions are special cases of the Dolph-Tchebyscheff distribution, the binomial distribution corresponding to an infinite ratio between main- and side-lobe levels and the edge distribution to a ratio of unity. The uniform distribution is, however, not a special case of the Dolph-Tchebyscheff distribution.

Referring to Fig. 4-29, we may draw a number of general conclusions regarding the relation between patterns and amplitude distributions. We note that if the amplitude tapers to a small value at the edge of the array (binomial distribution), minor lobes can be eliminated. On the other hand, if the distribution has an inverse taper with maximum amplitude at the edges and none at the center of the array (edge distribution), the minor lobes are accentuated being, in fact, equal to the "main" lobe. From this we may quite properly conclude that the minor-lobe level is closely related to the abruptness with which the amplitude distribution ends at the edge of the array. An abrupt discontinuity in the distribution results in large minor lobes, while a gradually tapered distribution approaching zero at the edge minimizes the discontinuity and the minor lobes. In the next section, we shall see that the abrupt discontinuity produces large higher "harmonic" terms in the Fourier series representing

[1] C. L. Dolph, A Current Distribution for Broadside Arrays Which Optimizes the Relationship between Beam Width and Side-lobe Level, *Proc. I.R.E.*, **34**, No. 6, 335–348, June, 1946.

H. J. Riblet, discussion on Dolph's Paper, *Proc. I.R.E.*, **35**, No. 5, 489–492, May, 1947.

the pattern. On the other hand, these higher harmonic terms are small when the distribution tapers gradually to a small value at the edge. There is an analogy between this situation and the Fourier analysis of wave shapes. Thus, a square wave has relatively large higher harmonics, whereas a pure sine wave has none, the square wave being analogous to the uniform array distribution while the pure sine wave is analogous to the binomial distribution.

The preceding discussion has been concerned with arrays of discrete sources separated by finite distances. However, the general conclusions concerning amplitude distributions which we have drawn can be extended to large arrays of continuous distributions of an infinite number of point sources, such as might exist in the case of a continuous current distribution on a metal sheet or in the case of a continuous field distribution across the mouth of an electromagnetic horn. If the amplitude distribution follows a Gauss error curve, which is similar to a binomial distribution for discrete sources, then minor lobes are absent but the beam width is relatively large. An increase of amplitude at the edge reduces the beam width but results in minor lobes, as we have seen. Thus, in the case of a high-gain parabolic reflector type of antenna, the illumination of the reflector by the primary antenna is usually arranged to taper toward the edge of the parabola. However, a compromise is generally made between beam width and side-lobe level so that the illumination is not zero at the edge but has an appreciable value as in a Dolph-Tchebyscheff distribution.

4-8. Linear Arrays with Nonuniform Amplitude Distributions. The Dolph-Tchebyscheff Optimum Distribution. In this section linear in-phase arrays with nonuniform amplitude distributions are analyzed, and the development and application of the Dolph-Tchebyscheff distribution are discussed.

Let us consider a linear array of an even number n_e of isotropic point sources of uniform spacing d arranged as in Fig. 4-30a. All sources are in the same phase. The direction $\theta = 0$ is taken normal to the array with the origin at the center of the array as shown. The individual sources have the amplitudes A_0, A_1, A_2, etc., as indicated, the amplitude distribution being symmetrical about the center of the array. The total field E_{n_e} from the even number of sources at a large distance in a direction θ is then the sum of the fields of the symmetrical pairs of sources, or

$$E_{n_e} = 2A_0 \cos \frac{\psi}{2} + 2A_1 \cos \frac{3\psi}{2} + \cdots + 2A_k \cos \left(\frac{n_e - 1}{2} \psi \right) \quad (4\text{-}95)$$

where

$$\psi = \frac{2\pi d}{\lambda} \sin \theta = d_r \sin \theta \quad (4\text{-}96)$$

Each term in (4-95) represents the field due to a symmetrically deposed pair of the sources.

Now let

$$2(k + 1) = n_e$$

where $k = 0, 1, 2, 3 \ldots$ so that

$$\frac{n_e - 1}{2} = \frac{2k + 1}{2}$$

Then (4-95) becomes

$$E_{n_e} = 2 \sum_{k=0}^{k=N-1} A_k \cos\left(\frac{2k + 1}{2}\psi\right) \qquad (4\text{-}97)$$

where $N = n_e/2$

Next let us consider the case of a linear array of an odd number n_0 of

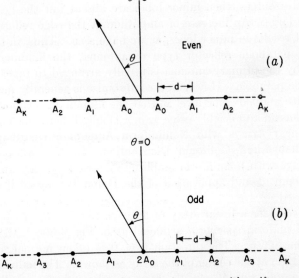

Fig. 4-30. Linear broadside arrays of n isotropic sources with uniform spacing for n even and n odd.

isotropic point sources of uniform spacing arranged as in Fig. 4-30b. The amplitude distribution is symmetrical about the center source. The amplitude of the center source is taken as $2A_0$, the next as A_1, the next as A_2, etc. The total field E_{n_0} from the odd number of sources at a large distance in a direction θ is then

$$E_{n_0} = 2A_0 + 2A_1 \cos\psi + 2A_2 \cos 2\psi + \cdots + 2A_k \cos\left(\frac{n_0 - 1}{2}\psi\right) \qquad (4\text{-}98)$$

Now for this case let

$$2k + 1 = n_0$$

where $k = 0, 1, 2, 3 \ldots$. Then (4-98) becomes

$$E_{n_0} = 2 \sum_{k=0}^{k=N} A_k \cos\left(2k\,\frac{\psi}{2}\right) \tag{4-99}$$

where $N = (n_0 - 1)/2$

The series expressed by (4-98) or by (4-99) may be recognized as a finite Fourier series of N terms.[1] For $k = 0$ we have a constant term $2A_0$ representing the contribution of the center source. For $k = 1$ we have the term $2A_1 \cos \psi$ representing the contribution of the first pair of sources on either side of the center source. For each higher value of k we have a higher harmonic term which in each case represents the contribution of a pair of symmetrically disposed sources. Thus, the total field pattern is simply the sum of a series of terms of increasing order in the same way that the wave form of an alternating current can be represented as a Fourier series involving, in general, a constant term, a fundamental term, and higher harmonic terms. The field pattern of an even number of sources as given by (4-95) or (4-97) is also a finite Fourier series but one which has no constant term and only odd harmonics. The coefficients $A_0, A_1, \ldots$ in both series are arbitrary and express the amplitude distribution.

To illustrate the Fourier nature of the field-pattern expression, let us consider the simple example of an array of nine isotropic point sources spaced $\frac{1}{2}$ wavelength apart, having the same amplitude and phase. Hence, the coefficients are related as follows: $2A_0 = A_1 = A_2 = A_3 = A_4 = \frac{1}{2}$. The number of sources is odd; hence the expression for the field pattern is then given by (4-99) as

$$E_9 = \tfrac{1}{2} + \cos \psi + \cos 2\psi + \cos 3\psi + \cos 4\psi \tag{4-100}$$

The first term ($k = 0$) is a constant so that the field pattern is a circle of amplitude $\frac{1}{2}$ as shown in Fig. 4-31a. The second term ($k = 1$) may be regarded as the fundamental term of the Fourier series and gives the pattern of the two sources (A_1 in Fig 4-30b) either side of the center. This pattern has 4 lobes of maximum amplitude of unity as illustrated in Fig. 4-31b. The next term ($k = 2$) may be regarded as the second harmonic term and gives the pattern of the next pair of sources (A_2 in Fig. 4-30b). This pattern has 8 lobes as shown by Fig. 4-31c. The last two terms represent the third and fourth harmonics, and the patterns have

[1] Irving Wolff, Determination of the Radiating System Which Will Produce a Specified Directional Characteristic, *Proc. I.R.E.*, **25**, 630–643, May, 1937.

12 and 16 lobes, respectively, as indicated by Figs. 4-31d and (e). The above relations may be summarized as in Table 4-4.

TABLE 4-4

k	Sources	Spacing	Fourier term	Pattern
0	1	0	Constant	Circle
1	2	1 λ	Fundamental	4 lobes
2	2	2 λ	2d harmonic	8 lobes
3	2	3 λ	3d harmonic	12 lobes
4	2	4 λ	4th harmonic	16 lobes

The algebraic sum of the patterns given by the five terms is the total far-field pattern of the array which is presented in Fig. 4-31f. If the middle source of the array has zero amplitude or is omitted, the total pattern is then the sum of the four terms for which $k = 1, 2, 3$, and 4. If in addition the pair of sources A_1 is omitted, the total pattern is the sum of three terms for which $k = 2, 3$, and 4. Since these are higher

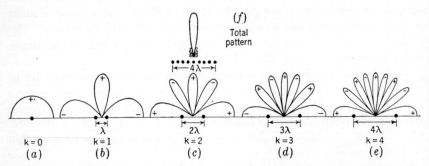

FIG. 4-31. Resolution of total pattern of array of nine isotropic sources into Fourier components due to center source and pairs of symmetrically disposed sources. The relative field pattern of the entire array is shown by (f). The lower halves of patterns are not shown. (Note that the end-fire lobes are wider than the broadside lobes.)

harmonic terms, we may properly expect that in this case the minor lobes of the total pattern will be accentuated. It is apparent from the above discussion that the field pattern of any symmetrical amplitude distribution can be expressed as a series of the form of (4-97) or (4-99).

Proceeding now to the Dolph-Tchebyscheff amplitude distribution, it will be shown that the coefficients of the pattern series[1] can be uniquely determined so as to produce a pattern of minimum beam width for a

[1] Equations (4-95), (4-97), (4-98), and (4-99).

specified side-lobe level.   The first step in the development of the Dolph-Tchebyscheff distribution is to show that (4-97) and (4-99) can be regarded as polynomials of degree $n_e - 1$ and $n_0 - 1$, that is, polynomials of degree equal to the number of sources less 1.   In the present discussion we shall consider only the case of the broadside type of array, that is, where $\delta = 0$.   Thus,

$$\psi = d_r \sin \theta \qquad (4\text{-}101)$$

Now by de Moivre's theorem,

$$e^{jm\psi/2} = \cos m \frac{\psi}{2} + j \sin m \frac{\psi}{2} = \left(\cos \frac{\psi}{2} + j \sin \frac{\psi}{2} \right)^m \qquad (4\text{-}102)$$

On taking real parts of (4-102) we have

$$\cos m \frac{\psi}{2} = \mathrm{Re} \left(\cos \frac{\psi}{2} + j \sin \frac{\psi}{2} \right)^m \qquad (4\text{-}103)$$

Expanding (4-103) as a binomial series gives

$$\cos m \frac{\psi}{2} = \cos^m \frac{\psi}{2} - \frac{m(m-1)}{2!} \cos^{m-2} \frac{\psi}{2} \sin^2 \frac{\psi}{2}$$
$$+ \frac{m(m-1)(m-2)(m-3)}{4!} \cos^{m-4} \frac{\psi}{2} \sin^4 \frac{\psi}{2} - \cdots \qquad (4\text{-}104)$$

Putting $\sin^2 (\psi/2) = 1 - \cos^2 (\psi/2)$, and substituting particular values of m, (4-104) then reduces to the following:

$$\left.
\begin{aligned}
m = 0, \quad & \cos m \frac{\psi}{2} = 1 \\[4pt]
m = 1, \quad & \cos m \frac{\psi}{2} = \cos \frac{\psi}{2} \\[4pt]
m = 2, \quad & \cos m \frac{\psi}{2} = 2 \cos^2 \frac{\psi}{2} - 1 \\[4pt]
m = 3, \quad & \cos m \frac{\psi}{2} = 4 \cos^3 \frac{\psi}{2} - 3 \cos \frac{\psi}{2} \\[4pt]
m = 4, \quad & \cos m \frac{\psi}{2} = 8 \cos^4 \frac{\psi}{2} - 8 \cos^2 \frac{\psi}{2} + 1 \\[4pt]
\text{etc.}
\end{aligned}
\right\} \qquad (4\text{-}105)$$

Now let

$$x = \cos \frac{\psi}{2} \qquad (4\text{-}105a)$$

whereupon the equations of (4-105) become

$$
\left.
\begin{aligned}
\cos m \frac{\psi}{2} &= 1, &&\text{when } m = 0 \\[2mm]
\cos m \frac{\psi}{2} &= x, &&\text{when } m = 1 \\[2mm]
\cos m \frac{\psi}{2} &= 2x^2 - 1, &&\text{when } m = 2 \\[2mm]
\text{etc.}
\end{aligned}
\right\} \tag{4-106}
$$

The polynomials of (4-106) are called Tchebyscheff polynomials, which may be designated in general by

$$
T_m(x) = \cos m \frac{\psi}{2} \tag{4-107}
$$

For particular values of m, the first eight Tchebyscheff polynomials are

$$
\left.
\begin{aligned}
T_0(x) &= 1 \\
T_1(x) &= x \\
T_2(x) &= 2x^2 - 1 \\
T_3(x) &= 4x^3 - 3x \\
T_4(x) &= 8x^4 - 8x^2 + 1 \\
T_5(x) &= 16x^5 - 20x^3 + 5x \\
T_6(x) &= 32x^6 - 48x^4 + 18x^2 - 1 \\
T_7(x) &= 64x^7 - 112x^5 + 56x^3 - 7x
\end{aligned}
\right\} \tag{4-108}
$$

We note in (4-108) that the degree of the polynomial is the same as the value of m.

The roots of the polynomials occur when $\cos m(\psi/2) = 0$ or when

$$
m \frac{\psi}{2} = (2k - 1) \frac{\pi}{2} \tag{4-109}
$$

where $k = 1, 2, 3, \ldots$

The roots of x, designated x', are thus

$$
x' = \cos \left[(2k - 1) \frac{\pi}{2m} \right] \tag{4-109a}
$$

We have shown that $\cos m(\psi/2)$ can be expressed as a polynomial of degree m. Thus, (4-97) and (4-99) are expressible as polynomials of degree $2k + 1$ and $2k$, respectively, since each are the sums of cosine polynomials of the form $\cos m(\psi/2)$. For an even number n_e of sources $2k + 1 = n_e - 1$, while for an odd number n_0, $2k = n_0 - 1$. Therefore, (4-97) and (4-99), which express the field pattern of a symmetric in-phase equispaced linear array of n isotropic point sources, are polynomials of degree equal to the number of sources less 1. If we now set the array polynomial as given by (4-97) or (4-99) equal to the Tchebyscheff polynomial of like degree ($m = n - 1$) and equate the array coefficients to the coefficients of the Tchebyscheff polynomial, then the amplitude distribution given by these coefficients is a Tchebyscheff distribution and the field pattern of the array corresponds to the Tchebyscheff polynomial of degree $n - 1$.

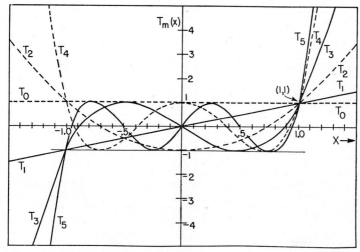

FIG. 4-32. Tchebyscheff polynomials of degree $m = 0$ through $m = 5$.

The Tchebyscheff polynomials of degree $m = 0$ through $m = 5$ are presented in Fig. 4-32. Referring to Fig. 4-32, the following properties of the polynomials are worthy of note:

1. All pass through the point $(1, 1)$.
2. For values of x in the range $-1 \leq x \leq +1$, the polynomials all lie between ordinate values of $+1$ and -1. All roots occur between $-1 \leq x \leq +1$, and all maximum values in this range are ± 1.

We may now describe Dolph's method of applying the Tchebyscheff polynomial to obtain an optimum pattern. Suppose that we have an array of six sources. The field pattern is then a polynomial of degree 5. If this polynomial is equated to the Tchebyscheff polynomial of degree 5, shown in Fig. 4-33, then the optimum pattern may be derived as follows: Let the ratio of the main-lobe maximum to the minor-lobe level be specified as R. That is,

$$R = \frac{\text{main-lobe maximum}}{\text{side-lobe level}}$$

The point (x_0, R) on the $T_5(x)$ polynomial curve then corresponds to the main-lobe maximum, while the minor lobes are confined to a maximum value of 1. The roots of the polynomial correspond to the nulls of the field pattern. The important property of the Tchebyscheff polynomial is that *if the ratio R is specified the beam width to the first null ($x = x_1'$) is minimized.* The corollary also holds that *if the beam width is specified the ratio R is maximized* (side-lobe level minimized).

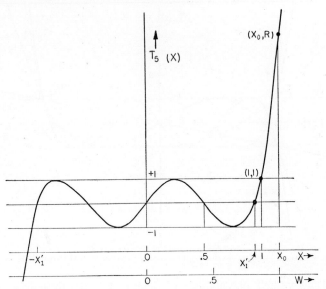

FIG. 4-33. Tchebyscheff polynomial of fifth degree with relation to coordinate scales.

The procedure will now be summarized. Let us write (4-97) and (4-99) again. It is to be noted that they are functions of $\psi/2$. Thus,

$$E_{n_e} = 2 \sum_{k=0}^{k=N-1} A_k \cos\left[(2k+1)\frac{\psi}{2}\right] \qquad (n \text{ even}) \qquad (4\text{-}110)$$

and

$$E_{n_o} = 2 \sum_{k=0}^{k=N} A_k \cos\left(2k\frac{\psi}{2}\right) \qquad (n \text{ odd}) \qquad (4\text{-}111)$$

Since we are usually interested only in the relative field pattern, the factor 2 before the summation sign in (4-110) and (4-111) may be dropped.

For an array of n sources, the first step is to select the Tchebyscheff polynomial of the same degree as the array polynomial, (4-110) or (4-111). This is given by

$$T_{n-1}(x) \qquad (4\text{-}112)$$

where n is the number of sources and $m = n - 1$. Next we choose R and solve

$$T_m(x_0) = R \qquad (4\text{-}113)$$

for x_0. Referring to Fig. 4-33, we note that, for $R > 1$, x_0 is also greater than 1. This presents a difficulty since according to (4-105a) x must be restricted to the range $-1 \leq x \leq +1$. If, however, a change of scale is made by introducing a new abscissa w (Fig. 4-33), where

$$w = \frac{x}{x_0} \qquad (4\text{-}114)$$

then the restriction of (4-105a) can be fulfilled by putting

$$w = \cos\frac{\psi}{2} \qquad (4\text{-}115)$$

where now the range of w is restricted to $-1 \leq w \leq +1$. The pattern polynomial, (4-110) or (4-111), may now be expressed as a polynomial in w. The final step is to equate the Tchebyscheff polynomial of (4-112) and the array polynomial obtained by substituting (4-115) into (4-110) or (4-111). Thus,

$$T_{n-1}(x) = E_n \qquad (4\text{-}115a)$$

The coefficients of the array polynomial are then obtained from (4-115a), yielding the Dolph-Tchebyscheff amplitude distribution which is an optimum for the side-lobe level specified.

As a proof of the optimum property of the Tchebyscheff polynomial, let us consider any other polynomial $P(x)$ of degree 5 which passes through (x_0, R) in Fig. 4-33 and the highest root x_1' and for all smaller values of x lies between $+1$ and -1. If the range in ordinate of $P(x)$ is less than ± 1, then this polynomial would give a smaller side-lobe level for this same beam width, and $T_5(x)$ would not be optimum. Since $P(x)$ lies between ± 1 in the range $-x_1' \leq x \leq +x_1'$ it must intersect the curve $T_5(x)$ in at least $m + 1 = 6$ points, including (x_0, R). Two polynomials of the same degree m which intersect in $m + 1$ points must be the same polynomial,[1] so that

$$P(x) = T_5(x)$$

and the $T_5(x)$ polynomial is, therefore, the optimum.

If the spacing between sources exceeds $\frac{1}{2}$ wavelength, it should be

---

[1] This follows from the fact that a polynomial of degree m has $m + 1$ arbitrary constants. Further, if $m + 1$ points on the polynomial's curve are specified, $m + 1$ independent equations with $m + 1$ unknowns can be written and the $m + 1$ constants thereby determined.

noted that as the spacing approaches 1 wavelength a large lobe develops at $\theta = \pm 90°$ which equals the main lobe when $d = \lambda$. However, if the individual sources of the array are nonisotropic, that is, are directional with the maximum at $\theta = 0$ and with little or no radiation at $\theta = \pm 90°$, then by pattern multiplication the lobes of the total pattern at $\theta = \pm 90°$ can be made small.

4-9. Example of Dolph-Tchebyscheff Distribution for an Array of Eight Sources. To illustrate the method for finding the Dolph-Tchebyscheff distribution, let us work the following problem:

An array of $n = 8$ in-phase isotropic sources, spaced $\frac{1}{2}$ wavelength apart, is to have a side-lobe level 26 db below the main-lobe maximum. Find the amplitude distribution fulfilling this requirement that produces the minimum beam width between first nulls, and plot the field pattern.

Since

$$\text{Side-lobe level in db below main-lobe maximum} = 20 \log_{10} R \quad (4\text{-}115b)$$

it follows that

$$R = 20 \quad (4\text{-}116)$$

The Tchebyscheff polynomial of degree $n - 1$ is $T_7(x)$. Thus, we set

$$T_7(x_0) = 20 \quad (4\text{-}117)$$

The value of x_0 may be determined by trial and error from the $T_7(x)$ expansion as given in (4-108), or x_0 may be calculated from

$$x_0 = \tfrac{1}{2}[(R + \sqrt{R^2 - 1})^{1/m} + (R - \sqrt{R^2 - 1})^{1/m}] \quad (4\text{-}118)$$

Substituting $R = 20$ and $m = 7$ in (4-118) yields

$$x_0 = 1.15 \quad (4\text{-}119)$$

Now substituting (4-115) in (4-110) and dropping the factor 2, we have

$$E_8 = A_0 w + A_1(4w^3 - 3w) + A_2(16w^5 - 20w^3 + 5w)$$
$$+ A_3(64w^7 - 112w^5 + 56w^3 - 7w) \quad (4\text{-}120)$$

But $w = x/x_0$ so that making this substitution in (4-120) and grouping terms of like degree,

$$E_8 = \frac{64A_3}{x_0^7} x^7 + \frac{16A_2 - 112A_3}{x_0^5} x^5 + \frac{4A_1 - 20A_2 + 56A_3}{x_0^3} x^3$$
$$+ \frac{A_0 - 3A_1 + 5A_2 - 7A_3}{x_0} x \quad (4\text{-}121)$$

The Tchebyscheff polynomial of like degree is

$$T_7(x) = 64x^7 - 112x^5 + 56x^3 - 7x \quad (4\text{-}122)$$

Now equating (4-121) and (4-122)

$$E_8 = T_7(x) \tag{4-123}$$

For (4-123) to be true requires that the coefficients of (4-121) equal the coefficients of the terms of like degree in (4-122). Therefore,

$$\frac{64A_3}{x_0^7} = 64 \tag{4-124}$$

or

$$A_3 = x_0^7 = 1.15^7 = 2.66 \tag{4-125}$$

In a similar way we find that

$$\left.\begin{array}{l} A_2 = 4.56 \\ A_1 = 6.82 \\ A_0 = 8.25 \end{array}\right\} \tag{4-126}$$

The relative amplitudes of the 8 sources are then

$$1,\ 1.7,\ 2.6,\ 3.1,\ 3.1,\ 2.6,\ 1.7,\ 1$$

To obtain the field pattern given by the Dolph-Tchebyscheff distribu-

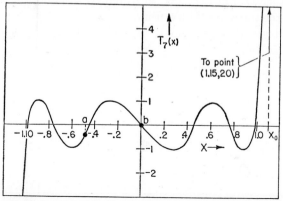

FIG. 4-34.   Tschebyscheff polynomial of the seventh degree.

ion, we recall that $\psi/2 = (d_r \sin \theta)/2$, $\cos (\psi/2) = w$, and $w = x/x_0$, rom which

$$x = x_0 \cos \frac{d_r \sin \theta}{2} \tag{4-127}$$

The value of x corresponding to a given value of θ, as obtained from 4-127), is then introduced in the appropriate Tchebyscheff polynomial, in his case $T_7(x)$, or scaled from a graph of this polynomial, as shown in

Fig. 4-34. The value of the polynomial for this value of x is then the relative field strength in the direction θ. In general, as θ ranges from $-\pi/2$ to $+\pi/2$, the variables $\psi/2$, w, and x range as indicated by Table 4-5.

TABLE 4-5

Variable	Range		
θ	$-\dfrac{\pi}{2}$	0	$+\dfrac{\pi}{2}$
$\dfrac{\psi}{2}$	$-\dfrac{d_r}{2}$	0	$+\dfrac{d_r}{2}$
w	$\cos\dfrac{d_r}{2}$	1	$\cos\dfrac{d_r}{2}$
x	$x_0 \cos\dfrac{d_r}{2}$	x_0	$x_0 \cos\dfrac{d_r}{2}$

Thus, in general, as θ ranges from $-\pi/2$ to 0 to $+\pi/2$, x ranges from some point, such as a in Fig. 4-34, to x_0 and back again to a, the ordinate value giving the relative field intensity.

In our problem, $d_r = \pi$, and $x_0 = 1.15$, so that the range of x is as shown in Table 4-6.

TABLE 4-6

Variable	Range		
θ	$-\dfrac{\pi}{2}$	0	$+\dfrac{\pi}{2}$
x	0	1.15	0

Hence, at $\theta = -90°$ we start at the origin in Fig. 4-34 (point b), and as θ approaches $0°$ we proceed to the right along the polynomial curve reaching the point $(x_0, R = 1.15, 20)$ when $\theta = 0°$. As θ continues to increase we retrace the polynomial curve, reaching the origin when $\theta = 90°$. Thus, the pattern is symmetrical about the $\theta = 0°$ direction.

As a preliminary step to plotting the field pattern, it is usually helpful to make a plot of x vs. θ from (4-127). Then, knowing the values of x for the nulls and maxima of the $T_m(x)$ curve, the corresponding values of θ may be determined. As many intermediate points as are needed may also be obtained in the same manner. Following this procedure, the field pattern for our problem of the eight-source array is presented in Fig. 4-35a in rectangular coordinates and in Fig. 4-35b in polar coordinates.

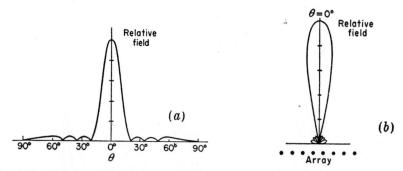

Fig. 4-35.   Relative field pattern of broadside array of eight isotropic sources spaced $\frac{1}{2}$ wavelength apart.   The amplitude distribution gives a minimum beam width for a side-lobe level one-twentieth of the main lobe.   The pattern is shown in rectangular coordinates at (a) and in polar at (b).   Both diagrams show the pattern only from $-90°$ to $+90°$, the other half of the pattern being identical.

4-10. Comparison of Amplitude Distributions for Eight-source Arrays. In the problem worked in the preceding section, the side-lobe level was 26 db below the maximum of the main beam ($R = 20$). It is of interest to compare the amplitude for this case with the distributions for other side-lobe levels. This is done in Fig. 4-36, in which the relative amplitude distributions are shown for eight-source arrays with side-lobe levels ranging from 0 db to an infinite number of decibels below the main beam maximum. The infinite db case corresponds to $R = \infty$ (zero side-lobe level) and is identical with Stone's binomial distribution. The relative amplitudes for this case are 1, 7, 21, 35, 35, 21, 7, 1. The ratio of amplitudes of the center sources to the edge sources is 35 to 1. Such a large ratio would be very difficult to achieve in practice. As the side-lobe level increases (R decreases), the amplitude distribution becomes more uniform, the ratio of the center to edge amplitudes being only about 3 to 1 for the 26-db ($R = 20$) case. The 20-db case ($R = 10$) is more uniform, with an amplitude ratio of only 1.7 to 1. The 14-db case ($R = 5$) exhibits a still more uniform distribution but shows an inversion, the maximum amplitude having shifted to the outermost sources (1 and 8). The uniform distribution is not a special case of the Dolph-Tchebyscheff distribution, an inversion occurring before the uniform case is reached. As the side-lobe level is raised still further, the distribution tends more toward an edge type, the amplitude of the inner sources decreasing still further. In the extreme case, where the side lobes are equal to the main-lobe level (0 db, or $R = 1$), the amplitudes of all of the inner sources are zero, and the distribution is of the edge type discussed in connection with Fig. 4-29. Thus, both the binomial and edge distributions are special cases of the Dolph-Tchebyscheff distribution, but the uniform amplitude distribution is not. The point of nearest approach to the uniform distribution is for an R value between 5 and 10. Referring to Fig. 4-20 and interpolating for $n = 8$ between the curves for $n = 10$ and $n = 5$, it is interesting to note that the ratio of the main-lobe maximum to the minor-lobe maxima ranges from about 4.3 to 8 for an array of eight sources of uniform amplitude.

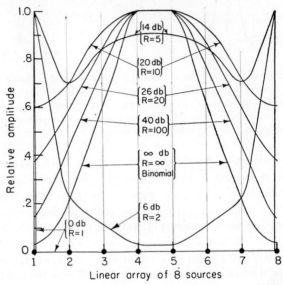

FIG. 4-36. Comparison of Dolph-Tchebyscheff amplitude distribution envelopes for various side-lobe levels.

The Dolph-Tchebyscheff optimum amplitude distribution, as discussed in the preceding sections, is optimum only if $d \geq \lambda/2$, which covers the cases of most interest for broadside arrays. By a generalization of the method, however, cases with smaller spacings can also be optimized.[1]

In conclusion, it should be pointed out that the properties of the Tchebyscheff polynomials may be applied not only to antenna patterns as discussed above but also to other situations. It is necessary, however, that the function to be optimized be expressible as a polynomial.

4-11. Continuous Arrays. In the preceding sections, the discussion has been restricted to arrays of discrete point sources, that is, to arrays of a finite number of sources separated by finite distances. We now proceed

[1] H. J. Riblet, *Proc. I.R.E.*, **35**, No. 5, 489–492, May, 1947.

to a consideration of *continuous* arrays of point sources, that is, arrays of an infinite number of sources separated by infinitesimal distances. By Huygens' principle, a continuous array of point sources is equivalent to a continuous field distribution. In this way, our discussion of continuous arrays can be extended to include the radiation patterns of field distributions across apertures, as, for example, the pattern of an electromagnetic horn where the field distribution across the mouth of the horn is known.

We shall now develop an expression for the far field of a continuous array of point sources of uniform amplitude and of the same phase. Let the array of length a be parallel to the y axis with its center at the origin

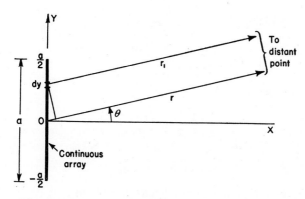

Fig. 4-37.   Continuous broadside array of point sources of length a.

as indicated in Fig. 4-37. Then the field dE at a distant point in the direction θ due to the point sources in the infinitesimal length dy at a distance y from the origin is

$$dE = \frac{A}{r_1} e^{i\omega\left(t-\frac{r_1}{c}\right)} = \frac{A}{r_1} e^{i(\omega t - \beta r_1)} \qquad (4\text{-}128)$$

where $\beta = \omega/c = 2\pi/\lambda$ and A is a constant involving amplitude. The total field E at the distant point is then the integrated value of (4-128) over the array of length a as given by

$$E = \int_{-a/2}^{a/2} \frac{A}{r_1} e^{i(\omega t - \beta r_1)} \, dy \qquad (4\text{-}129)$$

Both A and the time factor may be taken outside the integral, and r_1 may also be if $r_1 \gg y$. Thus,

$$E = \frac{A e^{i\omega t}}{r_1} \int_{-a/2}^{a/2} e^{-i\beta r_1} \, dy \qquad (4\text{-}130)$$

But, referring to Fig. 4-37,

$$r_1 = r - y \sin \theta \tag{4-131}$$

Substituting (4-131) in (4-130) and taking the constant factor $e^{-j\beta r}$ outside the integral, we have

$$E = A' \int_{-a/2}^{a/2} e^{j\beta y \sin \theta} \, dy \tag{4-132}$$

where

$$A' = \frac{Ae^{j(\omega t - \beta r)}}{r_1} \tag{4-133}$$

Integrating (4-132) yields

$$E = \frac{2A'}{\beta \sin \theta} \frac{e^{j\frac{\beta a}{2} \sin \theta} - e^{-j\frac{\beta a}{2} \sin \theta}}{2j} \tag{4-134}$$

which may be written as

$$E = \frac{2A'}{\beta \sin \theta} \sin \left(\frac{\beta a}{2} \sin \theta \right) \tag{4-135}$$

Let

$$\psi' = \beta a \sin \theta = a_r \sin \theta \tag{4-136}$$

where $a_r = \beta a = 2\pi a/\lambda$ = array length in radians
Then

$$E = \frac{2A'}{\beta \sin \theta} \sin \frac{\psi'}{2} \tag{4-137}$$

But from (4-136)

$$\beta \sin \theta = \frac{\psi'}{a}$$

so that (4-137) becomes

$$E = aA' \frac{\sin (\psi'/2)}{\psi'/2} \tag{4-138}$$

Normalizing (4-138) gives finally

$$E = \frac{\sin (\psi'/2)}{\psi'/2} \tag{4-139}$$

Equation (4-139) expresses the far field, or Fraunhofer diffraction pattern, of a continuous broadside array of length a, having uniform amplitude and phase. For n discrete, equally spaced sources, it was previously shown by (4-52) that the normalized value of the total field is

$$E = \frac{\sin{(n\psi/2)}}{n\sin{(\psi/2)}} \tag{4-140}$$

where $\psi = d_r \cos\phi + \delta$

For in-phase sources, $\delta = 0$. Comparing Figs. 4-18 and 4-37 we note that $\phi = \theta + \pi/2$, so that

$$\psi = -d_r \sin\theta = -\beta d \sin\theta \tag{4-141}$$

For small values of ψ, which occur for small values of θ, d, or both, (4-140) can be expressed as

$$E = \frac{\sin{(n\psi/2)}}{n\psi/2} = \frac{\sin{((\beta nd/2)\sin\theta)}}{(\beta nd/2)\sin\theta} \tag{4-142}$$

The length a of the array of discrete sources is

$$a = d(n-1) \tag{4-143}$$

where n = number of sources
d = spacing

If $n \gg 1$, $a \simeq nd$, and (4-142) becomes

$$E = \frac{\sin{((\beta a/2)\sin\theta)}}{(\beta a/2)\sin\theta} = \frac{\sin{((a_r/2)\sin\theta)}}{(a_r/2)\sin\theta} \tag{4-144}$$

where $a_r = \beta a = 2\pi a/\lambda$

By (4-136) this can now be expressed as

$$E = \frac{\sin{(\psi'/2)}}{\psi'/2} \tag{4-145}$$

which is identical with the value obtained in (4-139) for the continuous array. Thus, the field pattern for an array of many discrete sources $n \gg 1$) and for small values of ψ is the same as the pattern of a continuous array of the same length. If the array is long, that is, if $nd \gg \lambda$, the main beam and the first minor lobes are confined to small values of θ. It, therefore, follows that the main features of the pattern of a large array are the same, whether the array has many discrete sources or is a continuous distribution of sources. Many of the conclusions derived in previous sections concerning amplitude distributions for arrays of discrete sources can also be applied to continuous arrays provided that the arrays are large.

The null directions θ_0 of the continuous array pattern are given by

$$\frac{\psi'}{2} = \pm K\pi \tag{4-146}$$

where $K = 1, 2, 3 \ldots$

Thus,

$$\theta_0 = \arcsin\left(\pm\frac{K\lambda}{a}\right) \tag{4-147}$$

For a long array (4-147) can be expressed

$$\theta_0 \simeq \pm\frac{K}{a_\lambda} \text{ rad} \simeq \pm\frac{57.3K}{a_\lambda} \text{ deg} \tag{4-148}$$

where $a_\lambda = a/\lambda$

The beam width between first nulls $(K = 1)$ for a long array is then

$$2\theta_{01} \simeq \frac{2}{a_\lambda} \text{ rad} \simeq \frac{115}{a_\lambda} \text{ deg} \tag{4-149}$$

It is to be noted that (4-147), (4-148), and (4-149) are identical with the expressions given for the broadside array of discrete sources, if nd is replaced by a (see Table 4-2). Therefore, the null locations for arrays of either discrete or continuous sources are the same provided only that $n \gg 1$.

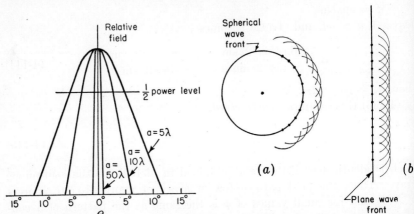

FIG. 4-38. Main-lobe field patterns of continuous uniform broadside arrays 5, 10, and 50 wavelengths long.

FIG. 4-39. Spherical and plane wave fronts with secondary waves of Huygens.

The field patterns of the main beam of continuous arrays of point source 5, 10, and 50 wavelengths long are compared in Fig. 4-38. It may be noted that the beam width between half-power points, θ_{HP}, of a long uniform broadside array is given approximately by

$$\theta_{HP} = 0.9\theta_{01} = \frac{0.9}{a_\lambda} \text{ rad} \tag{4-150}$$

or

$$\theta_{HP} = \frac{51}{a_\lambda} \text{ deg} \tag{4-151}$$

4-12. Huygens' Principle.[1]   The principle proposed by Christian Huygens (1629–1695), now often called Huygens' principle, has been of fundamental importance to the development of wave theory.   According to Huygens, each point of a wave front can be considered as the source of a secondary spherical wave.   The secondary spherical waves from the points on a wave front then combine to form a new wave front, the new

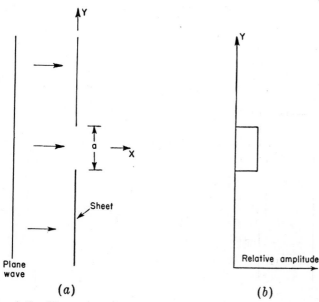

FIG. 4-40.   Plane wave incident on opaque sheet with slot of width a.

wave front being the envelope of the secondary wavelets.   Thus a spherical wave from a single point source propagates as a spherical wave as indicated in Fig. 4-39a.   On the other hand, an infinite plane wave continues as a plane wave as suggested by Fig. 4-39b.

[1] J. C. Slater and N. H. Frank, "Introduction to Theoretical Physics," McGraw-Hill Book Company, Inc., New York, 1933, Chaps. 26 and 27.

Max Born, "Optik," Verlag Julius Springer, Berlin, 1933, Sec. 44, p. 142.

Arnold Sommerfeld, Theorie der Beugung, Chap. 20 of "Differential und Integralgleichungen der Mechanik und Physik," Frank and von Mises, Editors, Friedrich Vieweg & Sohn, Brunswick, 1935.

J. A. Stratton, "Electromagnetic Theory," McGraw-Hill Book Company, Inc., New York, 1941, p. 460.

J. C. Slater, "Microwave Transmission," McGraw-Hill Book Company, Inc., New York, 1942, p. 256.

R. C. Spencer, Fourier Integral Methods of Pattern Analysis, *Radiation Lab. M.I.T. Rep.* 762-1, 1946.

B. B. Baker and E. T. Copson, "The Mathematical Theory of Huygens' Principle," Oxford University Press, New York, 1939.

Let us consider now the situation shown in Fig. 4-40a in which an infinite plane electromagnetic wave is incident on an infinite flat sheet which is opaque to the waves. The sheet has a slot of width a and of infinite length in the direction normal to the page. The field everywhere to the right of the sheet is the result of the section of the wave that passes through the slot. If a is many wavelengths, the field distribution across the slot may be assumed, in the first approximation, to be uniform as

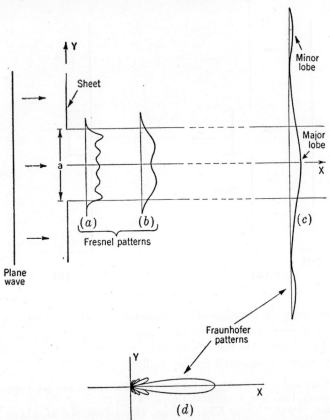

Fig. 4-41.   Fresnel and Fraunhofer patterns of a slot of width a.

shown in Fig. 4-40b. By Huygens' principle the field everywhere to the right of the sheet is the same as though each point in the plane of the slot is the source of a new spherical wave. Each of these point sources is of equal amplitude and phase. Thus, by Huygens' principle the slotted sheet with a uniform field across the opening can be replaced by a continuous array of point sources which just fills the opening. The field pattern in the x-y plane (Fig-40a) is then calculated the same as for continuous linear array of point sources of length a oriented parallel to the y axis.

The far field, or Fraunhofer diffraction pattern, of such an array was shown in the preceding section to be given by

$$E = \frac{\sin (\psi'/2)}{\psi'/2} \tag{4-152}$$

where $\psi' = (2\pi a/\lambda) \sin \theta$ and where θ is in the x-y plane (Fig. 4-37). This pattern, in the x-y plane, is independent of the extent of the array in the z direction (normal to the page).

In deriving (4-152), *i.e.*, (4-145) of Sec. 4-11, the total field at a point was obtained by integrating the contributions from a continuous array of sources distributed over a length a. For points at a great distance from the array the integral can be simplified, and the integration is easy, as demonstrated in the preceding section. For points near to the array, however, the integral does not simplify in this way but can be reduced to a form known as Fresnel's integral. This integral is often evaluated graphically with the aid of a curve known as a Cornu spiral. The field variation near the slot as obtained in this way is commonly called a Fresnel diffraction pattern. Along a straight line parallel to the slot and a short distance from it, the field variation is as suggested at (*a*) in Fig. 4-41, the variation approximating the uniform distribution of field at the slot as shown in Fig. 4-40*b*. As the distance x from the slot is increased, the Fresnel patterns change through a series of transitional forms, such as suggested at (*b*) in Fig. 4-41, until at large distances we enter the Fraunhofer region and the pattern assumes a form as suggested by (*c*) in Fig. 4-41. Ordinarily the Fraunhofer pattern is obtained by rotating the slot around its center so that the field is observed at a constant radius rather than at a constant distance x. The resulting field pattern in polar coordinates is then as suggested at (*d*) in Fig. 4-41. Once we have entered the Fraunhofer region, this pattern is the same at all greater distances. For a point to be in the Fraunhofer region, it must be at a sufficient distance from the slot so that we can make the assumption that lines extending from the edges of the slot to the point are parallel. This is commonly assumed to be the case when the point is at a distance r from the slot given by

$$r \geq \frac{2a^2}{\lambda} \tag{4-153}$$

where a is the width or aperture of the slot, which is assumed to be large. Thus, the larger the aperture or the shorter the wavelength, the greater must be the distance at which the pattern is measured if we wish to avoid the effects of Fresnel diffraction.

A nearly uniform type of field distribution across an aperture such as discussed above in connection with Figs. 4-40 and 4-41 occurs in optics when a beam of light is incident on a slit. It also may be realized by the field distribution across the mouth of a long electromagnetic horn antenna as in Fig. 4-42a. Since the pattern of a uniform field distribution is the same as the pattern of a uniform distribution of point sources of equal extent, another form of antenna equivalent to the optical slit or electromagnetic horn is a uniform current sheet. This can be approximated by a "billboard" type of array, as in Fig. 4-42b, having many dipole antennas carrying equal currents. The expressions which have been developed can thus be applied to a calculation of the Fraunhofer diffraction pattern of an optical slit or the far field of a horn or uniform current sheet. If the field or current distribution across the slit or antenna aperture is not uniform, the form factor for the distribution will appear in the integral for the field expression. The result may or may not be integrable analytically. However, if the aperture is large, the relations developed for amplitude distributions of arrays of discrete sources can be applied to the case of continuous arrays of sources.

It should be mentioned that Huygens' principle is not without its limitations. Thus, it neglects the vector nature of the electromagnetic field. It also neglects the effect of currents which flow at the edge of the slot, as in Figs. 4-40 and 4-41, or at the edge of the horn, as in Fig. 4-42a.

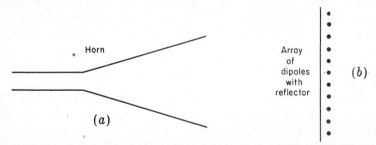

Fig. 4-42.   Electromagnetic horn antenna and array of dipoles with reflector.

However, if the aperture is sufficiently large and we confine our attention to directions roughly normal to aperture, the scalar theory of Huygens' principle gives satisfactory results.

4-13. Rectangular-area Broadside Arrays. The method of obtaining the field patterns of linear arrays discussed in the preceding sections can be easily extended to the case of rectangular broadside arrays, that is, arrays of sources which occupy a flat area of rectangular shape, as in Fig. 4-43. For such a rectangular array, the field pattern in the x-y plane (as a function of θ) depends only on the y dimension (a) of the array,

while the field pattern in the x-z plane (as a function of ϕ) depends only
on the z dimension (b) of the array.   The assumption is made that the
field or current distribution across the array in the y direction is the same
for any values of z between $\pm b/2$.   Likewise, it is assumed that the
amplitude distribution across the array in the z direction is the same for
all values of y between $\pm a/2$.   Therefore, the field pattern in the x-y
plane is calculated as though the array consists only of a single linear
array of height a coincident with the y axis (y array).   In the same way,
the pattern in the x-z plane is obtained by calculating the pattern of a

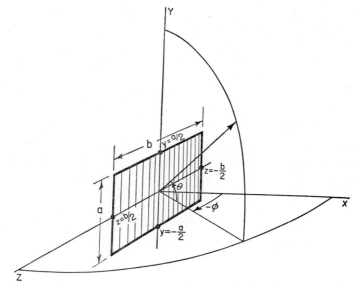

Fig. 4-43.   Rectangular broadside array of height a and length b with relation to
coordinates.

single linear array of length b coincident with the z axis (z array).   If
the array also has depth in the x direction, that is, has end-fire directivity,
then the pattern in the x-y plane is the product of the patterns of the
single linear x and y arrays, while the pattern in the x-z plane is the product
of the patterns of the x and z arrays.

If the area occupied by the array is not rectangular in shape, the above
principles do not hold.   However, the approximate field patterns may be
obtained in the case of an array of elliptical area, for example, by assuming
that it is a rectangular area as in Fig. 4-44a or in the case of a circular
area by assuming that it is square as in Fig. 4-44b.

From the field patterns in two planes (x-y and x-z) of a rectangular
array the beam widths between half-power points can be obtained.   If

the minor lobes are not large, the directivity D is then given approximately by

$$D = 41{,}253/\theta_1^0 \phi_1^0 \qquad (4\text{-}154)$$

where θ_1^0 and ϕ_1^0 are the half-power beam widths in degrees in the x-y and x-z planes, respectively.

An expression for the directivity of a large rectangular broadside array

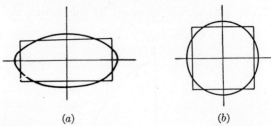

(a)   (b)

Fig. 4-44. Elliptical array with equivalent rectangular array (a) and circular array with equivalent square array (b).

of height a and width b (Fig. 4-43) and with a uniform amplitude distribution may also be derived directly as follows: By (2-38) the directivity of an antenna is given by

$$D = \frac{4\pi \, f(\theta, \phi)_{\text{max}}}{\iint f(\theta, \phi) \sin \theta \, d\theta \, d\phi} \qquad (4\text{-}155)$$

where $f(\theta, \phi)$ is the space power pattern, which varies as the square of the space field pattern. From (4-152) the space field pattern of a large rectangular array is

$$E(\theta, \phi) = \frac{\sin ((a_r \sin \theta)/2)}{(a_r \sin \theta)/2} \frac{\sin ((b_r \sin \phi)/2)}{(b_r \sin \phi)/2} \qquad (4\text{-}156)$$

where $a_r = 2\pi a/\lambda$
$\quad\quad b_r = 2\pi b/\lambda$

The main-beam maximum is in the direction $\theta = \phi = 0$ in Fig. 4-43. In (4-156), $\theta = 0$ at the equator, while in (4-155), $\theta = 0$ at the north pole. For large arrays and relatively sharp beams we can therefore replace $\sin \theta$ and $\sin \phi$ in (4-156) by the angles, while $\sin \theta$ in (4-155) can be set equal to unity. Assuming that the array is unidirectional (no field in $-x$ direction), the integral in the denominator of (4-155) then becomes

$$\int_{-\pi/2}^{\pi/2} \int_{-\pi/2}^{\pi/2} \frac{\sin^2 (\pi a \theta/\lambda)}{(\pi a \theta/\lambda)^2} \frac{\sin^2 (\pi b \phi/\lambda)}{(\pi b \phi/\lambda)^2} \, d\theta \, d\phi \qquad (4\text{-}157)$$

Making the limits of integration $-\infty$ to $+\infty$ instead of $-\pi/2$ to $+\pi/2$, (4-157) may be evaluated as λ^2/ab. Therefore, the approximate directivity D of a large unidirectional rectangular broadside array with a uniform amplitude distribution is

$$D = \frac{4\pi ab}{\lambda^2} = 12.6 \frac{ab}{\lambda^2} \tag{4-158}$$

As an example, the directivity of a broadside array of height $a = 10\ \lambda$ and length $b = 20\ \lambda$ is from (4-158) equal to 2,520, or 34 db.

By the approximate formula of (4-154), and taking the half-power beam widths given by (4-151), the directivity of a large unidirectional broadside array with a uniform amplitude distribution is approximately

$$D = \frac{41{,}253ab}{51^2\,\lambda^2} = 15.9 \frac{ab}{\lambda^2} \tag{4-159}$$

This is about 25 per cent, or 1 db, higher than the value given by (4-158).

PROBLEMS

4-1. *a.* Show that the relative $E(\phi)$ pattern of an array of two identical isotropic in-phase point sources arranged as in the figure is given by $E(\phi) = \cos\,[(d_r/2)\sin\phi]$, where $d_r = 2\pi d/\lambda$.

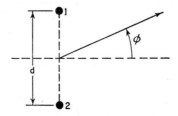

b. Show that the maxima, nulls, and half-power points of the pattern are given by the following relations:

$$\text{Maxima:} \quad \phi = \arcsin\left(\pm\frac{k\lambda}{d}\right)$$

$$\text{Nulls:} \quad \phi = \arcsin\left[\pm\frac{(2k+1)\,\lambda}{2d}\right]$$

$$\text{Half-power points:} \quad \phi = \arcsin\left[\pm\frac{(2k+1)\,\lambda}{4d}\right]$$

where $k = 0, 1, 2, 3 \ldots$

c. For $d = \lambda$ find the maxima, nulls, and half-power points, and from these points and any additional points that may be needed plot the $E(\phi)$ pattern for $0° \le \phi \le 360°$. There are four maxima, four nulls, and eight half-power points.

d. Repeat for $d = 3\lambda/2$.

e. Repeat for $d = 4\lambda$.

f. Repeat for $d = \lambda/4$. Note that this pattern has two maxima and two half-power points but no nulls. The half-power points are minima.

4-2. a. Derive an expression for $E(\phi)$ for an array of four identical isotropic point sources arranged as in the figure.

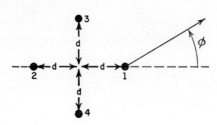

The spacing d between each source and the center point of the array is $3\lambda/8$. Sources 1 and 2 are in phase, and sources 3 and 4 in opposite phase.

b. Plot, approximately, the normalized field pattern.

4-3. a. What is the expression for $E(\phi)$ for an array of two point sources arranged as in the figure for Prob. 1. The spacing d is $3\lambda/8$. The amplitude of source 1 in the ϕ plane is given by $|\cos \phi|$, and the phase by ϕ. The amplitude of source 2 is given by $|\cos (\phi - 45°)|$, and the phase by $\phi - 45°$.

b. Plot the normalized amplitude and the phase of $E(\phi)$ referring the phase to the center point of the array.

4-4. a. Derive an expression for $E(\phi)$ for a linear in-phase broadside array of four identical isotropic point sources. Take $\phi = 0$ in the broadside direction. The spacing between sources is $5\lambda/8$.

b. Plot, approximately, the normalized field pattern ($0° \le \phi \le 360°$).

c. Repeat parts a and b with the changed condition that the amplitudes of the four sources are proportional to the coefficients of the binomial series for $(a + b)^n$.

4-5. a. Calculate and plot $\cos \theta$ as x, and $\cos 3\theta$ as y, for $-1 \le x \le +1$. Compare with the curve for $T_3(x)$.

b. Calculate and plot $\cos \theta$ as x, and $\cos 6\theta$ as y, for $-1 \le x \le +1$. Compare with the curve for $T_6(x)$.

4-6. a. Find the Dolph-Tchebyscheff current distribution for the minimum beam width of a linear in-phase broadside array of five isotropic point sources. The spacing between sources is $\frac{1}{2}$ wavelength, and the side-lobe level is to be 20 db down. Take $\phi = 0$ in the broadside direction.

b. Locate the nulls and maxima of the minor lobes.

  c. Plot, approximately, the normalized field pattern ($0° \leq \phi \leq 360°$).

  d. What is the half-power beam width?

4-7. *a.* Find the Dolph-Tchebyscheff current distribution for the minimum beam width of a linear in-phase broadside array of eight isotropic sources. The spacing between elements is $\frac{3}{4}$ wavelength, and the side-lobe level is to be 40 db down. Take $\phi = 0$ in the broadside direction.

  b. Locate the nulls and the maxima of the minor lobes.

  c. Plot, approximately, the normalized field pattern ($0° \leq \phi \leq 360°$).

  d. What is the half-power beam width?

4-8. *a.* Derive an expression for $E(\psi)$ for an array of n identical isotropic point sources where $\psi = f(\phi, d, \delta)$. ϕ is the azimuthal position angle with $\phi = 0$ in the direction of the array. δ is the phase lag between sources as one moves along the array in the $\phi = 0°$ direction and d is the spacing.

  b. Plot the normalized field as ordinate and ψ as abscissa for $n = 2, 4, 6, 8, 10,$ and 12 for $0° \leq \psi \leq 180°$.

4-9. *a.* Plot $E(\phi)$ for an end-fire array of $n = 10$ identical isotropic point sources spaced $3 \lambda/8$ apart with $\delta = -3\pi/4$.

  b. Repeat with $\delta = -\pi[(3/4) + (1/n)]$.

4-10. *a.* Calculate the directivity of a broadside array of two identical isotropic in-phase point sources spaced $\frac{1}{2}$ wavelength apart along the polar axis, the field pattern being given by

$$E = \cos\left(\frac{\pi}{2} \cos \theta\right)$$

where θ is the polar angle.

  b. Show that the directivity for a broadside array of two identical isotropic in-phase point sources spaced a distance d is given by

$$D = \frac{2}{1 + (\lambda/2\pi d) \sin (2\pi d/\lambda)}$$

4-11. *a.* Calculate the directivity of an end-fire array of two identical isotropic point sources in phase opposition, spaced $\frac{1}{2}$ wavelength apart along the polar axis, the relative field pattern being given by

$$E = \sin\left(\frac{\pi}{2} \cos \theta\right)$$

where θ is the polar angle.

  b. Show that the directivity of an ordinary end-fire array of two identical isotropic point sources spaced a distance d is given by

$$D = \frac{2}{1 + (\lambda/4\pi d) \sin (4\pi d/\lambda)}$$

4-12. A broadcasting station requires the horizontal plane pattern indicated by the figure. The maximum field intensity is to be radiated northeast with as little decrease as possible in field intensity in the 90° sector between north and east. No nulls are permitted in this sector. Nulls may occur in any direction in the complementary 270° sector. However, it is required that nulls must be present for the directions of due west and due southwest, in order to prevent interference with other stations in these directions.

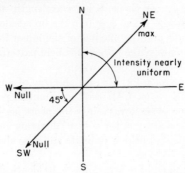

Design a four-vertical-tower array to fulfill these requirements. The currents are to be equal in magnitude in all towers, but the phase may be adjusted to any relationship. There is also no restriction on the spacing or geometrical arrangements of the towers. Plot the field pattern.

4-13. Calculate and plot the field and phase patterns for an array of two isotropic sources of the same amplitude and phase, for two cases:

$a.$ $\quad d = \dfrac{3}{4}\lambda$

$b.$ $\quad d = \dfrac{3}{2}\lambda$

Plot the field pattern in polar coordinates and phase pattern in rectangular coordinates with
1. Phase center at source 1
2. Phase center at mid-point

4-14. Calculate and plot the field and phase patterns of an array of two nonisotropic dissimilar sources for which the total field is given by

$$E = \cos\phi + \sin\phi\,\underline{/\psi}$$

where $\psi = d_r \cos\phi + \delta = \dfrac{\pi}{2}(\cos\phi + 1)$

Take source 1 as the reference for phase.

4-15. Calculate the Dolph-Tchebyscheff distribution of a six-source broadside array for $R = 5$, 7, and 10. Explain the variation.

4-16. In Case 5 of Sec. 4-2 for two isotropic point sources of unequal amplitude and any phase difference show that the phase angle of the total field with mid-point of the array as phase center is given by

$$\arctan \left(\frac{a - 1}{a + 1} \tan \frac{\psi}{2} \right)$$

4-17. Calculate and plot the field and phase patterns for the cases of Fig. 4-21 and 4-22 and compare with the curves shown.

4-18. *a.* What is an expression for the field pattern of an array of five identical isotropic point sources arranged in line and spaced a distance d apart? The phase lead of source 2 over 1, 3 over 2, etc., is α.

　　　 b. What value should α have to make the array a broadside type? For this broadside case what are the relative current magnitudes of the sources for

　　　　 1. Maximum directivity
　　　　 2. No side lobes
　　　　 3. Side lobes equal in magnitude to "main" lobe

4-19. A broadcast array of two vertical towers with equal currents is to have a horizontal plane pattern with a broad maximum of field intensity to the north and a null at an azimuth angle of 131° measured counterclockwise from the north. Specify the arrangement of the towers, their spacing, and phasing. Calculate and plot the field pattern in the horizontal plane.

4-20. A broadcast array with three vertical towers arranged in a straight horizontal line is to have a horizontal plane pattern with a broad maximum of field intensity to the north and nulls at azimuth angles of 105°, 147°, and 213° measured counterclockwise from the north. The towers need not have equal currents. For the purpose of analysis the center tower (No. 2) may be regarded as two towers, one belonging to an array of towers 1 and 2 and the other to an array of towers 2 and 3. Specify the arrangement of towers, their spacing, currents, and phasing. Calculate and plot the field pattern in the horizontal plane.

4-21. A broadcast array of four vertical towers with equal currents is to have a symmetrical four-lobed pattern in the horizontal plane with maximum field intensity to the north, east, south, and west and a reduced field intensity to the northeast, southeast, southwest, and northwest equal to one-half the maximum. Specify the array arrangement, orientation, spacing, and phasing. Calculate and plot the field pattern in the horizontal plane.

4-22. *a.* Calculate and plot the field pattern of a linear array of eight isotropic point sources of equal amplitude spaced 0.2 wavelength apart for the ordinary end-fire condition.

　　　 b. Repeat, assuming that the phasing satisfies the Hansen and Woodyard increased directivity condition.

　　　 c. Calculate the directivity in both cases by graphical integration of the entire pattern.

4-23. Calculate and plot the patterns in both planes perpendicular to a rectangular sheet carrying a current of uniform density and everywhere of the same direction and phase if the sheet measures 10 by 20 wavelengths. What is the approximate directivity?

4-24. *a.* Calculate and plot the field pattern of a linear end-fire array of 12 isotropic point sources of equal amplitude spaced $\frac{1}{4}$ wavelength apart for the ordinary end-fire condition.

　　b. Calculate the directivity by graphical integration of the entire pattern. Note that it is the power pattern (square of field pattern) which is to be integrated. It is most convenient to make the array axis coincide with the polar or *z* axis of Fig. 2-2 so that the pattern is a function only of θ.

　　c. Calculate the directivity by the approximate half-power beam-width method, and compare with that obtained in (*b*).

4-25. *a.* Calculate and plot the pattern of a linear broadside array of 12 isotropic point sources of equal amplitude spaced $\frac{1}{4}$ wavelength apart with all sources in the same phase.

　　b. Calculate the directivity by graphical integration of the entire pattern, and compare with the directivity obtained in Prob. 24 for the same size array operating end fire.

　　c. Calculate the directivity by the approximate half-power beam-width method, and compare with that obtained in (*b*).

4-26. *a.* Calculate and plot the pattern of a linear end-fire array of 12 isotropic point sources of equal amplitude spaced $\frac{1}{4}$ wavelength apart and phased to fulfill the Hansen and Woodyard increased-directivity condition.

　　b. Calculate the directivity by graphical integration of the entire pattern, and compare with the directivity obtained in Prob. 4-24 and 4-25.

　　c. Calculate the directivity by the approximate half-power beam-width method, and compare with that obtained in (*b*).

CHAPTER 5

THE ELECTRIC DIPOLE AND
THIN LINEAR ANTENNAS

5-1. The Short Electric Dipole. Since any linear antenna may be considered as consisting of a large number of very short conductors connected in series, it is of interest to examine first the radiation properties of short conductors. From a knowledge of the properties of short conductors, we can then proceed to a study of long linear conductors such as are commonly employed in practice.

A short linear conductor is often called a short *dipole*. In the following discussion, a short dipole is always of finite length even though it may be very short. If the dipole is vanishingly short, it is an infinitesimal dipole.

Let us consider a short dipole such as shown in Fig. 5-1a. The length L is very short compared to the wavelength $(L \ll \lambda)$. Plates at the ends of the dipole provide capacitance loading. The short length and the presence of these plates result in a uniform current I along the entire length L of the dipole. The dipole may be energized by a balanced transmission line, as shown. It is assumed that the transmission line does not radiate and, therefore, its presence will be disregarded. Radiation from the end plates is also considered to be negligible. The diameter d of the dipole is small compared to its length $(d \ll L)$. Thus, for purposes

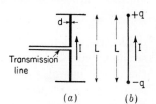

Fig. 5-1. A short dipole antenna (a) and its equivalent (b).

of analysis we may consider that the short dipole appears as in Fig. 5-1b. Here it consists simply of a thin conductor of length L with a uniform current I and point charges q at the ends. The current and charge are related by

$$\frac{dq}{dt} = I \tag{5-1}$$

5-2. The Fields of a Short Dipole.[1] Let us now proceed to find the

[1] J. Aharoni, "Antennae," Oxford University Press, New York, 1946, p. 116.

A. Alford, Ultra-short Electromagnetic Waves: Radiation, *Elec. Eng.*, July, 1943.

Ramo and Whinnery, "Fields and Waves in Modern Radio," John Wiley and Sons, Inc., New York, 1944, p. 430.

fields everywhere around a short dipole. Let the dipole of length L be placed coincident with the z axis and with its center at the origin as in Fig. 5-2. The relation of the electric field components, E_θ and E_ϕ, is then as shown. It is assumed that the medium surrounding the dipole is air or vacuum.

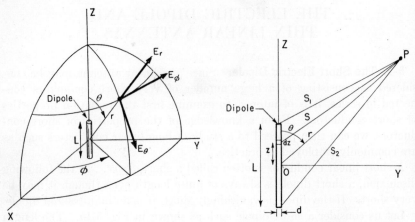

FIG. 5-2. Relation of dipole to coordinates.   FIG. 5-3. Geometry for short dipole.

Electric and magnetic fields can be expressed in terms of vector and scalar potentials. Since we will be interested not only in the fields near the dipole but also at distances which are large compared to the wavelength, we must use retarded potentials, that is, expressions involving $t - r/c$. For a dipole located as in Fig. 5-2 or Fig. 5-3, the retarded vector potential of the electric current has only one component, namely, A_z. Its value is

$$A_z = \frac{\mu}{4\pi} \int_{-L/2}^{L/2} \frac{[I]}{s} \, dz \qquad (5\text{-}2)$$

where $[I]$ is the retarded current given by

$$[I] = I_0 e^{j\omega\left(t - \frac{s}{c}\right)} \qquad (5\text{-}3)$$

In (5-2) and (5-3)

z = distance to a point on the conductor

I_0 = peak value in time of current (uniform along dipole)

μ = permeability of free space

If the distance from the dipole is large compared to its length ($r \gg L$) and if the wavelength is large compared to the length ($\lambda \gg L$), we can put $s = r$ and neglect the phase differences of the field contributions from different parts of the wire. The integrand in (5-2) can then be regarded as a constant, so that (5-2) becomes

$$A_z = \frac{\mu L I_0 e^{i\omega\left(t-\frac{r}{c}\right)}}{4\pi r} \tag{5-4}$$

The retarded scalar potential V of a charge distribution is

$$V = \frac{1}{4\pi\epsilon} \int_V \frac{[\rho]}{s} \, d\tau \tag{5-5}$$

where $[\rho]$ is the retarded charge density given by

$$[\rho] = \rho_0 e^{i\omega\left(t-\frac{s}{c}\right)} \tag{5-6}$$

and $d\tau$ = infinitesimal volume element
    ϵ = dielectric constant of free space
Since the region of charge in the case of the dipole being considered is confined to the points at the ends as in Fig. 5-1b, (5-5) reduces to

$$V = \frac{1}{4\pi\epsilon} \left\{ \frac{[q]}{s_1} - \frac{[q]}{s_2} \right\} \tag{5-7}$$

From (5-1) and (5-3)

$$[q] = \int [I] \, dt = I_0 \int e^{i\omega\left(t-\frac{s}{c}\right)} \, dt = \frac{[I]}{j\omega} \tag{5-8}$$

Substituting (5-8) into (5-7),

$$V = \frac{I_0}{4\pi\epsilon j\omega}$$

$$\left[\frac{e^{i\omega\left(t-\frac{s_1}{c}\right)}}{s_1} - \frac{e^{i\omega\left(t-\frac{s_2}{c}\right)}}{s_2} \right] \tag{5-9}$$

Referring to Fig. 5-4, when $r \gg L$, the lines connecting the ends of the dipole and the point P may be considered as parallel so that

$$s_1 = r - \frac{L}{2} \cos\theta \tag{5-10}$$

and

$$s_2 = r + \frac{L}{2} \cos\theta \tag{5-11}$$

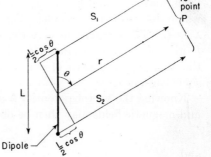

FIG. 5-4. Relations for short dipole when $r \gg L$.

Substituting (5-10) and (5-11) into (5-9) and clearing fractions, we have

$$V = \frac{I_0 e^{i\omega\left(t-\frac{r}{c}\right)}}{4\pi\epsilon j\omega}\left[\frac{e^{i\frac{\omega L \cos\theta}{2c}}\left(r + \frac{L}{2}\cos\theta\right) - e^{-i\frac{\omega L \cos\theta}{2c}}\left(r - \frac{L}{2}\cos\theta\right)}{r^2}\right] \quad (5\text{-}12)$$

where the term $L^2/4 \cos^2\theta$ in the denominator has been neglected in comparison with r^2 by assuming that $r \gg L$. By de Moivre's theorem (5-12) becomes,

$$V = \frac{I_0 e^{i\omega\left(t-\frac{r}{c}\right)}}{4\pi\epsilon j\omega r^2}\left[\left(\cos\frac{\omega L \cos\theta}{2c} + j\sin\frac{\omega L \cos\theta}{2c}\right)\left(r + \frac{L}{2}\cos\theta\right)\right.$$
$$\left. - \left(\cos\frac{\omega L \cos\theta}{2c} - j\sin\frac{\omega L \cos\theta}{2c}\right)\left(r - \frac{L}{2}\cos\theta\right)\right] \quad (5\text{-}13)$$

If the wavelength is much greater than the length of the dipole ($\lambda \gg L$), then

$$\cos\frac{\omega L \cos\theta}{2c} = \cos\frac{\pi L \cos\theta}{\lambda} \simeq 1 \quad (5\text{-}14)$$

and

$$\sin\frac{\omega L \cos\theta}{2c} \simeq \frac{\omega L \cos\theta}{2c} \quad (5\text{-}15)$$

Introducing (5-14) and (5-15) into (5-13), the expression for the scalar potential then reduces to

$$V = \frac{I_0 L \cos\theta\, e^{i\omega\left(t-\frac{r}{c}\right)}}{4\pi\epsilon c}\left(\frac{1}{r} + \frac{c}{j\omega}\frac{1}{r^2}\right) \quad (5\text{-}16)$$

Equations (5-4) and (5-16) express the vector and scalar potentials everywhere due to a short dipole. The only restrictions are that $r \gg L$ and $\lambda \gg L$. These equations give the vector and scalar potentials at a point P in terms of the distance r to the point from the center of the dipole, the angle θ, the length of the dipole L, the current on the dipole, and some constants.

Knowing the vector potential $\mathbf{A}$ and the scalar potential V, the electric and magnetic fields may then be obtained from the relations

$$\mathbf{E} = -j\omega\mathbf{A} - \nabla V \quad (5\text{-}17)$$

and

$$\mathbf{H} = \frac{1}{\mu}\nabla \times \mathbf{A} \quad (5\text{-}18)$$

It will be desirable to obtain $\mathbf{E}$ and $\mathbf{H}$ in polar coordinates. The polar coordinate components for the vector potential are

$$\mathbf{A} = \mathbf{a}_r A_r + \mathbf{a}_\theta A_\theta + \mathbf{a}_\phi A_\phi \quad (5\text{-}19)$$

Since the vector potential for the dipole has only a z component, $A_\phi = 0$, and A_r and A_θ are given by (see Fig. 5-5)

$$A_r = A_z \cos \theta \qquad (5\text{-}20)$$
$$A_\theta = -A_z \sin \theta \qquad (5\text{-}21)$$

where A_z is as given by (5-4). In polar coordinates the gradient of V is

$$\nabla V = \mathbf{a}_r \frac{\partial V}{\partial r} + \mathbf{a}_\theta \frac{1}{r} \frac{\partial V}{\partial \theta} + \mathbf{a}_\phi \frac{1}{r \sin \theta} \frac{\partial V}{\partial \phi} \qquad (5\text{-}22)$$

Calculating now the electric field $\mathbf{E}$ from (5-17), let us first express $\mathbf{E}$ in its polar coordinate components. Thus,

$$\mathbf{E} = \mathbf{a}_r E_r + \mathbf{a}_\theta E_\theta + \mathbf{a}_\phi E_\phi \qquad (5\text{-}23)$$

From (5-17), (5-19) and (5-22) the three components of E are then

$$E_r = -j\omega A_r - \frac{\partial V}{\partial r} \qquad (5\text{-}24)$$

$$E_\theta = -j\omega A_\theta - \frac{1}{r} \frac{\partial V}{\partial \theta} \qquad (5\text{-}25)$$

$$E_\phi = -j\omega A_\phi - \frac{1}{r \sin \theta} \frac{\partial V}{\partial \phi} \qquad (5\text{-}26)$$

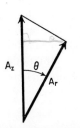 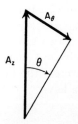

Fig. 5-5. Resolution of vector potential into A_r and A_θ components.

In (5-26) $A_\phi = 0$. The second term is also zero since V in (5-16) is independent of ϕ so that $\partial V/\partial \phi = 0$. Therefore, $E_\phi = 0$. Substituting (5-20) into (5-24) and (5-21) into (5-25), we have

$$E_r = -j\omega A_z \cos \theta - \frac{\partial V}{\partial r} \qquad (5\text{-}27)$$

and

$$E_\theta = j\omega A_z \sin \theta - \frac{1}{r} \frac{\partial V}{\partial \theta} \qquad (5\text{-}28)$$

Introducing now the values of A_z from (5-4) and V from (5-16) into (5-27) and (5-28) and performing the indicated operations, we obtain

$$E_r = \frac{I_0 L \cos \theta \, e^{j\omega\left(t-\frac{r}{c}\right)}}{2\pi\epsilon} \left(\frac{1}{cr^2} + \frac{1}{j\omega r^3}\right) \qquad (5\text{-}29)$$

and

$$E_\theta = \frac{I_0 L \sin \theta \, e^{j\omega\left(t-\frac{r}{c}\right)}}{4\pi\epsilon} \left(\frac{j\omega}{c^2 r} + \frac{1}{cr^2} + \frac{1}{j\omega r^3}\right) \qquad (5\text{-}30)$$

In obtaining (5-29) and (5-30) the relation was used that $\mu\epsilon = 1/c^2$, where $c =$ velocity of light.

Turning our attention now to the magnetic field, this may be calculated by (5-18). In polar coordinates the curl of $\mathbf{A}$ is

$$\nabla \times \mathbf{A} = \frac{\mathbf{a}_r}{r^2 \sin \theta} \left[\frac{\partial (r \sin \theta) A_\phi}{\partial \theta} - \frac{\partial (r A_\theta)}{\partial \phi} \right]$$
$$+ \frac{\mathbf{a}_\theta}{r \sin \theta} \left[\frac{\partial A_r}{\partial \phi} - \frac{\partial (r \sin \theta) A_\phi}{\partial r} \right]$$
$$+ \frac{\mathbf{a}_\phi}{r} \left[\frac{\partial (r A_\theta)}{\partial r} - \frac{\partial A_r}{\partial \theta} \right] \quad (5\text{-}31)$$

Since $A_\phi = 0$, the first and fourth terms of (5-31) are zero. From (5-4) and (5-20) and (5-21) we note that A_r and A_θ are independent of ϕ, so that the second and third terms of (5-31) are also zero. Thus, only the last two terms in (5-31) contribute so that $\mathbf{A}$, and by (5-18) also $\mathbf{H}$, have only a ϕ component. Introducing (5-20) and (5-21) into (5-31), performing the indicated operations, and substituting this result into (5-18), we have

$$|\mathbf{H}| = H_\phi = \frac{I_0 L \sin \theta \, e^{j\omega\left(t - \frac{r}{c}\right)}}{4\pi} \left(\frac{j\omega}{cr} + \frac{1}{r^2} \right) \quad (5\text{-}32)$$

and

$$H_r = H_\theta = 0 \quad (5\text{-}33)$$

Thus, the fields from the dipole have only three components E_r, E_θ, and H_ϕ. The components E_ϕ, H_r, and H_θ are everywhere zero.

When r is very large, the terms in $1/r^2$ and $1/r^3$ in (5-29), (5-30), and (5-32) can be neglected in favor of the terms in $1/r$. Thus, in the far field E_r is negligible, and we have effectively only two field components, E_θ and H_ϕ, given by

$$E_\theta = \frac{j\omega I_0 L \sin \theta \, e^{j\omega\left(t - \frac{r}{c}\right)}}{4\pi\epsilon c^2 r} \quad (5\text{-}34)$$

and

$$H_\phi = \frac{j\omega I_0 L \sin \theta \, e^{j\omega\left(t - \frac{r}{c}\right)}}{4\pi c r} \quad (5\text{-}35)$$

Taking the ratio of E_θ to H_ϕ as given by (5-34) and (5-35), we obtain

$$\frac{E_\theta}{H_\phi} = \frac{1}{\epsilon c} = \sqrt{\frac{\mu}{\epsilon}} = 377 \text{ ohms} \quad (5\text{-}36)$$

This is the intrinsic impedance of free space for a plane wave.

Comparing (5-34) and (5-35) we note that E_θ and H_ϕ are in time phase in the far field. We note also that the field patterns of both are proportional to $\sin\theta$. The pattern is independent of ϕ, so that the space pattern is doughnut-shaped, being a figure of revolution of the pattern in Fig. 5-6a about the axis of the dipole. Referring to the near-field expressions given by (5-29), (5-30), and (5-32), we note that for a small r the electric field has two components E_r and E_θ, which are both in time phase quadrature with the magnetic field, as in a resonator. At intermediate distances, E_θ and E_ϕ can approach time quadrature so that the total electric field vector rotates in a plane parallel to the direction of propagation, thus exhibiting the phenomenon of cross-field.[1] For the E_θ and H_ϕ components, the near-field patterns are the same as the far-field patterns, being proportional to $\sin\theta$ (Fig. 5-6a). However, the near-field pattern for E_r is proportional to $\cos\theta$ as indicated by Fig. 5-6b. The space pattern for E_r is a figure of revolution of this pattern around the dipole axis.

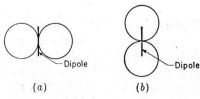

(a)   (b)

FIG. 5-6. Near- and far-field patterns of E_θ and H_ϕ components for short dipole (a) and near-field pattern of E_r component (b).

Let us now consider the situation at very low frequencies. This will be referred to as the *quasi-stationary*, or d-c, case. Since from (5-8),

$$[I] = I_0 e^{j\omega\left(t-\frac{r}{c}\right)} = j\omega[q] \qquad (5\text{-}37)$$

(5-29) and (5-30) can be rewritten as

$$E_r = \frac{[q]L\cos\theta}{2\pi\epsilon}\left(\frac{j\omega}{cr^2} + \frac{1}{r^3}\right) \qquad (5\text{-}38)$$

and

$$E_\theta = \frac{[q]L\sin\theta}{4\pi\epsilon}\left(-\frac{\omega^2}{c^2 r} + \frac{j\omega}{cr^2} + \frac{1}{r^3}\right) \qquad (5\text{-}39)$$

The magnetic field is given by (5-32) as

$$H_\phi = \frac{[I]L\sin\theta}{4\pi}\left(\frac{j\omega}{cr} + \frac{1}{r^2}\right) \qquad (5\text{-}40)$$

At low frequencies, ω approaches zero so that the terms with ω in the numerator can be neglected. As $\omega \to 0$, we also have

$$[q] = q_0 e^{j\omega\left(t-\frac{r}{c}\right)} = q_0 \qquad (5\text{-}41)$$

[1] See "Very High Frequency Techniques," by Radio Research Laboratory Staff, McGraw-Hill Book Company, Inc., New York, 1947, p. 199.

and

$$[I] = I_0 \qquad (5\text{-}42)$$

Thus, for the quasi-stationary, or d-c, case, the field components become from (5-38), (5-39), and (5-40),

$$E_r = \frac{q_0 L \cos \theta}{2\pi\epsilon r^3} \qquad (5\text{-}43)$$

$$E_\theta = \frac{q_0 L \sin \theta}{4\pi\epsilon r^3} \qquad (5\text{-}44)$$

$$H_\phi = \frac{I_0 L \sin \theta}{4\pi r^2} \qquad (5\text{-}45)$$

The restriction that $r \gg L$ still applies.

The expressions for the electric field, (5-43) and (5-44), are identical to those obtained in electrostatics for the field of two point charges, $+q_0$ and $-q_0$, separated by a distance L. The relation for the magnetic field, (5-45), may be recognized as the Biot-Savart relation for the magnetic field of a short element carrying a steady or slowly varying current. Since in the expressions for the quasi-stationary case the fields decrease as $1/r^2$ or $1/r^3$, the fields are confined to the vicinity of the dipole and there is negligible radiation. In the general expressions for the fields, (5-38), (5-39), and (5-40), it is the $1/r$ terms which are important in the far field and hence take into account the radiation.

The expressions for the fields from a short dipole developed above are summarized in Table 5-1.

If we had been interested only in the far field, the development beginning with (5-5) could have been much simplified. The scalar potential V does not contribute to the far field, so that both **E** and **H** may be determined from **A** above. Thus, from (5-17), **E** and **H** of the far field may be obtained very simply from

$$| \mathbf{E} | = E_\theta = -j\omega A_\theta \qquad (5\text{-}45a)$$

and

$$| \mathbf{H} | = H_\phi = \frac{E_\theta}{Z} = -\frac{j\omega}{Z} A_\theta \qquad (5\text{-}45b)$$

where $Z = \sqrt{\mu/\epsilon} = 377$ ohms

Or **H** may be obtained as before from (5-18) and **E** from this. Thus,

$$| \mathbf{H} | = H_\phi = \frac{1}{\mu} | \nabla \times \mathbf{A} | \qquad (5\text{-}45c)$$

and neglecting terms in $1/r^2$,

$$| \mathbf{E} | = E_\theta = ZH_\phi = \frac{Z}{\mu} | \nabla \times \mathbf{A} | \qquad (5\text{-}45d)$$

TABLE 5-1
FIELDS OF A SHORT ELECTRIC DIPOLE*

Component	General expression	Far field	Quasi-stationary
E_r	$\dfrac{[I]L\cos\theta}{2\pi\epsilon}\left(\dfrac{1}{cr^2}+\dfrac{1}{j\omega r^3}\right)$	0	$\dfrac{q_0 L\cos\theta}{2\pi\epsilon r^3}$
E_θ	$\dfrac{[I]L\sin\theta}{4\pi\epsilon}\left(\dfrac{j\omega}{c^2 r}+\dfrac{1}{cr^2}+\dfrac{1}{j\omega r^3}\right)$	$\dfrac{[I]Lj\omega\sin\theta}{4\pi\epsilon c^2 r}=\dfrac{j60\pi[I]\sin\theta}{r}\dfrac{L}{\lambda}$	$\dfrac{q_0 L\sin\theta}{4\pi\epsilon r^3}$
H_ϕ	$\dfrac{[I]L\sin\theta}{4\pi}\left(\dfrac{j\omega}{cr}+\dfrac{1}{r^2}\right)$	$\dfrac{[I]Lj\omega\sin\theta}{4\pi cr}=\dfrac{j[I]\sin\theta}{2r}\dfrac{L}{\lambda}$	$\dfrac{I_0 L\sin\theta}{4\pi r^2}$

*The restriction applies that $r \gg L$ and $\lambda \gg L$. The quantities in the table are in mks units, that is, E in volts per meter, H in amperes per meter, I in amperes, r in meters, etc. $[I]$ is as given by (5-37). Three of the field components of an electric dipole are everywhere zero, that is,

$$E_\phi = H_r = H_\theta = 0$$

5-3. Radiation Resistance of Short Electric Dipole. Let us now calculate the radiation resistance of the short dipole of Fig. 5-1. This may be done as follows. The Poynting vector of the far field is integrated over a large sphere to obtain the total power radiated. This power is then equated to I^2R where I is the rms current on the dipole and R is a resistance, called the radiation resistance of the dipole.

The *average* Poynting vector is given by

$$\mathbf{P} = \tfrac{1}{2} \operatorname{Re} (\mathbf{E} \times \mathbf{H}^*) \tag{5-46}$$

The far-field components are E_θ and H_ϕ so that the radial component of the Poynting vector is

$$P_r = \tfrac{1}{2} \operatorname{Re} E_\theta H_\phi^* \tag{5-47}$$

where E_θ and H_ϕ^* are complex.

The far-field components are related by the intrinsic impedance of the medium. Hence,

$$E_\theta = H_\phi Z = H_\phi \sqrt{\frac{\mu}{\epsilon}} \tag{5-48}$$

Thus, (5-47) becomes

$$P_r = \tfrac{1}{2} \operatorname{Re} Z H_\phi H_\phi^* = \tfrac{1}{2} \mid H_\phi \mid^2 \operatorname{Re} Z = \tfrac{1}{2} \mid H_\phi \mid^2 \sqrt{\frac{\mu}{\epsilon}} \tag{5-49}$$

The total power radiated W is then

$$W = \iint P_r \, ds = \tfrac{1}{2} \sqrt{\frac{\mu}{\epsilon}} \int_0^{2\pi} \int_0^{\pi} \mid H_\phi \mid^2 r^2 \sin\theta \, d\theta \, d\phi \tag{5-50}$$

where the angles are as shown in Fig. 5-2 and H_ϕ is the absolute value of the magnetic field, which from (5-35) is

$$\mid H_\phi \mid = \frac{\omega I_0 L \sin\theta}{4\pi cr} \tag{5-51}$$

Substituting this into (5-50) we have

$$W = \frac{1}{32} \sqrt{\frac{\mu}{\epsilon}} \frac{\beta^2 I_0^2 L^2}{\pi^2} \int_0^{2\pi} \int_0^{\pi} \sin^3\theta \, d\theta \, d\phi \tag{5-52}$$

Upon integrating, (5-52) becomes

$$W = \sqrt{\frac{\mu}{\epsilon}} \frac{\beta^2 I_0^2 L^2}{12\pi} \tag{5-53}$$

This is the *average* power or rate at which energy is streaming out of a sphere surrounding the dipole. Hence, it is equal to the power radiated. Assuming no losses, it is also equal to the power delivered to the dipole.

Therefore, W must be equal to the square of the rms current I flowing on the dipole times a resistance R called the radiation resistance of the dipole. Thus,

$$\sqrt{\frac{\mu}{\epsilon}} \frac{\beta^2 I_0^2 L^2}{12\pi} = \left(\frac{I_0}{\sqrt{2}}\right)^2 R \qquad (5\text{-}54)$$

Solving for R,

$$R = \sqrt{\frac{\mu}{\epsilon}} \frac{\beta^2 L^2}{6\pi} \qquad (5\text{-}55)$$

For air or vacuum $\sqrt{\mu/\epsilon} = 377 = 120\pi$ ohms so that (5-55) becomes

$$R = 80\pi^2 \left(\frac{L}{\lambda}\right)^2 = 80\pi^2 L_\lambda^2 \qquad (5\text{-}56)$$

As an example suppose that $L_\lambda = 1/10$. Then $R = 7.9$ ohms. If $L_\lambda = 0.01$, then $R = 0.08$ ohm. Thus, the radiation resistance of a short dipole is small.

In developing the field expressions for the short dipole, which were used in obtaining (5-56), the restriction was made that $\lambda \gg L$. This made it possible to neglect the phase difference of field contributions from different parts of the dipole. If $L_\lambda = \frac{1}{2}$ we violate this assumption, but, as a matter of interest, let us find what the radiation resistance of a $\frac{1}{2}$-wavelength dipole is, when calculated in this way. Then for $L_\lambda = \frac{1}{2}$, we obtain $R = 197$ ohms. The correct value is 168 ohms (see Prob. 5-4), which indicates the magnitude of the error introduced by violating the restriction that $\lambda \gg L$ to the extent of taking $L = \lambda/2$.

5-4. The Fields of a Short Dipole by the Hertz Vector Method.

In Sec. 5-2 the fields of a short dipole were obtained by a method involving the use of vector and scalar potentials. Another equivalent method which is sometimes employed makes use of the Hertz vector. Since this method is frequently found in the literature, it will be of interest to use it to find the fields of a short electric dipole. The fields so obtained are identical with those found by the vector-scalar potential method, indicating the equivalence of the two procedures.

The retarded vector potential of any electric-current distribution is given by

$$\mathbf{A} = \frac{\mu}{4\pi} \int_V \frac{[\mathbf{J}]}{r} \, d\tau \qquad (5\text{-}57)$$

where the retarded current density $[\mathbf{J}]$ is given by

$$[\mathbf{J}] = \mathbf{J}_0 e^{j\omega\left(t - \frac{r}{c}\right)} \qquad (5\text{-}58)$$

Multiplying numerator and denominator by ϵ (5-57) may be written as

$$\mathbf{A} = \mu\epsilon \frac{\partial \mathbf{\Pi}}{\partial t} \tag{5-59}$$

where

$$\frac{\partial \mathbf{\Pi}}{\partial t} = \frac{1}{4\pi\epsilon} \int_V \frac{[\mathbf{J}]}{r} \, d\tau \tag{5-60}$$

where t represents time and τ volume. The quantity $\mathbf{\Pi}$ is the retarded Hertz vector or retarded Hertzian potential. Since $[\mathbf{J}]$ is the only time dependent quantity on the right side of (5-60), we have for the retarded Hertz vector

$$\mathbf{\Pi} = \frac{1}{4\pi\epsilon} \int_V \frac{\int [\mathbf{J}] \, dt}{r} \, d\tau = \frac{1}{4\pi\epsilon j\omega} \int_V \frac{[\mathbf{J}]}{r} \, d\tau \tag{5-61}$$

Since

$$\mathbf{\Pi} = \mathbf{\Pi}_0 e^{j\omega\left(t - \frac{r}{c}\right)},$$

we obtain from (5-59)

$$\mathbf{A} = j\omega\mu\epsilon\mathbf{\Pi} \tag{5-62}$$

and

$$\mathbf{\Pi} = -\frac{j}{\omega\mu\epsilon} \mathbf{A} \tag{5-63}$$

If the retarded Hertz vector is known, both $\mathbf{E}$ and $\mathbf{H}$ everywhere can be calculated from the relations

$$\mathbf{E} = \omega^2\mu\epsilon\mathbf{\Pi} + \nabla (\nabla \cdot \mathbf{\Pi}) \tag{5-64}$$

$$\mathbf{H} = j\omega\epsilon \nabla \times \mathbf{\Pi} \tag{5-65}$$

Thus, $\mathbf{E}$ and $\mathbf{H}$ are derivable from a single potential function, $\mathbf{\Pi}$. Substituting (5-63) into (5-64) and (5-65), these relations may be also re-expressed in terms of $\mathbf{A}$ alone. Thus,

$$\mathbf{E} = -j\omega\mathbf{A} - \frac{j}{\omega\mu\epsilon} \nabla (\nabla \cdot \mathbf{A}) \tag{5-66}$$

$$\mathbf{H} = \frac{1}{\mu} \nabla \times \mathbf{A} \tag{5-67}$$

Let us now find the retarded Hertz vector for a short electric dipole. The vector potential for the dipole has only a z component as given by (5-4). Therefore, from (5-63) the Hertz vector has only a z component given by

$$\Pi_z = -\frac{j I_0 L e^{j\omega\left(t - \frac{r}{c}\right)}}{4\pi r\omega\epsilon} \tag{5-68}$$

In polar coordinates $\mathbf{\Pi}$ has two components, obtained in the same way as the components of $\mathbf{A}$ in (5-20) and (5-21). Thus,

$$\mathbf{\Pi} = \mathbf{a}_r \Pi_z \cos \theta - \mathbf{a}_\theta \Pi_z \sin \theta \qquad (5\text{-}69)$$

Substituting (5-68) into (5-69), and this in turn in (5-65) and performing the indicated operations, yields the result that

$$H_\phi = \frac{[I]L \sin \theta}{4\pi} \left(\frac{j\omega}{cr} + \frac{1}{r^2} \right) \qquad (5\text{-}70)$$

This result is identical with that obtained previously in (5-32). We could have anticipated this result since substituting (5-63) into (5-65) gives (5-67), from which (5-32) was obtained.

Substituting (5-68) into (5-69) and this in turn in (5-64) then gives the electric field $\mathbf{E}$ everywhere. The expressions for the two components, E_r and E_θ, so obtained are identical with those arrived at in (5-29) and (5-30) by the use of vector and scalar potentials.

5-5. The Thin Linear Antenna.[1] In this section expressions for the far-field patterns of thin linear antennas will be developed. It is assumed that the antennas are symmetrically fed at the center by a balanced two-wire transmission line. The antennas may be of any length, but it is assumed that the current distribution is sinusoidal. Current-distribution

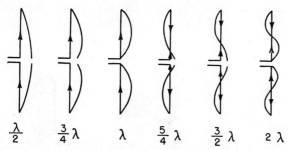

$$\frac{\lambda}{2} \qquad \frac{3}{4}\lambda \qquad \lambda \qquad \frac{5}{4}\lambda \qquad \frac{3}{2}\lambda \qquad 2\lambda$$

Fig. 5-7. Approximate natural current distribution for thin, linear center-fed antennas of various lengths.

measurements indicate that this is a good assumption provided that the antenna is thin, that is, when the conductor diameter is less than, say, $\lambda/100$. Thus, the sinusoidal current distribution approximates the natural distribution on thin antennas. Examples of the approximate natural-current distributions on a number of thin, linear center-fed antennas of

[1] Ramo and Whinnery, "Fields and Waves in Modern Radio," John Wiley and Sons, Inc., New York, 1944, p. 432.

different length are illustrated in Fig. 5-7. The currents are in phase over each $\frac{1}{2}$-wavelength section and in opposite phase over the next.

Referring to Fig. 5-8, let us now proceed to develop the far-field equations for a symmetrical, thin, linear, center-fed antenna of length L. The retarded value of the current at any point z on the antenna referred to a point at a distance s is

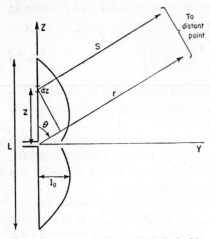

$$[I] = I_0$$
$$\sin\left[\frac{2\pi}{\lambda}\left(\frac{L}{2} \pm z\right)\right]e^{j\omega\left(t-\frac{s}{c}\right)} \quad (5\text{-}71)$$

In (5-71) the function

$$\sin\left[\frac{2\pi}{\lambda}\left(\frac{L}{2} \pm z\right)\right]$$

is the form factor for the current on the antenna. The expression $(L/2) + z$ is used when $z < 0$ and $(L/2) - z$ is used when $z > 0$. By regarding the antenna as made up of a series of infinitesimal dipoles of

FIG. 5-8. Relations for symmetrical, thin, linear, center-fed antenna of length L.

length dz, the field of the entire antenna may then be obtained by integrating the fields from all of the dipoles making up the antenna. The far fields dE_θ and dH_ϕ at a distance s from the infinitesimal dipole dz are (see Table 5-1),

$$dE_\theta = \frac{j60\pi[I]\sin\theta\,dz}{s\lambda} \quad (5\text{-}72)$$

$$dH_\phi = \frac{j[I]\sin\theta\,dz}{2s\lambda} \quad (5\text{-}73)$$

Since $E_\theta = ZH_\phi = 120\pi H_\phi$, it will suffice to calculate H_ϕ. The value of the magnetic field H_ϕ for the entire antenna is the integral of (5-73) over the length of the antenna. Thus,

$$H_\phi = \int_{-L/2}^{L/2} dH_\phi \quad (5\text{-}74)$$

Now introducing the value of $[I]$ from (5-71) into (5-73) and substituting this into (5-74) we have

$$H_\phi = \frac{jI_0\sin\theta\,e^{j\omega t}}{2\lambda}\left\{\int_{-L/2}^{0}\frac{1}{s}\sin\left[\frac{2\pi}{\lambda}\left(\frac{L}{2}+z\right)\right]e^{-j\frac{\omega s}{c}}\,dz\right.$$
$$\left.+\int_{0}^{L/2}\frac{1}{s}\sin\left[\frac{2\pi}{\lambda}\left(\frac{L}{2}-z\right)\right]e^{-j\frac{\omega s}{c}}\,dz\right\} \quad (5\text{-}75)$$

In (5-75), $1/s$ affects only the amplitude, and hence at a large distance it may be regarded as a constant. Also at a large distance, the difference between s and r can be neglected in its effect on the amplitude although its effect on the phase must be considered. Further, from Fig. 5-8,

$$s = r - z \cos \theta \qquad (5\text{-}76)$$

Substituting (5-76) into (5-75) and also r for s in the amplitude factor, (5-75) becomes

$$H_\phi = \frac{jI_0 \sin \theta \, e^{i\omega\left(t-\frac{r}{c}\right)}}{2\lambda r} \left\{ \int_{-L/2}^{0} \sin\left[\frac{2\pi}{\lambda}\left(\frac{L}{2}+z\right)\right] e^{i\frac{\omega \cos \theta}{c}z} \, dz \right.$$
$$\left. + \int_{0}^{L/2} \sin\left[\frac{2\pi}{\lambda}\left(\frac{L}{2}-z\right)\right] e^{i\frac{\omega \cos \theta}{c}z} \, dz \right\} \qquad (5\text{-}77)$$

Since $\beta = \omega/c = 2\pi/\lambda$ and $\beta/4\pi = \frac{1}{2}\lambda$, (5-77) may be rewritten as

$$H_\phi = \frac{j\beta I_0 \sin \theta \, e^{i\omega\left(t-\frac{r}{c}\right)}}{4\pi r} \left\{ \int_{-L/2}^{0} e^{j\beta z \cos \theta} \sin\left[\beta\left(\frac{L}{2}+z\right)\right] dz \right.$$
$$\left. + \int_{0}^{L/2} e^{j\beta z \cos \theta} \sin\left[\beta\left(\frac{L}{2}-z\right)\right] dz \right\} \qquad (5\text{-}78)$$

The integrals are of the form

$$\int e^{ax} \sin(c+bx) \, dx = \frac{e^{ax}}{a^2+b^2} [a \sin(c+bx) - b \cos(c+bx)] \qquad (5\text{-}79)$$

where for the first integral

$$a = j\beta \cos \theta$$
$$b = \beta$$
$$c = \beta L/2$$

For the second integral a and c are the same as in the first integral, but $b = -\beta$. Carrying through the two integrations, adding the results, and simplifying yields

$$H_\phi = \frac{j[I_0]}{2\pi r} \left[\frac{\cos((\beta L \cos \theta)/2) - \cos(\beta L/2)}{\sin \theta} \right] \qquad (5\text{-}80)$$

Multiplying H_ϕ by $Z = 120\pi$ gives E_θ as

$$E_\theta = \frac{j60[I_0]}{r} \left[\frac{\cos((\beta L \cos \theta)/2) - \cos(\beta L/2)}{\sin \theta} \right] \qquad (5\text{-}81)$$

where $[I_0] = I_0 \, e^{i\omega\left(t-\frac{r}{c}\right)}$

Equations (5-80) and (5-81) are the expressions for the far fields, H_ϕ and E_θ, of a symmetrical, center-fed, thin linear antenna of length L.

The shape of the far-field pattern is given by the factor in the brackets. The factors preceding the brackets in (5-80) and (5-81) give the instantaneous magnitude of the fields as functions of the antenna current and the distance r. To obtain the rms value of the field, we let $[I_0]$ equal the rms current at the location of the current maximum. There is no factor involving phase in (5-80) or (5-81), since the center of the antenna is taken as the phase center. Hence any phase change of the fields as a function of θ will be a jump of 180° when the pattern factor changes sign.

As examples of the far-field patterns of linear center-fed antennas, three antennas of different lengths will be considered. Since the amplitude factor is independent of the length, only the relative field patterns as given by the pattern factor will be compared.

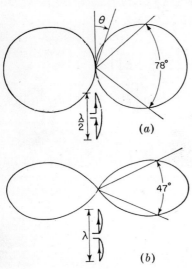

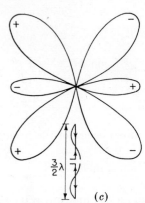

FIG. 5-9. Far-field patterns of $\frac{1}{2}$-wavelength, full-wavelength, and $\frac{3}{2}$-wavelength antennas. The antennas are center-fed, and the current distribution is assumed to be sinusoidal.

Case 1. $\frac{1}{2}$-*wavelength Antenna.* When $L = \lambda/2$, the pattern factor becomes

$$E = \frac{\cos\left(\frac{\pi}{2}\cos\theta\right)}{\sin\theta} \qquad (5\text{-}84)$$

This pattern is shown in Fig. 5-9a. It is only slightly more directional than the pattern of an infinitesimal or short dipole which is given by sin θ. The beam width between half-power points of the $\frac{1}{2}$-wavelength antenna is 78° as compared to 90° for the short dipole.

Case 2. *Full-wave Antenna.* When $L = \lambda$, the pattern factor becomes

$$E = \frac{\cos\left(\pi\cos\theta\right) + 1}{\sin\theta} \qquad (5\text{-}85)$$

This pattern is shown in Fig. 5-9b.

Case 3. $\frac{3}{2}$-*wavelength Antenna.* When $L = 3 \lambda/2$, the pattern factor is

$$E = \frac{\cos \left(\frac{3}{2} \pi \cos \theta \right)}{\sin \theta} \tag{5-86}$$

The pattern for this case is presented in Fig. 5-9c. With the mid-point of the antenna as phase center, the phase shifts 180° at each null, the relative phase of the lobes being indicated by the + and − signs. In all three cases, (*a*), (*b*), and (*c*), the space pattern is a figure of revolution of pattern shown around the axis of the antenna.

5-6. Radiation Resistance of $\frac{1}{2}$-wavelength Antenna. To find the radiation resistance, the Poynting vector is integrated over a large sphere yielding the power radiated, and this power is then equated to $(I_0/\sqrt{2})^2 R_0$, where R_0 is the radiation resistance at a current maximum point and I_0 is the peak value in time of the current at this point. The total power radiated W was given in (5-50)[1] in terms of H_ϕ for a short dipole. In (5-50), $| H_\phi |$ is the absolute value. Hence, the corresponding value of H_ϕ for a linear antenna is obtained from (5-80) by putting $| j[I_0] | = I_0$. Substituting this into (5-50), we obtain

$$W = \frac{15 I_0^2}{\pi} \int_0^{2\pi} \int_0^\pi \frac{\left[\cos \left(\frac{\beta L}{2} \cos \theta \right) - \cos \frac{\beta L}{2} \right]^2}{\sin \theta} \, d\theta \, d\phi \tag{5-87}$$

$$= 30 I_0^2 \int_0^\pi \frac{\left[\cos \left(\frac{\beta L}{2} \cos \theta \right) - \cos \frac{\beta L}{2} \right]^2}{\sin \theta} \, d\theta \tag{5-88}$$

Equating the radiated power as given by (5-88) to $I_0^2 R_0/2$ we have

$$W = \frac{I_0^2 R_0}{2} \tag{5-89}$$

and

$$R_0 = 60 \int_0^\pi \frac{\left[\cos \left(\frac{\beta L}{2} \cos \theta \right) - \cos \frac{\beta L}{2} \right]^2}{\sin \theta} \, d\theta \tag{5-90}$$

where the radiation resistance R_0 is referred to the current maximum. In the case of a $\frac{1}{2}$-wavelength antenna this is at the center of the antenna or at the terminals of the transmission line (see Fig. 5-7).

Proceeding now to evaluate (5-90), let

$$u = \cos \theta \qquad \text{and} \qquad du = - \sin \theta \, d\theta \tag{5-91}$$

[1] $W = \iint \mathbf{P} \cdot d\mathbf{s} = \frac{1}{2} \sqrt{\mu/\epsilon} \iint | H_\phi |^2 \, ds$

by which (5-90) is transformed to

$$R_0 = 60 \int_{-1}^{+1} \frac{\left(\cos \frac{\beta L}{2} u - \cos \frac{\beta L}{2} \right)^2}{1 - u^2} \, du \tag{5-92}$$

But

$$\frac{1}{1 - u^2} = \frac{1}{(1 + u)(1 - u)} = \frac{1}{2} \left(\frac{1}{1 + u} + \frac{1}{1 - u} \right) \tag{5-93}$$

Also putting $k = \beta L/2$, (5-92) becomes

$$R_0 = 30 \int_{-1}^{+1} \left[\frac{(\cos ku - \cos k)^2}{1 + u} + \frac{(\cos ku - \cos k)^2}{1 - u} \right] du \tag{5-94}$$

This integral gives the radiation resistance for a thin linear antenna of any length L. For the special case being considered where $L = \lambda/2$, we have $k = \pi/2$. Thus, in the case of a thin $\frac{1}{2}$-wavelength antenna, (5-94) reduces to

$$R_0 = 30 \int_{-1}^{+1} \left[\frac{\cos^2 (\pi u/2)}{1 + u} + \frac{\cos^2 (\pi u/2)}{1 - u} \right] du \tag{5-95}$$

Now in the first term let

$$1 + u = \frac{v}{\pi} \quad \text{and} \quad du = \frac{dv}{\pi} \tag{5-96}$$

and in the second term let

$$1 - u = \frac{v'}{\pi} \quad \text{and} \quad du = -\frac{dv'}{\pi} \tag{5-97}$$

Noting also that $(v - \pi)/2 = (\pi - v')/2$, Eq. (5-95) becomes

$$R_0 = 60 \int_0^{2\pi} \frac{\cos^2 ((v - \pi)/2)}{v} \, dv \tag{5-98}$$

But $\cos^2 (x/2) = \frac{1}{2}(1 + \cos x)$ so that

$$R_0 = 30 \int_0^{2\pi} \frac{1 + \cos (v - \pi)}{v} \, dv = 30 \int_0^{2\pi} \frac{1 - \cos v}{v} \, dv \tag{5-99}$$

The last integral in (5-99) is a form which is tabulated. This integral is often designated as Cin (x) (see Appendix). Thus,

$$\text{Cin} (x) = \int_0^x \frac{1 - \cos v}{v} \, dv = \ln \gamma x - \text{Ci} (x)$$

$$= 0.577 + \ln x - \text{Ci} (x) \tag{5-100}$$

where $\gamma = e^c = 1.781$, or $\ln \gamma = c = 0.577 = $ Euler's constant

The part of this integral given by

$$\text{Ci}(x) = \ln \gamma x - \text{Cin}(x) \qquad (5\text{-}101)$$

is called the cosine integral. The value of this integral is given by

$$\text{Ci}(x) = \int_{\infty}^{x} \frac{\cos v}{v}\, dv = \ln \gamma x - \frac{x^2}{2!2} + \frac{x^4}{4!4} - \frac{x^6}{6!6} + \cdots \qquad (5\text{-}102)$$

When x is small ($x < 0.2$),

$$\text{Ci}(x) \simeq \ln \gamma x = 0.577 + \ln x \qquad (5\text{-}103)$$

When x is large ($x \gg 1$),

$$\text{Ci}(x) = \frac{\sin x}{x} \qquad (5\text{-}104)$$

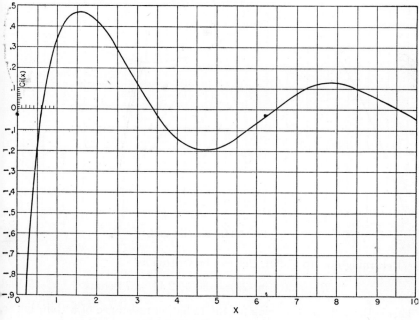

FIG. 5-10.   Cosine integral.

A curve of the cosine integral as a function of x is presented in Fig. 5-10. It is to be noted that $\text{Ci}(x)$ converges around zero at large values of x. From (5-102) and (5-100) we obtain $\text{Cin}(x)$ as an infinite series,

$$\text{Cin}(x) = \frac{x^2}{2!2} - \frac{x^4}{4!4} + \frac{x^6}{6!6} - \cdots \qquad (5\text{-}105)$$

While discussing Cin (x) and Ci (x), mention may be made of another integral which commonly occurs in impedance calculations. This is the sine integral,[1] Si (x), given by

$$Si\ (x) = \int_0^x \frac{\sin v}{v}\,dv = x + \frac{x^3}{3!3} + \frac{x^5}{5!5} + \cdots \tag{5-106}$$

When x is small $(x < 0.5)$,

$$Si\ (x) \simeq x \tag{5-107}$$

When x is large $(x \gg 1)$,

$$Si\ (x) \simeq \frac{\pi}{2} - \frac{\cos x}{x} \tag{5-108}$$

A curve of the sine integral as a function of x is presented in Fig. 5-11. It is to be noted that Si (x) converges around $\pi/2$ at large values of x.

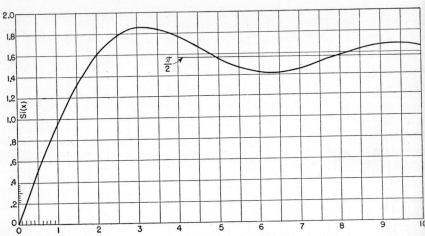

FIG. 5-11. Sine integral.

Returning now to (5-99), this can be written as

$$R_0 = 30\ Cin\ (2\pi) = 30 \times 2.44 = 73\ \text{ohms} \tag{5-109}$$

This is the well-known value for the radiation resistance of a thin, linear, center-fed, $\frac{1}{2}$-wavelength antenna with sinusoidal current distribution. The terminal impedance also includes some inductive reactance in series with R_0 (see Chap. 10). To make the reactance zero, that is, to make the antenna resonant, requires that the antenna be a few per cent less than $\frac{1}{2}$ wavelength. This shortening also results in a reduction in the value of the radiation resistance.

[1] See Appendix.

In some cases it may be impossible or at least very tedious to integrate the radiation-resistance expression analytically. In such cases one can carry out the integration graphically.[1]

5-7. Radiation Resistance at a Point Which Is Not a Current Maximum.

If we calculate, for example, the radiation resistance of a $\frac{3}{4}$-wavelength antenna (see Fig. 5-7) by the above method, we obtain its value at a current maximum. This is not the point at which the transmission line is connected. Neglecting antenna losses, the value of radiation resistance so obtained is the resistance R_0 which would appear at the terminals of a transmission line connected at a current maximum in the antenna, *provided* that the current distribution on the antenna is the same as when it is center-fed as in Fig. 5-7. Since a change of the feed point from the center of the antenna may change the current distribution, the radiation resistance R_0 is not the value which would be measured on a $\frac{3}{4}$-wavelength antenna or on any symmetrical antenna whose length is not an odd number of $\frac{1}{2}$ wavelengths. However, R_0 can be easily transformed to the value which would appear across the terminals of the transmission line connected at the center of the antenna.

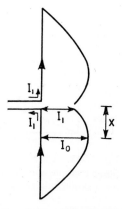

Fig. 5-12. Relation of current I_1 at transmission-line terminals to current I_0 at current maximum.

This may be done by equating (5-89) to the power supplied by the transmission line, given by $I_1^2 R_1/2$, where I_1 is the current amplitude at the terminals and R_1 is the radiation resistance at this point. See Fig. 5-12. Thus,

$$\frac{I_1^2}{2} R_1 = \frac{I_0^2}{2} R_0 \qquad (5\text{-}110)$$

where R_0 is the radiation resistance calculated at the current maximum. Thus, the radiation resistance appearing at the terminals is

$$R_1 = \left(\frac{I_0}{I_1}\right)^2 R_0 \qquad (5\text{-}111)$$

The current I_1 at a distance x from the nearest current maximum, as shown in Fig. 5-12, is given by

$$I_1 = I_0 \cos \beta x \qquad (5\text{-}112)$$

[1] An example of such a calculation is given in N. Marchand, "Ultrahigh Frequency Transmission and Radiation," John Wiley and Sons, Inc., New York, 1947, p. 163.

Therefore, (5-111) can be expressed

$$R_1 = \frac{R_0}{\cos^2 \beta x} \qquad (5\text{-}113)$$

When $x = 0$, $R_1 = R_0$; but when $x = \lambda/4$, $R_1 = \infty$ if $R_0 \neq 0$. However, the radiation resistance measured at a current minimum ($x = \lambda/4$) is not infinite as would be calculated from (5-113), since an actual antenna is not infinitesimally thin and the current at a minimum point is not zero. Nevertheless, the radiation resistance at a current minimum may in practice be very large, that is, thousands of ohms.

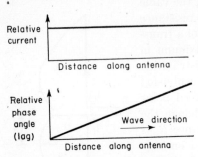

FIG. 5-13. Current amplitude and phase relations along an antenna carrying a single uniform traveling wave.

5-8. Fields of a Thin Linear Antenna with a Uniform Traveling Wave. The foregoing discussion has been confined to the case of antennas with sinusoidal current distributions. This current distribution may be regarded as the standing wave produced by two uniform (unattenuated) traveling waves of equal amplitude moving in opposite directions along the antenna. If, however, only one such wave is present on the antenna, the current distribution is uniform. The amplitude is a constant along the antenna, and the phase changes linearly with distance as suggested by Fig. 5-13.

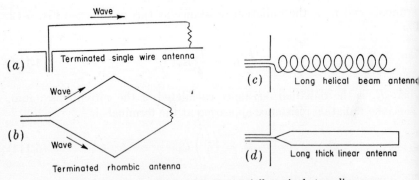

FIG. 5-14. Various antennas having essentially a single traveling wave.

The condition of a uniform traveling wave on an antenna is one of considerable importance, as this condition may be approximated in a number of antenna systems. For example, a single-wire antenna terminated in its characteristic impedance, as in Fig. 5-14a, may have essentially uniform traveling wave.[1] This type of antenna is often referred to as a Beverage or wave antenna. A terminated rhombic antenna (Fig. 5-14b) may also have essentially a single traveling wave. Other types of antennas that have, in the first approximation, a single outgoing traveling wave, are a long helical beam antenna and a long, thick linear antenna as illustrated in Fig. 5-14c and (d). These antennas have no terminating impedance but behave similar to terminated antennas. Thus, the thick linear conductor has a current distribution similar to a thin terminated linear conductor, and the patterns are similar if the conductor diameter is not too large. The results for a traveling wave on a linear conductor can be applied to a helix, as shown in Chap. 7, by considering that the helix consists of a number of short linear segments. On the linear antennas, the phase velocity of the traveling wave is substantially equal to the velocity of light. However, the phase velocity along the conductor of a helical beam antenna may differ appreciably from the velocity of light. Hence, to make the results applicable to any of the antenna types shown in Fig. 5-14, the fields from an antenna with a traveling wave will be developed for the general case where the phase velocity v of the wave along the conductor may have any arbitrary value.[2]

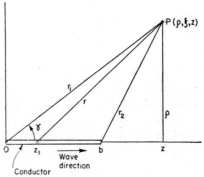

FIG. 5-15. Relation of conductor of length b with single traveling wave to cylindrical coordinate system.

Proceeding now to find the field radiated by a traveling wave on a thin linear conductor, let us consider a conductor of length b coincident with the z axis and with one end at the origin of a cylindrical coordinate system (ρ, ξ, z) as in Fig. 5-15. It is assumed that a single, uniform traveling wave is moving to the right along the conductor.

[1] Since the fields of an antenna are not confined to the immediate vicinity of the antenna, it is not possible to provide a nonreflecting termination with a lumped impedance. However, a lumped impedance may greatly reduce reflections at the termination.

[2] A. Alford, A discussion of methods employed in calculations of electromagnetic fields of radiating conductors, *Elec. Commun.*, **15**, 70–88, July, 1936. Treats case where velocity is equal to light.

J. D. Kraus and J. C. Williamson, Characteristics of helical antennas radiating in the axial mode, *J. Applied Phys.*, **19**, 87–96, January, 1948. Treats general case.

J. Grosskopf, Über die Verwendung zweier Lösungsansätze der Maxwellschen Gleichungen bei der Berechnung der electromagnetischen Felder strahlender Leiter, *Hochfrequenztechnik und Electroakustik*, **49**, 205–211, June, 1937. Treats case where velocity is equal to light.

Since the current is entirely in the z direction, the magnetic field has but one component H_ξ. The ξ direction is normal to the page at P in Fig. 5-15, and its positive sense is outward from the page. The magnetic field H_ξ can be obtained from the Hertz vector **II**. Since the current is entirely in the z direction, the Hertz vector has only a z component. Thus,

$$H_\xi = j\omega\epsilon(\nabla \times \mathbf{II})_\xi = -j\omega\epsilon \frac{\partial \Pi_z}{\partial \rho} \tag{5-114}$$

where Π_z is the z component of the retarded Hertz vector at the point P, as given by

$$\Pi_z = \frac{1}{4\pi j\omega\epsilon} \int_0^b \frac{[I]}{r}\, dz_1 \tag{5-115}$$

where

$$[I] = I_0 \sin \omega\left(t - \frac{r}{c} - \frac{z_1}{v}\right) \tag{5-116}$$

where $z_1 =$ a point on the conductor
and

$$v = pc \qquad \text{or} \qquad p = \frac{v}{c} \tag{5-117}$$

In (5-117), p is the ratio of the velocity along the conductor v to the velocity of light c. This ratio will be called the *relative phase velocity*.

All the conditions required for calculating the magnetic field due to a single traveling wave on the linear conductor are contained in the relations (5-114) through (5-117). That is, if $[I]$ in (5-116) is substituted into (5-115), and Π_z from this equation into (5-114), and the indicated operations performed, we obtain the field H_ξ. Let us now proceed to carry through this calculation. To do this, let

$$u = t - \frac{r}{c} - \frac{z_1}{v} \tag{5-118}$$

Now since

$$r = [(z - z_1)^2 + \rho^2]^{\frac{1}{2}} \tag{5-119}$$

we have

$$\frac{du}{dz_1} = \frac{z - z_1}{rc} - \frac{1}{pc} \tag{5-120}$$

Equation (5-115) now becomes

$$\Pi_z = \frac{I_0 c}{4\pi j\omega\epsilon} \int_{u_1}^{u_2} \frac{\sin \omega u}{z - z_1 - r/p}\, du \tag{5-121}$$

where the new limits are

$$u_1 = t - \frac{r_1}{c} \qquad \text{and} \qquad u_2 = t - \frac{r_2}{c} - \frac{b}{v} \tag{5-122}$$

Introducing (5-121) into (5-114) we have

$$H_\xi = -\frac{I_0 c}{4\pi} \frac{\partial}{\partial \rho} \int_{u_1}^{u_2} \frac{\sin \omega u}{z - z_1 - r/p} \, du \tag{5-123}$$

Confining our attention now to the far field, that is, at a large distance r, which is very much larger than b, the quantity z_1 can be neglected and the denominator of the integrand considered to be a constant $z - r/p$. Therefore (5-123) becomes

$$H_\xi = -\frac{I_0 c}{4\pi\omega} \frac{\partial}{\partial \rho} \left(\frac{-\cos \omega u_2 + \cos \omega u_1}{z - r/p} \right) \tag{5-124}$$

Performing the differentiation with respect to ρ, (5-124) becomes,

$$H = \frac{I_0 c}{4\pi r}$$
$$\cdot \left[\frac{(z - r/p)(\sin \omega u_2 - \sin \omega u_1) + (\lambda/2\pi)(\cos \omega u_2 - \cos \omega u_1)}{(z - r/p)^2} \right] \tag{5-125}$$

At arbitrarily large distances, that is, where

$$\left| z - r/p \right| \gg \frac{\lambda}{2\pi}$$

and for the case where

$$\sin \omega u_2 - \sin \omega u_1 \neq 0$$

(5-125) reduces to

$$H_\xi = \frac{I_0}{4\pi r} \frac{\sin \gamma}{\cos \gamma - 1/p} (\sin \omega u_2 - \sin \omega u_1) \tag{5-126}$$

where the relations have been introduced for $r \gg b$ that

$$\frac{z}{r} = \cos \gamma \qquad \text{and} \qquad \frac{\rho}{r} = \sin \gamma \tag{5-127}$$

Introducing the values of u_1 and u_2 into (5-126) from (5-122) and by trigonometric manipulation, (5-127) can be put in the form,

$$H_\xi = \frac{I_0 p}{2\pi r_1} \left\{ \frac{\sin \gamma}{1 - p \cos \gamma} \left[\sin \frac{\omega b}{2pc} (1 - p \cos \gamma) \right] \right\}$$
$$\Big/ \left[\omega\left(t - \frac{r_1}{c}\right) + \frac{\omega b}{2pc}(1 - p \cos \gamma) \right] \tag{5-128}$$

Equation (5-128) gives the instantaneous magnetic field at large distances from the linear antenna carrying a single traveling wave of amplitude I_0, in terms of the distance r_1, direction angle γ, relative phase velocity p, radian frequency ω, conductor length b, time t, and velocity of light c. The distant or far electric field E_γ is obtained from H_ξ by $E_\gamma = H_\xi Z$ where $Z = 377$ ohms.

In (5-128) the shape of the field pattern is given by the expression in

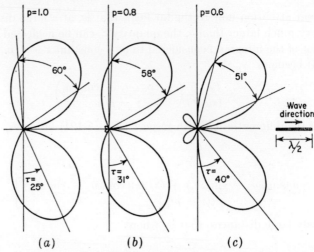

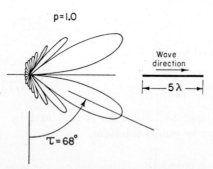

Fig. 5-16. Far-field patterns of linear $\frac{1}{2}$-wavelength antenna carrying a uniform traveling wave (to right) for three conditions of relative phase velocity ($p = 1.0$, 0.8, and 0.6). The tilt angle τ and the half-power beam widths are indicated for each pattern.

the braces { }. The expression indicated as an angle $\angle$ gives the phase of the field referred to the origin of the coordinates (see Fig. 5-15) as the phase center. The relative phase pattern at a constant distance is given by the right-hand term, $(\omega b / 2pc) (1 - p \cos \gamma)$.

Several examples will now be considered to illustrate the nature of the field patterns obtained on linear conductors carrying a uniform traveling wave.

Case 1. *Linear $\frac{1}{2}$-wavelength Antenna.* Let us consider a linear antenna, $\frac{1}{2}$ wavelength long as measured in free-space wavelengths. Assuming that $p = 1$, that is, the phase velocity along the antenna is equal to that of light, the pattern calculated from (5-128) is as shown by Fig. 5-16a. The difference between this pattern and that for a linear $\frac{1}{2}$-wavelength antenna with a sinusoidal current distribution or standing wave (Fig. 5-9a) is striking. The lobes are sharper and also tilted forward in the case of the traveling wave

Fig. 5-17. Far-field pattern of linear five-wavelength antenna carrying a uniform traveling wave ($p = 1$).

antenna (Fig. 5-16a). The tilt is in the direction of the traveling wave. The tilt angle τ of the direction of maximum radiation is 25° and the beam width between half-power points is about 60°. This is in contrast to $\tau = 0$ and a beam width of 78° for the $\frac{1}{2}$-wavelength antenna with a sinusoidal current distribution or standing wave.

As the phase velocity of the traveling wave on the $\frac{1}{2}$-wavelength antenna is reduced, the tilt angle is increased and the beam width reduced further as illustrated by the patterns of Figs. 5-16b and (c) which are for the cases of $p = 0.8$ and $p = 0.6$, respectively.

Case 2. Linear Antenna 5 Wavelengths Long. The field pattern for a 5-wavelength linear antenna with a single traveling wave is presented in Fig. 5-17 for the case where $p = 1$ (that is, $v = c$). This pattern is typical of those for long, terminated antennas, the radiation being beamed forward in a cone having the antenna as its axis. The tilt angle for this antenna is about 68°. As the length of the antenna is increased, the tilt angle increases further, reaching a value of about 78° when the length is 20 wavelengths for $p = 1$.

PROBLEMS

5-1. *a.* Two equal static electric charges of opposite sign separated by a distance L constitute a static electric dipole. Show that the electric potential at a distance r from such a dipole is given by

$$V = \frac{QL \cos \theta}{4\pi\epsilon r^2}$$

where Q is the magnitude of each charge and θ is the angle between the radius r and the line joining the charges (axis of dipole). It is assumed that r is very large compared to L.

   b. Find the vector value of the electric field **E** at a large distance from a static electric dipole by taking the gradient of the potential expression in part (a).

5-2. Using the value of the Hertz vector for a short oscillating dipole as given in (5-68) obtain **E** and **H** by the Hertz vector method, that is, by performing the operations indicated in (5-64) and (5-65), and confirm the fact that the fields so obtained are identical with the fields given in the column headed "General Expression" in Table 5-1.

5-3. The instantaneous current distribution of a thin linear center-fed antenna 2 wavelengths long is sinusoidal as shown.

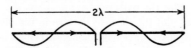

   a. Calculate and plot the pattern of the far field.

   b. What is the radiation resistance referred to a current loop?

   c. What is the radiation resistance at the transmission-line terminals as shown?

d. What is the radiation resistance $\lambda/8$ from a current loop?

5-4. Assume that the current is of uniform magnitude and in phase along the entire length of a $\lambda/2$ thin linear element.

    a. Calculate and plot the pattern of the far field.

    b. What is the radiation resistance?

    c. Tabulate for comparison

        (1) Radiation resistance of part *b* above.

        (2) Radiation resistance at the current loop of a $\lambda/2$ thin linear element with sinusoidal in-phase current distribution.

        (3) Radiation resistance of a $\lambda/2$ dipole calculated by means of the short dipole formula.

    d. Discuss the three results tabulated in part *c* and reasons for the differences.

5-5. Calculate and plot the radiation-field pattern in the plane of two thin linear $\frac{1}{2}$-wavelength antennas with equal in-phase currents and the spacing relationship shown. Assume sinusoidal current distributions.

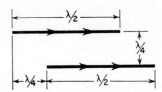

5-6. *a.* Express in integral form the retarded vector potential at a distance r from the center of a thin linear $\frac{1}{2}$-wavelength antenna. The antenna is parallel to the y axis, and its center is at the origin. The current is in phase along the antenna, and its magnitude corresponds to a cosine function of distance from the origin.

    b. What relations involving the vector potential yield the electric and magnetic fields (**E** and **H**) at a large distance?

    c. What is the integral form for the retarded Hertz vector at a distance r from the $\frac{1}{2}$-wavelength antenna of part (*a*)?

5-7. Calculate the field pattern in the plane of the full-wave antenna shown in the

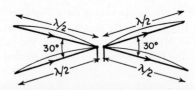

figure. Assume that the current distribution on each wire is sinusoidal and that all currents are in phase. Plot the pattern.

5-8. *a.* Calculate and plot the far-field pattern in the plane of a thin linear element one free-space wavelength long, carrying a single uniform traveling wave for 2 cases of the relative phase velocity $p = 1$ and 0.5.

    b. Repeat for the single case of an element 10 λ long and $p = 1$.

CHAPTER 6

THE LOOP ANTENNA

This chapter is devoted to the loop antenna. First, the field pattern of a small loop is derived very simply by considering that the loop is square and consists of four short linear dipoles. The same field equations are then developed by a somewhat longer method based on the assumption that the small loop is equivalent to a short magnetic dipole. Finally, the general case of the loop antenna with uniform current is treated for loops of any size. Although most of the development concerns circular loops, square loops are also discussed, and it is shown that the far fields of circular and square loops of the same area are the same when they are small but different when they are large.

6-1. The Small Loop. A very simple method of finding the field pattern of a small loop is treated in this section. Consider a circular loop of radius a with a uniform in-phase current as suggested by Fig. 6-1a. The

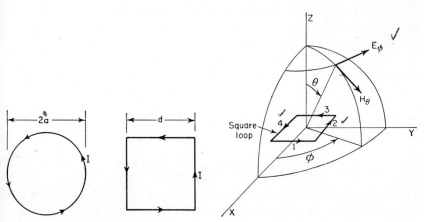

FIG. 6-1. Circular loop (a) and square loop (b).

FIG. 6-2. Relation of square loop to coordinates.

radius a is very small compared to the wavelength ($a \ll \lambda$). Suppose now that the circular loop is represented by a square loop of side length d, also with a uniform in-phase current, as shown in Fig. 6-1b. In this way, the loop can be treated as four short linear dipoles, whose properties we have already investigated in Chap. 5. Let d be chosen so that the area of the square loop is the same as the area of the circular loop. That is,

$$d^2 = \pi a^2 \tag{6-1}$$

If the loop is oriented as in Fig. 6-2, its far electric field has only an E_ϕ component. To find the far-field pattern in the y-z plane, it is only necessary to consider two of the four small linear dipoles (2 and 4). A cross section through the loop in the y-z plane is presented in Fig. 6-3.

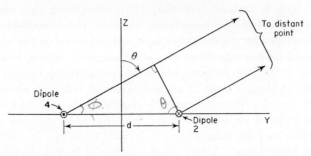

Fig. 6-3. Construction for finding far field of dipoles 2 and 4 of square loop.

Since the individual small dipoles 2 and 4 are nondirectional in the y-z plane, the field pattern of the loop in this plane is the same as that for two isotropic point sources as treated in Sec. 4-2. Thus,

$$E_\phi = -E_{\phi 0}\, e^{i\psi/2} + E_{\phi 0}\, e^{-i\psi/2} \tag{6-2}$$

where $E_{\phi 0}$ = electric field from individual dipole and

$$\psi = \frac{2\pi d}{\lambda} \sin\theta = d_r \sin\theta \tag{6-3}$$

It follows that

$$E_\phi = -2jE_{\phi 0} \sin\left(\frac{d_r}{2}\sin\theta\right) \tag{6-4}$$

The factor j in (6-4) indicates that the total field E_ϕ is in phase quadrature with the field $E_{\phi 0}$ of the individual dipole. This may be readily seen by a vector construction of the type of Fig. 4-1b of Chap. 4. Now if $d \ll \lambda$, (6-4) can be written

$$E_\phi = -jE_{\phi 0}\, d_r \sin\theta \tag{6-5}$$

The far field of the individual dipole was developed in Chap. 5, being given in Table 5-1. In developing the dipole formula, the dipole was in the z direction, whereas in the present case it is in the x direction (see

Figs. 6-2 and 6-3).   The angle θ in the dipole formula is measured from the dipole axis and is $90°$ in the present case.   The angle θ in (6-5) is a different angle with respect to the dipole, being as shown in Figs. 6-2 and 6-3.   Thus, we have for the far field $E_{\phi 0}$ of the individual dipole

$$E_{\phi 0} = \frac{j60\pi[I]L}{r\lambda} \tag{6-6}$$

where $[I]$ is the retarded current on the dipole and r is the distance from the dipole.   Substituting (6-6) in (6-5) then gives

$$E_\phi = \frac{60\pi[I]Ld_r \sin \theta}{r\lambda} \tag{6-7}$$

But the length L of the short dipole is the same as d, that is, $L = d$. Noting also that $d_r = 2\pi d/\lambda$ and that the area A of the loop is d^2, (6-7) becomes

$$E_\phi = \frac{120\pi^2[I] \sin \theta}{r} \frac{A}{\lambda^2} \tag{6-8}$$

This is the instantaneous value of the E_ϕ component of the far field of a small loop of area A.   The peak value of the field is obtained by replacing $[I]$ by I_0, where I_0 is the peak current in time on the loop.   The other component of the far field of the loop is H_θ, which is obtained from (6-8) by dividing by the intrinsic impedance of the medium, in this case, free space.   Thus,

$$H_\theta = \frac{E_\phi}{120\pi} = \frac{\pi[I] \sin \theta}{r} \frac{A}{\lambda^2} \tag{6-9}$$

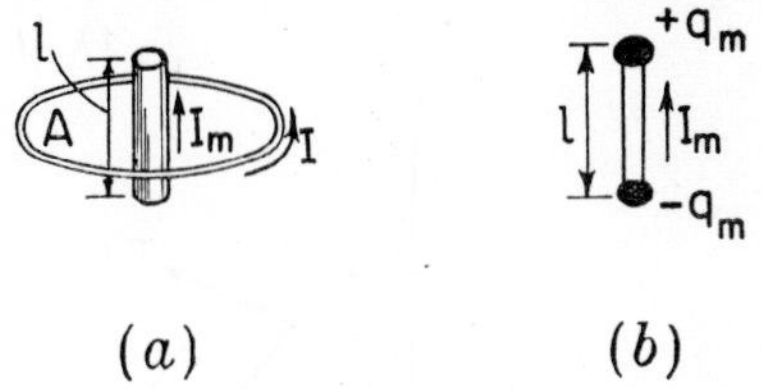

(a)   (b)

FIG. 6-4.   (a) Relation of small loop of area A to short magnetic dipole of length l.   (b) Short magnetic dipole.

6-2. The Short Magnetic Dipole. Equivalence to a Loop.   Another method of treating the small loop is by making use of its equivalence to a short magnetic dipole.   Thus, a small loop of area A and carrying a uniform in-phase electric current I is replaced by an equivalent magnetic dipole of length l as shown in Fig. 6-4a.   The magnetic dipole is assumed to carry a fictitious magnetic current I_m.

The relation between the loop and its equivalent magnetic dipole will now be developed.   The moment of the magnetic dipole is $q_m l$ where q_m is the pole strength at each end as in Fig. 6-4b.   The magnetic current is related to this pole strength by

$$I_m = -\mu \frac{dq_m}{dt} \tag{6-10}$$

where $I_m = I_{m0}e^{j\omega t}$

Integrating (6-10) with respect to time,

$$q_m = -\frac{I_m}{j\omega\mu} \tag{6-11}$$

The magnetic moment of the loop is IA. Equating this to the moment of the magnetic dipole, we have

$$q_m l = IA \tag{6-12}$$

Substituting (6-11) in (6-12),

$$\frac{I_m l}{j\omega\mu} = -IA \tag{6-13}$$

This may be reexpressed as,

$$I_m l = -j\omega\mu IA = -j2\pi f \frac{\lambda}{\lambda} \mu IA = -j2\pi \frac{Z_0}{\lambda} IA \tag{6-14}$$

or

$$I_m l = -j240\pi^2 I \frac{A}{\lambda} \tag{6-15}$$

In retarded form (6-15) is

$$[I_m]l = -j240\pi^2 [I] \frac{A}{\lambda} \tag{6-16}$$

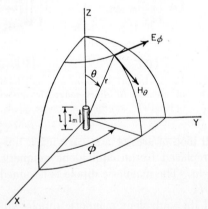

FIG. 6-5. Relation of short magnetic dipole to coordinates.

where $[I_m] = I_{m0}e^{j\omega\left(t-\frac{r}{c}\right)}$

$$[I] = I_0 e^{j\omega\left(t-\frac{r}{c}\right)}$$

Equations (6-15) and (6-16) relate a loop of area A and carrying a current I to its equivalent magnetic dipole of length l carrying a fictitious magnetic current I_m.

6-3. The Short Magnetic Dipole. Far Fields. In this section the far fields of a short magnetic dipole will be calculated. Then applying the equivalence relation between a loop and magnetic dipole developed in Sec. 6-2, we obtain the far field of a small circular loop.

The method of finding the fields of a short magnetic dipole is formally the same as that employed in Sec. 5-2 to find the far field of a short electric dipole. The only difference is that electric current I is replaced by a fictitious magnetic current I_m and that $\mathbf{E}$ is replaced by $\mathbf{H}$. Then with the magnetic dipole oriented as in Fig. 6-5, the retarded vector potential $\mathbf{F}$ of the *magnetic* current is

$$\mathbf{F} = \frac{\mu}{4\pi} \iiint \frac{[\mathbf{J}_m]}{r} \, d\tau = \mathbf{k} \frac{\mu}{4\pi} \int_{-l/2}^{+l/2} \frac{[I_m]}{r} \, dz \qquad \frac{\text{volts}^2 \text{ sec}}{\text{amp meter}} \qquad (6\text{-}17)$$

The vector potential $\mathbf{F}$ has only a z component F_z. Introducing the value of the retarded current

$$F_z = \frac{\mu I_{m0}}{4\pi} \int_{-l/2}^{+l/2} \frac{e^{j\omega\left(t-\frac{r}{c}\right)}}{r} \, dz \qquad (6\text{-}18)$$

If $r \gg l$ and $\lambda \gg l$, the phase difference of the contributions of the various current elements of length dz along the magnetic dipole can be neglected. Hence, the integrand in (6-18) may be regarded as a constant, and (6-18) becomes

$$F_z = \frac{\mu I_{m0} l e^{j\omega\left(t-\frac{r}{c}\right)}}{4\pi r} \qquad (6\text{-}19)$$

The electric field $\mathbf{E}$ is obtained from $\mathbf{F}$ by the relation,

$$\mathbf{E} = \frac{1}{\mu} \nabla \times \mathbf{F} \qquad (6\text{-}20)$$

Resolving F_z into its spherical or polar coordinate components F_θ and F_r and taking the curl of $\mathbf{F}$ as in (6-20), the E_ϕ component of the electric field is found to be

$$E_\phi = \frac{[I_m]l \sin\theta}{4\pi} \left(\frac{j\omega}{cr} + \frac{1}{r^2}\right) \qquad (6\text{-}21)$$

This is the only component of the electric field produced by a magnetic dipole oriented as in Fig. 6-5. It is interesting to note that (6-21) is identical with the expression for H_ϕ developed for a short electric dipole, provided that E in (6-21) is replaced by H and I_m by I (see Table 5-1).

The relation of (6-21) applies at any distance from the magnetic dipole, provided only that $r \gg l$ and $\lambda \gg l$. At a large distance r the second term of (6-21) can be neglected, and (6-21) becomes

$$E_\phi = \frac{j[I_m]\omega l \sin\theta}{4\pi cr} = \frac{j[I_m]\sin\theta}{2r} \frac{l}{\lambda} \qquad (6\text{-}22)$$

This is the far electric field from a short magnetic dipole of length l and carrying a fictitious magnetic current I_m. The far magnetic field H_θ of the magnetic dipole is related to E_ϕ by the intrinsic impedance of the medium, in this case, free space. Hence

$$H_\theta = \frac{j[I_m] \sin \theta}{240\pi r} \frac{l}{\lambda} \qquad (6\text{-}23)$$

Substituting now for the moment $[I_m]l$ in (6-22) and (6-23) the equivalent value for a loop as given by (6-16), we obtain

$$E_\phi = \frac{120\pi^2 [I] \sin \theta}{r} \frac{A}{\lambda^2} \qquad (6\text{-}24)$$

and

$$H_\theta = \frac{\pi [I] \sin \theta}{r} \frac{A}{\lambda^2} \qquad (6\text{-}25)$$

These are then the far-field equations for a small loop of area A carrying a current I. They are identical with (6-8) and (6-9) developed in Sec. 6-1 by the method using a square loop of four short linear electric dipoles. The field pattern in the plane of a circular loop with uniform current is by symmetry a circle. The far-field pattern in the plane of a small square loop with uniform current may also be shown to be a circle (Prob. 6-6). Thus, it appears that the far fields of *small* circular and square loops are identical *provided that both have the same area.*

Both E_ϕ and H_θ vary as the sine of the angle θ as illustrated in Fig. 6-6. The fields are independent of ϕ. Hence, the space patterns are figures of revolution of the pattern of Fig. 6-6 around the polar axis, the form being that of a doughnut. This pattern is identical in shape to that of a short electric dipole oriented parallel to the polar or z axis.

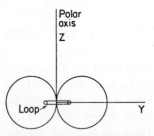

FIG. 6-6. Far-field pattern for a small loop.

6-4. Comparison of Far Fields of Small Loop and Short Dipole. It is of interest to compare the far-field expressions for a small loop with those for a short electric dipole. The comparison is made in Table 6-1. The presence of the operator j in the dipole expressions and its absence in the loop equations indicate that the fields of the electric dipole and of the loop are in time phase quadrature, the current I being in the same phase in both dipole and loop. This quadrature relationship is a fundamental difference between the fields of loops and dipoles.

The formulas in Table 6-1 apply to a loop oriented as in Fig. 6-2 and a dipole oriented parallel to the polar or z axis. The formulas are exact only for vanishingly small loops and dipoles. However, they are good approximations for loops up to $\frac{1}{10}$ wavelength in diameter and dipoles up to $\frac{1}{10}$ wavelength long.

TABLE 6-1

FAR FIELDS OF SMALL ELECTRIC DIPOLES AND LOOPS

Field	Electric dipole	Loop
Electric	$E_\theta = \dfrac{j60\pi[I] \sin \theta}{r} \dfrac{L}{\lambda}$	$E_\phi = \dfrac{120\pi^2[I] \sin \theta}{r} \dfrac{A}{\lambda^2}$
Magnetic	$H_\phi = \dfrac{j[I] \sin \theta}{2r} \dfrac{L}{\lambda}$	$H_\theta = \dfrac{\pi[I] \sin \theta}{r} \dfrac{A}{\lambda^2}$

6-5. The Loop Antenna. General Case. The general case of a loop antenna with uniform, in-phase current will now be discussed. The size of the loop is not restricted to a small value compared to the wavelength as in the preceding sections but may assume any value. The method of treatment follows that given by Foster.[1]

Let the loop of radius a be located with its center at the origin of the coordinates as in Fig. 6-7. The current I is uniform and in phase around the loop. Although this condition is readily obtained when the loop is small, it is not a natural condition for large loops energized at a point. For loops with perimeters of about $\frac{1}{4}$ wavelength or larger, phase shifters of some type must be introduced at intervals around the periphery in order to approximate a uniform, in-phase current on the loop. Assuming that the current is uni-

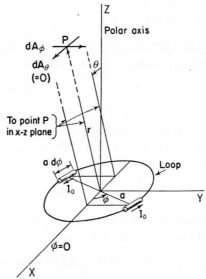

FIG. 6-7. Loop of any radius a with relation to coordinates.

[1] Donald Foster, Loop Antennas with Uniform Current, *Proc. I.R.E.*, **32**, 603–607, October, 1944.

A discussion of circular loops of circumference less than $\frac{1}{2}$ wavelength ($C_\lambda < \frac{1}{2}$) with nonuniform current distribution is given by G. Glinski, Note on Circular Loop Antennas with Nonuniform Current Distribution, *J. Applied Phys.*, **18**, 638–644, July, 1947.

form and in phase, the far-field expressions will be derived with the aid of the vector potential of the electric current. The vector potential will first be developed for a pair of short, diametrically opposed electric dipoles of length $a\,d\phi$, as in Fig. 6-7. Then integrating over the loop, the total vector potential is obtained, and from this the far-field components are derived.

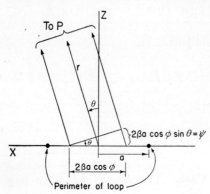

FIG. 6-8. Cross section in x-z plane through loop of Fig. 6-7.

Since the current is confined to the loop, the only component of the vector potential having a value is A_ϕ. The other components are zero: $A_\theta = A_r = 0$. The infinitesimal value at the point P of the ϕ component of A from two diametrically opposed infinitesimal dipoles is

$$dA_\phi = \frac{\mu\,dM}{4\pi r} \qquad (6\text{-}26)$$

where dM is the current moment due to one pair of diametrically opposed infinitesimal dipoles of length, $a\,d\phi$. In the $\phi = 0$ plane (Fig. 6-7) the ϕ component of the retarded current moment due to one dipole is

$$[I]\,a\,d\phi\,\cos\phi \qquad (6\text{-}27)$$

where $[I] = I_0 e^{j\omega\left(t-\frac{r}{c}\right)}$ and I_0 is the peak current in time on the loop.

Figure 6-8 is a cross section through the loop in the x-z plane of Fig. 6-7. Referring now to Fig. 6-8, the resultant moment dM at a large distance due to a pair of diametrically opposed dipoles is

$$dM = 2j[I]a\,d\phi\,\cos\phi\,\sin\frac{\psi}{2} \qquad (6\text{-}28)$$

where $\psi = 2\beta a\,\cos\phi\,\sin\theta$ radians
Introducing this value for ψ into (6-28) we have

$$dM = 2j[I]a\,\cos\phi\,[\sin\,(\beta a\,\cos\phi\,\sin\theta)]\,d\phi \qquad (6\text{-}29)$$

Now substituting (6-29) into (6-26) and integrating,

$$A_\phi = \frac{j\mu[I]a}{2\pi r}\int_0^\pi \sin\,(\beta a\,\cos\phi\,\sin\theta)\,\cos\phi\,d\phi \qquad (6\text{-}30)$$

or

$$A_\phi = \frac{j\mu[I]a}{2r}\,J_1(\beta a\,\sin\,\theta) \qquad (6\text{-}31)$$

where J_1 is a Bessel function of the first order and of argument $(\beta a\,\sin\,\theta)\cdot$ The integration of (6-30) is performed on equivalent dipoles which are all situated at the origin but have different orientations with respect to ϕ. The retarded current $[I]$ is referred to the origin and, hence, is constant in the integration.

The far electric field of the loop has only a ϕ component given by

$$E_\phi = -j\omega A_\phi \tag{6-32}$$

Substituting the value of A_ϕ from (6-31) into (6-32) yields,

$$E_\phi = \frac{\mu\omega[I]a}{2r} J_1(\beta a \sin \theta) \tag{6-33}$$

or

$$E_\phi = \frac{60\pi\beta a[I]}{r} J_1(\beta a \sin \theta) \tag{6-34}$$

This expression gives the instantaneous electric field at a large distance r from a loop of any radius a. The peak value of E_ϕ is obtained by putting $[I] = I_0$, where I_0 is the peak value (in time) of the current on the loop. The magnetic field H_θ at a large distance is related to E_ϕ by the intrinsic impedance of the medium, in this case, free space. Thus,

$$H_\theta = \frac{\beta a[I]}{2r} J_1(\beta a \sin \theta) \tag{6-35}$$

This expression gives the instantaneous magnetic field at a large distance r from a loop of any radius a.

6-6. Far-field Patterns of Circular Loop Antennas with Uniform Current. The far-field patterns for a loop of any size are given by (6-34) and (6-35). They differ in magnitude by a factor ($E_\phi = H_\theta Z$). For a loop of a given size, βa is constant and the shape of the far-field pattern is given as a function of θ by

$$J_1(C_\lambda \sin \theta) \tag{6-36}$$

where C_λ is the circumference of the loop in wavelengths. That is,

$$C_\lambda = \frac{2\pi a}{\lambda} = \beta a \tag{6-37}$$

The value of $\sin \theta$ as a function of θ ranges in magnitude between zero and unity. When $\theta = 90°$, the relative field is $J_1(C_\lambda)$, and as θ decreases to zero, the values of the relative field vary in accordance with the J_1 curve from $J_1(C_\lambda)$ to zero. This is illustrated by Fig. 6-9 in which a rectified first-order Bessel curve is shown as a function of $C_\lambda \sin \theta$.

As an example, let us find the pattern for a loop 1 wavelength in diameter ($C_\lambda = \pi = 3.14$). The relative field in the direction $\theta = 90°$ is then 0.285. As θ decreases, the field intensity rises, reaching a maximum of 0.582 at angle θ of about 36°. As θ decreases further, the field intensity also decreases, reaching zero at $\theta = 0°$. The pattern in the other four quadrants is symmetrical, the complete pattern being as presented in Fig. 6-10b.

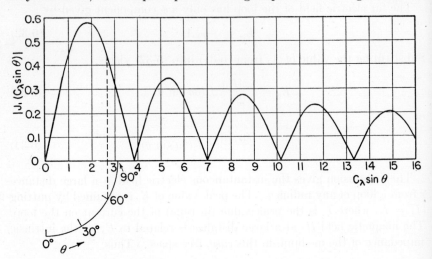

FIG. 6-9. Pattern chart for loops with uniform current as given by first-order Bessel curve as a function of $C_\lambda \sin \theta$.

It is possible to obtain the pattern by a graphical construction. This is illustrated for the case we have just considered of $C_\lambda = \pi$ by the auxiliary circle quadrant in Fig. 6-9. The angle θ is laid off around the arc of the circle. The radius of the circle is equal to $C_\lambda \sin 90° = C_\lambda$, which in this case is π. The field in the direction $\theta = 60°$, for instance, is then given by drawing a perpendicular to the axis of the abscissa and continuing this perpendicular until it intersects the J_1 curve giving a value of relative field, in this case, of 0.443, as shown in Fig. 6-9.

Turning now to a consideration of loops of other size, it is to be noted from Fig. 6-9 that the maximum field is in the direction $\theta = 90°$ for all loops which are less than 1.84 wavelengths in circumference (less than 0.585 wavelength in diameter). As an example, the pattern for a loop $\frac{1}{10}$ wavelength in diameter is presented in Fig. 6-10a. The pattern is practically a sine pattern as would be obtained with a very small loop.

By way of contrast, the pattern for a loop 5 wavelengths in diameter is shown in Fig. 6-10c. In this case, which is typical for large circular loops with uniform current, the maximum field is in a direction nearly normal to the plane of the loop, while the field in the direction of the plane of the loop is small.

All patterns in Fig. 6-10 are adjusted to the same maximum. The space patterns for the three cases in Fig. 6-10 are figures of revolution of

the patterns around the polar axis.　It is to be noted that the field exactly
normal to the loop is always zero, regardless of the size of the loop.

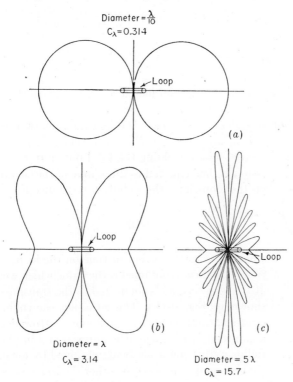

FIG. 6-10.　Far-field patterns of loops of 0.1, 1, and 5 wavelengths diameter. Uniform,
in-phase current is assumed on the loops.

6-7. The Small Loop as a Special Case.　The relations of (6-34) and
(6-35) apply to loops of any size.　It will now be shown that for the special
case of a small loop, these expressions reduce to the ones obtained previously.

For small arguments of the first-order Bessel function, the following
approximate relation can be used.[1]

$$J_1(x) = \frac{x}{2} \qquad (6\text{-}38)$$

where x is any variable.　When $x = \frac{1}{3}$, the approximation of (6-38) is
about 1 per cent in error.　The relation becomes exact as x approaches
zero.　Thus, if the perimeter of the loop is $\frac{1}{3}$ wavelength or less ($C_\lambda < \frac{1}{3}$),

---

[1] For small arguments, the J_1 curve is nearly linear (see Fig. 6-9).　The general rela-
tion for a Bessel function of any order n is $J_n(x) \simeq x^n/n!2^n$, where $|x| \ll 1$.

(6-38) may be applied to (6-34) and (6-35) with an error which is about 1 per cent or less. Equations (6-34) and (6-35) then become

$$E_\phi = \frac{60\pi\beta a[I]\beta a \sin\theta}{2r} = \frac{120\pi^2[I]\sin\theta}{r}\frac{A}{\lambda^2} \qquad (6\text{-}39)$$

$$H_\theta = \frac{\beta a[I]\beta a \sin\theta}{4r} = \frac{\pi[I]\sin\theta}{r}\frac{A}{\lambda^2} \qquad (6\text{-}40)$$

These far-field equations for a small loop are identical with those obtained in earlier sections (see Table 6-1).

6-8. Radiation Resistance of Loops.[1] To find the radiation resistance of a loop antenna, the Poynting vector is integrated over a large sphere yielding the total power W radiated. This power is then equated to the square of the effective current on the loop times the radiation resistance R_r.

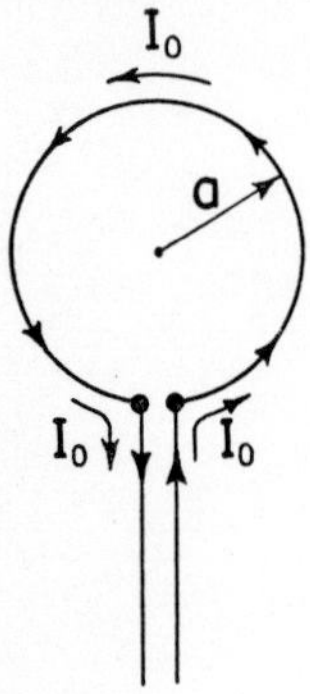

$$W = \frac{I_0^2}{2}R_r \qquad (6\text{-}41)$$

where I_0 = peak current in time on the loop. The radiation resistance so obtained is the value which would appear at the loop terminals connected to the transmission line as shown in Fig. 6-11. The situation shown in Fig. 6-11 occurs naturally only on small loops. However, it will be assumed that the current is uniform and in phase for any radius a, this condition being obtained by means of phase shifters, multiple feeds, or other devices (see Sec. 14-20).

Fig. 6-11. Loop and transmission line.

The average Poynting vector of a far field is given by

$$P_r = \tfrac{1}{2}|H|^2 \operatorname{Re} Z \qquad (6\text{-}42)$$

where $|H|$ is the absolute value of the magnetic field and Z is the intrinsic impedance of the medium, which in this case is free space. Substituting the absolute value of H_θ from (6-35) for $|H|$ in (6-42) yields

$$P_r = \frac{15\pi(\beta a I_0)^2}{r^2} J_1^2(\beta a \sin\theta) \qquad (6\text{-}43)$$

The total power radiated W is the integral of P_r over a large sphere. That is,

$$W = \iint P_r\, ds = 15\pi(\beta a I_0)^2 \int_0^{2\pi} \int_0^{\pi} J_1^2(\beta a \sin\theta)\sin\theta\, d\theta\, d\phi \qquad (6\text{-}44)$$

[1] The procedure follows that given by Foster, Loop Antennas with Uniform Current, *Proc. I.R.E.*, **32**, 603–607, October, 1944.

or

$$W = 30\pi^2(\beta a I_0)^2 \int_0^\pi J_1^2(\beta a \sin \theta) \sin \theta \, d\theta \qquad (6\text{-}45)$$

In the case of a loop that is small in terms of wavelengths, the approximation of (6-38) can be applied. Thus (6-45) reduces to

$$W = \frac{15}{2}\pi^2(\beta a)^4 I_0^2 \int_0^\pi \sin^3 \theta \, d\theta = 10\pi^2\beta^4 a^4 I_0^2 \qquad (6\text{-}46)$$

But the area $A = \pi a^2$ so (6-46) becomes

$$W = 10\beta^4 A^2 I_0^2 \qquad (6\text{-}47)$$

Assuming no antenna losses, this power equals the power delivered to the loop terminals as given by (6-41). Therefore,

$$R_r \frac{I_0^2}{2} = 10\beta^4 A^2 I_0^2 \qquad (6\text{-}48)$$

and

$$R_r = 31{,}171\left(\frac{A}{\lambda^2}\right)^2 = 197 C_\lambda^4 \quad \text{ohms} \qquad (6\text{-}49)$$

or

$$R_r \simeq 31{,}200\left(\frac{A}{\lambda^2}\right)^2 \quad \text{ohms} \qquad (6\text{-}50)$$

This is the radiation resistance of a small single-turn loop antenna, circular or square, with uniform in-phase current. The relation is about 2 per cent in error when the loop perimeter is $\frac{1}{3}$ wavelength. A circular loop of this perimeter has a diameter of about $\frac{1}{10}$ wavelength. Its radiation resistance by (6-50) is nearly 2.5 ohms.

The radiation resistance of a small loop consisting of one or more turns is given by[1]

$$R_r = 31{,}200\left(n\frac{A}{\lambda^2}\right)^2 \quad \text{ohms}$$

where n = number of turns

Let us now proceed to find the radiation resistance of a circular loop of any radius a. To do this we must integrate (6-45). However, the integral of (6-45) may be reexpressed. Thus, in general,[2]

$$\int_0^\pi J_1^2(x \sin \theta) \sin \theta \, d\theta = \frac{1}{x}\int_0^{2x} J_2(y) \, dy \qquad (6\text{-}51)$$

---

[1] A. Alford and A. G. Kandoian, Ultrahigh-frequency Loop Antennas, Trans. *A.I.E.E.*, **59**, 843–848, 1940.

[2] G. N. Watson, "A Treatise on the Theory of Bessel Functions," Cambridge University Press, London, 1922.

where y is any function

Applying (6-51) to (6-45) we obtain

$$W = 30\pi^2 \beta a I_0^2 \int_0^{2\beta a} J_2(y)\ dy \tag{6-52}$$

Equating (6-52) and (6-41) and putting $\beta a = C_\lambda$ yields

$$R_r = 60\pi^2 C_\lambda \int_0^{2C_\lambda} J_2(y)\ dy \quad \text{ohms} \tag{6-53}$$

This is the radiation resistance as given by Foster for a single-turn circular loop with uniform in-phase current and of any circumference C_λ.

When the loop is large ($C_\lambda \geq 5$), we can use the approximation

$$\int_0^{2C_\lambda} J_2(y)\ dy \simeq 1 \tag{6-54}$$

so that (6-53) reduces to

$$R_r = 60\pi^2 C_\lambda = 592 C_\lambda = 3{,}720\frac{a}{\lambda} \tag{6-55}$$

For a loop of 10 wavelengths perimeter, the radiation resistance by (6-55) is nearly 6,000 ohms.

For values of C_λ between $\frac{1}{3}$ and 5 the integral in (6-53) can be evaluated using the transformation

$$\int_0^{2C_\lambda} J_2(y)\ dy = \int_0^{2C_\lambda} J_0(y)\ dy - 2J_1(2C_\lambda) \tag{6-56}$$

where the expressions on the right of (6-56) are tabulated functions.[1]

For perimeters of over 5 wavelengths ($C_\lambda > 5$) one can also use the asymptotic development,

$$\int_0^{2x} J_2(y)\ dy \simeq 1 - \frac{1}{\sqrt{\pi x}}\left[\sin\left(2x - \frac{\pi}{4}\right) + \frac{11}{16x}\cos\left(2x - \frac{\pi}{4}\right)\right] \tag{6-57}$$

where $x = \beta a = C_\lambda$

For small values of x, one can use a series obtained by integrating the ascending power series for J_2. Thus,

$$\int_0^{2x} J_2(y)\ dy = \frac{x^3}{3}\left(1 - \frac{x^2}{5} + \frac{x^4}{56} - \frac{x^6}{1{,}080} + \frac{x^8}{31{,}680} - \cdots\right) \tag{6-58}$$

When $x = C_\lambda = 2$ (perimeter 2 wavelengths), the result with four terms

[1] The integral involving J_0 for the interval $0 \leq x \leq 5$ (where $x = C_\lambda$) is given by A. N. Lowan and M. Abramowitz, *J. Math. Phys.*, **22**, 2–12, May, 1943; and also by *Natl. Bur. Standards Tech. Memo* 20.

Values of J_1 are given in many tables. See, for example, Jahnke and Emde, "Tables of Functions," B. G. Teubner, Leipzig, 1933, p. 157.

is about 2 per cent in error. This same percentage error is obtained with one term when the perimeter is about $\frac{1}{3}$ wavelength.

A graph showing the radiation resistance of single-turn loops with uniform current as a function of the circumference in wavelengths is presented in Fig. 6-12. The data for the curve are based on Foster's formulas

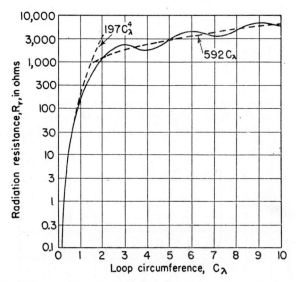

FIG. 6-12. Radiation resistance of single-turn circular loop with uniform, in-phase current as a function of the loop circumference in wavelengths, C_λ.

as given above. Curves for the approximate formulas of small and large loops are shown by the dashed lines.

6-9. Directivity of Circular Loop Antennas with Uniform Current. The directivity D of an antenna was defined in (2-31) as the ratio of maximum radiation intensity to the average radiation intensity. The maximum radiation intensity for a loop antenna is given by r^2 times (6-43). The average radiation intensity is given by (6-45) divided by 4π. Thus, the directivity of a loop is

$$D = \frac{2C_\lambda J_1^2(C_\lambda \sin\theta)}{\int_0^{2C_\lambda} J_2(y)\,dy} \qquad (6\text{-}59)$$

This is Foster's expression for the directivity of a circular loop with uniform in-phase current of any circumference C_λ. The angle θ in (6-59) is the value for which the field is a maximum.

For a small loop $(C_\lambda < \frac{1}{3})$, the directivity expression reduces to

$$D = \frac{3}{2}\sin^2\theta = \frac{3}{2} \qquad (6\text{-}60)$$

since the field is a maximum at $\theta = 90°$. The value of $\frac{3}{2}$ is the same as for a short electric dipole. This is to be expected since the pattern of a short dipole is the same as for a small loop.

For a large loop ($C_\lambda > 5$), (6-59) reduces to

$$D = 2C_\lambda J_1^2(C_\lambda \sin \theta) \tag{6-61}$$

From Fig. 6-9 we note that for any loop with $C_\lambda \geq 1.84$, the maximum value of $J_1(C_\lambda \sin \theta)$ is 0.582. Thus, the directivity expression of (6-61) for a large loop becomes

$$D = 0.68C_\lambda \tag{6-62}$$

The directivity of a loop antenna as a function of the loop circumference C_λ is presented in Fig. 6-13. Curves based on the approximate relations of (6-60) and (6-62) for small and large loops are indicated by dashed lines.

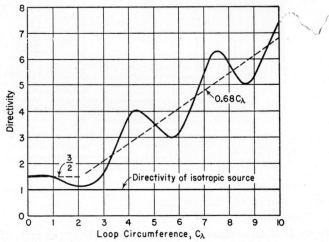

Fig. 6-13. Directivity of circular loop antenna with uniform, in-phase current as a function of loop circumference in wavelengths, C_λ. (After Foster.)

6-10. Table of Loop Formulas. The relations developed in the preceding sections are summarized in Table 6-2. The general and large loop formulas are based on Foster's results.

6-11. Square Loops. It was shown in Sec. 6-3 that the far-field patterns of square and circular loops of the same area are identical when the loops are small ($A < \lambda^2/100$). As a generalization, we may say that the properties depend only on the area and that the shape of the loop has no effect when the loop is small. However, this is not the case when the loop is large. The pattern of a circular loop of any size is independent of the angle ϕ but is a function of θ (see Fig. 6-2). On the other hand, the pattern of a large square loop is a function of both θ and ϕ. Referring to Fig. 6-14, the pattern in a plane normal to the plane of the loop and parallel to two sides (1 and 3), as indicated by the line AA', is simply the pattern of two point sources representing sides 2 and 4 of the loop. The pattern in a

TABLE 6-2

FORMULAS FOR CIRCULAR LOOPS WITH UNIFORM CURRENT

Quantity	General expression (any size loop)	Small loop* $A < \lambda^2/100$ $C_\lambda < \frac{1}{3}$	Large loop $C_\lambda > 5$
Far E_ϕ	$\dfrac{60\pi[I]C_\lambda J_1(C_\lambda \sin \theta)}{r}$	$\dfrac{120\pi^2[I]\sin \theta}{r}\dfrac{A}{\lambda^2}$	Same as general
Far H_θ	$\dfrac{[I]C_\lambda J_1(C_\lambda \sin \theta)}{2r}$	$\dfrac{\pi[I]\sin \theta}{r}\dfrac{A}{\lambda^2}$	Same as general
Radiation resistance, ohms	$60\pi^2 C_\lambda \displaystyle\int_0^{2C_\lambda} J_2(y)\ dy$	$31,200\left(\dfrac{A}{\lambda^2}\right)^2 = 197C_\lambda^4$	$3,720\dfrac{a}{\lambda} = 592C_\lambda$
Directivity	$\dfrac{2C_\lambda J_1^2(C_\lambda \sin \theta)}{\int_0^{2C_\lambda} J_2(y)\ dy}$	$\dfrac{3}{2}$	$4.25\dfrac{a}{\lambda} = 0.68C_\lambda$

A = area of loop; C_λ = circumference of circular loop, wavelengths.

*The small loop formulas apply not only to circular loops but also to square loops of area A and in fact to small loops of any shape having an area A. The formula involving C_λ applies, of course, only to a circular loop.

plane normal to the plane of the loop and passing through diagonal corners, as indicated by the line BB', is different. The complete range in the pattern variation as a function of ϕ is contained in this 45° interval between AA' and BB' in Fig. 6-14.

An additional difference of large circular and square loops is in the θ patterns. For instance, Fig. 6-10c shows the pattern as a function of θ for a circular loop 5 wavelengths in diameter. By way of comparison, the pattern for a square loop of the same area is presented in Fig. 6-15. The square loop is 4.44 wavelengths on a side. The pattern is in a plane perpendicular to the plane of the loop and parallel to the sides (plane contains AA' in Fig. 6-14). Comparing Figs. 6-10c and 6-15, we note that the pattern lobes of the circular loop decrease in magnitude as θ approaches 90° while the lobes of the square loop are of equal magnitude. This illustrates the difference of the Bessel function pattern of the circular loop and the trigonometric function pattern of the square loop. In the above discussion, uniform in-phase currents are assumed.

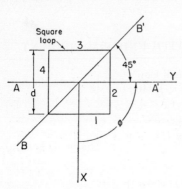

FIG. 6-14. Large square loop.

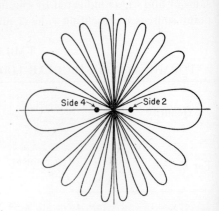

FIG. 6-15. Pattern of square loop with uniform, in-phase current. The loop is 4.44 wavelengths on a side. The pattern is in a plane normal to the plane of the loop and through the line AA' of Fig. 6-14.

PROBLEMS

6-1. Calculate and plot the far-field pattern normal to the plane of a circular loop $\frac{3}{4}$ wavelength in diameter with a uniform in-phase current distribution.

6-2. Calculate and plot the far-field pattern in a plane normal to the plane of a square loop and parallel to one side. The loop is 1 wavelength on a side. Assume uniform in-phase currents.

6-3. What is the maximum effective aperture of a thin loop antenna 0.1 wavelength in diameter with a uniform in-phase current distribution?

6-4. What is the radiation resistance of the loop of Prob. 6-1?

6-5. A circular loop antenna with uniform in-phase current has a diameter D. What is

     a. The far-field pattern (calculate and plot)

     b. The radiation resistance

     c. The directivity

for each of three cases where

      (1) $D = \lambda/4$

      (2) $D = 1.5\,\lambda$

      (3) $D = 8\,\lambda$

6-6. Resolving the small square loop with uniform current into 4 short dipoles, show that the far-field pattern in the plane of the loop is a circle.

CHAPTER 7

THE HELICAL ANTENNA

7-1. Introduction. The helical antenna, which is discussed in this chapter, may be regarded as the connecting link between the linear antenna and the loop antenna, discussed in preceding chapters. The helical antenna is the general form of antenna of which the linear and loop antennas are special cases. Thus, a helix of fixed diameter collapses to a loop as the spacing approaches zero. On the other hand, a helix of fixed spacing between turns straightens out into a linear conductor as the diameter approaches zero.

A helix may radiate in many modes. Two of these radiation modes will be considered in some detail. These are: (1) the axial mode of radiation[1] and (2) the normal mode of radiation.[2]

In the axial mode of radiation the field is a maximum in the direction of the helix axis and is circularly polarized or nearly so. The axial mode of radiation occurs when the helix circumference is of the order of 1 wavelength. For a given helix, this mode of radiation persists over a relatively wide frequency range.

In the normal mode of radiation, the field is a maximum in a direction normal to the helix axis, and for a certain relation between the spacing and diameter the field is, in theory, circularly polarized. For the normal mode the dimensions of the helix must be small compared to the wavelength, so that from band width and efficiency considerations this mode is not readily applicable in practice.

[1] J. D. Kraus, Helical Beam Antenna, *Electronics*, **20**, 109–111, April, 1947.

J. D. Kraus and J. C. Williamson, Characteristics of Helical Antennas Radiating in the Axial Mode, *J. Applied Phys.*, **19**, 87–96, January, 1948.

O. J. Glasser and J. D. Kraus, Measured Impedances of Helical Beam Antennas, *J. Applied Phys.*, **19**, 193–197, February, 1948.

J. D. Kraus, Helical Beam Antennas for Wide-band Applications, *Proc. I.R.E.*, **36**, 1236–1242, October, 1948.

J. D. Kraus, The Helical Antenna, *Proc. I.R.E.*, **37**, 263–272, March, 1949.

J. D. Kraus, Helical Beam Antenna Design Techniques, *Communications*, **29**, 6–9, 34–35, September, 1949.

T. E. Tice and J. D. Kraus, The Influence of Conductor Size on the Properties of Helical Beam Antennas, *Proc. I.R.E.*, **37**, 1296, November, 1949.

[2] H. A. Wheeler, A Helical Antenna for Circular Polarization, *Proc. I.R.E.*, **35**, 1484–1488, December, 1947.

The axial and normal radiation mode patterns of a helix are compared with the radiation patterns for straight conductors and loops in Fig. 7-1.

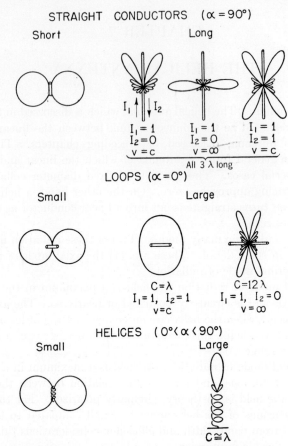

STRAIGHT CONDUCTORS $(\alpha = 90°)$

LOOPS $(\alpha = 0°)$

HELICES $(0° < \alpha < 90°)$

FIG. 7-1. Patterns of straight conductor, loop, and helix compared. I_1 and I_2 represent current magnitudes of waves traveling in opposite directions on antennas. If $I_2 = I_1$ there is a pure standing wave. If $I_2 = 0$, only a pure traveling wave is present. (v = velocity of wave along antenna, c = velocity of light, C = circumference).

It is to be noted that the patterns of a short linear conductor, a small loop, and a small helix are the same.

7-2. Helix Dimensions. The following symbols will be used to describe a helix (see Fig. 7-2):

D = diameter of helix (center to center)
C = circumference of helix = πD
S = spacing between turns (center to center)
α = pitch angle = arctan $S/\pi D$

L = length of 1 turn
n = number of turns
A = axial length = nS
d = diameter of helix conductor

The diameter D and circumference C refer to the imaginary cylinder whose surface passes through the center line of the helix conductor. A subscript λ signifies that the dimension is measured in *free-space wavelengths*. For example: D_λ is the helix diameter in free-space wavelengths.

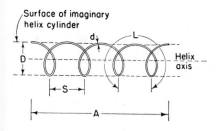

FIG. 7-2. Helix and associated dimensions.

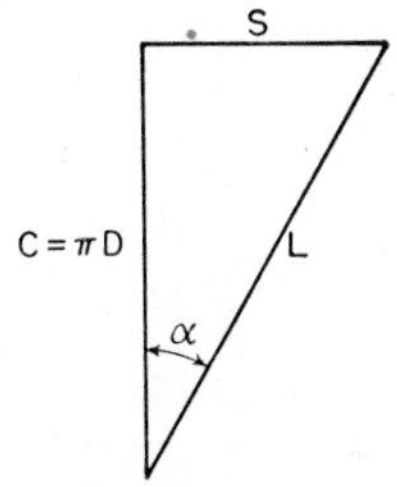

FIG. 7-3. Relation between circumference, spacing, turn length, and pitch angle of a helix.

If 1 turn of a circular helix is unrolled on a flat plane, the relation between the spacing S, circumference C, turn length L, and pitch angle α, are as illustrated by the triangle in Fig. 7-3.

The dimensions of a helix are conveniently represented by a diameter-spacing chart or, as in Fig. 7-4, by a circumference-spacing chart. On this chart the dimensions of a helix may be expressed either in rectangular coordinates by the spacing S_λ and circumference C_λ or in polar coordinates by the length of 1 turn L_λ and the pitch angle α. When the spacing is zero, $\alpha = 0$, and the helix becomes a loop. On the other hand, when the diameter is zero, $\alpha = 90°$, and the helix becomes a linear conductor. Thus, in Fig. 7-4 the ordinate axis represents loops while the abscissa axis represents linear conductors. The entire area between the two axes represents the general case of the helix.

Suppose that we have a 1-turn helix with a turn length of 1 wavelength $(L_\lambda = 1)$. When $\alpha = 0$, the helix is a loop of 1 wavelength circumference or of diameter equal to $1/\pi$ wavelengths. As the pitch angle α increases, the circumference decreases and the dimensions of the helix move along the $L_\lambda = 1$ curve in Fig. 7-4, until, when $\alpha = 90°$, the "helix" is a straight conductor 1 wavelength long.

7-3. Radiation and Transmission Modes of Helices. In discussing the helix, it is necessary to distinguish between transmission and radiation modes.

The term "transmission mode" is used to describe the manner in which an electromagnetic wave is propagated along an infinite helix as though

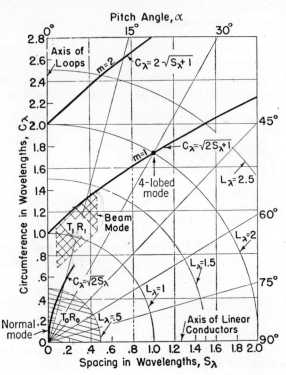

FIG. 7-4. Spacing-circumference chart for helices showing regions for different modes of operation.

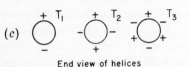

FIG. 7-5. Approximate instantaneous charge distributions on helices for different transmission modes.

the helix constituted an infinite transmission line or wave guide. A variety of different transmission modes is possible.

The term "radiation mode" is used to describe the general form of the far-field pattern of a finite helix. Although an infinite variety of patterns is possible, two kinds are of particular interest. One is the axial or beam mode of radiation (R_1 mode), and the other is the normal mode of radiation (R_0 mode).

The lowest transmission mode for a helical conductor has adjacent regions of positive and negative charge separated by many turns.   This mode is designated as the T_0 transmission mode and the instantaneous charge distribution is as suggested by Fig. 7-5a. The T_0 mode is important when the length of 1 turn is small compared to the wavelength ($L \ll \lambda$) and is the mode occurring on low-frequency inductances. It is also the important transmission mode in the traveling-wave tube.[1]   Since the adjacent regions of positive and negative charge are separated by an appreciable axial distance, a substantial axial component of the electric field is present, and in the traveling-wave tube this field interacts with the electron stream.   If the criterion $L_\lambda < \frac{1}{2}$ is arbitrarily selected as a boundary for the T_0 transmission mode, the region of the helix dimensions for which this mode is important is shown by the shaded area in Fig. 7-4.

A helix excited in the T_0 transmission mode may radiate.   Let us consider the case when the helix is very short ($nL \ll \lambda$) and the current is assumed to be of uniform magnitude and in phase along the entire helix.   It is theoretically possible to approximate this condition on a small, end-loaded helix. Although the radiation resistance of such a small helix would be very low, let us assume that appreciable radiation can be obtained.   The maximum field from the helix is then normal to the helix axis for all helix dimensions provided only that $nL \ll \lambda$.

Fig. 7-6.   A small helix and its radiation pattern.

Thus, this condition is called a "normal radiation mode" (R_0).[2]   Any component of the field has a sine variation with θ as shown in Fig. 7-6.   The space pattern is a figure of revolution of the pattern shown, around the polar axis.   The field is, in general, elliptically polarized but for certain helix dimensions may be circularly polarized and for other dimensions, linearly polarized.   The transmission mode and radiation mode appropriate for very small helices can be described by combining the T_0 and R_0 designa-

[1] R. Komfner, The Traveling Wave Tube as Amplifier at Microwaves, *Proc. I.R.E.*, **35**, No. 2, 124–127, February, 1947.

    J. R. Pierce and L. M. Field, Traveling Wave Tubes, *Proc. I.R.E.*, **35**, No. 2, 108–111, February, 1947.

    J. R. Pierce, Theory of the Beam-type Traveling Wave Tube, *Proc. I.R.E.*, **35**, No. 2, 111–123, February, 1947.

    C. C. Cutler, Experimental Determination of Helical Wave Properties, *Proc. I.R.E.*, **35**, No. 2, 230–233, February, 1948.

    L. J. Chu and J. D. Jackson, Field Theory of Traveling Wave Tubes, *Proc. I.R.E.*, **36**, No. 7, 853–863, July, 1948.

[2] Any radiation mode, in general, may be arbitrarily designated by the shorthand notation $R_{\cos \theta_m}$ where θ_m is the angle from the helix axis to the direction of maximum radiation.   For the normal mode $\theta_m = 90°$ so that the designation is R_0.

tions as $T_0 R_0$. This designation is applied in Fig. 7-4 to the region of helix dimensions near the origin.

A first-order transmission mode on the helix, designated T_1, becomes permissible when the helix circumference C_λ in free-space wavelengths is of the order of 1 wavelength. For small pitch angles, this mode has regions of adjacent positive and negative charge separated by approximately $\frac{1}{2}$ turn or near the opposite ends of a diameter as shown in Fig. 7-5b and also in end view by Fig. 7-5c. It is found that radiation from helices with circumferences of the order of 1 wavelength ($C_\lambda \sim 1$) and a number of turns ($n > 1$) is usually a well-defined beam with a maximum in the direction of the helix axis. Hence, this type of operation is called the "axial or beam mode of radiation" and since $\theta_m = 0$ the designation is R_1. A helix radiating in the axial mode may be spoken of as a "helical beam antenna." The field in the axial direction from a helix radiating in the axial mode is circularly polarized or nearly so.

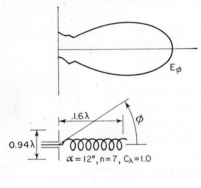

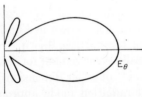

Measured field patterns of a 7-turn 12° helix with a circumference of 1 wavelength are shown in Fig. 7-7. There are two patterns. Referring to the helix in Fig. 7-7, the E_ϕ pattern shows the variation with ϕ of the E_ϕ component (parallel to the page) of the field. The E_θ pattern shows the variation with ϕ of the E_θ component (normal to the page). Both patterns are functions of ϕ and are measured in the plane of the page. Both patterns in Fig. 7-7 are adjusted to the same maximum. However, the actual difference between the maxima of E_ϕ and E_θ is small, since the field is nearly circularly polarized.

Fig. 7-7. Field patterns of 12°, 7-turn helix radiating in the axial mode. The helix circumference is 1 wavelength. Both E_ϕ and E_θ patterns are shown as a function of ϕ. E_ϕ is in the plane of the page, and E_θ is normal to the page.

The axial mode of radiation with patterns similar to those of Fig. 7-7 occurs over a considerable range of helix dimensions (C_λ and S_λ or L_λ and α), as shown by the crosshatched area in Fig. 7-4. Being associated with the T_1 transmission mode, the combined designation appropriate to this region of helix dimensions is $T_1 R_1$ as shown in Fig. 7-4.

Still higher order transmission modes, T_2, T_3, and so forth, become permissible for larger values of C_λ. For small pitch angles, the approximate charge distribution around the helix for these modes is as suggested by Fig. 7-5c.

In Fig. 7-4, the normal radiation mode region (T_0R_0) is shown as a shaded area. The axial or beam mode region (T_1R_1) is shown as a cross-hatched area. In general, the radiation mode associated with helix dimensions outside these areas is multi-lobed or, in some cases, conical, as illustrated by the patterns in Fig. 7-8. Another example is the four-lobed mode[1] that occurs when the spacing is 1 wavelength and the length of one turn is 2 wavelengths $(\alpha = 30°)$, the radiation being both normal and axial. See Fig. 7-9.

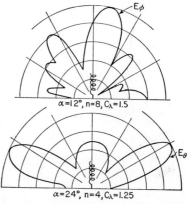

FIG. 7-8.   Examples of multilobed and conical patterns.

7-4. The Normal Radiation Mode.   Consider a helix oriented with its axis coincident with the polar or z axis as in Fig. 7-10a. If the dimen-

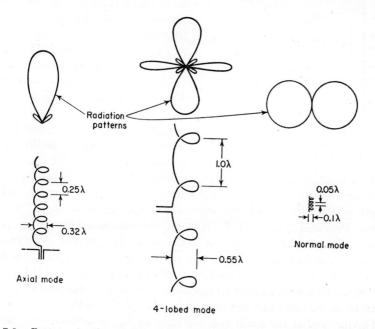

IG. 7-9.   Patterns for three helix radiation modes, the relative size of helices to produce the different modes at the same wavelength is indicated.

[1] H. Chireix, U.S. Patent 1,843,445, Feb. 2, 1932.

sions of the helix are small $(nL \ll \lambda)$, the maximum radiation is always in a direction normal to the helix axis (see pattern in Fig. 7-6). Hence, the

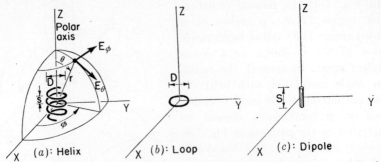

FIG. 7-10(a), (b), and (c). Dimensions and coordinates for helix, loop, and dipole.

maximum field of a small helix oriented as in Fig. 7-10a is in the x-y plane with zero field in the direction of the z axis.

When the pitch angle is zero, the helix becomes a loop as in Fig. 7-10b

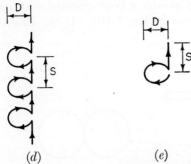

(d)   (e)

FIG. 7-10(d) and (e).   Modified helix for normal mode calculations.

When the pitch angle is 90°, the helix straightens out into a linear antenna as in Fig. 7-10c, the loop and straight antenna being limiting cases of the helix.

The far field of the helix may be described by two components of the electric field, E_ϕ and E_θ, as shown in Fig. 7-10a. Let us now develop expressions for the far-field pattern of these components for a small helix. The development is facilitated by assuming that the helix consists of a number of small loops and short dipoles connected in series as in Fig. 7-10d. The diameter D of the loops is the same as the helix diameter, and the length of the dipoles S is the same as the spacing between turns of the helix. Provided that the helix is small, the modified form of Fig. 7-10 is equivalent to the true helix of Fig. 7-10a. The current is assumed to be uniform in magnitude and in phase over the entire length of the helix. Since the helix is small, the far-field pattern is independent of the number of turns. Hence, it suffices to calculate the far-field patterns of a single small loop and one short dipole as illustrated in Fig. 7-10e.

The far field of the small loop has only an E_ϕ component. Its value is given in Table 6-1, as

$$E_\phi = \frac{120\pi^2 [I] \sin \theta}{r} \frac{A}{\lambda^2} \qquad (7-$$

where the area of the loop $A = \pi D^2/4$
The far field of the short dipole has only an E_θ component. Its value is
given in the same table as

$$E_\theta = j\,\frac{60\pi[I]\sin\theta}{r}\,\frac{S}{\lambda} \tag{7-2}$$

where S has been substituted for L as the length of the dipole.

Comparing (7-1) and (7-2), the j operator in (7-2) and its absence in
(7-1) indicates that E_ϕ and E_θ are in phase quadrature. The ratio of the
magnitudes of (7-1) and (7-2) then gives the axial ratio of the polarization
ellipse of the far field. Hence, dividing the magnitude of (7-2) by (7-1)
we obtain for the axial ratio AR,

$$\text{AR} = \frac{|E_\theta|}{|E_\phi|} = \frac{S\lambda}{2\pi A} = \frac{2S\lambda}{\pi^2 D^2} \tag{7-3}$$

Three special cases of the polarization ellipse are of interest. (1) When
$E_\phi = 0$, the axial ratio is infinite and the polarization ellipse is a vertical
line indicating linear vertical polarization. The helix in this case is a
vertical dipole. (2) When $E_\theta = 0$, the axial ratio is zero[1] and the polarization ellipse is a horizontal line indicating linear horizontal polarization.
The helix in this case is a horizontal loop. (3) The third special case of
interest occurs when $|E_\theta| = |E_\phi|$. For this case the axial ratio is unity,
and the polarization ellipse is a circle, indicating circular polarization.
Thus, setting (7-3) equal to unity yields

$$\pi D = \sqrt{2S\lambda} \qquad \text{or} \qquad C_\lambda = \sqrt{2S_\lambda} \tag{7-4}$$

This relation was first obtained by Wheeler in an equivalent form.[2] The
radiation is circularly polarized, not only in all directions in the x-y plane
of Fig. 7-10a but in all directions in space except in the direction of the
polar axis where the field is zero.

We have considered three special cases of the polarization ellipse involving linear and circular polarization. In the general case, the radiation
is elliptically polarized. Therefore, the radiation from a helix of constant
turn length changes progressively through the following forms as the pitch
angle is varied. When $\alpha = 0$, we have a loop (Fig. 7-10b) and the polarization is linear and horizontal. As α increases, let us consider the helix
dimensions as we move along a constant L_λ line in Fig. 7-4. As α increases

[1] The axial ratio is here allowed to range from 0 to infinity, instead of from 1 to
infinity as customarily (Sec. 15-11), in order to distinguish between linear vertical and
linear horizontal polarization.

[2] H. A. Wheeler, A Helical Antenna for Circular Polarization, *Proc. I.R.E.*, **35**, 1484–
1488, December, 1947.

from zero, the polarization becomes elliptical with the major axis of the polarization ellipse horizontal. When α reaches a value such that $C_\lambda = \sqrt{2S_\lambda}$ the polarization is circular. With the aid of Fig. 7-3, this value of α is given by

$$\alpha = \arcsin \frac{-1 + \sqrt{1 + L_\lambda^2}}{L_\lambda} \tag{7-5}$$

As α increases still further, the polarization again becomes elliptical but with the major axis of the polarization ellipse vertical. Finally, when α reaches 90°, we have a dipole (Fig. 7-10c) and the polarization is linear and vertical. Wheeler's relation for circular polarization from a helix radiating in the normal mode as given by (7-4) or (7-5) is shown in Fig. 7-4 by the curve marked $C_\lambda = \sqrt{2S_\lambda}$.

In the preceding discussion on the normal mode of radiation, the assumption is made that the current is uniform in magnitude and in phase over the entire length of the helix. This condition could be approximated if the helix is very small ($nL \ll \lambda$) and is end-loaded. However, the band width of such a small helix would be very narrow, and the radiation efficiency would be low. The band width and radiation efficiency could be increased by increasing the size of the helix, but to approximate the uniform, in-phase current distribution requires that some type of phase shifter be placed at intervals along the helix. This may be inconvenient or impractical. Hence, the production of the normal mode of radiation from a helix has serious practical limitations.

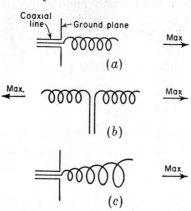

FIG. 7-11. Arrangements for producing the axial mode of radiation.

An antenna having four slanting dipoles that is suggestive of a modified helix radiating in the normal mode has been built by Brown and Woodward[1] (see Fig. 14-39f). Their arrangement is based on a design described by Lindenblad.[2]

7-5. Arrangements for Producing the Axial Mode of Radiation. When the helix circumference C_λ is increased to the order of 1 wavelength, the axial or beam mode of radiation is obtained. This radiation mode is generated in practice with great ease. In fact, the dimensions of the

[1] G. H. Brown and O. M. Woodward, Circularly Polarized Omnidirectional Antenna, *RCA Rev*, **8**, 259–269, June, 1947.

[2] N. E. Lindenblad, Antennas and Transmission Lines at the Empire State Television Station, *Communications*, **21**, 10–14, 24–26, April, 1941.

helix are so noncritical that a helical beam antenna is one of the simplest types of antennas it is possible to make.

The arrangement illustrated in Fig. 7-11a affords a simple method of generating the axial mode of radiation from a helix. The radiation is in the form of a unidirectional beam as in Fig. 7-7.

The radiation is a maximum in the direction of the helix axis and is circularly polarized, or nearly so. The helix is operated in conjunction with a ground plane and is energized by a coaxial transmission line. The inner conductor of the line connects to the helix, and the outer conductor terminates in the ground plane. The ground plane should be at least $\frac{1}{2}$ wavelength in diameter. An axial mode helical antenna of 7 turns and pitch angle of 12.5° is shown in the photograph of Fig. 7-12.

FIG. 7-12.   Pole-mounted helical beam antenna (or axial mode helix) of 7 turns with pitch angle of 12.5°.

An arrangement for energizing a helix in the beam mode with a two-wire transmission line is shown in Fig. 7-11b. The antenna in this case produces a bidirectional pattern as indicated. The above helices are of uniform cross section. The beam mode of radiation can also be generated with a tapered helix as in Fig. 7-11c.

The diameter, the spacing, or both may be tapered (see Sec. 7-16). If the taper is moderate, the effect is small, owing to the noncritical nature of the helix dimensions when radiating in the axial mode.

The following discussion will be restricted to uniform helices.

7-6. Current Distribution on Helices. When the circumference of the helix is less than about $\frac{2}{3}$ wavelengths ($C_\lambda < \frac{2}{3}$) the current distribution is nearly sinusoidal as on a long straight antenna. As an example,[1] the absolute magnitude of the measured current distribution on a 12°, 7-turn helix with a circumference of about 0.6 wavelength ($C_\lambda \simeq 0.6$) is presented

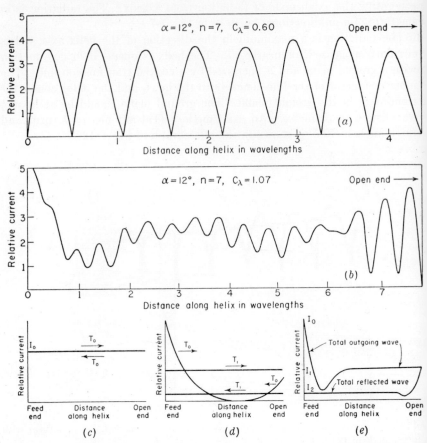

FIG. 7-13.   (*a*) Measured current distribution on helix of 0.6 wavelength circumference.

    (*b*) Measured current distribution on same helix at higher frequency ($C_\lambda = 1.07$) with radiation in the axial mode.

    (*c*) Resolution of current distribution when $C_\lambda < \frac{2}{3}$ into two T_0 transmission mode waves of nearly constant amplitude I_0 traveling in opposite directions.

    (*d*) Resolution of current distribution on helix radiating in the axial mode ($\frac{3}{4} < C_\lambda < \frac{4}{3}$) into two outgoing waves and two reflected waves.

    (*e*) Resolution of current distribution on helix radiating in the axial mode into a total outgoing and a total reflected wave.

in Fig. 7-13*a*. When the frequency is raised so that the circumference of this helix is about one wavelength ($C_\lambda \simeq 1$), the measured current is of

---

[1] Kraus and Williamson, *loc. cit.*

distinctly different form as shown in Fig. 7-13b. This type of distribution is characteristic of helices radiating in the axial mode.

Thus, a helix with a circumference too small for the axial mode of radiation ($C_\lambda < \frac{2}{3}$) has a nearly sinusoidal type of current distribution, caused by alternate reinforcement and cancellation of two oppositely directed traveling waves on the helix of nearly equal amplitude I_0 as suggested in Fig. 7-13c. Both traveling waves are of the T_0 transmission-mode type.

When the circumference of the helix is of the order of 1 wavelength and radiation is in the axial mode ($\frac{3}{4} < C_\lambda < \frac{4}{3}$), the current distribution is relatively uniform over the central region of the helix since the outgoing waves are large in comparison with those returning. By assuming two outgoing traveling waves of different phase velocity, one (T_0 mode) attenuated and the other (T_1 mode) constant, and two smaller returning traveling waves of different phase velocity, one (T_0 mode) attenuated and the other (T_1 mode) constant, Marsh[1] has been able to account in detail for the complex appearance of a measured current distribution such as in Fig. 7-13b. The T_0 mode waves are rapidly attenuated while the T_1 mode waves are of relatively constant amplitude as suggested in Fig. 7-13d, so that in the central region of the helix only the relatively constant T_1 mode waves are of importance.

Continuing the discussion of the current distribution on helices radiating in the axial mode ($\frac{3}{4} < C_\lambda < \frac{4}{3}$), the two outgoing waves may be combined into a single total outgoing wave ($T_0 + T_1$ waves) and the two reflected waves into a single total reflected wave as in Fig. 7-13e. The total outgoing wave attenuates rapidly near the input end but reaches a relatively constant value about 1 wavelength from the input terminals (as measured along the helical conductor). This value is maintained to the open end of the helix. A dip in the total outgoing wave occurs where the two component outgoing waves (T_0 and T_1) of different phase velocity are in phase opposition and of nearly equal amplitude. The total reflected wave starts back from the open end exhibiting a similar behavior. It decreases rapidly at first but reaches a relatively constant value about 1 wavelength along the helix from the open end. This amplitude is usually very much less than that of the total outgoing wave,[2] so that the reflected wave

<hr/>

[1] James A. Marsh, Measured Current Distributions on Helical Antennas, submitted to *Proc. I.R.E.*

[2] This may be deduced from Fig. 7-13b by noting that the SWR of current on the helix approaches unity about 1 wavelength (or 1 turn in this case) from the open end. More detailed data are given by Marsh. A few earlier measurements were made by Milton Aronoff, "Measured Phase Velocity and Current Distribution Characteristics of Helical Antennas Radiating in the Beam Mode," master's thesis, Department of Electrical Engineering, The Ohio State University, 1948.

can usually be neglected in calculating helix patterns. Furthermore, if the helix is long, the outgoing T_0 wave can also be neglected and the pattern calculated entirely on the basis of a single outgoing T_1 wave of constant amplitude.

7-7. Terminal Impedance of Helices.[1] When the helix circumference

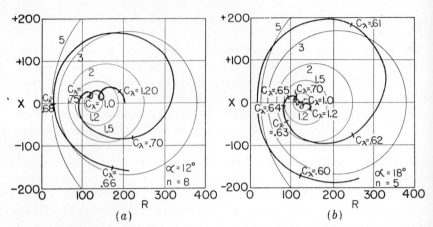

Fig. 7-14. Measured impedance spiral for 12°, 8-turn helix (*a*) and 18°, 5-turn helix (*b*). The helices are of fixed physical size. The impedance (resistance R and reactance X, in ohms) is shown as a function of frequency, the circumference in wavelengths at a given frequency being indicated at intervals along the spirals.

is less than about $\frac{2}{3}$ wavelength $(C_\lambda < \frac{2}{3})$, the terminal impedance is highly sensitive to changes in frequency. However, when the helix circumference is of the order of 1 wavelength $(\frac{3}{4} < C_\lambda < \frac{4}{3})$ and the helix is radiating in the axial mode, the terminal impedance is nearly constant as a function of frequency, provided that the pitch angle and number of turns are not too small. This is illustrated by the impedance spirals of Fig. 7-14 which show the measured terminal impedance of 12° and 18° helices as a function of the frequency, the helix circumference in wavelengths for a given frequency being indicated at intervals along the spirals.

When the circumference is too small for the axial mode of radiation, the impedance variation is similar to that on a mismatched transmission line of considerable length. On the other hand, the impedance variation, or lack of it, when the helix radiates in the axial mode, is similar to that on a transmission line terminated in approximately its characteristic impedance. This relatively constant terminal impedance of a helix radiating in the axial mode may be explained by the marked attenuation

[1] O. J. Glasser and J. D. Kraus, Measured Impedances of Helical Beam Antennas, *J. Applied Phys.*, **19**, 193–197, February, 1948.

of both the total outgoing and total reflected waves. Thus, relatively little
energy reflected from the open end of the helix reaches the input. The
SWR of current at the input terminals
is given by

$$SWR = \frac{I_0 + I_2}{I_0 - I_2}$$

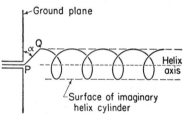

where I_0 and I_2 are as indicated in
Fig. 7-13e. Since I_2 is very small
compared to I_0, the SWR at the terminals is nearly unity, like on a transmission line terminated in approximately its characteristic impedance.

Fig. 7-15. Terminal arrangement of
helical beam antenna.

The impedance spirals of Fig. 7-14 are measured on helices having the
terminal arrangement shown in Fig. 7-15. Beyond point Q, the helix lies
in the surface of the imaginary helix cylinder. Between points P and Q,
the helix conductor lies in a plane through the helix axis and at approximately the same pitch angle as for the helix proper. The helix axis coincides with the center conductor of the coaxial line feeding the antenna.
All terminal impedances are referred to the point P. Variations in the
arrangement of the conductor between P and Q produce changes in the
details of the impedance spirals. The nature of the dielectric structure
supporting the helix and the size and shape of the ground plane also have
an effect on the detail but not on the general form of the impedance
spirals, it being assumed that the amount of dielectric is not excessive and
that the size of the ground plane is not too small. The conductor diameter
d has relatively little effect on the helix characteristics when the helix is
radiating in the axial mode.[1] However, at frequencies outside the axial
mode the effect of d may be considerable. In general, the terminal impedance of helical antennas radiating in the axial mode is nearly a pure
resistance with a value between 100 and 200 ohms. Based on a large
number of impedance measurements, the terminal impedance of an axially
fed helix (as in Fig. 7-15) is given within about ± 20 per cent by the
empirical relation, $R = 140 \, C_\lambda$ ohms. This applies to helices with
$12° < \alpha < 15°$, $\frac{3}{4} < C_\lambda < \frac{4}{3}$, and $n > 3$.

**7-8. Axial Mode Patterns and the Phase Velocity of Wave Propagation
on Helices.**[2] As a first approximation, a helical antenna radiating in the
axial mode may be assumed to have a single traveling wave of uniform
amplitude along its conductor. By the principle of pattern multiplication,

---

[1] T. E. Tice and J. D. Kraus, The Influence of Conductor Size on the Properties of
Helical Beam Antennas, *Proc. I.R.E.*, **37**, 1296, November, 1949.

[2] J. D. Kraus, The Helical Antenna, *Proc. I.R.E.*, **37**, 263–272, March, 1949.

the far-field pattern of a helix, such as shown in Fig. 7-15, is the product of the pattern for 1 turn and the pattern for an array of n isotropic point sources as in Fig. 7-16.   The number n equals the number of turns.

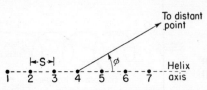

FIG. 7-16. Array of isotropic point sources, each source representing 1 turn of the helix.

The spacing S between sources is equal to the turn spacing. When the helix is long (say, $nS_\lambda > 1$), the array pattern is much sharper than the single-turn pattern and hence largely determines the shape of the total far-field pattern. Hence, the approximate far-field pattern of a long helix is given by the array pattern.   Assuming now that the far-field variation is given by the array pattern or factor and that the phase difference between sources of the array is equal to the phase shift over 1 turn length L_λ for a single traveling wave, it is possible to obtain a simple, approximate expression for the phase velocity required to produce axial mode radiation.   This value of phase velocity is then used in pattern calculations.

The array pattern or array factor E for an array of n isotropic point sources arranged as in Fig. 7-16 is given by (4-51).   Thus,

$$E = \frac{\sin (n\psi/2)}{\sin (\psi/2)} \qquad (7\text{-}6)$$

where n = number of sources and

$$\psi = S_r \cos \phi + \delta \qquad (7\text{-}7)$$

where $S_r = 2\pi S/\lambda$
In the present case, (7-7) becomes

$$\psi = 2\pi \left(S_\lambda \cos \phi - \frac{L_\lambda}{p} \right) \qquad (7\text{-}8)$$

where $p = v/c$ = relative phase velocity of wave propagation along the helical conductor, v being the phase velocity along the helical conductor and c being the velocity of light in free space.

If the fields from all sources are in phase at a point on the helix axis ($\phi = 0$), the radiation will be in the axial mode.   For the fields to be in phase (ordinary end-fire condition) requires that

$$\psi = -2\pi m \qquad (7\text{-}9)$$

where $m = 0, 1, 2, 3 \ldots$
The minus sign in (7-9) results from the fact that the phase of source 2 is retarded by $2\pi L_\lambda/p$ with respect to source 1.   Source 3 is similarly retarded with respect to source 2, etc.

Now putting $\phi = 0$ and equating (7-8) and (7-9), we have

$$\frac{L_\lambda}{p} = S_\lambda + m \qquad (7\text{-}10)$$

When $m = 1$ and $p = 1$, we have the relation

$$L_\lambda - S_\lambda = 1 \qquad \text{or} \qquad L - S = \lambda \qquad (7\text{-}11)$$

This is an approximate relation between the turn length and spacing required for a helix radiating in the axial mode. Since for a helix $L^2 = \pi^2 D^2 + S^2$, (7-11) can be rewritten as

$$D_\lambda = \frac{\sqrt{2S_\lambda + 1}}{\pi} \qquad \text{or} \qquad C_\lambda = \sqrt{2S_\lambda + 1} \qquad (7\text{-}12)$$

Equation (7-12) is shown graphically by the curve marked $C_\lambda = \sqrt{2S_\lambda + 1}$ in Fig. 7-4. The curve defines approximately the upper limit of the axial or beam mode region.

When $m = 1$, (7-10) is appropriate for a helix operating in the first-order (T_1) transmission mode. When $m = 2$, (7-10) is appropriate for the T_2 transmission mode, etc. A curve for $m = 2$ is shown in Fig. 7-4 by the line marked $C_\lambda = 2\sqrt{S_\lambda + 1}$. Hence, m corresponds to the order of the transmission mode on a helix radiating a maximum field in the axial direction. The case of particular interest here is where $m = 1$.

The case where $m = 0$ does not represent a realizable condition, unless p exceeds unity, since when $m = 0$ and $p = 1$ in (7-10) we have $L = S$. This is the condition for an end-fire array of isotropic sources excited by a straight wire connecting them ($\alpha = 90°$). However, the field in the axial direction of a straight wire is zero so that there can be no axial mode of radiation in this case.

Returning now to a consideration of the case where $m = 1$ and solving (7-10) for p, we have

$$p = \frac{L_\lambda}{S_\lambda + 1} \qquad (7\text{-}13)$$

From the triangle of Fig. 7-3, (7-13) can also be expressed

$$p = \frac{1}{\sin \alpha + ((\cos \alpha)/C_\lambda)} \qquad (7\text{-}13a)$$

Equation (7-13a) gives the required variation in the relative phase velocity p as a function of the circumference C_λ for in-phase fields in the axial direction. The variation for helices of different pitch angles is illustrated in Fig. 7-17. These curves indicate that when a helix is radiating in the axial mode ($\frac{3}{4} < C_\lambda < \frac{4}{3}$) the value of p may be considerably less than unity. This is borne out by direct measurements of the phase velocity. In fact, the observed phase velocity is found to be slightly less than called for by (7-13) or (7-13a). Calculating the array pattern for a 7-turn helix using values of p from (7-13) and (7-13a) yields patterns much broader than observed. The p value of (7-13) or (7-13a) corresponds to the ordinary

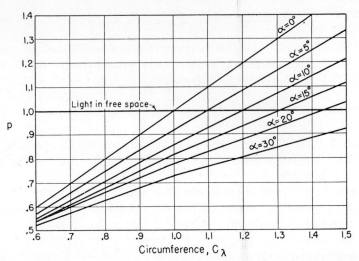

Fig. 7-17. Relative phase velocity p for different pitch angles α as a function of the helix circumference in free-space wavelengths C_λ for the condition of in-phase fields in the axial direction.

end-fire condition discussed in Chap. 4. If the increased directivity condition of Hansen and Woodyard is presumed to exist, (7-9) becomes

$$\psi = -\left(2\pi m + \frac{\pi}{n}\right) \tag{7-14}$$

Now equating (7-14) and (7-8), putting $\phi = 0$, and solving for p we have

$$p = \frac{L_\lambda}{S_\lambda + m + (1/2n)} \tag{7-15}$$

For the case of interest $m = 1$ and

$$p = \frac{L_\lambda}{S_\lambda + ((2n + 1)/2n)} \tag{7-16}$$

For large values of n, (7-16) reduces to (7-13). Equation (7-16) can also be expressed[1]

$$p = \frac{1}{\sin \alpha + [(2n + 1)/2n][(\cos \alpha)/C_\lambda]} \tag{7-17}$$

[1] It is to be noted that, as n becomes large, (7-17) reduces to (7-13a).

Using p as obtained from (7-16) or (7-17) to calculate the array factor yields patterns in good agreement with measured patterns. The p value from (7-16) or (7-17) also is in closer agreement with measured values of the relative phase velocity. Hence, it appears that the increased directivity condition is approximated as a natural condition on helices radiating in the axial mode.[1]

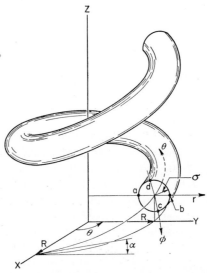

Another method of finding the relative phase velocity p on helical antennas radiating in the axial mode is by measuring the angle ϕ_0 at which the first minimum or null occurs in the far-field pattern. This corresponds to the first null in the array factor, which is at ψ_0 (see Fig. 4-20). Then in this case (7-9) becomes

FIG. 7-18. Helix showing points c and d at conductor surface.

$$\psi = -(2\pi m + \psi_0) \qquad (7\text{-}18)$$

Now equating (7-18) and (7-8) and putting $m = 1$ and solving for p, we have

$$p = \frac{L_\lambda}{S_\lambda \cos \phi_0 + 1 + (\psi_0/2\pi)} \qquad (7\text{-}19)$$

Three relations for the relative phase velocity p have been discussed for helices radiating in the axial mode with transmission in the T_1 mode. These are given by (7-13a), (7-17), and (7-19).

A fourth relation for p appropriate to the T_1 and higher order transmission modes on infinite helices has been obtained by Bagby[2] by applying boundary conditions approximating a helical conductor to a solution of the general wave equation expressed in a new coordinate system, called "helicoidal cylindrical coordinates." Bagby's solution is obtained by applying boundary conditions to the two points c and d in Fig. 7-18. His value of the relative phase velocity is given by

---

[1] The axial mode region is shown by the crosshatched area in Fig. 7-4. Helices with dimensions in this region radiate in the axial mode, and (7-13a), or more properly (7-17), applies. Outside this region these equations generally do not apply.

[2] C. K. Bagby, "A Theoretical Investigation of Electro-magnetic Wave Propagation on the Helical Beam Antenna," master's thesis, Department of Electrical Engineering, The Ohio State University, 1948.

$$p = \frac{C_\lambda}{m \cos \alpha + hR \sin \alpha} \qquad (7\text{-}20)$$

where

$$hR = \tan \alpha \, \frac{mJ_m^2(kR)}{J_{m-1}(kR)J_{m+1}(kR)} \qquad (7\text{-}21)$$

where m = order of transmission mode ($=1, 2, 3 \ldots$) ($m \neq 0$)
R = radius of helix cylinder
$kR = \sqrt{C_\lambda^2 - (hR)^2}$
h = arbitrary constant
J is a Bessel function of argument kR

The variation of p as a function of C_λ for a 13° helix as calculated by (7-20) and (7-21) for the case $m = 1$ is illustrated by the curve A_1 in Fig. 7-19. A curve for the T_1 transmission mode ($m = 1$) as calculated for the in-phase condition from (7-13a) is shown by B_1. A curve for the increased directivity condition on a 13°, 7-turn helix, with $m = 1$ is presented by C_1.

Curves for the T_2 transmission mode for each of the three cases considered above are also presented in Fig. 7-19. In addition, a curve of the measured relative phase velocity on a 13°, 7-turn helix is shown for circumferences between about 0.4 and 1.5 wavelengths. It is to be noted that in the circumference range where the helix is radiating in the axial mode ($\frac{3}{4} < C_\lambda < \frac{4}{3}$), the increased directivity curve, of the three calculated curves, lies closest to the measured curve.[1] The measured curve gives the value of the total or resultant phase velocity owing to all modes present (T_0, T_1, etc.) as averaged over the region of the helix between the third and sixth turns from the feed end. The vertical lines indicate the spread, if any, in values observed at one frequency. In general each transmission mode propagates with a different velocity so that when waves of more than one transmission mode are present the resultant phase velocity becomes a function of position along the helix and may vary over a considerable range of values.[2] When $\frac{3}{4} < C_\lambda < \frac{4}{3}$ the phase velocity as measured in the region between the third and sixth turns corresponds closely to that of the T_1 transmission mode. The T_0 mode is also present on the helix but is only important near the ends (see Fig. 7-13d). When the circumference $C_\lambda < \frac{2}{3}$, the T_0 mode may be obtained almost alone

[1] The increased directivity curve is the only curve calculated for a helix of 7 turns. The in-phase field's curve and Bagby's curve imply an infinite helix. The reason that the in-phase field curve can be considered as referring to an infinite helix follows from the fact that the increased directivity condition approaches the in-phase field condition as the number of turns becomes infinite.

[2] J. A. Marsh, Measured Current Distributions on Helical Antennas, submitted Proc. I.R.E.

over the entire helix (see Fig. 7-13c) and the measured phase velocity approaches that for a pure T_0 mode indicated by curve D in Fig. 7-19.

Theoretical values of the phase velocity for the T_0 transmission mode have been obtained by Pierce[1] and by Chu and Jackson[2] and a few meas-

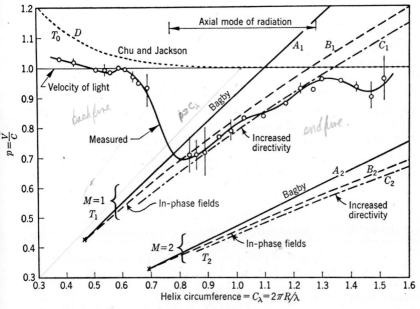

FIG. 7-19.   Relative phase velocity p as a function of the helix circumference in free-space wavelengths C_λ for 13° helices. The solid curve is measured on a 13°, 7-turn helix.. Curves A_1 and A_2 are as calculated by Bagby for T_1 and T_2 transmission modes on an infinite 13° helix. Curves B_1 and B_2 are calculated for in-phase fields and curves C_1 and C_2 for increased directivity for T_1 and T_2 transmission modes. Curve D is from data by Chu and Jackson as calculated for T_0 transmission mode.

urements have been given by Cutler.[3] Curve D in Fig. 7-19 is for a 13° helix and is based on data given by Chu and Jackson. This curve indi-cates that at small circumferences the relative velocity of a pure T_0 mode wave attains values considerably greater than that of light in free space. At $C_\lambda = \frac{2}{3}$, curve D has decreased to a value of nearly unity, and if no higher order transmission mode were permissible, the phase velocity would approach that of light for large circumferences. However, higher order

[1] J. R. Pierce, Theory of the Beam-type Traveling Wave Tube, *Proc. I.R.E.*, **35**, No. 2, 111–123, February, 1947.

[2] L. J. Chu and J. D. Jackson, Field Theory of Traveling Wave Tubes, *Proc. I.R.E.*, **36**, No. 7, 853–863, July, 1948.

[3] C. C. Cutler, Experimental Determination of Helical Wave Properties, *Proc. I.R.E.*, **35**, No. 2, 230–233, February, 1947.

modes are permissible, and when C_λ exceeds about $\frac{2}{3}$, the resultant velocity drops abruptly, as shown by the measured curve in Fig. 7-19. This change corresponds to a transition from the T_0 to the T_1 transmission mode. For a circumference in the transition region, such as 0.7 wavelength, both T_0 and T_1 modes are of about equal importance.

When C_λ is about $\frac{3}{4}$ or somewhat more, the measured phase velocity approaches a value associated with the T_1 mode. As C_λ increases further, the relative phase velocity increases in an approximately linear fashion, agreeing most closely with the theoretical curve for the increased directivity condition (curve C_1). When C_λ reaches about $\frac{4}{3}$, a still higher order transmission mode (T_2) appears to become partially effective, causing further dips in the measured curve. However, the radiation may no longer be in the axial mode.

7-9. Tables of Relative Phase Velocities. The formulas given in the preceding section for helical antennas operating in the first-order transmission mode ($m = 1$) are summarized in Table 7-1.

TABLE 7-1

RELATIVE PHASE VELOCITIES FOR
FIRST-ORDER TRANSMISSION MODE ON HELICAL ANTENNAS

Condition	Relative phase velocity
In-phase fields* (ordinary end-fire)	$p = \dfrac{L_\lambda}{S_\lambda + 1} = \dfrac{1}{\sin \alpha + [(\cos \alpha)/C_\lambda]}$
Increased directivity	$p = \dfrac{L_\lambda}{S_\lambda + [(2n + 1)/2n]}$ $= \dfrac{1}{\sin \alpha + [(2n + 1)/2n] \, [(\cos \alpha)/C_\lambda]}$
From first null of measured field pattern	$p = \dfrac{L_\lambda}{S_\lambda \cos \phi_0 + (\psi_0/2\pi) + 1}$
Helicoidal cylindrical coordinate solution	$p = \dfrac{C_\lambda}{\cos \alpha + hR \sin \alpha}$ where hR is as given by (7-21)

*It will be shown in Sec. 7-13 that this condition is also the one for circular polarization in the direction of the helix axis.

7-10. Axial Mode Array Factor Patterns and Effect of Number of Turns. As mentioned in Sec. 7-8, the approximate far-field pattern of a helix

radiating in the axial mode is given by the array factor for n isotropic
point sources, each source replacing a single turn of the helix (see Fig. 7-16).

The normalized array factor is

$$E = \sin \frac{\pi}{2n} \frac{\sin (n\psi/2)}{\sin (\psi/2)} \qquad (7\text{-}22)$$

where $\psi = 2\pi(S_\lambda \cos \phi - L_\lambda/p)$

The normalizing factor is $\sin (\pi/2n)$ instead of $1/n$ since the increased
directivity end-fire condition is assumed to exist (see Sec. 4-6a, Case 3).
For a given helix, S_λ and L_λ are known and p can be calculated from (4-16)
or (4-17). ψ is then obtained as a function of ϕ. From (7-22), these values
of ψ give the field pattern.

As an illustration, the calculated array factor patterns for a 7-turn 12°
helix with $C_\lambda = 0.95$ are shown in Fig. 7-20 for p values corresponding to

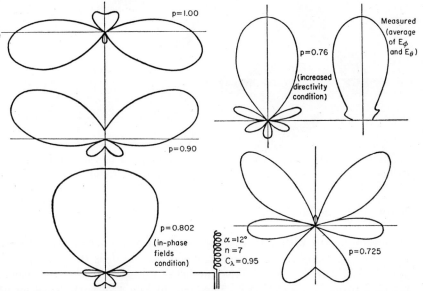

FIG. 7-20.   Array factor patterns for 12°, 7-turn helix with $C_\lambda = 0.95$. Patterns are
shown for $p = 1$, 0.9, 0.802 (in-phase fields or ordinary end-fire condition), 0.76 (increased directivity), and 0.725. A measured curve is also presented. All patterns are
adjusted to the same maximum.

increased directivity and also in-phase fields and for $p = 1$, 0.9, and 0.725.
A measured curve (average of E_ϕ and E_θ) is shown for comparison. It
is apparent that the pattern calculated for the increased directivity condition ($p = 0.76$) agrees most closely with the measured pattern. The
measured pattern was taken on a helix mounted on a ground plane 0.88
wavelength in diameter. The calculated patterns neglect the effect of a

ground plane. This effect is small if the back lobe is small compared to the front lobe as it is for $p = 0.802$ and $p = 0.76$.

In general, an increase in the number of turns causes a decrease in the beam width, as illustrated by the patterns in Fig. 7-21. This can be

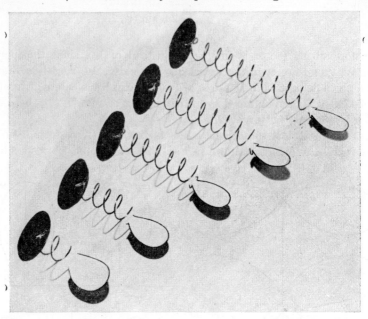

FIG. 7-21. Models showing effect of number of turns on measured field patterns. Helices have 12.2° pitch angle and 2, 4, 6, 8, 10 turns. Patterns shown are average of measured E_θ and E_ϕ patterns.

shown by calculating the array factor pattern for various values of n. In effect this has been done in Fig. 4-26 in which a curve for the beam width of end-fire arrays with increased directivity is presented as a function of nd_λ. In Fig. 4-26, n is the number of sources and d_λ is the spacing. To apply Fig. 4-26 to a helix, n is the number of turns and $d_\lambda = S_\lambda =$ spacing between turns in wavelengths. Thus, nd_λ in Fig. 4-26 is the axial length of the helix in wavelengths ($nd_\lambda = nS_\lambda = A_\lambda$). For long axial lengths, the beam width between first nulls varies in inverse proportion to the square root of the axial length. Thus, doubling the axial length of a helix reduces the beam width to $1/\sqrt{2} = 0.707$ of its original value.

Based on a large number of pattern measurements the beam width between half-power points and between first nulls is given by the following quasi-empirical relations,

$$\text{Beam width (half-power)} = \frac{52}{C_\lambda \sqrt{nS_\lambda}} \quad \text{deg} \qquad (7\text{-}23a)$$

$$\text{Beam width (first nulls)} = \frac{115}{C_\lambda \sqrt{nS_\lambda}} \quad \text{deg} \qquad (7\text{-}23b)$$

These apply to helices with $12° < \alpha < 15°$, $\frac{3}{4} < C_\lambda < \frac{4}{3}$, and $n > 3$.

The half-power beam width as given by (7-23a) is shown graphically in Fig. 7-22. Dividing the square of (7-23a) into the number of square

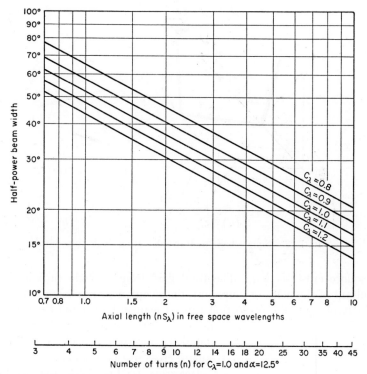

FIG. 7-22. Half-power beam width of axial mode helical antenna as a function of the axial length and circumference in free-space wavelengths and also as a function of the number of turns for $C_\lambda = 1.0$ and $\alpha = 12.5°$.

degrees in a sphere gives the approximate expression for the directivity D of an axial mode helix[1]

$$D = 15 \, C_\lambda^2 \, nS_\lambda \qquad (7\text{-}24)$$

7-11. Axial Mode Single-turn Patterns. In this section expressions will be developed for the far-field patterns from a single turn of a helix radiating in the axial mode. It is assumed that the single turn has a

[1] It is assumed that the patterns of both field components are of the same shape and are figures of revolution about the helix axis. The approximate directivity is then simply obtained as in (7-24) (see Appendix Sec. 20).

uniform traveling wave along its entire length. The product of the single-turn pattern and the array factor then gives the total helix pattern.

A circular helix may be treated approximately by assuming that it is

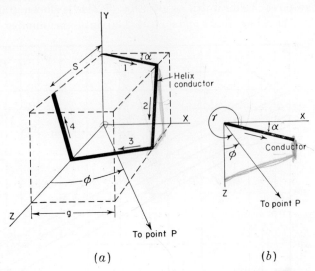

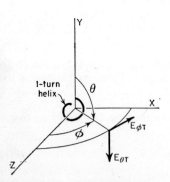

(a)   (b)

Fig. 7-23.   Square helix used in calculating single-turn pattern.

of square cross section. The total field from a single turn is then the resultant of the fields of four short, linear antennas as shown in Fig. 7-23a. A helix of square cross section can, of course, be treated exactly by this method. Measurements indicate that the difference between helices of circular and square cross section is small.

Referring to Fig. 7-24, the far electric field components, $E_{\phi T}$ and $E_{\theta T}$, in the x-z plane will be calculated as a function of ϕ for a single-turn helix.

Let the area of the square helix be equal to that of the circular helix so that

$$g = \frac{\sqrt{\pi} D}{2} \qquad (7\text{-}25a)$$

where g is as shown in Fig. 7-23a.

Fig. 7-24.   Field components with relation to single-turn helix.

The far magnetic field for a linear element with a uniform traveling wave is given in Chap. 5 by (5-128). Multiplying (5-128) by the intrinsic impedance Z of free space, putting $\gamma = (3\pi/2) + \alpha + \phi$, $t = 0$, and $b = g/\cos \alpha$, we obtain the expression for the ϕ component $E_{\phi 1}$ of the far field in the x-z plane due to element 1 of the square helix as follows,

$$E_{\phi 1} = k \frac{\sin \gamma}{A} \sin BA \;\Big/\!\!\left(-\frac{\omega r_1}{c} - BA\right) \qquad (7\text{-}25b)$$

where $k = \dfrac{I_0 p Z}{2\pi r_1}$

$A = 1 - p \cos \gamma$

$B = \dfrac{\omega g}{2pc \cos \alpha}$

The expressions for $E_{\phi 2}$, $E_{\phi 3}$, etc., due to elements 2, 3, and 4 of the square turn are obtained in a similar way (see Prob. 7-2a). Since the elements are all dissimilar sources, the total ϕ component, $E_{\phi T}$, from a single square turn is obtained by adding the fields from the four elements at each angle ϕ for which the total field is calculated (see Sec. 4-5). The sum of the fields from the four elements is then,

$$E_{\phi T} = k \frac{\sin \gamma}{A} \sin BA \;\Big/\!\!\left(-BA - \frac{\omega r_1}{c}\right)$$

$$+ k \frac{\sin \gamma'' \sin BA'' \sin \alpha \sin \phi}{A''(1 - \sin^2 \alpha \cos^2 \phi)^{\frac{1}{2}}}$$

$$\Big/\!\!\left[-BA'' - \frac{L\omega}{4pc} + \frac{\omega}{c}\left(\frac{S \cos \phi}{4} + g \sin \phi - r_1\right)\right]$$

$$+ k \frac{\sin \gamma'}{A'} \sin BA'$$

$$\Big/\!\!\left[-BA' - \frac{L\omega}{2pc} + \frac{\omega}{c}\left(\frac{S \cos \phi}{2} + g \sin \phi - r_1\right)\right]$$

$$+ k \frac{\sin \gamma'' \sin BA'' \sin \alpha \sin \phi}{A''(1 - \sin^2 \alpha \cos^2 \phi)^{\frac{1}{2}}}$$

$$\Big/\!\!\left[-BA'' - \frac{3L\omega}{4pc} + \frac{\omega}{c}\left(\frac{3S \cos \phi}{4} - r_1\right)\right] \quad (7\text{-}26)$$

where $\gamma = \dfrac{3\pi}{2} + \alpha + \phi$, $\gamma' = \dfrac{\pi}{2} - \alpha + \phi$, $\gamma'' = \arccos{(\sin \alpha \cos \phi)}$

$A = 1 - p \cos \gamma$, $A' = 1 - p \cos \gamma'$, $A'' = 1 - p \cos \gamma''$

When a helix of circular cross section is being calculated $L = \pi D/\cos \alpha$ in (7-26) while for a helix of square cross section $L = 4b$.

If the contributions of elements 2 and 4 are neglected, which is a good approximation when both α and ϕ are small, the expression for $E_{\phi T}$ is considerably simplified. Making this approximation, letting $k = 1$ and $r_1 = $ constant, we obtain

$$E_{\phi T} = \frac{\sin \gamma}{A} \sin BA \ \underline{/(-BA)}$$

$$+ \frac{\sin \gamma'}{A'} \sin BA'$$

$$\underline{/[-BA' - 2\sqrt{\pi}B + \pi(S_\lambda \cos \phi + \sqrt{\pi}D \sin \phi)]} \quad (7\text{-}27)$$

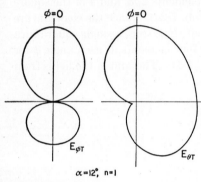

FIG. 7-25. Calculated single turn patterns for 12° helix.

Equation (7-27) applies specifically to helices of circular cross section, so that B in (7-27) is

$$B = \frac{D_\lambda \pi^{\frac{3}{2}}}{2p \cos \alpha} \quad (7\text{-}28)$$

Equation (7-27) gives the approximate pattern of the ϕ component of the far field in the x-z plane from a single-turn helix of circular cross section.

In the case of the θ component of the far field in the x-z plane, only elements 2 and 4 of the square turn contribute. Putting $k = 1$, the magnitude of the approximate θ pattern of the far field of a single-turn helix of circular cross section can be shown to be

$$|E_{\theta T}| = 2 \frac{\sin \gamma'' \sin BA'' \cos \alpha}{A''(1 - \sin^2 \alpha \cos^2 \phi)^{\frac{1}{2}}}$$

$$\cdot \sin \tfrac{1}{2}[\pi(S_\lambda \cos \phi - \sqrt{\pi}D_\lambda \sin \phi) - 2\sqrt{\pi}B] \quad (7\text{-}29)$$

where B is as given by (7-28) and γ'' and A'' are as in (7-26).

As an example, the $E_{\phi T}$ and $E_{\theta T}$ patterns for a single turn 12° helix with $C_\lambda = 1.07$ have been calculated and are presented in Fig. 7-25. Although the two patterns are of different form, both are broad in the axial direction ($\phi = 0$).

The individual E_ϕ patterns of elements 1 and 3 of the single turn are as suggested in Fig. 7-26. One lobe of each pattern is nearly in the axial direction, the tilt angle τ being nearly equal to the pitch angle α. The individual patterns add to give the $E_{\phi T}$ pattern for the single turn as shown (see also Fig. 7-25).

7-12. Complete Axial Mode Pattern. By the principle of pattern multiplication, the total far-field pattern of a helix radiating in the axial mode is the product of the single-turn pattern and the array factor. Thus the total ϕ component E_ϕ of the distant electric field of a helix of circular cross section is the product of (7-27) and (7-22) or

$$E_\phi = E_{\phi T}E \qquad (7\text{-}30a)$$

The total θ component E_θ is the product of (7-29) and (7-22) or

$$E_\theta = E_{\theta T}E \qquad (7\text{-}30b)$$

As examples, the approximate E_ϕ and E_θ patterns, as calculated by the above procedure, for a 12°, 7-turn uniform helix of circular cross section with $C_\lambda = 1.07$ are presented in Fig. 7-27 at (a) and (c). With reference to the helix shown at (e), E_ϕ is in the plane of the page and E_θ is normal to the page. The array factor is shown at (b). The single-turn patterns are as presented in Fig. 7-25. The value of p used in these calculations is approximately that for the increased directivity condition. The product of the single-turn patterns (Fig. 7-25) and the array factor pattern at (b) yields the total patterns at (a) and (c). The agreement with the measured patterns shown at (d) and (f) is satisfactory.

Comparing the patterns of Figs. 7-25 and 7-27, it is to be noted that the array factor is much sharper than the single turn patterns. Thus, the total E_ϕ and E_θ patterns (a) and (c), Fig. 7-27, are nearly the same, in spite of the difference in the single-turn patterns. Furthermore, the main lobes of the E_ϕ and E_θ

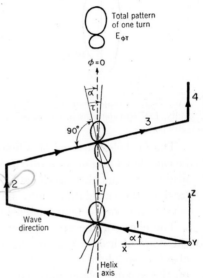

Fig. 7-26. Individual E_ϕ patterns of elements 1 and 3 and total pattern of single turn, $E_{\phi T}$. The single turn is shown in plan view (in x-z plane of Fig. 7-23). The single turn and coordinate axes have been rotated around the y axis so that the z-direction ($\phi = 0$) is toward the top of the page.

patterns are very similar to the array factor pattern. For long helices (say, $nS_\lambda > 1$) it is, therefore, apparent that a calculation of only the array factor suffices for an approximate pattern of any field component of the helix. Ordinarily the single-turn pattern need not be calculated except for short helices. However, to be able to neglect the single-turn pattern on long helices, it is necessary that the direction of maximum radiation from a single turn be approximately in the axial direction.

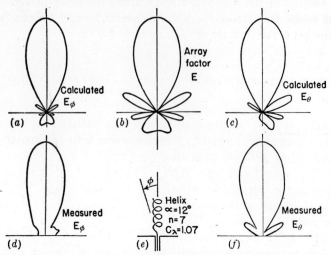

Fig. 7-27. Comparison of calculated and measured field patterns for a 12°, 7-turn helix, 1.07 wavelengths in circumference, radiating in the axial mode.

The far-field patterns of a helix radiating in the axial mode can, thus, be calculated to a good approximation from a knowledge of the dimensions of the helix and the wavelength. The value of the relative phase velocity used in the calculations may be computed for the increased directivity condition from the helix dimensions and number of turns.

The effect of the ground plane on the axial mode patterns is small if there are at least a few turns, since the returning wave on the helix and also the back lobe of the outgoing wave are both small. Hence, the effect of the ground plane may be neglected unless the helix is very short $(nS_\lambda < \frac{1}{2})$.

The approximate pattern of an axial mode helix can be calculated very simply, while including the approximate effect of the single-turn pattern, by assuming that the single-turn pattern is given by $\cos \phi$. Then the normalized total radiation pattern is expressed by

$$E = \left(\sin \frac{90°}{n}\right) \frac{\sin (n\psi/2)}{\sin (\psi/2)} \cos \phi \qquad (7\text{-}31a)$$

where n = number of turns and

$$\psi = 360°[S_\lambda(1 - \cos \phi) + (1/2n)] \qquad (7\text{-}31b)$$

The value of ψ in (7-31b) is for the increased directivity condition and is obtained by substituting (7-16) in (7-8) and simplifying. The first factor in (7-31a) is a normalizing factor, that is, makes the maximum value of E unity.

7-13. Axial Ratio and Conditions for Circular Polarization from Helices Radiating in the Axial Mode.[1]

In this section the axial ratio in the direction of the helix axis will be determined, and also the conditions necessary for circular polarization in this direction will be analyzed.

Consider the helix shown in Fig. 7-28. Let us calculate the electric field components E_ϕ and E_θ, as shown, at a large distance from the helix in the z direction. The helix is assumed to have a single uniform traveling wave as indicated. The relative phase velocity is p. The diameter of the helix is D, and the spacing between turns is S. Unrolling the helix in the x-z plane, the relations are as shown in Fig. 7-29. The helix as viewed from a point on the z axis is as indicated

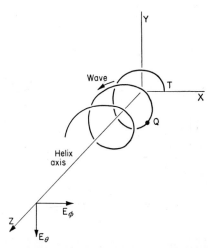

FIG. 7-28. Field components in the direction of the helix axis.

in Fig. 7-30. The angle ξ is measured from the x-z plane. The coordinates of a point Q on the helix can be specified as r, ξ, z. The point Q is at a distance l from the terminal point T as measured along the helix. From the geometric relations of Figs. 7-29 and 7-30, we can write

$$\left. \begin{aligned} & h = l \sin \alpha; \quad z_p - h = z_p - l \sin \alpha \\ & \alpha = \arctan \frac{S}{\pi D} = \arccos \frac{r\xi}{l} \\ & r\xi = l \cos \alpha \end{aligned} \right\} \qquad (7\text{-}32)$$

where z_p is the distance from the origin to the distant point P on the z axis.

At the point P the ϕ component E_ϕ of the electric field for a helix of an integral number of turns n is

$$E_\phi = E_0 \int_0^{2\pi n} \sin \xi \, e^{j\omega\left(t - \frac{z_p}{c} + \frac{l \sin \alpha}{c} - \frac{l}{pc}\right)} \, d\xi \qquad (7\text{-}33)$$

where E_0 is a constant involving the current magnitude on the helix.

From (7-32) the last two terms of the exponent in (7-33) may be rewritten. Thus,

$$\frac{l \sin \alpha}{c} - \frac{l}{pc} = \frac{r\xi}{c}\left(\tan \alpha - \frac{1}{p \cos \alpha}\right) = \frac{r\xi q}{c} \qquad (7\text{-}34)$$

[1] For a general discussion of elliptical and circular polarization see Secs. 14-10 to 14-18.

where

$$q = \tan \alpha - \frac{1}{p \cos \alpha} \tag{7-35}$$

When $\alpha = 0$, the helix becomes a loop and $q = -1/p$. The relation

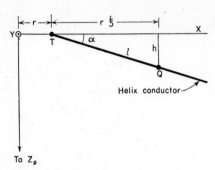

FIG. 7-29. Geometrical relations for calculating fields in z direction.

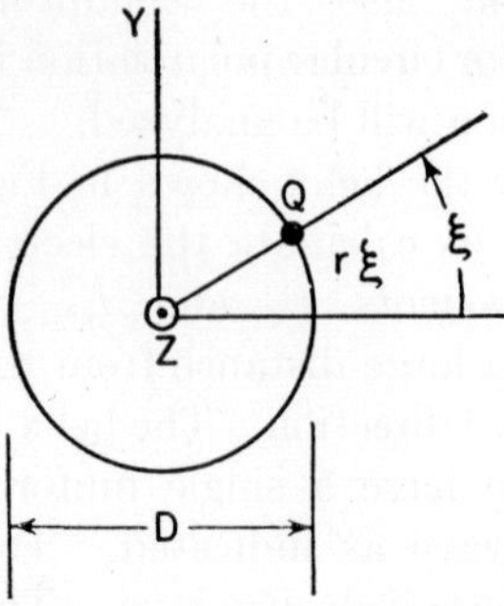

FIG. 7-30. Helix of Fig. 7-28 as viewed from the direction of the positive z axis.

being obtained is, thus, a general one, applying not only to helices but also to loops as a special case. Equation (7-33) now reduces to

$$E_\phi = E_0 \, e^{i(\omega t - \beta z_p)} \int_0^{2\pi n} \sin \xi \, e^{ik\xi} \, d\xi \tag{7-36}$$

where quantities independent of ξ have been taken outside the integral and where

$$\beta = \frac{\omega}{c} = \frac{2\pi}{\lambda}$$

and

$$k = \beta r q = L_\lambda \left(\sin \alpha - \frac{1}{p} \right) \tag{7-37}$$

On integration (7-36) becomes

$$E_\phi = \frac{E_1}{k^2 - 1} \left(e^{i2\pi n k} - 1 \right) \tag{7-38}$$

where $E_1 = E_0 \, e^{i(\omega t - \beta z_p)}$

In a similar way we have for the θ component E_θ of the electric field at the point P

$$E_\theta = E_0 \int_0^{2\pi n} \cos \xi \, e^{i\omega \left(t - \frac{z_p}{c} + \frac{l \sin \alpha}{c} - \frac{l}{pc} \right)} \, d\xi \tag{7-39}$$

Making the same substitutions as in (7-33), we obtain from (7-39)

$$E_\theta = \frac{jE_1 k}{(k^2 - 1)} \left(e^{j2\pi nk} - 1\right) \tag{7-40}$$

The condition for circular polarization in the direction of the z axis is

$$\frac{E_\phi}{E_\theta} = \pm j \tag{7-41}$$

The ratio of (7-38) to (7-40) gives

$$\frac{E_\phi}{E_\theta} = \frac{1}{jk} = -\frac{j}{k} \tag{7-42}$$

Accordingly, for circular polarization in the axial direction of a helix of an integral number of turns, k must equal ± 1.

Equation (7-42) indicates that E_ϕ and E_θ are in time phase quadrature. Therefore, the axial ratio AR is given by the magnitude of (7-42) or

$$\text{AR} = \frac{|E_\phi|}{|E_\theta|} = \left|\frac{1}{jk}\right| = \frac{1}{k} \tag{7-43}$$

The axial ratio will be restricted here to values between 1 and infinity. Hence, if (7-43) is less than 1, its reciprocal is taken.

Substituting the value of k from (7-37) into (7-43) yields

$$\text{AR} = \frac{1}{|\,L_\lambda[\sin\alpha - (1/p)]\,|} \tag{7-44}$$

or

$$\text{AR} = \left|\,L_\lambda\!\left(\sin\alpha - \frac{1}{p}\right)\right| \tag{7-45}$$

Either (7-44) or (7-45) is used so that $1 \leq \text{AR} \leq \infty$.

From (7-44) and (7-45), it appears that the axial ratio can be calculated from the turn length L_λ and pitch angle α of the helix, and the relative phase velocity p. If we introduce the value of p for the condition of in-phase fields (see Table 7-1), it is found that $\text{AR} = 1$. In other words, the in-phase field condition is also the condition for circular polarization in the axial direction.

This may also be shown by noting that (7-42) satisfies the condition for circular polarization when $k = -1$, or

$$L_\lambda\!\left(\sin\alpha - \frac{1}{p}\right) = -1 \tag{7-46}$$

Solving (7-46) for p, we obtain

$$p = \frac{L_\lambda}{S_\lambda + 1} \tag{7-47}$$

which is identical with the relation for in-phase fields (ordinary end-fire condition).

Our previous discussion on phase velocity indicated that p followed more closely the relation for increased directivity than the relation for in-phase fields. Thus, introducing p in (7-45) for the condition of increased directivity, we obtain

$$AR = \frac{2n + 1}{2n} \qquad (7\text{-}48)$$

where n is the number of turns of the helix. If n is large the axial ratio approaches unity and the polarization is nearly circular.

As an example, let us consider the axial ratio in the direction of the helix axis for a 13°, 7-turn helix. The axial ratio is unity if the relative velocity for the condition of in-phase fields is used. By (7-48) the axial ratio for the condition of increased directivity is $15/14 = 1.07$. This axial ratio is independent of the frequency or circumference C_λ as shown by the dashed line in Fig. 7-31. In this figure, the axial ratio is presented as a function of the helix circumference C_λ in free-space wavelengths.

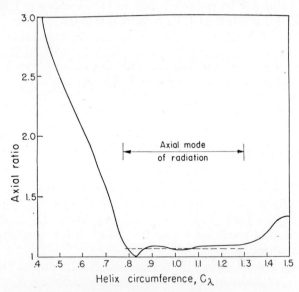

Fig. 7-31. Axial ratio as a function of helix circumference in free-space wavelengths for a 13°, 7-turn helical beam antenna.

If the axial ratio is calculated from (7-44) or (7-45), using the measured value of p shown in Fig. 7-19, an axial ratio variation is obtained as indicated by the solid curve in Fig. 7-31. This type of axial ratio vs. circumference curve is typical of ones measured on helical beam antennas.

Usually, however, the measured axial ratio increases more sharply as C_λ decreases to values less than about $\frac{3}{4}$ (see Fig. 7-34). This difference results from the fact that the calculation of axial ratio by (7-44) or (7-45) neglects the effect of the back wave on the helix. This is usually small when the helix is radiating in the axial mode but at lower frequencies or smaller circumferences ($C_\lambda < \frac{3}{4}$) the back wave is important. The back wave on the helix produces a wave reflected from the ground plane having the opposite direction of field rotation to that produced by the outgoing traveling wave on the helix. This causes the axial ratio to increase more rapidly than indicated in Fig. 7-31.

The foregoing discussion applies to helices of an integral number of turns. Let us now consider a long helix where the number of turns may assume nonintegral values. Hence, the length of the helical conductor will be specified as ξ_1 instead of $2\pi n$. It is further assumed that k is nearly unity. Thus, (7-36) becomes

$$E_\phi = \frac{E_1}{2j} \int_0^{\xi_1} [e^{j(k+1)\xi} - e^{j(k-1)\xi}]\, d\xi \qquad (7\text{-}49)$$

Since $k \simeq -1$, $k + 1 \simeq 0$, and it follows that

$$e^{j(k+1)\xi_1} \simeq 1 + j(k+1)\xi_1 \qquad (7\text{-}50)$$

Now integrating (7-49) and introducing the condition that k is nearly equal to -1 and the approximation of (7-50), we have

$$E_\phi = -\frac{E_1}{2}\left[j\xi_1 - \frac{e^{j(k-1)\xi_1} - 1}{k-1} \right] \qquad (7\text{-}51)$$

Similarly the θ component E_θ of the electric field is

$$E_\theta = -\frac{E_1}{2j}\left[j\xi_1 + \frac{e^{j(k-1)\xi_1} - 1}{k-1} \right] \qquad (7\text{-}52)$$

When the helix is very long

$$\xi_1 \gg 1$$

and (7-51) and (7-52) reduce to

$$E_\phi = -j\frac{E_1\xi_1}{2} \quad \text{and} \quad E_\theta = -\frac{E_1\xi_1}{2} \qquad (7\text{-}53)$$

Taking the ratio of E_ϕ to E_θ,

$$\frac{E_\phi}{E_\theta} = j \qquad (7\text{-}54)$$

which fulfills the condition for circular polarization.

Still another condition resulting in circular polarization is obtained when

$(k \pm 1)\xi_1 = 2\pi m$, where m is an integer. This condition is satisfied when either the positive or negative sign in $k \pm 1$ is chosen but not for both.

The important conditions for circular polarization are summarized as follows:

1. The radiation in the axial direction from a helical antenna of any pitch angle and of an integral number of 1 or more turns will be circularly polarized if $k = -1$ (in-phase fields or ordinary end-fire condition).

2. The radiation in the axial direction from a helical antenna of any pitch angle and a large number of turns, which are not necessarily an integral number, is nearly circularly polarized if k is nearly -1.

7-14. Wide-band Characteristics of Helical Antennas Radiating in the Axial Mode. The helical beam antenna has inherent broad-band properties, possessing desirable pattern, impedance, and polarization characteristics over a relatively wide frequency range. The natural adjustment of the phase velocity so that the fields from each turn add nearly in phase in the axial direction accounts for the persistence of the axial mode of radiation over a nearly 2 to 1 range in frequency. If the phase velocity were constant as a function of frequency, the axial mode patterns would be obtained only over a narrow frequency range. The terminal impedance is relatively constant over the same frequency range because of the large attenuation of the wave reflected from the open end of the helix. The polarization is nearly circular over the same range in frequency because the condition of fields in phase is also the condition for circular polarization.

As shown in Fig. 7-32a, the dimensions of a helix in free-space wavelengths move along a constant pitch-angle line as a function of frequency. If F_1 is the lower frequency limit of the axial mode of radiation and F_2 the upper frequency limit of this mode, then the range in dimensions for a 10° helix would be as suggested by the heavy line on the diameter-spacing chart of Fig. 7-32a. The center frequency F_0 is arbitrarily defined as $F_0 = (F_1 + F_2)/2$.

The properties of a helical beam antenna are a function of the pitch angle. The angle resulting in a maximum frequency range $F_2 - F_1$ of the axial mode of radiation is said to be an "optimum" pitch angle. To determine an optimum angle, the pattern, impedance, and polarization characteristics of helical antennas may be compared on a diameter-spacing chart as in Fig. 7-32b. The three contours indicate the region of satisfactory pattern, impedance, and polarization values as determined by measurements on helices of various pitch angle as a function of frequency. The axial length of the helices tested is about 1.6 wavelengths at the center frequency. The pattern contour in Fig. 7-32b indicates the approximate region of satisfactory patterns. A satisfactory pattern is considered to be one with a major lobe in the axial direction and with relatively small minor lobes.   Inside the pattern contour, the patterns are of this form and have half-power beam widths of less than 60° and as small as 30°.   Inside the impedance contour in Fig. 7-32b the terminal impedance

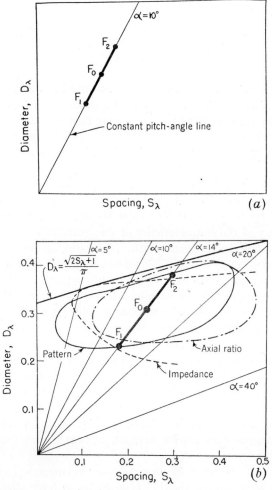

Fig. 7-32.   Diameter-spacing charts for helices with measured performance contours for axial mode of radiation (b).

is relatively constant and is nearly a pure resistance of 100 to 150 ohms. Inside the axial ratio contour, the axial ratio in the direction of the helix axis is less than 1.25.   Note that all contours lie below the line for which $D = \sqrt{2S_\lambda + 1}/\pi$.   This line may be regarded as an upper limit for the beam mode. It is apparent that the frequency range $F_2 - F_1$ is small if the pitch angle is either too small or too large. A pitch angle of about 12° or 14° would appear to be "optimum" for helices about 1.6 wavelengths long at the center frequency. Since the properties of the helix change slowly in the vicinity of the optimum angle, there is nothing critical about this value. The contours are arbitrary but are suitable for a general-purpose beam antenna of moderate directivity. The exact values of the frequency limits, F_1 and F_2, also are arbitrary but are relatively well defined by the close bunching of the contours near the frequency limits.

Based on the above conclusions, a 14°, 6-turn helix was constructed and its properties measured. The helix has a diameter of 0.31 wavelength at the center frequency (400 Mc). The diameter of the conductor is about 0.02 λ. Conductor diameters of 0.006 λ to 0.05 λ can be used with little difference in the properties of this helix in the frequency range of the beam mode.

The measured patterns between 275 and 560 Mc are presented in Fig. 7-33. It is apparent that the patterns are satisfactory over a frequency range from 300 Mc ($C_\lambda = 0.73$) to 500 Mc ($C_\lambda = 1.22$).

A summary of the characteristics of this antenna are given in Fig. 7-34 in which the half-power beam width, axial ratio, and standing-wave ratio are shown as a function of the helix circumference. The half-power beam width is taken between half-power points regardless of whether these occur on the major lobe or on minor lobes. This definition is arbitrary but is convenient to take into account a splitting up of the pattern into many lobes of large amplitude. Beam widths of 180° or more are arbitrarily plotted as 180°. The axial ratio is the value measured in the direction of the helix axis. The standing-wave ratio is the value measured on a 53-ohm coaxial line. A transformer section $\frac{1}{2}$ wavelength long at the center frequency is located at the helix terminals to transform the terminal resistance of approximately 130 to 53 ohms. Considered altogether, these pattern, polarization, and impedance characteristics represent remarkably good performance over a wide frequency range for a circularly polarized beam antenna.

Although the difference in characteristics between helices of 12° to 14° pitch angle is not large, the 14° type tends to have slightly better impedance characteristics while the 12° type tends to have slightly better patterns. The choice of a particular pitch angle as the optimum value is arbitrary but may very appropriately lie in the range of 12° to 14°.[1]

[1] Design data for a 12.5° helix are given by J. D. Kraus, Helical Beam Antenna Design Techniques, *Communications*, **29**, September, 1949.

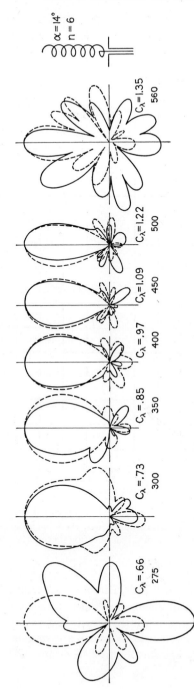

FIG. 7-33. Measured field patterns of 14°, 6-turn helix. Patterns are characteristic of the axial mode of radiation over a range of circumferences from about 0.73 to 1.22 wavelengths. Both the circumference and the frequency (in Mc) are indicated. The solid patterns are for the horizontally polarized field component (E_ϕ) and the dashed for the vertically polarized (E_θ). Both are adjusted to the same maximum.

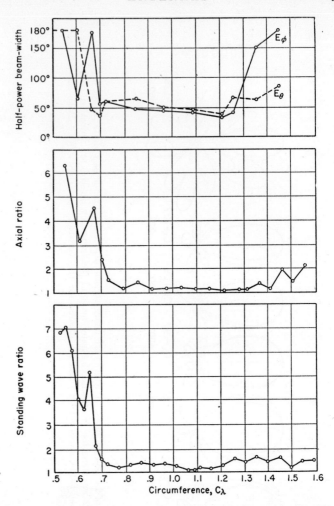

Fig. 7-34. Summary of measured performance of 14°, 6-turn helix. The curves show the half-power beam width for both field components, the axial ratio in the direction of the helix axis, and the SWR on a 53-ohm line as a function of the circumference in free-space wavelengths (C_λ).

7-15. Table of Pattern, Beam Width, Directivity, Terminal Resistance, and Axial-ratio Formulas. Expressions developed in the preceding sections for calculating the pattern, beam width, directivity, terminal resistance, and axial ratio for axial mode helical antennas are summarized in Table 7-2. These relations apply specifically to helices for $12° < \alpha < 15°$, $\frac{3}{4} < C_\lambda < \frac{4}{3}$, and $n > 3$.

TABLE 7-2

FORMULAS FOR AXIAL MODE HELICAL ANTENNAS

Pattern	$E = \left(\sin \dfrac{90°}{n}\right) \dfrac{\sin(n\psi/2)}{\sin(\psi/2)} \cos \phi$ where $\psi = 360°\left[S_\lambda(1 - \cos \phi) + \dfrac{1}{2n}\right]$
Beam width (half-power)	$B = \dfrac{52}{C_\lambda \sqrt{nS_\lambda}}$ deg
Beam width (first nulls)	$B = \dfrac{115}{C_\lambda \sqrt{nS_\lambda}}$ deg
Directivity	$D = 15\, C_\lambda^2\, n S_\lambda$
Terminal resistance	$R = 140\, C_\lambda$ ohms
Axial ratio	$AR = \dfrac{2n + 1}{2n}$ (increased directivity)
Axial ratio	$AR = \left| L_\lambda\left(\sin \alpha - \dfrac{1}{p}\right)\right|$ (p unrestricted)

n = number of turns of helix
C_λ = circumference in free-space wavelengths
S_λ = spacing between turns in free-space wavelengths

L_λ = turn length in free-space wavelengths
α = pitch angle
p = relative phase velocity
ϕ = angle with respect to helix axis

7-16. Tapered and Other Forms of Axial Mode Helical Antennas. The preceding sections have dealt with the uniform helix mounted on a flat ground plane and fed from the ground-plane end. This type is illustrated in Fig. 7-35a. Several other feed arrangements are also shown in Fig. 7-35. At (b) the ground plane is conical instead of flat. The types at (c) and (d) have a conductor coincident with the helix axis. The effect of this conductor is not large since the longitudinal field at the axis of the helix is small. The balanced helix at (e) produces opposite types of circular polarization from the two ends while that at (f) produces the same type from both ends. The polarizations indicated in the figure are according to the IRE definition (see Sec. 15-12). Forms (g), (h), and (i) are other modifications involving multiple helices of the same or different diameter.

A wide variety of nonuniform or tapered helices are also possible. These may be grouped into the following types: (1) α constant but S and D variable, (2) D constant but α and S variable, and (3) S constant but α and D variable. The taper may be of several kinds. For example, it may be of the increasing, decreasing, or envelope type. These combinations are suggested by the helices in Fig. 7-36. Several other kinds of tapered helices are shown in Fig. 7-37. The one at (a) has both a tapered and a uniform section. The helix at (b) involves still another kind of taper, that of conductor size. In this case the conductor is a flat strip of tapering width near the feed end and constant width at the open end.

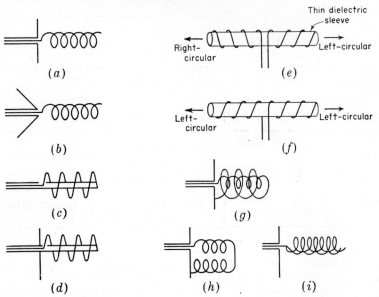

FIG. 7-35. Axial mode helices showing various constructional and feed arrangements.

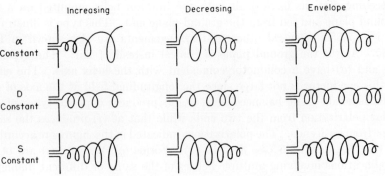

FIG. 7-36. Types of tapered axial mode helical antennas.

At the open end this construction approaches that of a helical slot in a conducting cylinder. A tapered strip conductor in combination with an increasing D taper is shown at (c). Tapered conductors of circular cross section can also be used as in (d) and (e). The one at (d) is tapered in both conductor and helix diameter while that at (e) is tapered only in

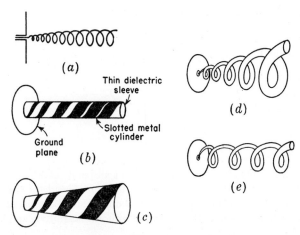

FIG. 7-37.   Additional tapered types.

conductor diameter. Since the characteristics of an axial mode helix are relatively insensitive to moderate changes in dimensions, the effect of moderate departures of the above types from a uniform helix is, in general, not large.

An interesting application of axial mode helices is to produce linear polarization. Two helices, one wound left-handed and the other right-handed but otherwise identical, are mounted as in Fig. 7-38a. The right-

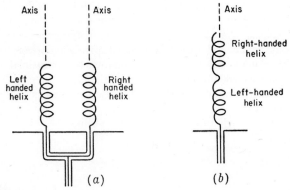

FIG. 7-38.   Helical antenna arrangements for producing linear polarization.

and left-circular polarization combine on the axis to give linear polarization. If the resulting field is vertically polarized, then rotating one helix 180° on its axis turns the plane of polarization to horizontal. Another method of obtaining linearly polarized radiation in the axial direction is by connecting a left- and a right-handed helix in series as in Fig. 7-38b.

PROBLEMS

7-1. *a.* What is the approximate relation required between the diameter D and height H of an antenna having the configuration shown, in order to ob-

tain a circularly polarized far field at all points at which the field is not zero. The loop is circular and is horizontal, and the linear conductor of length H is vertical. Assume D and H small compared to the wavelength, and assume the current of uniform magnitude and in phase over the system.

b. What is the pattern of the far circularly polarized field?

7-2. *a.* Prove that $\gamma'' = \arccos (\sin \alpha \cos \phi)$ in Eq. (7-26).

b. Confirm (7-29).

7-3. A helical beam antenna has $\alpha = 12°$, $n = 8$, $D = 22.5$ cm.

a. What is the value of p at 400 Mc for (1) in-phase fields? (2) increased directivity?

b. Calculate and plot the field patterns, assuming each turn is an isotropic point source for $p = 1, 0.9$, and 0.5, and also for p equal to the value for in-phase fields and for increased directivity.

c. Repeat (b), assuming each turn has a cosine field pattern.

7-4. A helix of uniform cross section consists of 6 turns. The diameter is 23.1 cm, and the turn spacing is 18.1 cm. Neglect the effect of the ground plane. Assume a phase velocity along the helical conductor satisfying the increased directivity condition. Calculate and plot the following patterns as a function of ϕ (0° to 360°) in the $\theta = 90°$ plane at 400 Mc. Use the square helix approximation.

a. $E_{\phi T}$ for a single turn and E_ϕ for the entire helix.

b. Repeat (a) neglecting the contribution of elements 2 and 4 of the square turn.

c. $E_{\theta T}$ for a single turn and E_θ for entire helix.

CHAPTER 8

THE BICONICAL ANTENNA AND ITS IMPEDANCE

8-1. Introduction. In the preceding chapters it is assumed that the antenna conductor is thin, in fact, infinitesimally thin. From known or assumed current distributions, the far-field patterns are calculated. The effect of the conductor thickness on the pattern is negligible provided that the diameter of the conductor is a small fraction of a wavelength. Thus, the patterns calculated on the basis of an infinitesimally thin conductor are applicable to conductors of moderate thickness, say for $d < 0.05 \lambda$ where d is the conductor diameter.

The radiation resistance of thin linear conductors and loops is calculated in Chaps. 5 and 6. This calculation is based on a knowledge of the pattern and a known or assumed current distribution. The values so obtained apply strictly to an infinitesimally thin conductor. The conductor thickness, up to moderate diameters, has only a small effect on the resistance at or near a current loop but may have a large effect on the resistance at or near a current minimum.[1]

In this chapter, we shall consider the problem of finding the input terminal resistance and also the reactance, taking into account the effect of conductor thickness. This problem is most simply approached by Schelkunoff's treatment of the biconical antenna[2] which will be outlined in the following sections. Beginning with the infinite biconical antenna, the analysis proceeds to terminated biconical antennas, that is, ones of finite length. This method of treatment bears a striking similarity to that usually employed with transmission lines in which the infinite transmission line is discussed first, followed by the terminated line of finite length.

8-2. The Characteristic Impedance of the Infinite Biconical Antenna. The infinite biconical antenna is analogous to an infinite uniform transmission line. The biconical antenna acts as a guide for a spherical wave in the same way that a uniform transmission line acts as a guide for a plane wave. The two situations are compared in Fig. 8-1.

---

[1] This is discussed in more detail in Chap. 9.

[2] S. A. Schelkunoff, "Electromagnetic Waves," D. Van Nostrand Company, Inc., New York, 1943, Chap. 11, p. 441.

The characteristic impedance of a biconical antenna will now be derived and will be shown to be uniform. Let a generator be connected to the terminals of an infinite biconical antenna as in Fig. 8-2. The generator causes waves with spherical phase fronts to travel radially outward from the terminals as suggested. The waves produce currents on the cones and a voltage between them. Let V be the voltage between points on the upper and lower cones a distance r from the terminals as in Fig. 8-2. Let I be

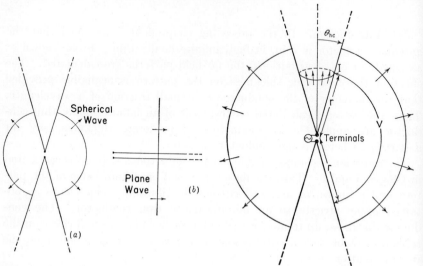

FIG. 8-1. An infinite biconical antenna (a) is analogous to an infinite uniform transmission line (b).

FIG. 8-2. Infinite biconical antenna showing voltage V and current I at a distance r from the terminals.

the total current on the surface of one of the cones at a distance r from the terminals. As on an ordinary transmission line, the ratio V/I is the characteristic impedance of the antenna. For the characteristic impedance to be uniform, it is necessary that the ratio V/I be independent of r.

Before V and I can be calculated, we must determine the nature of the electric and magnetic fields existing in the space between the conducting cones. Although the biconical transmission line can support an infinite number of transmission modes, let us assume that only the TEM or principal transmission mode is present. For the TEM mode, both **E** and **H** are entirely transverse, that is, they have no radial component. The **E** lines are along great circles passing through the polar axis as shown in Fig. 8-3. This satisfies the boundary conditions since **E** is normal to the surface of the cones. The **H** lines are circles lying in planes normal to the polar axis.

Maxwell's equation from Faraday's law for harmonically varying fields is

$$\nabla \times \mathbf{E} = -j\omega\mu\mathbf{H} \tag{8-1}$$

The biconical antenna is most readily handled in spherical coordinates.

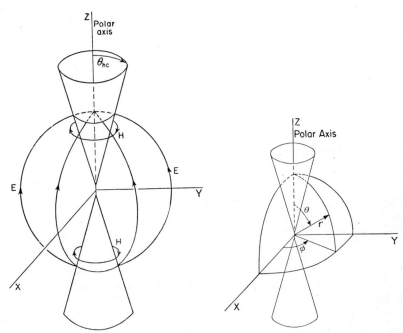

FIG. 8-3. **E** and **H** lines of outgoing TEM wave on biconical antenna.

FIG. 8-4. Biconical antenna with relation to spherical coordinates r, θ, ϕ.

Let the spherical coordinates r, θ, ϕ be related to the antenna as in Fig. 8-4. Expanding the left side of (8-1) in spherical coordinates, we have

$$\nabla \times \mathbf{E} = \frac{\mathbf{a}_r}{r^2 \sin\theta} \left[\frac{\partial(r \sin\theta \, E_\phi)}{\partial\theta} - \frac{\partial(rE_\theta)}{\partial\phi} \right]$$
$$+ \frac{\mathbf{a}_\theta}{r \sin\theta} \left[\frac{\partial E_r}{\partial\phi} - \frac{\partial(r \sin\theta \, E_\phi)}{\partial r} \right]$$
$$+ \frac{\mathbf{a}_\phi}{r} \left[\frac{\partial(rE_\theta)}{\partial r} - \frac{\partial E_r}{\partial\theta} \right] \tag{8-2}$$

Since **E** has only a θ component, which by symmetry is independent of ϕ, only the fifth term of (8-2) does not vanish. Thus,

$$\nabla \times \mathbf{E} = \frac{\mathbf{a}_\phi}{r} \frac{\partial(rE_\theta)}{\partial r} \tag{8-3}$$

Expanding the right side of (8-1) in spherical coordinates,

$$-j\omega\mu\mathbf{H} = -j\omega\mu(\mathbf{a}_r H_r + \mathbf{a}_\theta H_\theta + \mathbf{a}_\phi H_\phi) \tag{8-4}$$

Since $\mathbf{H}$ has only a ϕ component, (8-4) reduces to

$$-j\omega\mu\mathbf{H} = -\mathbf{a}_\phi j\omega\mu H_\phi \tag{8-5}$$

Now equating (8-3) and (8-5) we have

$$\frac{1}{r}\frac{\partial(rE_\theta)}{\partial r} = -j\omega\mu H_\phi \tag{8-6}$$

This is Maxwell's equation (8-1) reduced to a special form appropriate to a spherical wave.

Maxwell's equation from Ampère's law for harmonically varying fields in a nonconducting medium is

$$\nabla \times \mathbf{H} = j\omega\epsilon\mathbf{E} \tag{8-7}$$

$\mathbf{H}$ has only a ϕ component and $\mathbf{E}$ only a θ component. Since $E_r = 0$ it follows that

$$\frac{\partial(\sin\theta\, H_\phi)}{\partial\theta} = 0 \tag{8-8}$$

Hence, (8-7) can be reduced by a similar procedure as used for (8-1) to the form

$$\frac{\partial(rH_\phi)}{\partial r} = -j\omega\epsilon(rE_\theta) \tag{8-9}$$

Now differentiating (8-9) with respect to r and introducing (8-6), we obtain a wave equation in (rH_ϕ). Thus,

$$\frac{\partial^2(rH_\phi)}{\partial r^2} = -\omega^2\mu\epsilon(rH_\phi) \tag{8-10}$$

The condition of (8-8) requires that H_ϕ vary inversely as the sine of θ. That is,

$$H_\phi \propto \frac{1}{\sin\theta} \tag{8-11}$$

Hence, a solution of (8-10) which also fulfills (8-11) is

$$H_\phi = \frac{1}{r\sin\theta} H_0\, e^{-j\beta r} \tag{8-12}$$

where $\beta = \omega\sqrt{\mu\epsilon} = 2\pi/\lambda$

This solution represents an outgoing traveling wave on the antenna. Since the biconical antenna is assumed to be infinitely long, only the outgoing wave need be considered.

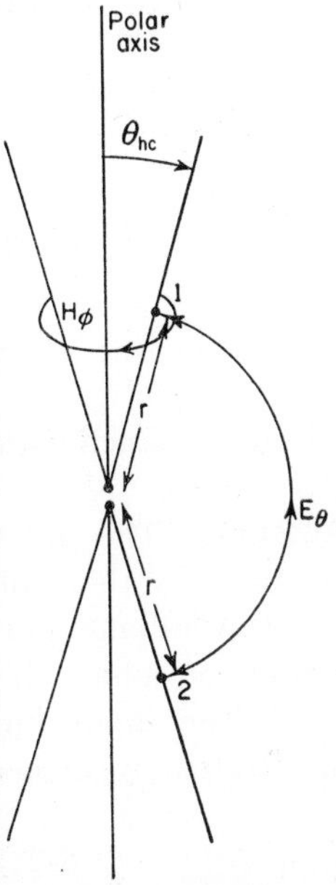

The electric and magnetic fields of a TEM wave are related by the intrinsic impedance Z_0 of the medium. Thus, we have

$$E_\theta = Z_0 H_\phi = \frac{Z_0}{r \sin \theta} H_0 e^{-i\beta r} \qquad (8\text{-}13)$$

Equations (8-12) and (8-13) give the variation of the magnetic and electric fields of a TEM outgoing wave in the space between the cones of a biconical antenna as a function of θ and r. The fields are independent of ϕ.

The voltage $V(r)$ between points 1 and 2 on the cones at a distance r from the terminals (see Fig. 8-5) can now be obtained by taking the line integral of E_θ along a great circle between the two points. Thus,

$$V(r) = \int_{\theta_{hc}}^{\pi - \theta_{hc}} E_\theta \, r \, d\theta \qquad (8\text{-}14)$$

FIG. 8-5. E_θ and H_ϕ field components at a distance r from the terminals of a biconical antenna.

where θ_{hc} is the half angle of the cone. Substituting (8-13) in (8-14) we have

$$V(r) = Z_0 H_0 e^{-i\beta r} \int_{\theta_{hc}}^{\pi - \theta_{hc}} \frac{d\theta}{\sin \theta} = Z_0 H_0 e^{-i\beta r} \ln \frac{\cot (\theta_{hc}/2)}{\tan (\theta_{hc}/2)} \qquad (8\text{-}15)$$

or

$$V(r) = 2 Z_0 H_0 e^{-i\beta r} \ln \cot \frac{\theta_{hc}}{2} \qquad (8\text{-}16)$$

The total current $I(r)$ on the cone at a distance r from the terminals can be obtained by applying Ampère's law. Thus,

$$I(r) = \int_0^{2\pi} H_\phi r \sin \theta \, d\phi = 2\pi r H_\phi \sin \theta \qquad (8\text{-}17)$$

Now substituting H_ϕ from (8-12) in (8-17) yields

$$I(r) = 2\pi H_0 e^{-i\beta r} \qquad (8\text{-}18)$$

The characteristic impedance Z_k of the biconical antenna is the ratio of $V(r)$ to $I(r)$ as given by (8-16) and (8-18) or

$$Z_k = \frac{V(r)}{I(r)} = \frac{Z_0}{\pi} \ln \cot \frac{\theta_{hc}}{2} \qquad (8\text{-}19)$$

For a medium of free space between the cones, $Z_0 = 120\pi$ so that (8-18) becomes

$$Z_k = 120 \ln \cot \frac{\theta_{hc}}{2} \quad \text{ohms} \tag{8-20}$$

When θ_{hc} is small ($\theta_{hc} < 20°$), $\cot(\theta_{hc}/2) \simeq 2/\theta_{hc}$ so that

$$Z_k = 120 \ln \frac{2}{\theta_{hc}} \quad \text{ohms} \tag{8-21}$$

Equations (8-20) and (8-21) are Schelkunoff's relations for the characteristic impedance of a biconical antenna. Since these equations are independent of r, the biconical antenna has a uniform characteristic impedance.

8-3. Input Impedance of the Infinite Biconical Antenna. The input impedance of a biconical antenna with TEM waves is given by the ratio $V(r)/I(r)$ as r approaches zero. For an infinite biconical antenna this ratio is independent of r, so that the input impedance of the infinite biconical antenna equals the characteristic impedance. The input impedance depends only on the TEM wave and is unaffected by higher order waves. Thus

$$Z_i = Z_k \tag{8-22}$$

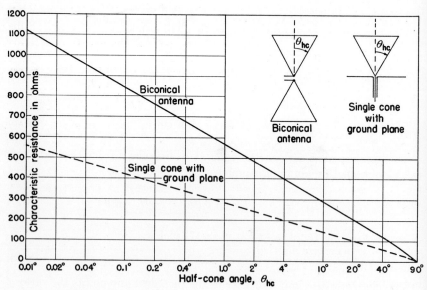

Fig. 8-6. Characteristic resistance of biconical antenna and of single cone with ground plane as a function of the half-cone angle in degrees. If the antenna is infinitely long, the terminal impedance is equal to the characteristic resistance as given in the figure.

where Z_i is the input impedance of the biconical antenna and Z_k is the characteristic impedance as given by (8-20) or for small cone angles by (8-21). The characteristic and input impedances are pure resistances so that they may be referred to as the characteristic resistance R_k and the input resistance R_i. They are given by

$$R_k = R_i = 120 \ln \cot \frac{\theta_{hc}}{2} \quad \text{ohms} \quad (8\text{-}23)$$

The variation of this resistance as a function of the half-cone angle θ_{hc} is presented by the solid curve in Fig. 8-6. An infinite biconical antenna of 2° total cone angle ($\theta_{hc} = 1°$) has a resistance of 568 ohms, while one with a total cone angle of 100° ($\theta_{hc} = 50°$) has a resistance of 91 ohms. If the lower cone is replaced by a large ground plane (see insert in Fig. 8-6), the resistance is one-half the value given by (8-23) as shown by the dashed line in Fig. 8-6.

8-4. Input Impedance of the Finite Biconical Antenna. In this section we will consider the finite biconical antenna. This is analogous to a finite or terminated transmission line.

A TEM mode wave can exist along the biconical conductors, but in the space beyond the cones transmission can be only in higher order modes. Schelkunoff has defined the sphere coinciding with the ends of the cones the *boundary sphere* as indicated in Fig. 8-7. The radius of the

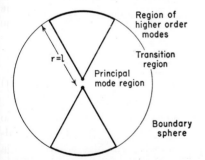

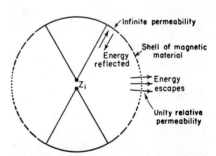

FIG. 8-7. Schelkunoff's finite biconical antenna and boundary sphere.

FIG. 8-8. Finite biconical antenna with boundary sphere replaced by a shell of magnetic material.

sphere is l, being equal to the length of the cones ($r = l$). Inside this sphere TEM waves can exist, and also higher order modes may be present, but outside only the higher order modes can exist.

When an outgoing TEM reaches the boundary sphere, part of its energy is reflected as a TEM wave. If the reflection at the sphere were uniform, there would be only this reflected TEM wave. However, the reflection at the sphere is not uniform, and some of the energy is reflected in higher order waves while some energy continues into space as higher order waves. It

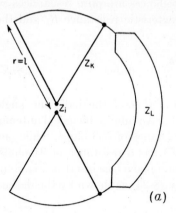

(a)

is as though the boundary sphere consists of a shell of magnetic material which is infinitely permeable near the cones and has a relative permeability of unity at the equator.[1] At the cones most of the outgoing TEM waves is reflected, but near the equator most of the energy escapes, as suggested in Fig. 8-8. It is but a step to imagine that, from the impedance viewpoint, the magnetic shell acts like a terminating or load impedance Z_L connected across the open end of the cones as suggested in Fig. 8-9a. Neglecting the effect of the end caps of the cones, the finite biconical antenna can now be treated as a transmission line of characteristic impedance Z_k terminated in the load impedance Z_L (see Fig. 8-9b). If the impedance Z_L can be found, the impedance Z_i at the input terminals of the biconical antenna is calculable as the impedance Z_L reflected back over a line

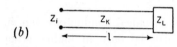

(b)

FIG. 8-9. Finite or terminated biconical antenna and equivalent transmission line.

of characteristic impedance Z_k and length l. Thus (see Appendix Sec. 3),

$$Z_i = Z_k \frac{Z_L + jZ_k \tan \beta l}{Z_k + jZ_L \tan \beta l} \qquad (8\text{-}24)$$

Thus, the problem resolves itself into one of finding Z_L. Reduced to simple terms, Schelkunoff's method of finding Z_L consists first of calculating Z_m at a current maximum on a very thin biconical antenna, a sinusoidal current distribution being assumed. In Fig. 8-10a a thin biconical antenna of length l is shown. Z_m is the impedance which appears between the current maximum on one cone and the corresponding point on the other cone. Since this impedance occurs $\frac{1}{4}$ wavelength from the open end of the antenna, Z_L is then equal to Z_m transformed over a line $\frac{1}{4}$ wavelength long as in Fig. 8-10b. Finally, the input impedance Z_i is Z_L transformed over a line of characteristic impedance Z_k and length l as in Fig. 8-9b.

The impedance Z_L is obtained from Z_m by the transmission-line relation (see Appendix Sec. 3)

---

[1] The shell is assumed to have zero electrical conductivity and a relative dielectric constant of unity.

$$Z_L = Z_k \frac{Z_m + jZ_k \tan \beta x}{Z_k + jZ_m \tan \beta x} \tag{8-25}$$

But the line is $\frac{1}{4}$ wavelength long so that $\beta x = \pi/2$ and (8-25) reduces to

$$Z_L = \frac{Z_k^2}{Z_m} \tag{8-26}$$

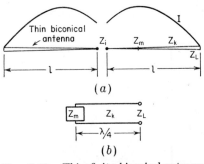

(a)

(b)

FIG. 8-10.   Thin finite biconical antenna and transmission line equivalent for finding Z_L.

Whereas Z_k is entirely real, Z_m in (8-26) may have both real and imaginary parts. Thus,

$$Z_m = R_m + jX_m$$

The real part R_m is the same as the radiation resistance at a current maximum of a very thin linear antenna. It has been calculated by Schelkunoff as[1]

$$R_m = 60 \text{ Cin } 2\beta l + 30(0.577 + \ln \beta l - 2 \text{ Ci } 2\beta l + \text{ Ci } 4\beta l) \cos 2\beta l$$
$$+ 30(\text{Si } 4\beta l - 2 \text{ Si } 2\beta l) \sin 2\beta l \qquad \text{ohms} \tag{8-27}$$

Provided only that the antenna is thin, the radiation resistance R_m is independent of the shape of the antenna (that is, whether cylindrical or conical). However, the radiation reactance depends on the shape and has been calculated by Schelkunoff for a thin cone as

$$X_m = 60 \text{ Si } 2\beta l + 30(\text{Ci } 4\beta l - \ln \beta l - 0.577) \sin 2\beta l$$
$$- 30(\text{Si } 4\beta l) \cos 2\beta l \qquad \text{ohms} \tag{8-28}$$

Now substituting (8-26) for Z_L into (8-24), the input impedance is

$$Z_i = Z_k \frac{Z_k + jZ_m \tan \beta l}{Z_m + jZ_k \tan \beta l} \tag{8-29}$$

where l = length of one cone
Z_k = value given by (8-21)
$Z_m = R_m + jX_m$, where R_m = value given by (8-27) and X_m = value given by (8-28).

The value of Z_m becomes independent of cone angle for thin cones. Thus, the real and imaginary parts of Z_m, as given by (8-27) and (8-28), are independent of the cone angle, being functions only of the cone length l. However, the characteristic impedance Z_k is a function of the cone

---

[1] l equals half the total length of the antenna. In Chap. 5, L is twice this value being equal to the total antenna length (that is, $L = 2l$).

angle. Hence, the input impedance Z_i as calculated by (8-29), is a function of both the cone angle and the cone length. The limitation in calculating Z_m that the cone angle be small also limits the use of (8-29) to small cone angles, say, half-cone angles of less than about 3 degrees.[1]

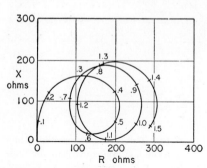

FIG. 8-11.   Resistance R_m and reactance X_m of radiation impedance Z_m of a biconical antenna as a function of the cone length in wavelengths (l_λ).

The radiation impedance Z_m at the current maximum of Schelkunoff's biconical antenna as given by (8-27) and (8-28) is presented in Fig. 8-11. The impedance is given as a function of cone length, l_λ, in wavelengths, where $l_\lambda = l/\lambda$. This impedance applies to small cone angles.

Introducing Z_m into (8-29), the input impedance can be obtained for cones of different characteristic impedance. As illustrations, the input impedance of a biconical antenna of 1,000 ohms characteristic impedance (half-cone angle, $\theta_{hc} = 0.027°$) and for one of 450 ohms characteristic impedance (half-cone angle, $\theta_{hc} = 2.7°$) are given in Fig. 8-12,[2] as functions of the cone length in wavelengths (l_λ). If the lower cone is replaced by a large ground plane (see insert in Fig. 8-6), the input impedance is halved.

It is significant that the terminal impedance of the thicker biconical antenna (lower characteristic impedance) is more constant as a function cone length than is the impedance of the thinner antenna. This difference in impedance behavior of thick and thin antennas is typical not only of conical antennas but also of antennas of other shapes, such as cylindrical antennas. We, thus, conclude that the impedance characteristics of a thick antenna are, in general, more suitable for wide-band applications than those of a thin antenna.

The curve in Fig. 8-12 for the 2.7° half-angle biconical antenna spirals inward and would eventually end at the point $R = 450$, $X = 0$, when the length l_λ becomes infinite. Likewise, the curve for the 0.027° antenna spirals into $R = 1000$, $X = 0$, when $l_\lambda = \infty$. The effect of the cone angle

[1] Approximate solutions for wide cone angles are discussed by

C. T. Tai, Application of a Variational Principle to Biconical Antennas, *J. Applied Phys.*, **20**, 1076–1084, November, 1949.

P. D. P. Smith, The Conical Dipole of Wide Angle, *J. Applied Phys.*, **19**, 11–23, January, 1948.

[2] The curves in Figs. 8-11 and 8-12 are plotted from data given by Schelkunoff, *loc. cit.*

is greatest near the second, fourth, or even, resonances ($l_\lambda \simeq \frac{1}{2}$, 1, etc.) and least near the first, third, or odd, resonances ($l_\lambda \simeq \frac{1}{4}$, $\frac{3}{4}$, etc.).

We note in Fig. 8-12 that the geometric mean resistance R_{12} of the resistance at the first and second resonances is about one-half the characteristic resistance of the biconical antenna. We take $R_{12} = \sqrt{R_1 R_2}$, where R_1 is the resistance at the first resonance ($l_\lambda \simeq \frac{1}{4}$) and R_2 is the resistance at the second resonance ($l_\lambda \simeq \frac{1}{2}$). Thus, for the antenna with 2.7° half-cone angle, $R_{12} = 224$ which is about half the characteristic resistance ($R_k = 450$). For the antenna with the 0.027° half-cone angle, $R_{12} = 500$ or half the characteristic resistance ($R_k = 1,000$). The geo-

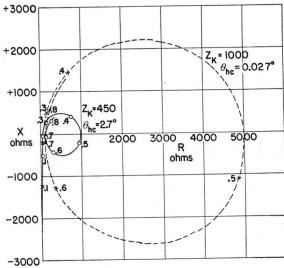

Fig. 8-12.   Calculated input impedance of biconical antennas with 2.7° half-cone angle (solid curve) and with 0.027° half-cone angle (dashed curve). The resistance R and reactance X of the input impedance Z_i are represented as a function of the length l of one cone in wavelengths, the length being indicated in 0.1-wavelength intervals.

metric mean resistance R_{23} of the resistance at the second and third resonances is closer to the characteristic resistance. We take $R_{23} = \sqrt{R_2 R_3}$, where R_3 is the resistance at the third resonance ($l_\lambda \simeq \frac{3}{4}$). Thus, for the antenna with the 2.7° half-cone angle, $R_{23} = 317$ ($R_k = 450$) while for the antenna with the 0.027° half-cone angle, $R_{23} = 710$ ($R_k = 1,000$). The geometric mean of successive higher resonant resistances would be expected to approach closer yet to the characteristic resistance around which the impedance spiral converges.

The impedance spirals in Fig. 8-12 are for a biconical antenna. If the lower cone is replaced by a large ground plane, the impedance values are halved. Measured impedances of single cones with ground plane are

presented in Fig. 8-13 for cones with half-angles of 5°, 10°, 20°, and 30°
and characteristic resistances ($R_k = Z_k$) of 188, 146, 104, and 80 ohms,
respectively.[1] The cones measured had a top hat consisting of an inverted
cone of 90° total included angle (see insert in Fig. 8-13). It is to be noted
that the trend toward reduced impedance variation with increasing cone
angle, as predicted by the calculated curves of Fig. 8-12, is continued for
the larger cone angles.

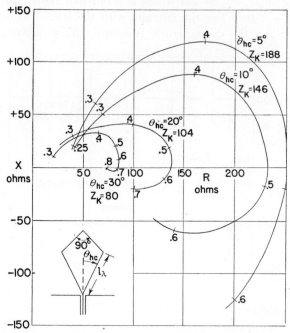

FIG. 8-13.　Measured input impedance of single cones with ground plane as a function
of cone length in wavelengths (l_λ). Impedance curves are presented for cones with
half-angles of 5°, 10°, 20°, and 30°.

8-5. Pattern of Biconical Antenna.　The far-field pattern of a biconical
antenna will be nearly the same as for an infinitesimally thin linear antenna
provided that the cone angle is small. It is assumed that the current
distribution is sinusoidal. Thus, Eqs. (5-80) and (5-81) can be used for thin
biconical antennas, the substitution being made that $L = 2l$, where l is the
length of one cone.

8-6. Input Impedance of Antennas of Arbitrary Shape.　Schelkunoff has
extended his analysis for thin biconical antennas, as outlined above, to

---

[1] The curves in Fig. 8-13 are plotted from data presented in Chap. 4 by A. Dorne, in
"Very High Frequency Techniques," by Radio Research Laboratory Staff, McGraw-
Hill Book Company, Inc., New York, 1947.

thin antennas of other shapes by considering the average characteristic impedance of the antenna. Whereas the characteristic impedance of a biconical antenna is uniform, the impedance of antennas of shape other than conical is nonuniform. Thus, as an approximation the input impedance of the cylindrical antenna in Fig. 8-14a can be calculated as though it were a biconical antenna of characteristic impedance equal to the *average* characteristic impedance of the cylindrical antenna. The cylindrical antenna is replaced by the equivalent biconical antenna as suggested in Fig. 8-14a. The transmission-line circuit, equivalent to the antenna, is shown in Fig. 8-14b, it being assumed that the line of length l

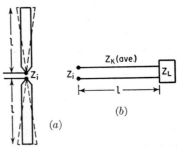

Fig. 8-14. Cylindrical antenna and equivalent biconical antenna and transmission line.

has a uniform characteristic impedance equal to the average characteristic impedance of the cylindrical antenna. This topic is discussed further in Sec. 9-11.

PROBLEMS

8-1. Confirm Schelkunoff's result that the characteristic impedance of an unsymmetrical biconical antenna (with unequal cone angles) is

$$Z_k = 60 \ln \left(\cot \frac{\theta'_{hc}}{2} \cot \frac{\theta''_{hc}}{2} \right)$$

where θ'_{hc} = half the upper cone angle

θ''_{hc} = half the lower cone angle

8-2. Prove that the characteristic impedance Z_k for a single cone and ground plane is half Z_k for a biconical antenna.

8-3. Calculate the terminal impedance of a conical antenna of 2° total angle operating against a very large ground plane. The length l of the cone is $\frac{3}{8}$ wavelength.

CHAPTER 9

THE CYLINDRICAL ANTENNA:
ITS CURRENT DISTRIBUTION AND IMPEDANCE

9-1. Introduction.[1] In previous chapters, the assumption is made that the current distribution on a finite antenna is sinusoidal. This assumption is a good one provided that the antenna is very thin. In this chapter, a method for calculating the current distribution of a cylindrical center-fed antenna will be discussed, taking into account the thickness of the antenna conductor.

This is a boundary-value problem. The antenna as a boundary-value problem was treated many years ago by Abraham,[2] who obtained an exact solution for a freely oscillating elongated ellipsoid of revolution. However, the earliest treatments of the cylindrical center-driven antenna as a boundary-value problem are those of Hallén[3] and L. V. King.[4] More recently the problem has been discussed by Synge and Albert.[5] Hallén's method leads to an integral equation, approximate solutions of which yield the current distribution. Knowing the current distribution and the voltage applied at the input terminals, the input impedance is then obtained as the ratio of the voltage to the current at the terminals.

Hallén's integral-equation method will not be presented in detail, but the important steps and results will be discussed in the following sections.

[1] In other chapters sufficient steps are given in most analyses that the reader should be able to supply the intermediate ones without undue difficulty. However, this is not the case in this chapter since in most instances a large number of steps is omitted between those given in order to reduce the length of the development.

[2] M. Abraham, Die electrischen Schwingungen um einen stabformingen Leiter, behandelt nach der Maxwellschen Theorie, *Ann. Physik*, **66**, 435–472, 1898.

[3] Erik Hallén, Theoretical Investigations into the Transmitting and Receiving Qualities of Antennae, *Nova Acta Regiae Soc. Sci. Upsaliensis*, Ser. IV, **11**, No. 4, 1–44, 1938.

[4] L. V. King, On the Radiation Field of a Perfectly Conducting Base-insulated Cylindrical Antenna Over a Perfectly Conducting Plane Earth, and the Calculation of the Radiation Resistance and Reactance, *Phil. Trans. Roy. Soc. (London)*, **236**, 381–422, 1937.

[5] G. E. Albert and J. L. Synge, The General Problem of Antenna Radiation. I, *Quart. Applied Math.*, **6**, 117–131, July, 1948.

J. L. Synge, The General Problem of Antenna Radiation and the Fundamental Integral Equation, With Application to an Antenna of Revolution. II, *Quart. Applied Math.*, **6**, 133–156, July, 1948.

9-2. Outline of the Integral-equation Method. Since this method is a long one, an outline of the important steps is given in this section.

The *objective* of the method is twofold:

1. To obtain the current distribution of a cylindrical center-fed antenna in terms of its length and diameter
2. To obtain the input impedance

An *outline of the procedure* is given by the following steps. These are treated more fully in the sections which follow.

1. The field **E** inside the conductor is expressed in terms of the current and skin effect resistance.
2. The field **E** outside the conductor is expressed in terms of the vector potential.
3. The tangential components of **E** are equated, obtaining a wave equation in the vector potential **A**.

Steps 1 through 3 are discussed in Sec. 9-3.

4. The wave equation in **A** is solved as the sum of a complementary function and a particular integral.
5. The constant C_2 in the solution is evaluated in terms of the conditions at the input terminals.
6. The vector potential **A** is expressed in terms of the antenna current **I**.
7. The value of C_2 from 5 and of **A** from 6 are inserted in the solution 4, obtaining Hallén's integral equation. This is an integral equation in the current I.

Steps 4 through 7 are discussed in Sec. 9-4.

8. A partial solution for the current I is then obtained by evaluating one of the integrals so that the current is expressed as the sum of several terms, some of which also involve I.
9. Neglecting certain terms in I, an approximate (zero order) solution is obtained for I.
10. This value of I is substituted back in the current equation obtaining a first-order approximation for the current. This process of iteration can be continued, yielding second-order and higher order solutions.
11. The constant C_1 is evaluated and an asymptotic expansion obtained for the current. That is,

$$I_z = \frac{jV_T}{60\,\Omega}\left[\frac{\sin \beta(l - |\,y\,|) + (b_1/\Omega) + (b_2/\Omega^2) + \cdots}{\cos \beta l + (d_1/\Omega) + (d_2/\Omega^2) + \cdots}\right]$$

where $\Omega = 2 \ln (2l/a)$, where l is the half-length of the antenna and

a the radius. The first-order approximation involves terms only as high as b_1/Ω and d_1/Ω. A second-order approximation involves b_2/Ω^2 and d_2/Ω^2, etc.

Steps 8 through 11 are discussed in Sec. 9-5.

12. The input impedance is then obtained as the ratio of the input terminal voltage V_T and the current at the input terminals I_T. This is discussed in Sec. 9-9.

9-3. The Wave Equation in the Vector Potential A.[1] Consider the center-fed cylindrical antenna of total length $2l$ and diameter $2a$ as shown in Fig. 9-1. Let us first state the boundary conditions. Since the tan-

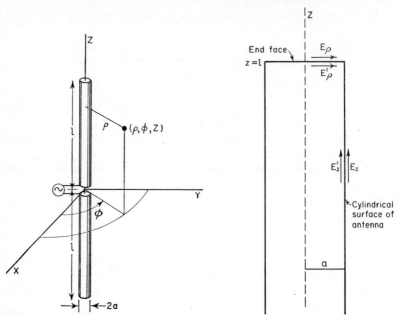

Fig. 9-1. Symmetrical center-fed cylindrical antenna with relation to coordinates.

Fig. 9-2. The tangential components of the electric field at the surface of the antenna are equal.

gential components of the electric field are equal at a boundary,

$$E_z' = E_z \tag{9-1}$$

along the cylindrical surface. In (9-1), E_z' is the field just inside the conductor ($\rho = a - da$), and E_z is the field just outside the surface of the

---

[1] The development in this section and in Sec. 9-4, leading up to Hallén's integral equation, follows the presentation of Ronald King and C. W. Harrison, Jr., The Distribution of Current Along a Symmetrical Center-Driven Antenna, *Proc. I.R.E.*, **31**, 548–567, October, 1943.

conductor ($\rho = a + da$) as indicated in Fig. 9-2. At the end faces of the antenna we have

$$E'_\rho = E_\rho \qquad (9\text{-}2)$$

where E'_ρ = the radial field just inside the face ($z = l - dl$)

E_ρ = the radial field just outside ($z = l + dl$) as suggested in Fig. 9-2

To simplify the problem, it is assumed that l is much larger than a ($l \gg a$) and that the radius is very small compared to the wavelength ($\beta a \ll 1$). The effect of the end face can then be neglected and the current I_z taken equal to zero at $z = \pm l$. Then,

$$E'_z = ZI_z \qquad (9\text{-}3)$$

where Z = the conductor impedance in ohms per meter length of the conductor due to skin effect

I_z = the total current

The electric field **E** outside the conductor is derivable entirely from the vector potential **A**. That is,

$$\mathbf{E} = -j\frac{c^2}{\omega}\,\nabla\,(\nabla \cdot \mathbf{A}) - j\omega\mathbf{A} \qquad (9\text{-}4)$$

Neglecting the end faces, the field **E** just outside the conductor will have only an E_z component. Since the current is entirely in the z direction, **A** has only a z component. Hence, at the conductor surface (9-4) becomes

$$E_z = -j\frac{\omega}{\beta^2}\left(\frac{\partial^2 A_z}{\partial z^2} + \beta^2 A_z\right) \qquad (9\text{-}5)$$

Now equating (9-3) and (9-5) in accordance with the boundary condition of (9-1), we obtain a wave equation,

$$\frac{\partial^2 A_z}{\partial z^2} + \beta^2 A_z = \frac{j\beta^2}{\omega}\,ZI_z \qquad (9\text{-}6)$$

This completes the first three steps in the outline of Sec. 9-2.

9-4. Hallén's Integral Equation. We next proceed to obtain a solution of (9-6), which is a one-dimensional wave equation in the vector potential A_z. The equation is of the second order and first degree. If the antenna conductivity is infinite, $Z = 0$ and the equation becomes homogeneous. However, when Z is not zero, the equation is not homogeneous and its solution is given as the sum of a complementary function A_c and a particular integral A_r.[1] That is

$$A_z = A_c + A_r \qquad (9\text{-}7)$$

---

[1] J. W. Mellor, "Higher Mathematics for Students of Chemistry and Physics," Longmans, Green & Co., Inc., New York, pp. 413–414.

Introducing the values of A_c and A_r (9-7) becomes

$$A_z = -\frac{j}{c}(C_1 \cos \beta z + C_2 \sin \beta z) + \frac{jz}{c}\int_0^z I(s) \sin \beta(z - s)\, ds \qquad (9\text{-}8)$$

Assume that the antenna is excited symmetrically by a pair of closely spaced terminals. Then

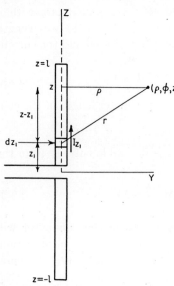

$$I_z(z) = I_z(-z)$$
and $$A_z(z) = A_z(-z) \qquad (9\text{-}9)$$

The constant C_2 in (9-8) may be evaluated as equal to one-half the applied terminal voltage V_T. Thus,

$$C_2 = \tfrac{1}{2}V_T \qquad (9\text{-}10)$$

Let us now express the vector potential A_z in terms of the current on the antenna. For a conductor of length $z = -l$ to $z = +l$, as shown in Fig. 9-3, the vector potential A_z at any point outside the conductor or at its surface is

$$A_z = \frac{\mu}{4\pi}\int_{-l}^{+l}\frac{[I_{z_1}]}{r}\, dz_1$$

$$= \frac{\mu e^{jwt}}{4\pi}\int_{-l}^{+l}\frac{I_{z_1}\,e^{-j\beta r}}{r}\, dz_1 \qquad (9\text{-}11)$$

Fig. 9-3. Construction for obtaining vector potential A_z.

where $r = [\rho^2 + (z - z_1)^2]^{\frac{1}{2}}$
z_1 = a point on the conductor $(-l \leq z_1 \leq +l)$

Inserting the values of C_2 and A_z from (9-10) and (9-11) in (9-8) and rearranging yields Hallén's integral equation,[1]

$$\frac{jc\mu\, e^{jwt}}{4\pi}\int_{-l}^{+l}\frac{I_{z_1}\,e^{-j\beta r}}{r}\, dz_1 = C_1 \cos \beta z + \frac{V_T}{2}\sin \beta|z|$$

$$- Z\int_0^z I(s) \sin(z - s)\, ds \qquad (9\text{-}12)$$

[1] An integral equation is an equation in which an unknown function appears under the integral sign. In this case, the unknown function is the antenna current I_{z_1}.

In the integral-equation approach to a boundary-value problem, the independent variable ranges over the boundary surface (in this case, the antenna) so that the boundary conditions are incorporated in the integral equation. This is in contrast to the situation with the differential equation approach, in which the independent variable ranges throughout space, with a solution being sought that satisfies the boundary conditions.

The absolute value sign on z in the second term of the right side of (9-12) has been introduced because of the symmetry condition of (9-9). Hallén's equation (9-12) is an equation in the current I_{z_1} on the conductor. If (9-12) could be solved for I_{z_1}, the current distribution could be obtained as a function of the antenna dimensions and the conductor impedance.

The term with Z has a negligible effect provided that the antenna is a good conductor. Thus, assuming that $Z = 0$ (conductivity infinite), we can put Hallén's integral equation in a simplified form as follows,

$$30j \int_{-l}^{+l} \frac{I_{z_1} e^{-i\beta r}}{r} \, dz_1 = C_1 \cos \beta z + \frac{V_T}{2} \sin \beta |z| \tag{9-13}$$

In (9-13) we have put $e^{iwt} = 1$ and written $c\mu/4\pi = 30$. This completes steps 4 through 7 of the outline of Sec. 9-2.

9-5. First-order Solution of Hallén's Equation.[1]
The problem now is to obtain a solution of (9-13) for the antenna current I_z which can be evaluated. As a first step in the solution, let the integral in (9-13) be expanded by adding and subtracting I_z. That is,

$$\int_{-l}^{+l} \frac{I_{z_1} e^{-i\beta r}}{r} \, dz_1 = \int_{-l}^{+l} \frac{I_z + I_{z_1} e^{-i\beta r} - I_z}{r} \, dz_1 \tag{9-14}$$

$$= I_y \int_{-l}^{+l} \frac{dz_1}{r} + \int_{-l}^{+l} \frac{I_{z_1} e^{-i\beta r} - I_z}{r} \, dz_1 \tag{9-15}$$

Integrating the first term in (9-15) and putting $\rho = a$ we have

$$\int_{-l}^{+l} \frac{dz_1}{r} = \Omega + \ln \left[1 - \left(\frac{z}{l} \right)^2 \right] + \delta \tag{9-16}$$

where

$$\Omega = 2 \ln \frac{2l}{a} = 2 \ln \frac{\text{total antenna length}}{\text{conductor radius}} \tag{9-17}$$

and

$$\delta = \ln \left\{ \frac{1}{4} \left[\sqrt{1 + \left(\frac{a}{l-z} \right)^2} + 1 \right] \left[\sqrt{1 + \left(\frac{a}{l+z} \right)^2} + 1 \right] \right\} \tag{9-18}$$

Substituting (9-16) into (9-15), and this in turn into (9-13), yields,

$$I_z = \frac{-j}{30\Omega} \left(C_1 \cos \beta z + \frac{1}{2} V_T \sin \beta |z| \right)$$
$$- \frac{1}{\Omega} \left\{ I_z \ln \left[1 - \left(\frac{z}{l} \right)^2 \right] + I_z \delta + \int_{-l}^{+l} \frac{I_{z_1} e^{-i\beta r} - I_z}{r} \, dz_1 \right\} \tag{9-19}$$

[1] The development in this and following sections is similar to that given by Erik Hallén, Theoretical Investigations into the Transmitting and Receiving Qualities of Antennae, *Nova Acta Regiae Soc. Sci. Upsaliensis*, Ser. IV, **11**, No. 4, 1–44, 1938; also by Ronald King and C. W. Harrison, Jr., The Distribution of Current Along a Symmetrical Center-driven Antenna, *Proc. I.R.E.*, **31**, 548–567, October, 1943.

At the end of the antenna the current is zero. Thus, when $z = l$, $I_z = 0$ so that (9-19) reduces to

$$0 = \frac{-j}{30\Omega}\left(C_1 \cos \beta l + \frac{1}{2} V_T \sin \beta l\right) + \frac{1}{\Omega}\int_{-l}^{+l} \frac{I_{z_1}e^{-j\beta r_1}}{r_1}\,dz_1 \qquad (9\text{-}20)$$

where $r_1 = \sqrt{(l - z_1)^2 + a^2}$

Now subtracting (9-20) from (9-19) as done by Hallén, we have

$$I_z = \frac{-j}{30\Omega}\left[C_1(\cos \beta z - \cos \beta l) + \frac{1}{2} V_T(\sin \beta|z| - \sin \beta l)\right]$$
$$- \frac{1}{\Omega}\left\{I_y \ln\left[1 - \left(\frac{z}{l}\right)^2\right] + I_z\delta + \int_{-l}^{+l} \frac{I_{z_1}e^{-j\beta r} - I_z}{r}\,dz_1 \right.$$
$$\left. - \int_{-l}^{+l} \frac{I_{z_1}e^{-j\beta r_1}}{r_1}\,dz_1\right\} \qquad (9\text{-}21)$$

Proceeding with Hallén's solution, the quantity in the braces in (9-21) is taken as zero so that the current I_z, given by the terms in the brackets, becomes a zero-order approximation, designated I_{z0}. Thus,

$$I_{z0} = -\frac{j}{30\Omega}\left(C_1 F_{0z} + \frac{1}{2} V_T G_{0z}\right) \qquad (9\text{-}22)$$

where the following symbols have been introduced

$$\begin{aligned}F_{0z} &= \cos \beta z - \cos \beta l \\ G_{0z} &= \sin \beta|z| - \sin \beta l\end{aligned} \qquad (9\text{-}23)$$

Substituting I_{z0}, as given by (9-22), for I_z on the right side of (9-21), a first-order approximation I_{z1} can be obtained for the current. That is,

$$I_{z1} = -\frac{j}{30\Omega}\left[C_1\left(F_{0z} + \frac{F_{1z}}{\Omega}\right) + \frac{1}{2} V_T\left(G_{0z} + \frac{G_{1z}}{\Omega}\right)\right] \qquad (9\text{-}24)$$

where $F_{1z} = F_1(z) - F_1(l)$

$$F_1(z) = -F_{0z} \ln\left[1 - \left(\frac{z}{l}\right)^2\right] + F_{0z}\delta - \int_{-l}^{+l} \frac{F_{0z_1}e^{-j\beta r} - F_{0z}}{r}\,dz_1$$

$$F_1(l) = -\int_{-l}^{+l} \frac{F_{0z_1}e^{-j\beta r_1}}{r_1}\,dz_1$$

$$G_{1z} = G_1(z) - G_1(l)$$

$G_1(z)$ is the same as $F_1(z)$ with G substituted for F and $G_1(l)$ is the same as $F_1(l)$ with G substituted for F.

If (9-24) is now substituted for I_z on the right side of (9-21), a second-order approximation for the current can be obtained. Continuing this process yields third-order and higher order approximations, and the solution for the antenna current I_z takes the form

$$I_z = \frac{-j}{30\Omega}\left[C_1\left(F_{0z} + \frac{F_{1z}}{\Omega} + \frac{F_{2z}}{\Omega^2} + \cdots\right)\right.$$
$$\left. + \frac{1}{2}V_T\left(G_{0z} + \frac{G_{1z}}{\Omega} + \frac{G_{2z}}{\Omega^2} + \cdots\right)\right] \quad (9\text{-}25)$$

Substituting I_z as given by (9-25) into (9-20) yields

$$C_1 = -\frac{1}{2}V_T\left[\frac{G_0(l) + (1/\Omega)G_1(l) + \cdots}{F_0(l) + (1/\Omega)F_1(l) + \cdots}\right] \quad (9\text{-}26)$$

Inserting C_1 from (9-26) in (9-25) and rearranging, the current is given by the asymptotic expansion,

$$I_z = \frac{jV_T}{60\Omega}\left[\frac{\sin\beta(l - |z|) + (b_1/\Omega) + (b_2/\Omega^2) + \cdots}{\cos\beta l + (d_1/\Omega) + (d_2/\Omega^2) + \cdots}\right] \quad (9\text{-}27)$$

where $b_1 = F_1(z)\sin\beta l - F_1(l)\sin\beta|z| + G_1(l)\cos\beta z - G_1(z)\cos\beta l$
$\quad d_1 = F_1(l)$
Neglecting b_2, d_2, and higher order terms, the first-order solution for the antenna current is

$$I_z = \frac{jV_T}{60\Omega}\left[\frac{\sin\beta(l - |z|) + (b_1/\Omega)}{\cos\beta l + (d_1/\Omega)}\right] \quad (9\text{-}28)$$

The quantities b_1 and d_1 have been calculated in terms of real and imaginary functions[1] by King and Harrison for several values of l and curves given.[2] This completes steps 8 through 11 of the outline of Sec. 9-2.

9-6. Length-Thickness Parameter Ω. The above development is based on the assumptions that $l \gg a$ and $\beta a \ll l$. The condition that $l \gg a$ will be arbitrarily taken to mean that

$$\frac{l}{a} \geq 60 \quad (9\text{-}29)$$

The ratio l/a equals the ratio of the total length of the cylindrical antenna to the diameter. Thus,

$$\frac{\text{Total length}}{\text{Diameter}} = \frac{2l}{2a} = \frac{l}{a}$$

When $l/a = 60$, the value of Ω from (9-17) is

$$\Omega = 2\ln\frac{2l}{a} = 2\ln 120 \simeq 9.6$$

[1] $b_1 = M_1{}^I + jM_1{}^{II}$ and $d_1 = A_1{}^I + jA_1{}^{II}$.
[2] Ronald King and C. W. Harrison, Jr., The Distribution of Current Along a Symmetrical Center-driven Antenna, *Proc. I.R.E.*, **31**, 548–567, October, 1943.

A graph of Ω as a function of the ratio of the total length to the conductor diameter is presented in Fig. 9-4.

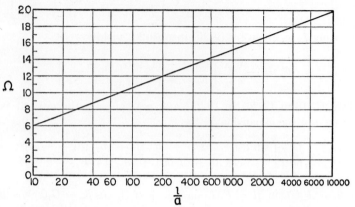

FIG. 9-4.　The coefficient Ω as a function of the total length to diameter ratio $(2l/2a)$ or length-to-radius ratio (l/a) of a cylindrical antenna.

Another factor which restricts l/a to large values $(l/a \geq 60)$ is that for asymptotic convergence of (9-27) Ω must exceed a certain value. If Ω is too small, the series may diverge.

9-7. Equivalent Radius of Antennas with Noncircular Cross Section. The above discussion in this and preceding sections deals with uniform cylindrical antennas, that is, antennas of circular cross section (radius = a). According to Hallén,[1] uniform antennas with noncircular cross section can also be treated by taking an equivalent radius. For square cross sections of side length g (Fig. 9-5), the equivalent radius is

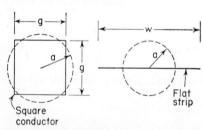

FIG. 9-5.　Conductors of square and flat cross section with equivalent circular conductors of radius a.

$$a = 0.59g$$

while for thin flat strips of width w the equivalent radius is

$$a = 0.25w$$

For any shape of cross section there exists an equivalent radius and hence a value of Ω. In all cases it is assumed that the cross section is uniform over the entire length of the antenna.

[1] Erik Hallén, Theoretical Investigations into the Transmitting and Receiving Qualities of Antennae, *Nova Acta Regiae Soc. Sci. Upsaliensis*, Ser. IV, **11**, No. 4, 1–44, 1938.

9-8. Current Distributions. The amplitude and phase of the current along cylindrical antennas of three lengths and two values of the total length-diamater ratio (l/a) are presented in Figs. 9-6, 9-7, and 9-8.

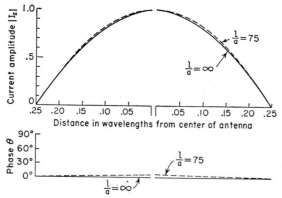

Fig. 9-6. Relative current amplitude and phase along a center-fed $\frac{1}{2}$-wavelength cylindrical antenna $(2l = \lambda/2)$ for total length-to-diameter ratios (l/a) of 75 and infinity (after King and Harrison). Distance from the center of the antenna is expressed in wavelengths.

Figure 9-6 is for a $\frac{1}{2}$-wavelength antenna $(2l = \lambda/2)$, Fig. 9-7 for a full-wavelength antenna $(2l = \lambda)$, and Fig. 9-8 for a $1\frac{1}{4}$-wavelength antenna $(2l = 1\frac{1}{4} \lambda)$. For each length the relative amplitude and phase of the current are presented for $\Omega = 10$ and $\Omega = \infty$ corresponding to total length-to-diameter ratios (l/a) of 75 and ∞. The amplitude curves are adjusted to the same maximum value, and all phase curves are adjusted to the same value at the ends of the antenna.

It is generally assumed that the current distribution of an infinitesimally thin antenna $(l/a = \infty)$ is sinusoidal, and that the phase is constant over a $\frac{1}{2}$-wavelength interval, changing abruptly by 180° between intervals. This behavior is illustrated by the solid curves in Figs. 9-6, 9-7, and 9-8.

The dashed curves illustrate the current amplitude and phase variation for $l/a = 75$ $(\Omega = 10)$. The difference between these curves and the solid curves $(l/a = \infty)$ is not large but is appreciable. The dashed curves $(l/a = 75)$ are from the distributions given by King and Harrison[1] as calculated from (9-28), the current being expressed in terms of its amplitude and the phase angle relative to a reference point. Thus,

$$I_z = |I_z| \underline{/\theta} \tag{9-30}$$

[1] Ronald King and C. W. Harrison, Jr., The Distribution of Current Along a Symmetrical Center-driven Antenna, *Proc. I.R.E.*, **31**, 548–567, October, 1943.

The effect of the length-thickness ratio on the current amplitude is well illustrated by Fig. 9-7 for a full-wavelength antenna.   When the antenna

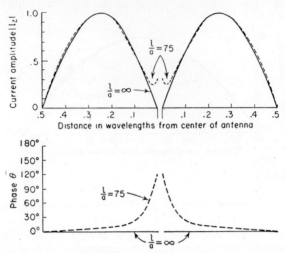

FIG. 9-7.   Relative current amplitude and phase along a center-fed full-wavelength cylindrical antenna ($2l = \lambda$) for total length-to-diameter ratios (l/a) of 75 and infinity (after King and Harrison).   Distance from the center of the antenna is expressed in wavelengths.

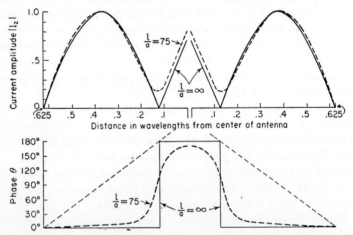

FIG. 9-8.   Relative current amplitude and phase along a center-fed $1\frac{1}{4}$-wavelength cylindrical antenna ($2l = 1\frac{1}{4}\lambda$) for total length-to-diameter ratios (l/a) of 75 and infinity (after King and Harrison).   Distance from the center of the antenna is expressed in wavelengths.

is infinitesimally thin, the current is zero at the center.   As the antenna becomes thicker, the current minimum increases and at the same time shifts slightly toward the end of the antenna. For still thicker antennas $(l/a < 75)$, Eq. (9-28) is no longer a good approximation for the current, but it might be expected that the above trend would continue.

The effect of the length-thickness ratio on the phase variation is well illustrated by Fig. 9-8 for a $1\frac{1}{4}$-wavelength antenna. When the antenna is infinitesimally thin, the phase varies as a step function, being constant over $\frac{1}{2}$ wavelength and changing by 180° at end of the $\frac{1}{2}$-wavelength interval (solid line, Fig. 9-8). This type of phase variation is observed in a pure standing wave. As the antenna becomes thicker, the phase shift at the end of the $\frac{1}{2}$-wavelength interval tends to become less abrupt (dashed curve for $l/a = 75$). For still thicker antennas $(l/a < 75)$, it might be expected that this trend would continue and for very thick antennas would tend to approach that of a pure traveling wave as indicated by the straight dashed lines in Fig. 9-8.

9-9. Input Impedance. The input impedance Z_T of a center-fed cylindrical antenna is found by taking the ratio of the input or terminal voltage V_T and the current I_T at the input terminals. That is,

$$Z_T = \frac{V_T}{I_T} = R_T + jX_T \tag{9-31}$$

where $I_T = I_z(0)$
$\quad R_T$ = terminal resistance
$\quad X_T$ = terminal reactance
Therefore, setting $z = 0$ in (9-28) and inserting this value of current in (9-31) yields Hallén's relation for the input impedance,

$$Z_T = -j60\,\Omega\left[\frac{\cos \beta l + (d_1/\Omega)}{\sin \beta l + (b_1/\Omega)}\right] \tag{9-32}$$

This is a first-order approximation for the input impedance. If the second-order terms are included [see (9-27)], Hallén's input-impedance expression has the form

$$Z_T = -j60\,\Omega\left[\frac{\cos \beta l + (d_1/\Omega) + (d_2/\Omega^2)}{\sin \beta l + (b_1/\Omega) + (b_2/\Omega^2)}\right] \tag{9-33}$$

This relation has been evaluated by Hallén[1] who has also presented the results in chart form.[2] Impedance spirals based on Hallén's data are presented in Fig. 9-9 for center-fed cylindrical antennas with ratios of total length to diameter (l/a) of 60 and 2,000. The half-length l of the

[1] Erik Hallén, On Antenna Impedances, *Trans. Roy. Inst. Technol.*, Stockholm, No. 13, 1947.

[2] Erik Hallén, "Admittance Diagrams for Antennas and the Relation Between Antenna Theories," Cruft Laboratory Tech. Rep. No. 46, Harvard University, 1948.

antenna is given along the spirals in free-space wavelengths. The impedance variation is that which would be obtained as a function of frequency for an antenna of fixed physical dimensions. The difference in the impedance behavior of the thinner antenna ($l/a = 2,000$) and of the thicker antenna ($l/a = 60$) is striking, the variation in impedance with frequency of the thicker antenna being much less than that of the thinner antenna.

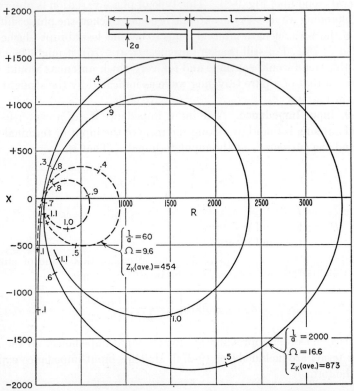

Fig. 9-9. Calculated input impedance ($R + jX$) in ohms for cylindrical center-fed antennas with ratios of total length to diameter ($2l/2a$) of 60 and 2,000 (after Hallén).

The impedance, given by (9-32) or (9-33), applies to center-fed cylindrical antennas of total length $2l$ and diameter $2a$. To obtain the impedance of a cylindrical stub antenna of length l and diameter $2a$ operating against a very large perfectly conducting ground plane, (9-32) and (9-33) are divided by 2. The impedance curve based on Hallén's calculations for a cylindrical stub antenna with an l/a ratio of 60 is given by the solid spiral in Fig. 9-10. The length l of the stub is indicated in free-space wavelengths along the spiral. The measured impedance variation of the same type of antenna ($l/a = 60$) as given by Dorne[1] is also shown in Fig. 9-10 by the dashed spiral. The agreement is good considering the fact that the measured curve includes the effect of the shunt capacitance at the gap and the small but finite antenna terminals.

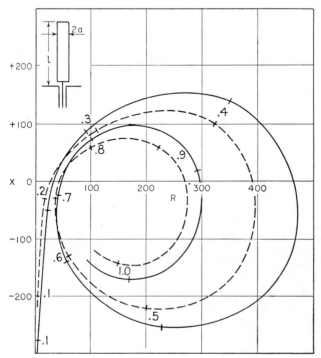

FIG. 9-10. Comparison of calculated (solid curve) and measured (dashed curve) input impedance ($R + jX$) in ohms for cylindrical stub antenna with ground plane for length-to-radius ratio (l/a) of 60.

The measured input impedance of a cylindrical stub antenna with an l/a ratio of 20 is shown in Fig. 9-11. Comparing this curve with the dashed curve of Fig. 9-10, it is apparent that the trend toward decreased impedance variation with smaller l/a ratio (increased thickness) suggested by Fig. 9-9 is continued to smaller l/a ratios. A measured impedance curve for $l/a = 472$ is also included in Fig. 9-11.[2]

[1] Chap. 4 by A. Dorne, "Very High Frequency Techniques," by Radio Research Laboratory Staff, McGraw-Hill Book Company, Inc., New York, 1947.

See also G. H. Brown and O. M. Woodward, Experimentally Determined Impedance Characteristics of Cylindrical Antennas, *Proc. I.R.E.*, **33**, 257–262, April, 1945.

D. D. King, The Measured Impedance of Cylindrical Dipoles, *J. Applied Phys.*, **17**, 844–852, October, 1946.

[2] The curves in Fig. 9-11 are based on data presented by Dorne.[1]

An antenna is said to be resonant when the input impedance is a pure resistance. On the impedance diagrams of Figs. 9-9, 9-10, and 9-11 resonance occurs where the spirals cross the $X = 0$ axis. At zero frequency all the impedance spirals start at $R = 0$ and $X = -\infty$. As the frequency increases, the reactance decreases and the resistance also increases although more slowly. The first resonance occurs when the length l of the antenna is about $\frac{1}{4}$ wavelength. The resistance at the first resonance is designated

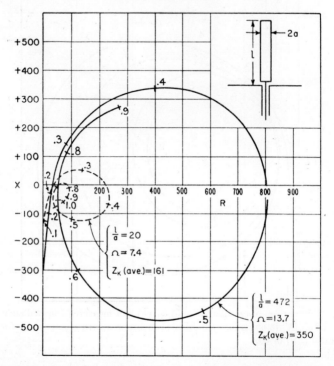

FIG. 9-11. Measured input impedance $(R + jX)$ in ohms of cylindrical stub antenna with ground plane for length-to-radius ratio (l/a) of 20 and 472.

R_1. As the frequency is increased, the length of the antenna becomes greater and the second resonance occurs when the length l is about $\frac{1}{2}$ wavelength. The resistance at the second resonance is designated R_2. At the third resonance (resistance $= R_3$), the antenna length l is about $\frac{3}{4}$ wavelength and at the fourth resonance (resistance $= R_4$) l is about 1 wavelength. As the frequency is increased indefinitely, an infinite number of such resonances can be obtained.

Since it is common practice to operate antennas at or near resonance, the values of the resonant resistances are of interest. Curves based on

Hallén's calculated graphs[1] are presented in Fig. 9-12 for the first four resonances of a cylindrical stub antenna with large ground plane as a function of the length-radius ratio (l/a). The lowest value of l/a for which Hallén gives data is 60, since the accuracy of (9-33) tends to deteriorate for smaller l/a values. Thus, the solid part of the curves

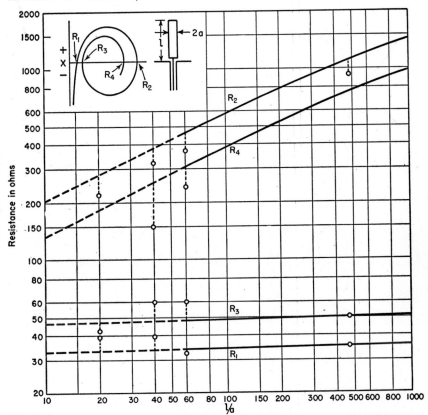

FIG. 9-12. Resonant resistance of cylindrical stub antenna with ground plane as a function of the length-to-radius ratio (l/a). Curves are shown for the first four resonances. For cylindrical center-fed antennas (total length $2l$) multiply the resistance by 2.

$(l/a > 60)$ are according to Hallén's calculated values. The dashed part of the curves are extrapolations to smaller values of l/a. The extrapolation is without theoretical basis but is probably not much in error. A few measured values of resonant resistance from Dorne's data[2] are shown as

[1] Erik Hallén, "Admittance Diagrams for Antennas and the Relation Between Antenna Theories," Cruft Laboratory Tech. Rep. No. 46, Harvard University, 1948.

[2] Chap. 4 by A. Dorne, "Very High Frequency Techniques," by Radio Research Laboratory Staff, McGraw-Hill Book Company, Inc., New York, 1947.

points in Fig. 9-12, the dotted lines indicating to which resonant resistance the points correspond.

Figure 9-12 illustrates the difference in the effect of antenna thickness on the resistance at odd and even resonances. The resistance at odd resonances (R_1, R_3, etc.) is nearly independent of the antenna thickness. The first resonant resistance R_1 is about 35 ohms, and the third resonant

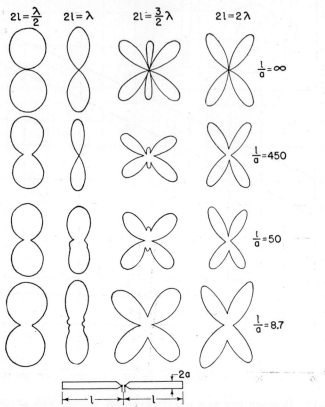

Fig. 9-13. Field patterns of cylindrical center-fed linear antennas of total length $2l$ as a function of the total length-to-diameter ratio (l/a) and also as a function of the total length ($2l$) in wavelengths.

resistance R_3 is about 50 ohms over a large range of l/a ratios. On the other hand, the antenna thickness has a large effect on the resistance at even resonances (R_2, R_4, etc.). The thicker the antenna, the smaller the resistance. For example, the second resonant resistance R_2 is about 200 ohms when $l/a = 10$ and increases to about 1,500 ohms at $l/a = 1,000$. The fourth resonant resistance behaves in a similar fashion, the values being somewhat less.

The difference in the resistance behavior at odd and even resonances is related to the current distribution. Thus, at odd resonances the antenna length l is an odd number of $\frac{1}{4}$ wavelengths long (approximately), and a current maximum appears at or near the input terminals. At even resonances the antenna length l is an even number of $\frac{1}{4}$ wavelengths long (approximately), and a current minimum appears at or near the input terminals. As indicated by the current distribution curves of Figs. 9-7 and 9-8, one of the most noticeable effects of an increase in antenna thickness is the increase of the current at current minima. Thus, when a current minimum is at or near the input terminals an increase in the antenna thickness raises the input current I_T for a constant input voltage V_T so that the resonant resistance given by the ratio V_T/I_T is reduced.

9-10. Patterns of Cylindrical Antennas. Formulas for calculating the far-field patterns of thin linear antennas were developed in Chap. 5. Although these relations apply strictly to infinitesimally thin conductors, they provide a first approximation to the pattern of even a relatively thick cylindrical antenna. This is illustrated by the patterns in Fig. 9-13 for center-fed linear cylindrical antennas of total length $2l$ equal to $\frac{1}{2}$, 1, $1\frac{1}{2}$, and 2 wavelengths. The calculated patterns for infinitesimally thin antennas are shown in the top row. Three of these patterns were given previously in Fig. 5-9. In the next three rows patterns measured by Dorne[1] are given for l/a ratios of 450, 50, and 8.7. The principal effect of increased antenna thickness appears to be that some of the pattern nulls are filled in and that some minor lobes are obliterated (note the patterns in the third column for $2l = 1\frac{1}{2}\ \lambda$).

9-11. The Thin Cylindrical Antenna. If the assumption is made that the cylindrical antenna is infinitesimally thin ($\Omega \rightarrow \infty$), the current distribution given by (9-27) or (9-28) reduces to

$$I_z = \frac{jV_T}{60\Omega} \frac{\sin \beta(l - |z|)}{\cos \beta l} \qquad (9\text{-}34)$$

Although Ω approaches infinity, the ratio V_T/Ω may be maintained constant by also letting V_T approach infinity. According to (9-34), the shape of the current distribution is sinusoidal. That is,

$$I_z = k \sin \beta(l - |z|) \qquad (9\text{-}35)$$

where k = a constant

The input impedance Z_T is the ratio V_T/I_T where I_T is the current at the terminals ($z = 0$). Thus from (9-34)

---

[1] Chap. 4 by A. Dorne, "Very High Frequency Techniques," by Radio Research Laboratory Staff, McGraw-Hill Book Company, Inc., New York, 1947.

$$Z_T = \frac{V_T}{I_T} = -j60\Omega \cot \beta l \qquad (9\text{-}36)$$

In (9-36) we may regard Ω as large but finite. The terminal impedance Z_T according to (9-36) is a pure reactance X_T. Equation (9-36) is identical to the relation for the input impedance of an open-circuited lossless transmission line of length βl (see Appendix Section 3) provided that 60Ω is taken equal to the characteristic impedance of the line. If, by analogy, 60Ω is taken equal to the average characteristic impedance Z_k (ave.) of the center-fed cylindrical antenna then, from the value of Ω given in Sec. 9-6,

$$Z_k \text{ (ave.)} = 60\Omega = 120 \ln \frac{2l}{a} \qquad (9\text{-}37)$$

This relation is of the same form as Schelkunoff's expression for the characteristic impedance Z_k of a thin biconical antenna given by (8-21) since for small cone angles $\theta_{hc} = a/l$ so that (8-21) becomes

$$Z_k = 120 \ln \frac{2l}{a} \qquad (9\text{-}38)$$

where a = end radius of the cone as shown in Fig. 9-14.

Fig. 9-14.   Biconical antenna of end radius a and length l.

The average characteristic impedance of a center-fed cylindrical antenna as given by Schelkunoff is

$$Z_k \text{ (ave.)} = 120\left(\ln \frac{2l}{a} - 1 \right) \qquad (9\text{-}39)$$

The average impedance of a cylindrical stub antenna with a large ground plane is one-half the value of (9-39).

As $l/a \rightarrow \infty$, (9-39) reduces to the form given in (9-37). However, for finite values of l/a the average characteristic impedance of a cylindrical antenna is the same as for a biconical antenna of the same length l but with an end radius a which is larger than the radius of the cylindrical conductor. This is suggested in Fig. 8-14a. For example, a cylindrical antenna with an l/a ratio of 500 has an average characteristic impedance equal to that of a biconical antenna of the same length with an end radius 2.8 times larger than the radius of the cylindrical conductor.

In Fig. 9-9 the calculated input impedance is presented for cylindrical center-fed antennas with total length-to-diameter ratios $(2l/2a = l/a)$ of 60 and 2,000. The average characteristic impedance of these antennas by (9-39) is 454 and 873 ohms, respectively. The curve for the l/a ratio of 60 [Z_k (ave.) = 454] has approximately the same form as the calculated impedance spiral in Fig. 8-12 for a 2.7° half-angle biconical antenna (Z_k = 450).

In Fig. 9-11 the measured input impedance is shown for cylindrical stub antennas with l/a ratios of 20 and 472. The average characteristic impedance of these antennas as given by one-half of (9-39) is 161 and 350 ohms, respectively. The curve for l/a = 20 [Z_k (ave.) = 161] is of the same general form (although displaced downward) as would be anticipated from Fig. 8-13 since a spiral for Z_k (ave.) = 161 should lie between those shown in Fig. 8-13 for Z_k = 146 and Z_k = 188.

9-12. Cylindrical Antennas with Conical Input Sections. It is common practice to construct cylindrical antennas with short conical sections at the input terminals as indicated at the bottom of Fig. 9-13. If the cylinders are of large cross section, the conical sections are particularly desirable in order to reduce the shunt capacitance at the gap. Since the measured impedance of an antenna includes the effect of the gap capacitance and the small but finite terminals, the measured impedances will differ more or less from the theoretical values. It is to be expected that measured values will agree better with calculated ones when end cones are used rather than when the ends of the cylinders are butted close together.

9-13. Antennas of Other Shapes: the Spheroidal Antenna. The solution of a boundary-value problem may be facilitated if the boundary can be specified by one coordinate of an appropriate coordinate system. A spherical antenna or one in the shape of an elongated ellipsoid of revolution (prolate spheroid) as in Fig. 9-15, is amenable to such treatment since the surface of the spheroid corresponds to a particular value of one coordinate of a spheroidal coordinate system. By varying the eccentricity of the ellipsoid, one may study the properties of the sphere at the one extreme of eccentricity and of a long thin conductor at the other extreme. This problem has been treated at length by Stratton and Chu[1] and by Page and Adams.[2]   Stratton and Chu give admittance and impedance

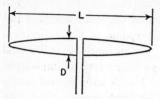

FIG. 9-15. Prolate spheroidal antenna.

curves for various length-to-diameter (L/D) ratios (see Fig. 9-15).   For long, thin ellipsoids the impedance characteristics are similar to those deduced by other methods.   The current distribution for thin $\frac{1}{2}$-wavelength spheroids is also found to be nearly sinusoidal.

A point of interest is that for spheroids of the order of $\frac{1}{2}$-wavelength long, the impedance variation with frequency decreases with decreasing L/D ratios (thicker spheroids).   That is to say, resonance with thick spheroids is broader than with thin ones.   This is in agreement with the well-known fact that thick antennas have broader band impedance characteristics than thin ones.

PROBLEMS

9-1. What is the initial relation used in developing Hallén's integral equation?

9-2. Indicate the principal steps required to arrive at the current distribution and terminal impedance of a cylindrical antenna by means of Hallén's integral equation.

[1] J. A. Stratton and L. J. Chu, Steady State Solutions of Electromagnetic Field Problems, *J. Applied Phys.*, **12**, 230–248, March, 1941.

[2] L. Page and N. I. Adams, The Electrical Oscillations of a Prolate Spheroid, *Phys. Rev.*, **53**, 819–831, 1938.

CHAPTER 10

SELF AND MUTUAL IMPEDANCES

10-1. Introduction. The impedance presented by an antenna to a transmission line can be represented by a two-terminal network. This is illustrated in Fig. 10-1 in which the antenna is replaced by an equivalent impedance Z connected to the terminals of the transmission line.[1] In designing a transmitter and its associated transmission line, it is convenient to consider that the antenna is simply a two-terminal impedance. This impedance into which the transmission line operates is called the *terminal* or *driving-point impedance*. If the antenna is isolated, that is, remote from the ground or other objects, and is lossless,[2] its terminal impedance is the same as the *self-impedance* of the antenna. This impedance has a real part called the *self-resistance* (radiation resistance) and an imaginary part called the *self-reactance*.

In case there are nearby objects, say, several other antennas, the terminal impedance can still be replaced by a two-terminal network. However, its value is determined not only by the self-impedance of the antenna but also by the mutual impedances between it and the other antennas and the currents flowing in them.

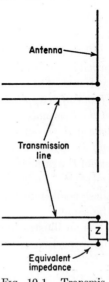

Fig. 10-1. Transmission line with antenna and with equivalent impedance.

---

[1] Because of the effect of the gap size at the center of the antenna and of the terminal arrangement, there may be some indefiniteness as to the value of the antenna impedance. Suppose, for example, that the antenna impedance Z is defined as that impedance which placed at the antenna terminals of the transmission line results in the same impedance at the left-hand end of the line (Fig. 10-1) as is actually measured. In general, this impedance is a function of the characteristics of the transmission line. Although this effect must sometimes be considered, it is usually negligible provided that the antenna gap or terminal spacing is small compared to the wavelength (gap of the order of 0.01 wavelength or less). See R. King and T. W. Winternitz, The Cylindrical Antenna with Gap, *Quart. Applied Math.*, **5**, 403–416, January, 1948.

[2] By lossless is meant that there is no Joule heating associated with the antenna. There may, of course, be radiation. If the antenna is not lossless, an equivalent loss resistance appears at the terminals in series with the self-resistance or radiation resistance.

251

In Chap. 5 an expression was developed for the radiation resistance (or self-resistance) of thin linear antennas. In the following sections this analysis is extended to yield expressions for both the self-resistance and the self-reactance. In addition, expressions are developed for the *mutual resistance* and mutual *reactance* of two thin linear antennas. These expressions will be used in Chap. 11 to find the driving-point impedance in an array of linear antennas. Even though the impedances apply strictly to infinitesimally thin antennas, they are useful in connection with practical types of cylindrical antennas, provided that the antennas are thin.

In developing the subject of antenna impedance, an important and much-used theorem is that of *reciprocity*. Accordingly, this topic is discussed first and then applied to the impedance problem.

10-2. Reciprocity Theorem for Antennas. The Rayleigh-Helmholtz reciprocity theorem[1] has been generalized by Carson[2] to include radiating systems. This theorem as applied to antennas may be stated as follows: *If an emf is applied to the terminals of an antenna A and the current measured at the terminals of another antenna B, then an equal current (in both amplitude and phase) will be obtained at the terminals of antenna A if the same emf is applied to the terminals of antenna B.* It is assumed that the emfs are of the same frequency and that the medium is linear, homogeneous, and isotropic. An important consequence of this theorem is the fact that under these conditions the transmitting and receiving patterns of an antenna are the same.

As an illustration of the reciprocity theorem for antennas, consider the following two cases.

Case 1. Let an emf V_a be applied to the terminals of antenna A as in Fig. 10-2a. This antenna acts as a transmitting antenna, and energy flows from it to antenna B, which may be considered as a receiving antenna, producing a current I_b at its terminals.[3] It is assumed that the generator supplying the emf and the ammeter for measuring the current have zero impedance, or if not zero, that the generator and ammeter impedances are equal.

[1] Lord Rayleigh, "The Theory of Sound," The Macmillan Company, New York, Vol. 1 (1877, 1937), pp. 98 and 150–157, and Vol. 2 (1878, 1929), p. 145.

[2] J. R. Carson, A Generalization of the Reciprocal Theorem, *Bell System Tech. J.*, **3**, 393–399, July, 1924.

J. R. Carson, Reciprocal Theorems in Radio Communication, *Proc. I.R.E.*, **17**, 952–956, June, 1929.

Stuart Ballantine, Reciprocity in Electromagnetic, Mechanical, Acoustical, and Interconnected Systems, *Proc. I.R.E.*, **17**, 929–951, June, 1929.

[3] Although the emf V_a and the current I_b are scalar space quantities, they are complex or vector quantities with respect to time phase. The term "phasor" is sometimes used to distinguish such a quantity from a true space vector.

Case 2. If an emf V_b is applied to the terminals of antenna B, then it acts as a transmitting antenna and energy flows from it to antenna A as in Fig. 10-2*b*, producing a current I_a at its terminals.

Now if $V_b = V_a$, then by the reciprocity theorem $I_a = I_b$.

The ratio of an emf to a current is an impedance. In Case 1 the ratio of V_a to I_b may be called the *transfer impedance* Z_{ab}, and in Case 2 the ratio V_b to I_a may be called the transfer impedance Z_{ba}. Then by the reciprocity theorem it follows that these impedances are equal. Thus,

$$\frac{V_a}{I_b} = Z_{ab} = Z_{ba} = \frac{V_b}{I_a} \tag{10-1}$$

In order to prove the reciprocity theorem for antennas, let the antennas and the space between them be replaced by a network of linear, passive,

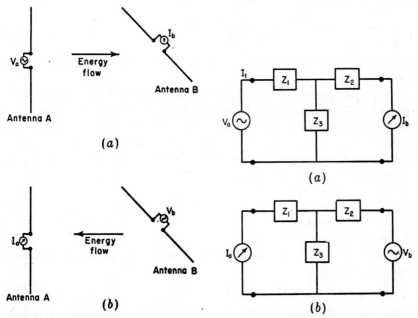

FIG. 10-2. Illustrations for reciprocity theorem.

FIG. 10-3. Equivalent circuits used in proof of reciprocity theorem.

bilateral impedances. Since any network can be reduced to an equivalent T section,[1] the antenna arrangement of Case 1 (see Fig. 10-2*a*) can be replaced by the network of Fig. 10-3*a*.

[1] W. L. Everitt, "Communication Engineering," McGraw-Hill Book Company, Inc., New York, 1937, p. 52.

The current through the meter is

$$I_b = I_1 \frac{Z_3}{Z_2 + Z_3} \tag{10-2}$$

where

$$I_1 = \frac{V_a}{Z_1 + [Z_2 Z_3/(Z_1 + Z_3)]} = \frac{V_a(Z_2 + Z_3)}{Z_1 Z_2 + Z_2 Z_3 + Z_3 Z_1} \tag{10-3}$$

Introducing (10-3) into (10-2) yields the current through the meter in terms of the emf V_a and the network impedances. Thus,

$$I_b = \frac{V_a Z_3}{Z_1 Z_2 + Z_2 Z_3 + Z_3 Z_1} \tag{10-4}$$

If the locations of the emf and current meter are interchanged, as in Fig. 10-3b, we obtain

$$I_a = \frac{V_b Z_3}{Z_1 Z_2 + Z_2 Z_3 + Z_3 Z_1} \tag{10-5}$$

Comparing (10-4) and (10-5), it follows that if $V_a = V_b$ then $I_a = I_b$, proving the theorem.

10-3. Self-impedance of a Thin Linear Antenna. In this section an *induced emf method*[1] as used by Carter is applied to the determination of the self-impedance of a thin linear antenna.[2] The antenna is center-fed with the lower end located at the origin of the coordinates as shown in Fig. 10-4. The antenna is situated in air or vacuum and is remote from other objects. Since the antenna is thin, a sinusoidal current distribution will be assumed with the maximum current I_1 at the terminals. Only lengths L which are an odd multiple of $\frac{1}{2}$ wavelength will be considered so that the current distribution is symmetrical, with a current maximum at the terminals. The current distribution shown in Fig. 10-4 is for the case where $L = \lambda/2$. The current at a distance z from the origin is designated I_z. Then,

$$I_z = I_1 \sin \beta z \tag{10-6}$$

---

[1] The relation of this method to the one used in Chap. 5, for the calculation of radiation resistance, is discussed in Sec. 10-10.

[2] P. S. Carter, Circuit Relations in Radiating Systems and Applications to Antenna Problems, *Proc. I.R.E.*, **20**, 1004–1041, June, 1932.

J. Aharoni, "Antennae," Oxford University Press. New York, 1946, pp. 174, 185.

A. A. Pistolkors, The Radiation Resistance of Beam Antennas, *Proc. I.R.E.*, **17**, 562–579, March, 1929.

R. Bechmann, Calculation of Electric and Magnetic Field Strengths of Any Oscillating Straight Conductors, *Proc. I.R.E.*, **19**, 461–466, March, 1931.

R. Bechmann, On the Calculation of Radiation Resistance of Antennas and Antenna Combinations, *Proc. I.R.E.*, **19**, 1471–1480, August, 1931.

Suppose that an emf V_{11} applied to the terminals of the antenna of Fig. 10-4 produces a current I_z at a distance z from the lower end. The ratio of V_{11} to I_z may be designated as the transfer impedance Z_{1z}. Thus,

$$Z_{1z} = \frac{V_{11}}{I_z} \tag{10-7}$$

Let the electric field parallel to the antenna at the point z be E_z. Then the emf dV_z induced by this field over a length dz of the antenna is $E_z\,dz$ or

$$dV_z = E_z\,dz \tag{10-8}$$

If the antenna is short-circuited and this in-finitesimal emf is applied at z, it will produce an infinitesimal current at the terminals which may be designated dI_1. The applied emf is equal in magnitude to the induced emf but opposite in sign. The ratio of the applied emf to dI_1 may be called the transfer impedance Z_{z1}. Then,

$$Z_{z1} = \frac{-dV_z}{dI_1} \tag{10-9}$$

Since the reciprocity theorem (Sec. 10-2) holds not only for two separate antennas but also for two points on the same antenna, it follows that the transfer impedances of (10-7) and (10-9) are equal. Therefore,

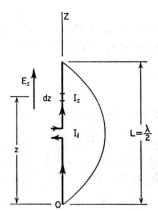

Fig. 10-4. Center-fed linear $\frac{1}{2}$-wavelength antenna.

$$\frac{V_{11}}{I_z} = Z_{1z} = Z_{z1} = \frac{-dV_z}{dI_1} = \frac{-E_z\,dz}{dI_1} \tag{10-10}$$

and

$$V_{11}\,dI_1 = -I_z E_z\,dz \tag{10-11}$$

The terminal impedance Z_{11} of the antenna is given by the ratio of V_{11} to the total terminal current I_1. Thus,

$$Z_{11} = \frac{V_{11}}{I_1} \tag{10-12}$$

The impedance Z_{11} is a constant and is independent of the current amplitude. This follows from the fact that the system is linear. Therefore, Z_{11} can also be expressed as the ratio of an infinitesimal emf dV_{11} at the terminals to an infinitesimal current dI_1 at the terminals, or

$$Z_{11} = \frac{V_{11}}{I_1} = \frac{dV_{11}}{dI_1} \tag{10-13}$$

from which

$$V_{11} \, dI_1 = I_1 \, dV_{11} \tag{10-14}$$

Substituting (10-14) into (10-11),

$$dV_{11} = \frac{-I_z}{I_1} E_z \, dz \tag{10-15}$$

Integrating (10-15) over the length of the antenna, we obtain

$$V_{11} = -\frac{1}{I_1} \int_0^L I_z E_z \, dz \tag{10-16}$$

where V_{11} is the emf which must be applied at the terminals to produce the current I_1 at the terminals. The terminal impedance Z_{11} is then

$$Z_{11} = \frac{V_{11}}{I_1} = -\frac{1}{I_1^2} \int_0^L I_z E_z \, dz \tag{10-17}$$

Since the antenna is isolated, this impedance is called the *self-impedance*. In (10-17) E_z is the z component of the electric field *at* the antenna caused by its own current. It will be convenient to indicate explicitly this type of field by the symbol E_{11} in place of E_z. Introducing also the value I_z from (10-6) into (10-17), we obtain for the self-impedance

$$Z_{11} = -\frac{1}{I_1} \int_0^L E_{11} \sin \beta z \, dz \tag{10-18}$$

To evaluate (10-18), it is first necessary to derive an expression for the field E_{11} along the antenna produced by its own current. Substituting this into (10-18) and integrating, it is possible to obtain an expression which can be evaluated numerically. The steps in this development are given in the following paragraphs.

If expressions can be written for the retarded scalar potential V due to charges on the antenna and for the retarded vector potential **A** due to currents on the antenna, then the electric field everywhere is derivable from the relation

$$\mathbf{E} = -\nabla V - j\omega \mathbf{A} \tag{10-19}$$

More particularly the z component of **E** is given by

$$E_z^\cdot = -\frac{\partial V}{\partial z} - j\omega A_z \tag{10-20}$$

Referring to Fig. 10-5, let the antenna be coincident with the z axis. A point on the antenna is designated z_1. A point P in space is given in cylindrical coordinates by ρ, ϕ, z. Other distances are as shown. Only lengths L which are an odd multiple of $\frac{1}{2}$ wavelength will be considered. Thus,

$$L = \frac{n\lambda}{2}$$

where $n = 1, 3, 5 \cdots$

The scalar potential V at any point is given by

$$V = \frac{1}{4\pi\epsilon_0} \iiint \frac{\rho}{r}\, d\tau \tag{10-21}$$

where ρ is the volume charge density, r the distance from the charge element to the point, and $d\tau$ is a volume element. From Fig. 10-5

$$r = \sqrt{\rho^2 + (z - z_1)^2}$$

In the case of a thin wire of length L, (10-21) reduces to

$$V = \frac{1}{4\pi\epsilon_0} \int_0^L \frac{\rho_L}{r}\, dz_1 \tag{10-22}$$

where ρ_L = the linear charge density on the wire

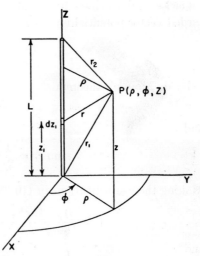

FIG. 10-5. Relation of coordinates to antenna.

The vector potential $\mathbf{A}$ at any point is given by

$$\mathbf{A} = \frac{\mu_0}{4\pi} \iiint \frac{\mathbf{J}}{r}\, d\tau \tag{10-23}$$

where $\mathbf{J}$ = the current density

In the case of a thin wire (10-23) reduces to

$$A_z = \frac{\mu_0}{4\pi} \int_0^L \frac{I_{z_1}}{r}\, dz_1 \tag{10-24}$$

where I_{z_1} = the current on the wire

By the continuity relation between current and linear charge density

$$\rho_L = -\int \frac{\partial I_{z_1}}{\partial z_1}\, dt \tag{10-25}$$

The current on the antenna is assumed to have a sinusoidal distribution as given by (10-6). Introducing the retarded time factor, we have for the retarded current

$$I_{z_1} = I_1 \sin \beta z_1\, e^{i\omega\left(t - \frac{r}{c}\right)} \tag{10-26}$$

Substituting (10-26) into (10-25) and performing the indicated operations, the retarded linear charge density is

$$\rho_L = \frac{j\beta I_1}{\omega} \cos \beta z_1 \, e^{i\omega\left(t - \frac{r}{c}\right)} \qquad (10\text{-}27)$$

Introducing (10-27) into (10-22) and noting that $\beta/\omega = 1/c$, the retarded scalar potential is

$$V = \frac{j I_1 e^{j\omega t}}{4\pi\epsilon_0 c} \int_0^L \frac{\cos \beta z_1 \, e^{-j\beta r}}{r} \, dz_1 \qquad (10\text{-}28)$$

Likewise, introducing (10-26) into (10-24), the z component of the retarded vector potential is

$$A_z = \frac{\mu_0 I_1 e^{j\omega t}}{4\pi} \int_0^L \frac{\sin \beta z_1 \, e^{-j\beta r}}{r} \, dz_1 \qquad (10\text{-}29)$$

By de Moivre's theorem

$$\cos \beta z_1 = \tfrac{1}{2}(e^{j\beta z_1} + e^{-j\beta z_1}) \qquad (10\text{-}30)$$

and

$$\sin \beta z_1 = \frac{1}{2j} (e^{j\beta z_1} - e^{-j\beta z_1}) \qquad (10\text{-}31)$$

Making these substitutions in (10-28) and (10-29)

$$V = \frac{j I_1 e^{j\omega t}}{8\pi\epsilon_0 c} \int_0^L \frac{e^{-j\beta(z_1+r)} + e^{j\beta(z_1-r)}}{r} \, dz_1 \qquad (10\text{-}32)$$

and

$$A_z = \frac{j\mu_0 I_1 e^{j\omega t}}{8\pi} \int_0^L \frac{e^{-j\beta(z_1+r)} - e^{j\beta(z_1-r)}}{r} \, dz_1 \qquad (10\text{-}33)$$

Equations (10-32) and (10-33) give the retarded scalar and vector potentials caused by current on the antenna with the assumed sinusoidal distribution. Substituting these equations into (10-20) yields an expression for the z component of the electric field everywhere. Thus,

$$E_z = -\frac{j I_1 e^{j\omega t}}{8\pi\epsilon_0 c} \int_0^L \frac{\partial}{\partial z} \left[\frac{e^{-j\beta(z_1+r)} + e^{j\beta(z_1+r)}}{r} \right] dz_1$$
$$+ \frac{\omega\mu_0 I_1 e^{j\omega t}}{8\pi} \int_0^L \left[\frac{e^{-j\beta(z_1+r)} + e^{j\beta(z_1-r)}}{r} \right] dz_1 \qquad (10\text{-}34)$$

$$E_z = -\frac{j I_1 e^{j\omega t}}{4\pi\epsilon_0 c} \left(\frac{e^{-j\beta r_1}}{r_1} + \frac{e^{-j\beta r_2}}{r_2} \right) \qquad (10\text{-}35)$$

where

$$r_1 = \sqrt{\rho^2 + z^2} \qquad (10\text{-}36)$$

and

$$r_2 = \sqrt{\rho^2 + (L - z)^2} \tag{10-37}$$

The factor $\frac{1}{4}\pi\epsilon_0 c \simeq 120\pi/4\pi = 30$. Also putting the time factor equal to its absolute value $e^{i\omega t} = 1$, and Eq. (10-35) becomes

$$E_z = -j30I_1\left(\frac{e^{-i\beta r_1}}{r_1} + \frac{e^{-i\beta r_2}}{r_2}\right) \tag{10-38}$$

At the antenna (10-36) and (10-37) become

$$r_1 = z \tag{10-39}$$

and

$$r_2 = L - z \tag{10-40}$$

Substituting these into (10-38) yields the value of the z component of the electric field E_{11} *at* the antenna due to its own current. Thus,

$$E_{11} = -j30I_1\left[\frac{e^{-i\beta z}}{z} + \frac{e^{-i\beta(L-z)}}{L - z}\right] \tag{10-41}$$

Introducing (10-41) into (10-18) we obtain the self-impedance Z_{11} of a thin linear antenna an odd number of $\frac{1}{2}$ wavelengths long. Hence,

$$Z_{11} = j30 \int_0^L \left[\frac{e^{-i\beta z}}{z} + \frac{e^{-i\beta(L-z)}}{L - z}\right] \sin \beta z \, dz \tag{10-42}$$

Applying de Moivre's theorem to $\sin \beta z$

$$Z_{11} = -15 \int_0^L \left[\frac{e^{-i2\beta z} - 1}{z} - \frac{e^{-i\beta L}(e^{i2\beta z} - 1)}{L - z}\right] dz \tag{10-43}$$

For $L = n\lambda/2$ where $n = 1, 3, 5, \ldots$, $e^{-i\beta L} = e^{-i\pi n} = -1$, so that Eq. (10-43) becomes

$$Z_{11} = -15 \int_0^L \left(\frac{e^{-i2\beta z} - 1}{z} + \frac{e^{i2\beta z} - 1}{L - z}\right) dz \tag{10-44}$$

or

$$Z_{11} = 15 \int_0^L \frac{1 - e^{-i2\beta z}}{z} dz + 15 \int_0^L \frac{1 - e^{i2\beta z}}{L - z} dz \tag{10-45}$$

In the first integral let

$$u = 2\beta z \quad \text{or} \quad du = 2\beta \, dz$$

The upper limit $z = L$ becomes $u = 2\beta L = 2\pi n$, while the lower limit is unchanged. The first integral then transforms to

$$15 \int_0^{2\pi n} \frac{1 - e^{-iu}}{u} du \tag{10-46}$$

In the second integral let

$$v = 2\beta(L - z) \qquad \text{or} \qquad dv = -2\beta\,dz$$

The upper limit becomes zero while the lower limit becomes $2\pi n$. The second integral then transforms to

$$-15 \int_{2\pi n}^{0} \frac{1 - e^{i(2\pi n - v)}}{v}\,dv = 15 \int_{0}^{2\pi n} \frac{1 - e^{-iv}}{v}\,dv \qquad (10\text{-}47)$$

Equations (10-46) and (10-47) are definite integrals of identical form. Since their limits are the same, they are equal. Therefore (10-45) becomes

$$Z_{11} = 30 \int_{0}^{2\pi n} \frac{1 - e^{-iu}}{u}\,du \qquad (10\text{-}48)$$

If we now put $w = ju$, (10-48) transforms to

$$Z_{11} = 30 \int_{0}^{j2\pi n} \frac{1 - e^{-w}}{w}\,dw \qquad (10\text{-}49)$$

The integral in (10-49) is an exponential integral with imaginary argument. It is designated by Ein (jy). Thus, [1]

$$\text{Ein}\,(jy) = \int_{0}^{iy} \frac{1 - e^{-w}}{w}\,dw \qquad (10\text{-}50)$$

In our case $y = 2\pi n$. This integral can be expressed in terms of the sine and cosine integrals discussed in Sec. 5-6. Thus,

$$\text{Ein}\,(jy) = \text{Cin}\,(y) + j\,\text{Si}\,(y) \qquad (10\text{-}51)$$

or

$$\text{Ein}\,(jy) = 0.577 + \ln y - \text{Ci}\,(y) + j\,\text{Si}\,(y) \qquad (10\text{-}52)$$

Hence, the self-impedance is

$$Z_{11} = R_{11} + jX_{11} = 30\,[\text{Cin}\,(2\pi n) + j\,\text{Si}\,(2\pi n)] \qquad (10\text{-}53)$$

or

$$Z_{11} = 30\,[0.577 + \ln\,(2\pi n) - \text{Ci}\,(2\pi n) + j\,\text{Si}\,(2\pi n)] \qquad \text{ohms} \qquad (10\text{-}54)$$

The self-resistance is

$$R_{11} = 30\,\text{Cin}\,(2\pi n) = 30\,[0.577 + \ln\,(2\pi n) - \text{Ci}\,(2\pi n)] \qquad \text{ohms} \qquad (10\text{-}55)$$

and the self-reactance is

$$X_{11} = 30\,\text{Si}\,(2\pi n) \qquad \text{ohms} \qquad (10\text{-}56)$$

---

[1] See for example, S. A. Schelkunoff, "Applied Mathematics for Engineers and Scientists," D. Van Nostrand Company, Inc., New York, 1948, p. 377.

These equations give the impedance values for a thin linear center-fed antenna that is an odd number (n) of $\frac{1}{2}$ wavelengths long. The current distribution is assumed to be sinusoidal (Fig. 10-6). The values are those appearing at the terminals at the center of the antenna.

In the case of a $\frac{1}{2}$-*wavelength antenna* as shown in Fig. 10-6a, $n = 1$, and we have for the self-resistance and self-reactance

$$R_{11} = 30 \operatorname{Cin} (2\pi) \quad (10\text{-}57)$$

and

$$X_{11} = 30 \operatorname{Si} (2\pi) \quad (10\text{-}58)$$

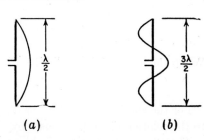

Fig. 10-6. One-half and three-halves wavelength antennas.

The value of (10-57) is identical with that given for the radiation resistance of a $\frac{1}{2}$-wavelength antenna, in Sec. 5-6, Eq. (5-109). Evaluating (10-57) and (10-58), see Appendix Section 19, we obtain for the self-impedance

$$Z_{11} = R_{11} + jX_{11} = 73 + j42.5 \text{ ohms} \quad (10\text{-}59)$$

Since X_{11} is not zero, an antenna an exact $\frac{1}{2}$ wavelength long is not resonant. To obtain a resonant antenna, it is common practice to shorten the antenna a few per cent to make $X_{11} = 0$. In this case the self-resistance is somewhat less than 73 ohms.

For a $\frac{3}{2}$-*wavelength antenna* as shown in Fig. 10-6b, $n = 3$, and the self-impedance is

$$Z_{11} = 30 \left[\operatorname{Cin} (6\pi) + j \operatorname{Si} (6\pi) \right]$$

or

$$Z_{11} = 105.5 + j45.5 \text{ ohms} \quad (10\text{-}60)$$

It is interesting that the self-reactance of center-fed antennas, an exact odd number of $\frac{1}{2}$ wavelengths long, is always positive since the sine integral Si $(2\pi n)$ is always positive. For large n the sine integral converges around a value of $\pi/2$ (see Fig. 5-11) which corresponds to a reactance of 47.1 ohms. It should be noted that for antenna lengths not an exact odd number of $\frac{1}{2}$ wavelengths the reactance may be positive or negative as illustrated for example by Fig. 9-9. However, the foregoing analysis of this section is limited to antennas that are an exact odd number of $\frac{1}{2}$ wavelengths long.

For large n, the self-resistance expression (10-55) approaches the value

$$R_{11} = 30[0.577 + \ln (2\pi n)] \quad (10\text{-}61)$$

since Ci $(2\pi n)$ approaches zero. Thus, the self-resistance continues to increase indefinitely with increasing n but at a logarithmic rate.

The more general situation, where the antenna length L is not restricted to an odd number of $\frac{1}{2}$ wavelengths, has also been treated.[1] The antenna is center-fed, and the current distribution is assumed to be sinusoidal (see Fig. 5-7). The self-resistance for this case is

$$R_{11} = 30\left[\left(1 - \cot^2\frac{\beta L}{2}\right)\text{Cin } 2\beta L + 4\cot^2\frac{\beta L}{2}\text{Cin }\beta L\right.$$

$$\left. + 2\cot\frac{\beta L}{2}\left(\text{Si } 2\beta L - 2\text{ Si }\beta L\right)\right] \quad \text{ohms} \quad (10\text{-}62)$$

When the length L is small, (10-62) reduces very nearly to

$$R_{11} = 5(\beta L)^2 \quad \text{ohms} \quad (10\text{-}63)$$

For the special case of $L = n\lambda/2$, where $n = 1, 3, 5 \ldots$, (10-62) reduces to the relation given previously by (10-55).

The above discussion of this section applies to balanced center-fed antennas. For a thin linear stub antenna of height l perpendicular to an infinite, perfectly conducting ground plane as in Fig. 10-7a, the self-impedance is one-half that for the corresponding balanced type (Fig. 10-7b). The general formula (10-62) for self-resistance can be converted for a stub antenna above a ground plane by changing the factor 30 to 15 and making the substitution $L = 2l$. The formulas (10-55) and (10-56) can be converted for a stub antenna with ground plane where the antenna is an odd number n of $\frac{1}{4}$ wave-

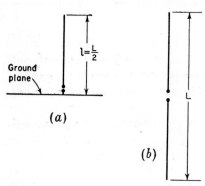

FIG. 10-7.   Stub antenna of length l at (a) and center-fed antenna of length L at (b).

lengths long by changing the factor 30 to 15. Thus, for a $\frac{1}{4}$-wavelength antenna perpendicular to an infinite perfectly conducting ground plane, the self-impedance is

$$Z_{11} = 36.5 + j21 \text{ ohms}$$

10-4. Mutual Impedance of Two Parallel Linear Antennas. The *mutual impedance* of two coupled circuits is defined in circuit-theory as the negative of the ratio of the emf V_{21} *induced* in circuit 2 by a current I_1 flowing in circuit 1 with circuit 2 open. Consider for example the coupled

[1] G. H. Brown and R. King, High Frequency Models in Antenna Investigations, *Proc. I.R.E.*, **22**, 457–480, April, 1934.

J. Labus, Recherische Ermittlung der Impedanz von Antennen, *Hochfrequenztechnik und Electroakustik*, 17, January, 1933.

circuit of Fig. 10-8 consisting of the primary and secondary coils of a transformer. The mutual impedance Z_{21} is then

$$Z_{21} = -\frac{V_{21}}{I_1} \qquad (10\text{-}64)$$

where V_{21} is the emf induced across the terminals of the open-circuited secondary by the current I_1 in the primary. The mutual impedance, so defined, is not the same as a transfer impedance such as discussed in connection with the reciprocity theorem in Sec. 10-2. In general, a *transfer impedance* is the ratio of an emf *impressed* in one circuit to the resulting current in another with all circuits closed. For example, if the generator in Fig. 8 is removed from the primary and is connected to the secondary terminals, the ratio of the emf V *applied* by this generator to the current I_1 in the closed primary circuit is a transfer impedance Z_T. Thus

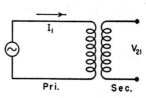

Fig. 10-8. Coupled circuit or transformer.

$$\frac{V}{I_1} = Z_T \qquad (10\text{-}65)$$

This impedance is not the same as the mutual impedance Z_{21} given in (10-64).

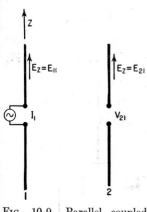

Fig. 10-9. Parallel coupled antennas.

Instead of the coupled circuit of Fig. 10-8, let us consider now the case of two coupled antennas 1 and 2 as shown in Fig. 10-9. Suppose a current I_1 in antenna 1 induces an emf V_{21} at the open terminals of antenna 2. Then the ratio of $-V_{21}$ to I_1 is the mutual impedance Z_{21}. Thus,

$$Z_{21} = \frac{-V_{21}}{I_1} \qquad (10\text{-}66)$$

If the generator is moved to the terminals of antenna 2, then by reciprocity the mutual impedance Z_{12} or ratio of $-V_{12}$ to I_2 is the same as before, where V_{12} is the emf induced at the open terminals of antenna 1 by the current I_2 in antenna 2. Thus,

$$\frac{-V_{21}}{I_1} = Z_{21} = Z_{12} = \frac{-V_{12}}{I_2} \qquad (10\text{-}67)$$

To calculate the mutual impedance, we need to know V_{21} and I_1. Let the antennas be in the z direction as shown in Fig. 10-9. The emf $-V_{11}$

induced in an antenna by its own current is indicated by (10-16). To obtain the emf V_{21} induced at the open terminals of antenna 2 by the current in antenna 1, we set $E_z = E_{21}$, $V_{11} = -V_{21}$, and $I_1 = I_2$ in (10-16). Then,

$$V_{21} = \frac{1}{I_2} \int_0^L I_z E_{21}\, dz \qquad (10\text{-}68)$$

where I_2 is the maximum current and I_z the value at a distance z from the lower end of antenna 2 with its terminals closed, and where E_{21} is the electric field along antenna 2 produced by the current in antenna 1. Assuming that this current distribution is sinusoidal as given by

$$I_z = I_2 \sin \beta z \qquad (10\text{-}69)$$

so that (10-68) becomes

$$V_{21} = \int_0^L E_{21} \sin \beta z\, dz \qquad (10\text{-}70)$$

then

$$Z_{21} = \frac{-V_{21}}{I_1} = -\frac{1}{I_1} \int_0^L E_{21} \sin \beta z\, dz \qquad (10\text{-}71)$$

This is the general expression for the mutual impedance of two thin linear, parallel, center-fed antennas with sinusoidal current distribution. We will consider first the situation where both antennas are the same length L, where L is an odd number of $\frac{1}{2}$ wavelengths long ($L = n\lambda/2$; $n = 1, 3, 5, \ldots$). A case of particular interest is where both antennas are $\frac{1}{2}$ wavelength long ($n = 1$). The relative positions of the antennas may be divided into three situations: side by side, collinear or end to end, and staggered or in echelon. These arrangements are illustrated in Fig.

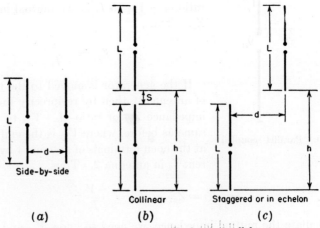

Side-by-side

Collinear

Staggered or in echelon

(a) (b) (c)

Fig. 10-10. Three arrangements of two parallel antennas.

10-10. Mutual-impedance expressions for the three arrangements are given in the following sections.

10-5. Mutual Impedance of Parallel Antennas Side by Side.[1] Let d be separation of the antennas. Referring to the arrangement of Fig. 10-10a and Fig. 10-11, the field E_{21} along antenna 2 produced by the current I_1 in antenna 1 is given by (10-38) where

$$r_1 = \sqrt{d^2 + z^2} \qquad (10\text{-}72)$$

and

$$r_2 = \sqrt{d^2 + (L - z)^2} \qquad (10\text{-}73)$$

Substituting this into (10-71), the mutual impedance becomes

$$Z_{21} = j30 \int_0^L \left[\frac{e^{-j\beta\sqrt{d^2+z^2}}}{\sqrt{d^2 + z^2}} \right.$$

$$\left. + \frac{e^{-j\beta\sqrt{d^2+(L-z)^2}}}{\sqrt{d^2 + (L - z)^2}} \right] \sin \beta z \, dz \qquad (10\text{-}74)$$

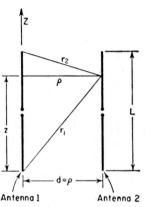

FIG. 10-11. Parallel coupled antennas with dimensions.

Carter has shown that upon integration of (10-74)

$$Z_{21} = 30\{2 \text{ Ei } (-j\beta d) - \text{Ei } [-j\beta(\sqrt{d^2 + L^2} + L)]$$
$$- \text{Ei } [-j\beta(\sqrt{d^2 + L^2} - L)]\} \qquad \text{ohms} \quad (10\text{-}75)$$

where the exponential integral

$$\text{Ei } (\pm jy) = \text{Ci } (y) \pm j \text{ Si } (y) \qquad (10\text{-}76)$$

Thus, the mutual resistance is,

$$R_{21} = 30\{2 \text{ Ci } (\beta d) - \text{Ci } [\beta(\sqrt{d^2 + L^2} + L)]$$
$$- \text{Ci } [\beta(\sqrt{d^2 + L^2} - L)]\} \qquad \text{ohms} \quad (10\text{-}77)$$

and the mutual reactance is

$$X_{21} = -30\{2 \text{ Si } (\beta d) - \text{Si } [\beta(\sqrt{d^2 + L^2} + L)]$$
$$- \text{Si } [\beta(\sqrt{d^2 + L^2} - L)]\} \qquad \text{ohms} \quad (10\text{-}78)$$

where

$$R_{21} + jX_{21} = Z_{21} = Z_{12} = R_{12} + jX_{12} \qquad (10\text{-}79)$$

[1] A number of mutual-impedance charts are presented by F. E. Terman, "Radio Engineers' Handbook," McGraw-Hill Book Company, Inc., New York, 1943, Sec. 11.

The mutual resistance and reactance calculated by (10-77) and (10-78) for the case of $\frac{1}{2}$-wavelength antennas $(L = \lambda/2)$ are presented by the

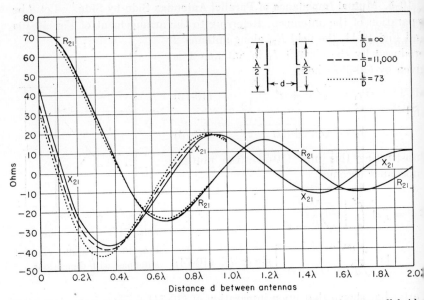

FIG. 10-12. Curves of mutual resistance (R_{21}) and reactance (X_{21}) of two parallel side by-side linear $\frac{1}{2}$-wavelength antennas as a function of distance between them. Solid curves are for infinitesimally thin antennas as calculated from Carter's formulas Dashed and dotted curves between 0 and 1.0 λ spacing are from Tai's data for antenna with L/D ratios of 11,000 and 73 respectively.

solid curves in Fig. 10-12 as a function of the spacing d. The mutual re sistance R_{21} is also listed in Table 10-1.

An integral-equation method for the calculation of the mutual im pedance of linear antennas has been presented by King and Harrison and by Tai.[2] The method is related to that discussed in Chap. 9. I this method the diameter of the antenna conductor is a factor. By wa of comparison, curves for the mutual resistance and reactance given b Tai are also shown in Fig. 10-12. The dashed curves are for a total length to-diameter ratio (L/D) of 11,000 (very thin antenna) and the dotte curves for a ratio of 73.

In Table 10-1 the quantity $R_{11} - R_{21}$, which is important in arra calculations, is also tabulated. When d is small, it has been shown b Brown[3] that this quantity is given approximately by the simple relation

[1] R. King and C. W. Harrison, Jr., "Mutual and Self Impedance for Coupled Antennas, *J. Applied Phys.*, **15**, 481–495, June, 1944.

[2] C. T. Tai, Coupled Antennas, *Proc. I.R.E.*, **36**, 487–500, April, 1948.

[3] G. H. Brown, private communication to the author, June 16, 1938.

$$R_{11} - R_{21} = 60\pi^2 \left(\frac{d}{\lambda}\right)^2 = 592.2 \left(\frac{d}{\lambda}\right)^2 \quad \text{ohms} \quad (10\text{-}80)$$

here λ = the free-space wavelength

This relation is accurate to within 1 per cent when $d \leq 0.05 \lambda$ and to within about 5 per cent when $d \leq 0.1 \lambda$.

TABLE 10-1

UTUAL RESISTANCE VS. SPACING FOR THIN CENTER-FED SIDE-BY-
SIDE $\frac{1}{2}$-WAVELENGTH ANTENNAS ($\beta L = 180°$), WITH SINUSOIDAL
CURRENT DISTRIBUTION

Spacing d	Mutual resistance R_{21}, ohms	Self minus mutual resistance $(R_{11} - R_{21})$, ohms
0.00	73.13	0.00
0.01	73.07	0.06
0.05	71.65	1.48
0.10	67.5	5.63
0.125	64.4	8.7
0.15	60.6	12.5
0.20	51.6	21.5
0.25	40.9	32.2
0.3	29.4	43.7
0.4	+ 6.3	66.8
0.5	−12.7	85.8
0.6	−23.4	96.5
0.7	−24.8	97.9
0.8	−18.6	91.7
0.9	− 7.2	80.3
1.0	+ 3.8	69.3
1.1	+12.1	61.0
1.2	+15.8	57.3
1.3	+12.4	60.7
1.4	+ 5.8	67.3
1.5	− 2.4	75.5
1.6	− 8.3	81.4
1.7	−10.7	83.8
1.8	− 9.4	82.5
1.9	− 4.8	77.9
2.0	+ 1.1	72.0

In the more general situation where the antenna length L is not re-
ricted to an odd number of $\frac{1}{2}$ wavelengths, the mutual resistance and

reactance are given by Brown and King[1] as

$$R_{21} = 30 \, \frac{1}{\sin^2 (\beta L/2)} \left\{ 2(2 + \cos \beta L) \, \mathrm{Ci} \, \beta d \right.$$

$$- \, 4 \cos^2 \frac{\beta L}{2} \left[\mathrm{Ci} \, \frac{\beta}{2} (\sqrt{4d^2 + L^2} - L) + \mathrm{Ci} \, \frac{\beta}{2} (\sqrt{4d^2 + L^2} + L) \right]$$

$$+ \, \cos \beta L [\mathrm{Ci} \, \beta(\sqrt{d^2 + L^2} - L) + \mathrm{Ci} \, \beta(\sqrt{d^2 + L^2} + L)]$$

$$+ \, \sin \beta L \left[\mathrm{Si} \, \beta(\sqrt{d^2 + L^2} + L) - \mathrm{Si} \, \beta(\sqrt{d^2 + L^2} - L) \right.$$

$$\left. \left. - \, 2 \, \mathrm{Si} \, \frac{\beta}{2} (\sqrt{4d^2 + L^2} + L) + 2 \, \mathrm{Si} \, \frac{\beta}{2} (\sqrt{4d^2 + L^2} - L) \right] \right\} \text{ ohms} \quad (10\text{-8}$$

and

$$X_{21} = 30 \, \frac{1}{\sin^2 (\beta L/2)} \left\{ -2(2 + \cos \beta L) \, \mathrm{Si} \, \beta L \right.$$

$$+ \, 4 \cos^2 \frac{\beta L}{2} \left[\mathrm{Si} \, \frac{\beta}{2} (\sqrt{4d^2 + L^2} - L) + \mathrm{Si} \, \frac{\beta}{2} (\sqrt{4d^2 + L^2} + L) \right]$$

$$- \, 2 \cos \beta L [\mathrm{Si} \, \beta(\sqrt{d^2 + L^2} - L) + \mathrm{Si} \, \beta(\sqrt{d^2 + L^2} + L)]$$

$$+ \, \sin \beta L \left[\mathrm{Ci} \, \beta(\sqrt{d^2 + L^2} + L) - \mathrm{Ci} \, \beta(\sqrt{d^2 + L^2} - L) \right.$$

$$\left. \left. - \, 2 \, \mathrm{Ci} \, \frac{\beta}{2} (\sqrt{4d^2 + L^2} + L) + 2 \, \mathrm{Ci} \, \frac{\beta}{2} (\sqrt{4d^2 + L^2} - L) \right] \right\} \text{ ohms} \quad (10\text{-8}$$

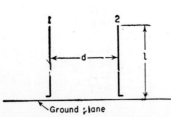

FIG. 10-13. Two coupled linear parallel stub antennas.

In the special case of $L = n\lambda/$ where n is odd, (10-81) and (10-8 reduce to the relations given previous. by (10-77) and (10-78).

The above relations of this sectic apply to balanced center-fed antenna The mutual impedance of two stub a tennas of height $l = L/2$ above an i finite, perfectly conducting grour plane as in Fig. 10-13 is one-half th; given by (10-77) and (10-78) or (10-81) and (10-82). These relations a converted to the ground-plane case by changing the factor 30 to 15 a making the substitution $L = 2l$.

[1] G. H. Brown and R. King, High Frequency Models in Antenna Investigation Proc. I.R.E., **22**, 457–480, April, 1934.

10-6. Mutual Impedance of Parallel Collinear Antennas. Let each antenna be an odd number of $\frac{1}{2}$ wavelengths long and arranged as in Fig. 10-10b. For the case where h is greater than L, Carter[1] gives the mutual resistance and reactance as

$$R_{21} = -15 \cos \beta h \left[-2 \text{ Ci } 2\beta h + \text{Ci } 2\beta(h - L) \right.$$
$$\left. + \text{Ci } 2\beta(h + L) - \ln\!\left(\frac{h^2 - L^2}{h^2}\right) \right]$$
$$+ 15 \sin \beta h [2 \text{ Si } 2\beta h - \text{Si } 2\beta(h - L) - \text{Si } 2\beta(h + L)] \qquad \text{ohms} \qquad (10\text{-}83)$$

and

$$X_{21} = -15 \cos \beta h [2 \text{ Si } 2\beta h - \text{Si } 2\beta(h - L) - \text{Si } 2\beta(h + L)]$$
$$+15 \sin \beta h \left[2 \text{ Ci } 2\beta h - \text{Ci } 2\beta(h - L) \right.$$
$$\left. - \text{Ci } 2\beta(h + L) - \ln\!\left(\frac{h^2 - L^2}{h^2}\right) \right] \qquad \text{ohms} \qquad (10\text{-}84)$$

Curves for R_{21} and X_{21} of parallel collinear $\frac{1}{2}$-wavelength antennas ($L = \lambda/2$) are presented in Fig. 10-14 as a function of the spacing s where $s = h - L$ (see Fig. 10-10b).

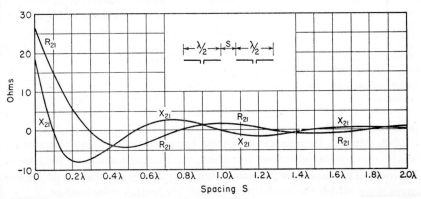

Fig. 10-14. Curves of mutual resistance (R_{21}) and reactance (X_{21}) of two parallel collinear infinitesimally thin $\frac{1}{2}$-wavelength antennas as a function of the spacing s between adjacent ends.

10-7. Mutual Impedance of Parallel Antennas in Echelon. For this case the antennas are staggered or in echelon as in Fig. 10-10c. Each

[1] P. S. Carter, Circuit Relations in Radiating Systems and Applications to Antenna Problems, *Proc. I.R.E.*, **20**, 1004–1041, June, 1932.

antenna is an odd number of $\frac{1}{2}$ wavelengths long. The mutual resistance and reactance of two such antennas are given by Carter[1] as

$$R_{21} = -15 \cos \beta h(-2 \text{ Ci } A - 2 \text{ Ci } A'$$
$$+ \text{ Ci } B + \text{ Ci } B' + \text{ Ci } C + \text{ Ci } C')$$
$$+15 \sin \beta h(2 \text{ Si } A - 2 \text{ Si } A'$$
$$- \text{ Si } B + \text{ Si } B' - \text{ Si } C + \text{ Si } C') \qquad \text{ohms} \qquad (10\text{-}85)$$

and

$$X_{21} = -15 \cos \beta h(2 \text{ Si } A + 2 \text{ Si } A'$$
$$- \text{ Si } B - \text{ Si } B' - \text{ Si } C - \text{ Si } C')$$
$$+15 \sin \beta h(2 \text{ Ci } A - 2 \text{ Ci } A'$$
$$- \text{ Ci } B + \text{ Ci } B' - \text{ Ci } C + \text{ Ci } C') \qquad \text{ohms} \qquad (10\text{-}86)$$

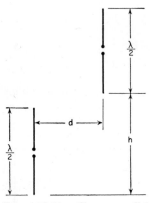

where $A \;\; = \beta(\sqrt{d^2 + h^2} + h)$
$A' = \beta(\sqrt{d^2 + h^2} - h)$
$B \;\; = \beta[\sqrt{d^2 + (h - L)^2} + (h - L)]$
$B' = \beta[\sqrt{d^2 + (h - L)^2} - (h - L)]$
$C \;\; = \beta[\sqrt{d^2 + (h + L)^2} + (h + L)]$
$C' = \beta[\sqrt{d^2 + (h + L)^2} - (h + L)]$

Values of the mutual resistance in ohms as calculated from (10-85) are listed in Table 10-2[2] as a function of d and h for the case where the antennas are $\frac{1}{2}$ wavelength long ($L = \lambda/2$) as indicated in Fig. 10-15.

Fig. 10-15. Two parallel linear $\frac{1}{2}$-wavelength antennas in echelon.

The staggered or echelon arrangement is the more general situation of which the side-by-side position (Sec. 10-5) and the collinear position (Sec. 10-6) are special cases.

10-8. Mutual Impedance of Other Configurations. There are many other antenna configurations for which the mutual impedance may be of interest. The variety is enormous, but two will be mentioned and references given which the reader may consult for further information.

1. *Parallel Antennas of Unequal Height.* This case has been treated by Cox.[3] His data apply specifically to stub antennas perpendicular to an infinite, perfectly conducting ground, but can be used with symmetrical

[1] Carter, *op. cit.*

[2] All but a few values are from a table by A. A. Pistolkors, The Radiation Resistance of Beam Antennas, *Proc. I.R.E.*, **17**, 562–579, March, 1929.

[3] C. R. Cox, Mutual Impedance Between Vertical Antennas of Unequal Heights, *Proc. I.R.E.*, **35**, 1367–1370, November, 1947.

TABLE 10-2

MUTUAL RESISTANCE AS A FUNCTION OF d AND h (FIG. 10-15) FOR THIN $\frac{1}{2}$-WAVELENGTH ANTENNAS IN ECHELON

Spacing d	Spacing h						
	0.0 λ	0.5 λ	1.0 λ	1.5 λ	2.0 λ	2.5 λ	3.0 λ
0.0 λ	+73.1	+26.4	−4.1	+1.8	−1.0	+0.6	−0.4
0.5 λ	−12.7	−11.8	−0.8	+0.8	−1.0	+0.5	−0.3
1.0 λ	+3.8	+8.8	+3.6	−2.9	+1.1	−0.4	+0.1
1.5 λ	−2.4	−5.8	−6.3	+2.0	+0.6	−1.0	+0.9
2.0 λ	+1.1	+3.8	+6.1	+0.2	−2.6	+1.6	−0.5
2.5 λ	−0.8	−2.8	−5.7	−2.4	+2.7	−0.3	−0.1
3.0 λ	+0.4	+1.9	+4.5	+3.2	−2.1	−1.6	+1.7
3.5 λ	−0.3	−1.5	−3.9	−3.8	+0.7	+2.7	−1.0
4.0 λ	+0.2	+1.1	+3.1	+3.7	+0.5	−2.5	−0.1
4.5 λ	−0.2	−0.9	−2.5	−3.4	−1.3	+2.0	+1.1
5.0 λ	+0.2	+0.7	+2.1	+3.1	+1.8	−1.4	−1.9
5.5 λ	−0.1	−0.6	−1.8	−2.9	−2.2	+0.5	+1.8
6.0 λ	+0.1	+0.5	+1.6	+2.6	+2.3	−0.1	−2.0
6.5 λ	−0.1	−0.5	−1.2	−2.3	−2.3	−0.5	+1.7
7.0 λ	+0.1	+0.4	+1.1	+2.1	+2.3	+0.9	−1.3
7.5 λ	0.0	−0.3	−1.0	−1.9	−2.1	−1.0	+0.7

center-fed antennas of twice the length by multiplying the resistance and reactance values by two.

2. *V or skew antennas.* Some antenna systems involve nonparallel linear radiators. The mutual impedance of such inclined antennas has been discussed by a number of writers,[1] but very few numerical data are available.

10-9. Comparison of Self-impedance Formulas. It is interesting to compare the formulas for self-resistance and reactance of thin linear center-fed antennas derived in this chapter with those for thin center-fed biconical antennas discussed in Chap. 8 for the case where the antennas are an odd number n of $\frac{1}{2}$ wavelengths long. This is done in Table 10-3. A case of particular interest is for antennas $\frac{1}{2}$ wavelength long ($n = 1$),

[1] P. S. Carter, Circuit Relations in Radiating Systems and Applications to Antenna Problems, *Proc. I.R.E.*, **20**, 1004–1041, June, 1932.

F. H. Murray, Mutual Impedance of Two Skew Antenna Wires, *Proc. I.R.E.*, **21**, 154–158, January, 1933.

F. B. Pidduck, "Currents in Aerials and High-frequency Networks," Oxford University Press, New York, 1946, p. 21.

TABLE 10-3

Case		Self-resistance R_{11}	Self-reactance X_{11}
Thin linear antenna (Carter)	Antenna odd no. n $\frac{1}{2}$ wavelengths long	30 Cin $(2\pi n)$	30 Si $(2\pi n)$
	$\frac{1}{2}$-wavelength antenna $(n = 1)$	73.13	42.5
Thin biconical antenna (Schelkunoff)	Antenna odd no. n $\frac{1}{2}$ wavelengths long	60 Cin $(n\pi) - 30[0.577$ $+ \ln \dfrac{n\pi}{2} - 2$ Ci $(n\pi)$ $+ $ Ci $(2n\pi)]$	60 Si $(n\pi) + 30$ Si $(2n\pi)$
	$\frac{1}{2}$-wavelength antenna $(n = 1)$	73.3	153.6

and the values for this case are also tabulated. The self-resistances are in close agreement for the two antennas, but the self-reactance of the thin biconical antenna is nearly four times as much as for the thin linear antenna.

10-10. A Discussion of the Methods Used for Calculating Antenna Impedances. In this and preceding chapters a number of methods for calculating the impedance of antennas of finite length have been discussed. In this section, a brief summary and comparison of these methods is presented.[1]

The methods may be classified into three principal types: (1) the boundary-value problem approach, (2) the transmission-line method, and (3) the Poynting vector method.

1. *The Boundary-value Problem Approach.* This method might be considered as the most basic approach. The fundamental field equations are expressed in terms of a coordinate system most appropriate to the antenna shape. A solution of this equation is then obtained which satisfies the boundary condition, usually that the tangential component of the electric field vanishes at the conductor surface. From this the current distribution is determined and the input impedance then obtained as the ratio of the applied terminal emf to the current at the terminals. No assumption is made as to the current distribution; it is determined by the solution.

The principal disadvantage of the method is that antenna shapes to

[1] A discussion is given by R. E. Burgess, Aerial Characteristics, *Wireless Engr.*, **21**, 154–160, April, 1944.

which it can be applied exactly are limited. In fact, the spheroidal antenna is the only shape which yields to an exact analysis. In this case, spheroidal coordinates are used and the antenna surface made to correspond to a fixed value of one coordinate. The free oscillations of a prolate spheroid (football shape, see Fig. 9-15) have been studied by Abraham.[1] Forced oscillations, as produced by a transmission line connected at the center, have been treated by Stratton and Chu[2] and by Page and Adams.[3] A good discussion of the general subject is given by Aharoni.[4]

Antennas are rarely made spheroidal in shape so that the results are not directly applicable to most practical types of antennas. An exception to this is the limiting case of a long, thin spheroidal antenna which may be considered as approximating a long, thin cylindrical conductor.

A direct attack on the cylindrical antenna as a boundary-value problem has been formulated by Hallén who obtained an integral equation in the antenna current I. This method is discussed in Chap. 9. The solution of this equation is a formidable problem. Approximate solutions have been obtained yielding the current distribution. The terminal impedance is found by taking the ratio of the emf applied at the antenna terminals to the terminal current. Results are most reliable for thin antennas. Both the resistive and reactive components of the self-impedance are obtained. Recently this method has been extended to finding the mutual impedance between antennas.

In Hallén's treatment the effect of the end cap on the cylindrical conductor is neglected by assuming that the antenna length is much greater than the diameter. Provided that the inside diameter of the hollow cylindrical conductor is sufficiently small that it cannot transmit a guided wave,[5] the difference in effect of an open or closed end is not large since the current flowing around an open end and into the interior of the hollow conductor vanishes in a short distance. The effect of neglecting the end caps is certainly no larger than that of changing the length of the antenna by an amount equal to the conductor diameter.

2. *The Transmission-line Method.* In this method, the antenna is treated as a terminated transmission line. This approach lends itself most appropriately to the biconical antenna with its uniform characteristic

---

[1] M. Abraham, Die electrischen Schwingungen um einen stabformingen Leiter, behandelt nach der Maxwellschen Theorie, *Ann. Physik*, **66**, 435–472, 1898.

[2] J. A. Stratton and I. J. Chu, Steady State Oscillations of Electromagnetic Field Problems, *J. Applied Phys.*, **12**, 230–248, March, 1941.

[3] L. Page and N. L. Adams, The Electrical Oscillations of a Prolate Spheroid, *Phys. Rev.*, **53**, 819–831, 1938.

[4] J. Aharoni, "Antennae," Oxford University Press, New York, 1946, pp. 62–86.

[5] The inside diameter would need to be at least 0.58λ in order to transmit a guided wave (TE_{11} mode) inside the antenna conductor even if this mode were to be excited.

impedance. This method has been used by Schelkunoff[1] and is discussed in Chap. 8. The equivalent terminating impedance of a biconical antenna has been calculated by him for thin cones with an assumed sinusoidal current distribution. The classification of this approach as a "transmission-line method" is arbitrary. It may also be called a boundary-value method since the solution is subject to the boundary conditions that the tangential **E** along the cones is zero and that the fields at the boundary sphere are continuous.

3. *The Poynting Vector Method.* The general approach in this method is to integrate the Poynting vector over a surface enclosing the antenna or to perform an equivalent calculation. Two limiting cases of this method have been discussed: (a) where the surface of integration coincides with the surface of the antenna and (b) where the surface of integration is a sphere at a large distance from the antenna.

a. Integration over antenna surface. This is the so-called emf method employed by Carter, Pistolkors, Bechmann, and others and discussed in previous sections of this chapter. The terminal voltage V_{11} required to produce a terminal current I_1 in an infinitesimally thin antenna is shown to be

$$V_{11} = -\int_0^L E_z \sin \beta z \, dz \qquad (10\text{-}87a)$$

The terminal impedance is then

$$Z_{11} = \frac{V_{11}}{I_1} = -\frac{1}{I_1} \int_0^L E_z \sin \beta z \, dz \qquad (10\text{-}87b)$$

as in (10-18). The complex power supplied to the antenna is

$$W = \tfrac{1}{2} V_{11} I_1^* \qquad (10\text{-}88a)$$

where V_{11} is given by (10-87a) and I_1^* is the complex conjugate of I_1.

The power W in (10-88a) should also be given by the integral of the normal component of the complex Poynting vector over the antenna surface. Thus,

$$W = \frac{1}{2} \iint (\mathbf{E} \times \mathbf{H}^*) \cdot d\mathbf{s} \qquad (10\text{-}88b)$$

Assuming that the antenna is in the z direction, the element of surface $ds = dl \, dz$, where dl is a segment of arc on a circle enclosing the antenna as in Fig. 10-16. Hence, (10-88b) can be expressed

$$W = \frac{1}{2} \iint E_z' H_\phi^* \, dl \, dz \qquad (10\text{-}89a)$$

[1] S. A. Schelkunoff, "Electromagnetic Waves," D. Van Nostrand Company, Inc., New York, 1943.

Since E_z' is not a function of ϕ, and recalling that the line integral $\oint H_\phi^* \, dl$ equals the current I_z^* in the wire (Ampère's law), (10-89a) becomes

$$W = \frac{1}{2} \int E_z' I_z^* \, dz \qquad \text{watts} \qquad (10\text{-}89b)$$

Both E_z' and I_z^* are functions of z. Let it be assumed that I_z^* is a sinusoidal function of z, that is, $I_z^* = I_1^* \sin \beta z$, where I_1^* is the maximum or terminal current. Then

$$W = \frac{1}{2} I_1^* \int_0^L E_z' \sin \beta z \, dz \qquad (10\text{-}90)$$

Actually the perfectly conducting metal parts of an antenna can neither absorb nor radiate power so that the only contribution to (10-88b) would come from the gap at the center of the antenna. Thus, if the terminals are at a current maximum, (10-90) reduces to

$$W = \frac{1}{2} I_1^* \int_{\text{gap}} E_z' \, dz \qquad (10\text{-}91a)$$

where the gap or terminal voltage is equal to the line integral of the field across the gap. Therefore, provided

$$\int_{\text{gap}} E_z' \, dz = -\int_0^L E_z \sin \beta z \, dz = V_{11} \qquad (10\text{-}91b)$$

the complex power W obtained by the emf method is equivalent to that calculated by the Poynting vector integration and it is convenient to classify the emf method as a Poynting vector integration. The terminal impedance Z_{11} is the ratio of W to $\frac{1}{2}$ the square of the absolute value of the terminal current I_1 or

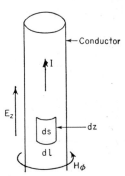

$$Z_{11} = \frac{2W}{|I_1|^2} = \frac{V_{11} I_1^*}{I_1 I_1^*} = \frac{V_{11}}{I_1} \qquad (10\text{-}91c)$$

The emf method yields both the resistive and reactive components of the self-impedance of thin antennas in terms of widely available tabulated functions. It is applicable not only to self-imped-ance but also to mutual-impedance calculations. The principal attractiveness of this method is its relative simplicity as contrasted with method 1 and also method 2.

FIG. 10-16. Antenna conductor and surface element.

b. *Integration over large sphere.* In this method the normal component of the Poynting vector is integrated over the surface of a large sphere enclosing the antenna. The power flowing through this sphere is all radiated power, the reactive power being confined to regions near the antenna. Hence, this method yields only the real or resistive component of the antenna impedance.

Examples of this method are given in Chap. 5 in the calculation of the radiation resistance of a thin linear antenna and also in Chap. 6 in finding the radiation resistance of thin loops. In this method a current distribution is assumed, and the radiated field pattern of this distribution is calculated. The average Poynting vector P_r at any point of the far field is given by

$$P_r = H^2 Z_0 \qquad \text{watts/meter}^2 \qquad (10\text{-}92)$$

where H is the rms magnetic-field intensity and Z_0 is the intrinsic impedance of the medium (= 377 ohms for free space). Integrating P_r over a large sphere yields the power W radiated. The terminal radiation resistance R is then given by the ratio of the power W to the rms terminal current I squared. Thus,

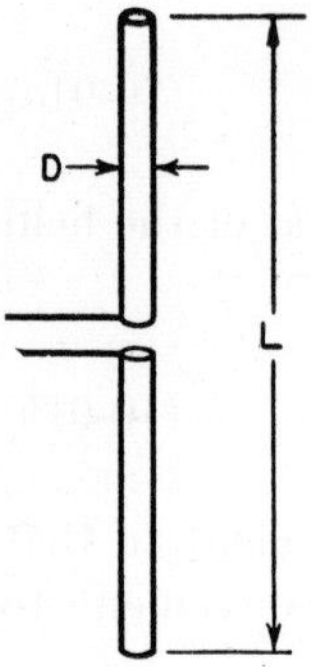

$$R = \frac{W}{I^2} = \frac{Z_0 \iint H^2 \, ds}{I^2} \qquad (10\text{-}93)$$

The accuracy of this method depends on how closely the assumed current distribution corresponds to the actual distribution. In the case of linear antennas a sinusoidal distribution is assumed. This is a good approximation if the antenna is thin and yields quite accurate values of resistance provided that the terminals are at or near a current maximum.

Fig. 10-17. Cylindrical center-fed antenna.

10-11. Simple Empirical Method. A very simple empirical method for calculating the approximate self-impedance of cylindrical center-fed antennas is outlined in this section.

The terminal resistance at first and third resonances is relatively independent of the ratio L/D of antenna length to diameter (Fig. 10-17). Hence, let us arbitrarily take the following values (see Fig. 9-12):

Resonance	Resistance, ohms	Antenna length, L
First, R_1.............	67	$L = 0.48\,A\lambda$
Third, R_3.............	95	$L = 1.44\,A\lambda$

where

$$A = \frac{L/D}{(L/D) + 1} \qquad (10\text{-}94)$$

Let the geometric mean of the resistances at an odd resonance and at the next higher even resonance be called the *natural resistance* R_n to distinguish it from the characteristic resistance. Then assuming R_n to be constant, the resistance at the second and fourth resonances is given by

$$R_2 = \frac{R_n^2}{R_1} = \frac{R_n^2}{67} \quad (L = 0.96A\lambda) \tag{10-95}$$

and

$$R_4 = \frac{R_n^2}{R_3} = \frac{R_n^2}{95} \quad (L = 1.92A\lambda) \tag{10-96}$$

where the natural resistance is given by the empirical relation

$$R_n = 150 \log_{10} \frac{L}{D} \quad \text{ohms} \tag{10-97}$$

where L is the total length and D the diameter of the antenna.

This gives four values which can be entered on an impedance diagram. An approximate impedance spiral for the antenna can then be sketched

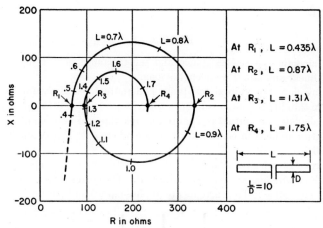

Fig. 10-18.   Impedance spiral for cylindrical antenna with length-to-diameter ratio (L/D) of 10 as constructed from empirical formula.

and lengths between resonances estimated as indicated in the example of Fig. 10-18.   This example is for the case of $L/D = 10$.

For *cylindrical stub antennas* mounted on large ground planes as in Fig. 10-19, the first and third resonant resistances are as follows:

Resonance	Resistance, ohms	Antenna length, l
First, R_1.............	34	$l = 0.24 A'\lambda$
Third, R_3.............	48	$l = 0.72 A'\lambda$

where

$$A' = \frac{l/r}{(l/r) + 1} \tag{10-98}$$

where l is the length of the stub antenna and r is the radius. The second and fourth resonant resistances are then

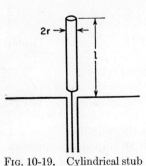

$$R_2 = \frac{(R_n')^2}{R_1} = \frac{(R_n')^2}{34} \qquad (l = 0.48A'\lambda) \quad (10\text{-}99)$$

and

$$R_4 = \frac{(R_n')^2}{R_3} = \frac{(R_n')^2}{48} \qquad (l = 0.96A'\lambda) \quad (10\text{-}100)$$

where the natural resistance for stub antennas is given by

$$R_n' = 75 \log_{10} \frac{l}{r} \quad \text{ohms} \quad (10\text{-}101)$$

FIG. 10-19. Cylindrical stub antenna.

PROBLEMS

10-1. Calculate the self-resistance and self-reactance of a thin, symmetrical center-fed linear antenna $\frac{5}{2}$ wavelengths long.

10-2. Calculate the mutual resistance and mutual reactance for two parallel side-by-side thin linear $\frac{1}{2}$-wave antennas with a separation of 0.15 wavelength.

10-3. Calculate the mutual resistance and reactance of two parallel thin linear $\frac{1}{2}$-wavelength antennas in echelon for the case where $d = 0.25\ \lambda$ and $h = 1.25\ \lambda$ (see Fig. 10-15).

10-4. Prove Brown's relation $R_{11} - R_{21} = 60\pi(d/\lambda)^2$ given in (10-80).

10-5. Three antennas are arranged as shown. The currents are of the same magnitude in all antennas. The currents are in phase in (a) and (c), but the current in

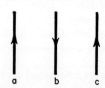

(b) is in antiphase. The self-resistance of each antenna is 100 ohms, while the mutual resistances are: $R_{ab} = R_{bc} = 40$ ohms and $R_{ac} = -10$ ohms. What is the radiation resistance of each of the antennas? The resistances are referred to the terminals, which are in the same location in all antennas.

CHAPTER 11

ARRAYS OF LINEAR ANTENNAS

11-1. Introduction. In discussing arrays of linear antennas a number of topics treated in previous chapters form an essential background. These topics are: arrays of point sources (Chap. 4), linear antennas (Chap. 5), and impedances of linear antennas (Chap. 10). It is assumed that the reader is already familiar with these subjects.

In this chapter arrays of thin linear antennas are analyzed in some detail. The *far-* or *radiation-field pattern,* the *driving-point impedance,* and the *gain in field intensity* are determined in that order for several different types of arrays. The method of analysis is general and can be applied to other arrays, the specific types discussed serving merely as examples. The simplest type of array will be considered first. This is an array of two driven ½-wavelength elements. The term "element" is taken to mean the basic unit antenna of which the array is constructed. It is assumed in this chapter that the elements are thin and linear.

11-2. Array of Two Driven ½-wavelength Elements. Broadside Case. Consider two center-fed ½-wavelength elements arranged side by side with a spacing d as in Fig. 11-1. Two special cases will be considered: the *broadside case*[1] treated in this section in which the two elements are fed with equal *in-phase* currents, and the *end-fire case*[2] (Sec. 11-3) in which the two elements are fed with equal currents in *opposite phase*. The more general case where the currents are equal in magnitude but in any phase relation is treated in Sec. 11-4.

11-2a. *Field Patterns.* The first part of the analysis will be to determine the absolute far-field patterns. It is convenient to obtain two pattern expressions, one for the horizontal plane and one for the vertical plane. Ordinarily, the relative patterns would be sufficient. However, the absolute patterns will be needed in gain calculations. Let the elements be

---

[1] In the so-called "broadside case" there is always a major lobe of radiation broadside to the array, although at large spacings there may be an end-fire lobe of equal magnitude (as for example when the spacing is 1 wavelength).

[2] In the so-called "end-fire case" the pattern always has zero radiation broadside. The maximum radiation is always end fire if the spacing is ½ wavelength or less. However, for greater spacings the maximum radiation is, in general, not end fire. Since spacings of ½ wavelength or less are of principal interest, the array may be referred to as an end-fire type.

vertical as shown in Fig. 11-2a. It is assumed that the array is in free space, that is, at an infinite distance from the ground or other objects. The field intensity $E_1(\phi)$ from a single element as a function of ϕ and at a large distance D $(D \gg d)$ in a horizontal plane ($\theta = 90°$ or x-y plane in Fig. 11-2a) is

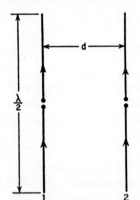

$$E_1(\phi) = kI_1 \qquad (11\text{-}1)$$

where k is a constant involving the distance D, and I_1 is the terminal current. Equation (11-1) is the absolute field pattern in the horizontal plane. It is independent of ϕ so that the relative pattern is a circle as indicated in Fig. 11-2b.

Next let the elements be replaced by isotropic point sources of equal amplitude. The pattern $E_{iso.}(\phi)$ as a function of ϕ in the horizontal plane for two such isotropic in-phase point sources is given by (4-6) as

FIG. 11-1. Broadside array of two in-phase ½-wavelength elements.

$$E_{iso.}(\phi) = 2E_0 \cos\left(\frac{d_r \cos \phi}{2}\right) \qquad (11\text{-}2)$$

where d_r = the distance between sources expressed in radians

That is,

$$d_r = \frac{2\pi d}{\lambda} \qquad (11\text{-}3)$$

Applying the principle of pattern multiplication, we may consider that E_0 is the field intensity from a single element at a distance D. Thus,

$$E_0 = E_1(\phi) = kI_1 \qquad (11\text{-}4)$$

Introducing (11-4) into (11-2) yields the field intensity $E(\phi)$ as a function of ϕ in the horizontal plane at a large distance D from the array, or

$$E(\phi) = E_1(\phi) \, 2 \cos\left(\frac{d_r \cos \phi}{2}\right) = 2kI_1 \cos\left(\frac{d_r \cos \phi}{2}\right) \qquad (11\text{-}5)$$

This expression may be called the absolute field pattern in the horizontal plane. The electric field at points in this plane is everywhere vertically polarized. The shape of this pattern is illustrated in Fig. 11-2c, and also partially in Fig. 11-2a, for the case where $d = \lambda/2$. The maximum field intensity is at $\phi = 90°$ or broadside to the array.

The field intensity $E_1(\theta)$ as a function of θ from a single ½-wavelength element at a distance D in the vertical plane (y-z plane in Fig. 11-2a) is from (5-81) given by

$$E_1(\theta) = kI_1 \frac{\cos\left[(\pi/2) \cos \theta\right]}{\sin \theta} \qquad (11\text{-}6)$$

The shape of this pattern is shown in Fig. 11-2d. It is independent of the angle ϕ. The pattern $E_{\text{iso.}}(\theta)$ in the vertical plane for two isotropic sources in place of the two elements is

$$E_{\text{iso.}}(\theta) = 2E_0 \qquad (11\text{-}7a)$$

Applying the principle of pattern multiplication, we put

$$E_0 = E_1(\theta) \qquad (11\text{-}7b)$$

so that the field intensity $E(\theta)$ in the vertical plane at a distance D from the array is

$$E(\theta) = 2kI_1 \frac{\cos\left[(\pi/2)\cos\theta\right]}{\sin\theta} \qquad (11\text{-}8)$$

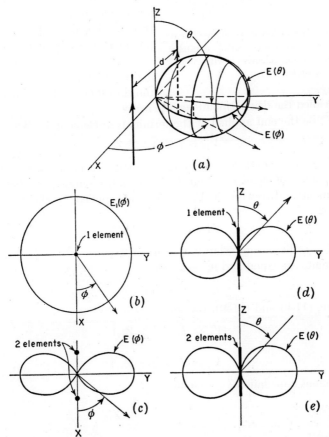

Fig. 11-2.   Patterns for broadside array of two linear in-phase $\frac{1}{2}$-wavelength elements with spacing d of $\frac{1}{2}$ wavelength.

This may be called the absolute field pattern in the vertical plane. This pattern has the same shape as the pattern for a single element in the vertical

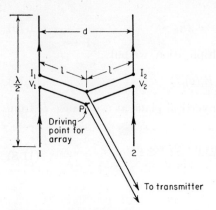

plane and is independent of the spacing. The relative pattern is presented in Fig. 11-2e and also partially in Fig. 11-2a. The relative three-dimensional field variation for the case where $d = \lambda/2$ is suggested in Fig. 11-2a. This pattern is actually bi-directional, only one-half being shown.

11-2b. *Driving-point Impedance.* Suppose that the array is energized by the transmission-line arrangement shown in Fig. 11-3. Two transmission lines of equal length l join at P to a third line extending to a transmitter. Let us find the driving-point impedance presented to the third line at the point P.[1] This

Fig. 11-3. Broadside array of two linear ½-wavelength elements with arrangement for driving elements with equal in-phase currents.

will be called the driving point for the array.

Let V_1 be the emf applied at the terminals of element 1. Then,

$$V_1 = I_1 Z_{11} + I_2 Z_{12} \qquad (11\text{-}9)$$

where I_1 is the current in element 1, I_2 the current in element 2, Z_{11} is the self-impedance of element 1, and Z_{12} is the mutual impedance between the two elements. Likewise, if V_2 is the emf applied at the terminals of element 2

$$V_2 = I_2 Z_{22} + I_1 Z_{12} \qquad (11\text{-}10)$$

where Z_{22} = the self-impedance of element 2
The currents are equal and in phase so

$$I_1 = I_2 \qquad (11\text{-}11)$$

Therefore, (11-9) and (11-10) become

$$V_1 = I_1(Z_{11} + Z_{12}) \qquad (11\text{-}12)$$

and

$$V_2 = I_2(Z_{22} + Z_{12}) \qquad (11\text{-}13)$$

The terminal impedance Z_1 of element 1 is

$$Z_1 = \frac{V_1}{I_1} = Z_{11} + Z_{12} \qquad (11\text{-}14)$$

[1] G. H. Brown, A Critical Study of the Characteristics of Broadcast Antennas as Affected by Antenna Current Distribution, *Proc. I.R.E.*, **24**, 48–81, January, 1936.
G. H. Brown, Directional Antennas, *Proc. I.R.E.*, **25**, 78–145, January, 1937.

and the terminal impedance Z_2 for element 2 is

$$Z_2 = \frac{V_2}{I_2} = Z_{22} + Z_{12} \tag{11-15}$$

Since the elements are identical

$$Z_{22} = Z_{11} \tag{11-16}$$

Therefore, the terminal impedances given by (11-14) and (11-15) are equal. That is,

$$Z_1 = Z_2 = Z_{11} + Z_{12} \tag{11-17}$$

Since $Z_1 = Z_2$ and $I_1 = I_2$ it is necessary that the emf V_1 applied at the terminals of element 1 be equal and in phase with respect to the emf V_2 applied at the terminals of element 2.

For the case where the spacing d is $\frac{1}{2}$-wavelength, the terminal impedance Z_1 of each element is

$$\begin{aligned} Z_1 = Z_{11} + Z_{12} &= R_{11} + R_{12} + j(X_{11} + X_{12}) \\ &= 73 - 13 + j(43 - 29) \\ &= 60 + j14 \quad \text{ohms} \end{aligned} \tag{11-18}$$

Suppose that the reactance of 14 ohms is tuned out at the terminals by a series capacitance.[1] The terminal impedance then becomes a pure resistance of 60 ohms. If the length l of each transmission line between the antenna terminals and P is $\frac{1}{2}$ wavelength, the driving-point impedance of the array at P is a pure resistance of 30 ohms. This value is independent of the characteristic impedance of the $\frac{1}{2}$-wavelength lines. However, a resistance of 30 ohms is too low to be matched readily by an open-wire transmission line. Therefore, a more practical arrangement would be to make l equal to $\frac{1}{4}$ wavelength. Suppose that we wish to have a driving-point resistance of 600 ohms. To do this, we let the characteristic impedance of each $\frac{1}{4}$-wavelength line be $\sqrt{1,200 \times 60} = 269$ ohms.[2] Each line transforms the 60 ohms to 1,200 ohms, and since two such lines are connected in parallel at P, the driving-point impedance for the array is a pure resistance of 600 ohms. This is the impedance presented to the line to the transmitter. For an impedance match this line should have a characteristic impedance of 600 ohms.

11-2c. *Gain in Field Intensity.* As the last part of the analysis of the

---

[1] It is often simpler to resonate the elements by shortening them slightly. This modifies the resistive component of the impedance and also alters the $E(\theta)$ field pattern, but to a first approximation these effects can usually be neglected.

[2] For the special case of a $\frac{1}{4}$-wavelength line, the general transmission-line formula (see Appendix) reduces to $Z_{in} = Z^2_0/Z_L$ where Z_{in} is the input impedance, Z_0 the characteristic impedance, and Z_L the load impedance. Thus, $Z_0 = \sqrt{Z_{in}Z_L}$.

array, let us determine the gain in field intensity for the array. This could be done by pattern integration as in Chap. 2, but with self- and mutual-impedance values available a shorter method is as follows.

Let the total power input (real power) to the array be W.* Assuming no heat losses, the power W_1 in element 1 is

$$W_1 = I_1^2(R_{11} + R_{12}) \tag{11-19}$$

the power W_2 in element 2 is

$$W_2 = I_2^2(R_{22} + R_{12}) \tag{11-20}$$

where I_1 and I_2 are rms currents.

But $R_{22} = R_{11}$ and $I_2 = I_1$. Making these substitutions and adding (11-19) and (11-20) to obtain the total power W, we have

$$W = W_1 + W_2 = 2I_1^2(R_{11} + R_{12}) \tag{11-21}$$

and

$$I_1 = \sqrt{\frac{W}{2(R_{11} + R_{12})}} \tag{11-22}$$

Suppose that we express the gain with respect to a single $\frac{1}{2}$-wavelength element as the reference antenna. Let the same power W be supplied to this antenna. Then assuming no heat losses, the current I_0 at its terminals is

$$I_0 = \sqrt{\frac{W}{R_{00}}} \tag{11-23}$$

where R_{00} is the self-resistance of the reference antenna.

In general, the *gain in field intensity*† of an array over a reference antenna is given by the ratio of the field intensity from the array to the field intensity from the reference antenna when both are supplied with the same power W. The comparison is, of course, made in the same direction from both the array and the reference antenna. In the present case it will be convenient to obtain two gain expressions, one for the horizontal plane and the other for the vertical plane.

* It is important that the antenna power W be considered constant. Most transmitters are essentially constant power devices which can be coupled to a wide range of antenna impedance. Until the antenna power was considered constant by G. H. Brown (*Proc. I.R.E.*, January, 1937) the advantages of closely spaced elements were not apparent. Prior to this time the antenna current had usually been considered constant.

† The *power gain* discussed in Chap. 2 is equal to the square of the *gain in field intensity*. The power gain is the ratio of the radiation intensities (power per unit solid angle) for the array and reference antennas, the radiation intensity being proportional to the square of the field intensity.

In the horizontal plane the field intensity $E_{\text{H.W.}}(\phi)$, as a function of ϕ, at a distance D from a single vertical center-fed $\frac{1}{2}$-wavelength reference antenna is of the form of (11-1). Thus,

$$E_{\text{H.W.}}(\phi) = kI_0 \tag{11-24}$$

where I_0 is the terminal current and "H.W." indicates "Half-Wavelength antenna." Substituting the value of I_0 from (11-23), we obtain

$$E_{\text{H.W.}}(\phi) = k\sqrt{\frac{W}{R_{00}}} \tag{11-25}$$

The field intensity $E(\phi)$ in the horizontal plane at a distance D from the array is given by (11-5). Introducing the value of the terminal current I_1 from (11-22) into (11-5) yields

$$E(\phi) = k\sqrt{\frac{2W}{R_{11} + R_{12}}} \cos\left(\frac{d_r \cos \phi}{2}\right) \tag{11-26}$$

The ratio of (11-26) to (11-25) gives the gain in field intensity of the array (as a function of ϕ in the horizontal plane) with respect to a vertical $\frac{1}{2}$-wavelength reference antenna with the same power input. This gain will be designated by the symbol $G_f(\phi)[\text{A./H.W.}]$ where the expression in the brackets is by way of explanation that the gain is that of the *Array* (A.) with respect to a *Half-Wavelength reference antenna* (H.W.)[1] in the same direction from both array and reference antenna. Thus,

$$G_f(\phi)\left[\frac{\text{A.}}{\text{H.W.}}\right] = \frac{E(\phi)}{E_{\text{H.W.}}(\phi)} = \sqrt{\frac{2R_{00}}{R_{11} + R_{12}}} \left| \cos\left(\frac{d_r \cos \phi}{2}\right) \right| \tag{11-27}$$

The absolute value bars || are introduced so that the gain will be confined to positive values (or zero) regardless of the values of d_r and ϕ. A negative gain would merely indicate a phase difference between the fields of the array and the reference antenna.

If the gain is the ratio of the *maximum* field of the array to the *maximum* field of the reference antenna it is designated by G_f (see Sec. 2-15).

The self-resistances $R_{00} = R_{11} = 73$ ohms. For the case where the spacing is $\frac{1}{2}$ wavelength, $d_r = \pi$ and $R_{12} = -13$ ohm so that (11-27) becomes

$$G_f(\phi)\left[\frac{\text{A.}}{\text{H.W.}}\right] = 1.56 \cos\left(\frac{\pi}{2} \cos \phi\right) \tag{11-28}$$

---

[1] Both the array and the $\frac{1}{2}$-wavelength reference antenna are assumed to be in free space. Thus, to be more explicit the expression $G_f(\phi)[\text{A.F.S./H.W.F.S.}]$, meaning the gain in field intensity of the *Array in Free Space* (A.F.S.) with respect to a *Half-Wavelength reference antenna in Free Space* (H.W.F.S.), might be used. However, to simplify the notation, the letters "F.S." will be omitted when *both* antennas are in free space.

In the broadside direction ($\phi = \pi/2$), the pattern factor becomes unity. The gain is then 1.56. This is the ratio of the maximum field of the array to the maximum field of the reference antenna (see Fig. 11-4). Hence, $G_f = 1.56$.

It is also of interest to find the angle ϕ_0 for which the gain is unity. For this condition (11-28) becomes

$$\cos\left(\frac{\pi}{2}\cos\phi_0\right) = 0.64 \qquad (11\text{-}29)$$

or

$$\phi_0 = \pm 56° \qquad \text{or} \qquad \pm 124°$$

These angles are shown in Fig. 11-4. The array has a gain of greater than unity in both broadside directions over an angle of 68°.

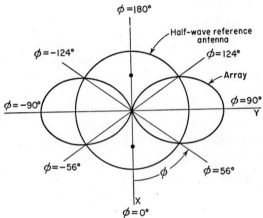

FIG. 11-4. Horizontal plane pattern of broadside array of two vertical in-phase $\frac{1}{2}$-wavelength elements spaced $\frac{1}{2}$ wavelength. The pattern of a single vertical $\frac{1}{2}$-wavelength reference antenna with the same power input is shown for comparison.

The gain as a decibel ratio is given by the relation

$$\text{Gain} = 20 \log_{10} G_f \qquad \text{db}$$

where G_f = the gain in field intensity
Thus, a field-intensity gain of 1.56 is equal to 3.86 db.

Turning our attention now to the gain in the vertical plane (y-z plane of Fig. 11-2a), the field intensity $E_{\text{H.W.}}(\theta)$ as a function of θ in this vertical plane at a distance D from a single vertical $\frac{1}{2}$-wavelength reference antenna with the same power input is of the form of (11-6). Thus,

$$E_{\text{H.W.}}(\theta) = kI_0 \frac{\cos\left[(\pi/2)\cos\theta\right]}{\sin\theta} \qquad (11\text{-}30)$$

where I_0 = the terminal current

Substituting its value from (11-23), we get

$$E_{\text{H.w.}}(\theta) = k\sqrt{\frac{W}{R_{00}}} \, \frac{\cos\left[(\pi/2) \cos\theta\right]}{\sin\theta} \qquad (11\text{-}31)$$

The field intensity $E(\theta)$ as a function of θ in the vertical plane at a distance D from the array is given by (11-8). Introducing the value of the terminal current I_1 from (11-22) into (11-8), we have

$$E(\theta) = k\sqrt{\frac{2W}{R_{11} + R_{12}}} \, \frac{\cos\left[(\pi/2) \cos\theta\right]}{\sin\theta} \qquad (11\text{-}32)$$

The ratio of (11-32) to (11-31) gives the gain in field intensity, $G_f(\theta)$[A./H.W.], of the array as a function of θ in the vertical plane over a vertical $\frac{1}{2}$-wavelength reference antenna with the same power input. Thus,

$$G_f(\theta)\left[\frac{\text{A.}}{\text{H.W.}}\right] = \frac{E(\theta)}{E_{\text{H.w.}}(\theta)} = \sqrt{\frac{2R_{00}}{R_{11} + R_{12}}} \qquad (11\text{-}33)$$

The gain is a constant, being independent of the angle θ. For the case where the spacing is $\frac{1}{2}$ wavelength, (11-33) becomes

$$G_f(\theta)\left[\frac{\text{A.}}{\text{H.W.}}\right] = 1.56 \text{ (or 3.86 db)} \qquad (11\text{-}34)$$

The shape of the pattern for the array and for the $\frac{1}{2}$-wavelength reference antenna is the same as shown in Fig. 11-5, but the ratio of the radius vectors in the same direction is a constant equal to 1.56.

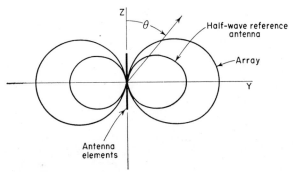

Fig. 11-5. Vertical-plane pattern of broadside array of two vertical in-phase $\frac{1}{2}$-wavelength elements spaced $\frac{1}{2}$ wavelength. The pattern of a single vertical $\frac{1}{2}$-wavelength reference antenna with the same power input is shown for comparison.

If the reference antenna is an isotropic source instead of a $\frac{1}{2}$-wavelength antenna, the gain in the vertical plane is a function of the angle θ. The maximum gain in field intensity of the array over an isotropic source with the same power input is $\sqrt{1.64}$ times greater than the voltage gain over a $\frac{1}{2}$-wavelength reference antenna. Thus, when the spacing is $\frac{1}{2}$ wavelength, the maximum gain in field intensity of the array with respect to an isotropic source is

$$G_f\left[\frac{\text{A.}}{\text{iso.}}\right] = 1.56 \times \sqrt{1.64} = 2.0 \ (\text{or } 6.0 \text{ db})$$

This value is in the broadside direction ($\phi = \theta = 90°$).

11-3. Array of Two Driven $\frac{1}{2}$-wavelength Elements. End-fire Case.
Consider an array of two center-fed vertical $\frac{1}{2}$-wavelength elements in free space arranged side by side with a spacing d and equal currents in opposite phase as in Fig. 11-6. The only difference between this case and the one discussed in Sec. 11-2 is that the currents in the elements are taken to be in the opposite phase instead of in the same phase. As in Sec. 11-2, the analysis will be divided into 3 subsections on the field patterns, driving-point impedance, and gain in field intensity.

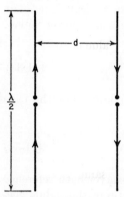

Fig. 11-6. End-fire array of two $\frac{1}{2}$-wavelength elements with currents of equal magnitude but opposite phase.

11-3a. *Field Patterns.* The field intensity $E_1(\phi)$ as a function of ϕ at a distance D in a horizontal plane (x-y or ϕ plane in Fig. 11-7a) from a single element is

$$E_1(\phi) = kI_1$$

where k = a constant involving the distance D
I_1 = the terminal current

Replacing the elements by isotropic point sources of equal amplitude, the pattern $E_{iso.}(\phi)$ in the horizontal plane for two such isotropic out-of-phase sources is given by (4-10) as

$$E_{iso.}(\phi) = 2E_0 \sin\left(\frac{d_r \cos\phi}{2}\right) \tag{11-35}$$

Applying the principle of pattern multiplication, we may consider that E_0 is the field intensity from a single element at a large distance D. Thus

$$E_0 = E_1(\phi) = kI_1 \tag{11-36}$$

and the field intensity $E(\phi)$ as a function of ϕ in the horizontal plane at a large distance D from the array is

$$E(\phi) = 2kI_1 \sin\left(\frac{d_r \cos\phi}{2}\right) \tag{11-37}$$

This is the absolute field pattern in the horizontal plane.   The electric field at points in this plane is everywhere vertically polarized.   The relative pattern for the case where the spacing d is $\frac{1}{2}$ wavelength is shown in Fig. 11-7b and also partially in Fig. 11-7a.   The maximum field in-

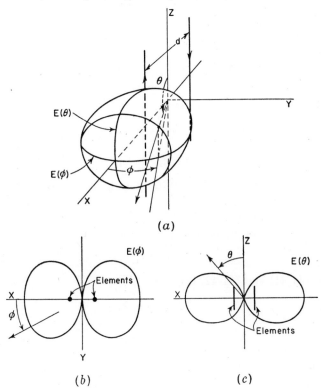

(a)

(b) (c)

FIG. 11-7.   Patterns for end-fire array of two linear out-of-phase $\frac{1}{2}$-wavelength elements with spacing d of $\frac{1}{2}$ wavelength.

tensity is at $\phi = 0°$ and $\phi = 180°$.   Hence, the array is commonly referred to as an "end-fire" type.

The field intensity $E_1(\theta)$ as a function of θ from a single $\frac{1}{2}$-wavelength element at a distance D in the vertical plane (x-z plane in Fig. 11-7a) is from (5-81) given by

$$E_1(\theta) = kI_1 \frac{\cos \left[(\pi/2) \cos \theta \right]}{\sin \theta} \tag{11-38}$$

The pattern $E_{iso.}(\theta)$ as a function of θ in the vertical plane for two isotropic sources in place of the two elements is from (4-10)

$$E_{iso.}(\theta) = 2E_0 \sin \left(\frac{d_r \sin \theta}{2} \right) \tag{11-39}$$

Note that θ is complementary to ϕ in (4-10), so $\cos \phi = \sin \theta$. Putting $E_0 = E_1(\theta)$ the field intensity $E(\theta)$ as a function of θ in the vertical plane at a large distance D from the array is

$$E(\theta) = 2kI_1 \frac{\cos \left[(\pi/2) \cos \theta\right]}{\sin \theta} \sin \left(\frac{d_r \sin \theta}{2}\right) \qquad (11\text{-}40)$$

This is the absolute field pattern in the vertical plane. The relative pattern is illustrated in Fig. 11-7c, and also partially in Fig. 11-7a, for the case where the spacing is $\frac{1}{2}$ wavelength. The relative three-dimensional field variation for this case $(d = \lambda/2)$ is suggested in Fig. 11-7a. This pattern is actually bidirectional, only one-half being shown.

11-3b. *Driving-point Impedance.* Let V_1 be the emf applied to the terminals of element 1. Then

$$V_1 = I_1 Z_{11} + I_2 Z_{12} \qquad (11\text{-}41)$$

Likewise, if V_2 is the emf applied to the terminals of element 2

$$V_2 = I_2 Z_{22} + I_1 Z_{12} \qquad (11\text{-}42)$$

The currents are equal in magnitude but opposite in phase so

$$I_2 = -I_1 \qquad (11\text{-}43)$$

Therefore, (11-41) and (11-42) become

$$V_1 = I_1 (Z_{11} - Z_{12}) \qquad (11\text{-}44)$$

and

$$V_2 = I_2 (Z_{22} - Z_{12}) \qquad (11\text{-}45)$$

The terminal impedance Z_1 of element 1 is

$$Z_1 = \frac{V_1}{I_1} = Z_{11} - Z_{12} \qquad (11\text{-}46)$$

and the terminal impedance Z_2 of element 2 is

$$Z_2 = \frac{V_2}{I_2} = Z_{22} - Z_{12} \qquad (11\text{-}47)$$

Therefore,

$$Z_1 = Z_2 = Z_{11} - Z_{12} \qquad (11\text{-}48)$$

or

$$\frac{V_1}{I_1} = \frac{V_2}{I_2} \qquad (11\text{-}49)$$

Since $I_2 = -I_1$ it follows from (11-49) that $V_2 = -V_1$. This means that the two elements must be energized with emfs which are equal in magnitude and opposite in phase. This may be done by means of a crossover in the transmission line from the driving point P to one of the elements as shown in Fig. 11-8. The length l of each line is the same.

For the case where the spacing between elements is $\frac{1}{2}$ wavelength, the terminal impedance of each element is

$$Z_1 = R_{11} - R_{12} + j(X_{11} - X_{12})$$
$$= 86 + j72 \quad \text{ohms} \quad (11\text{-}50)$$

Consider that the reactance of 72 ohms is tuned out by a series capacitance at the terminals of each element. The terminal impedance is then a pure resistance of 86 ohms. To obtain a driving-point resistance of 600 ohms, let the length l of the line from P to each element be $\frac{1}{4}$ wavelength and let the line impedance be $\sqrt{1,200 \times 86} = 322$ ohms. For an impedance match, the line from the driving point P to the transmitter should have a characteristic impedance of 600 ohms.

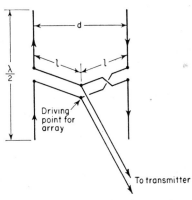

Fig. 11-8.   End-fire array of two linear $\frac{1}{2}$-wavelength elements with arrangement for driving elements with currents of equal magnitude but opposite phase.

11-3c. *Gain in Field Intensity.*   Using the same method as in Sec. 11-2c, the current I_1 in each element for a power input W to the array is given by

$$I_1 = \sqrt{\frac{W}{2(R_{11} - R_{12})}} \qquad (11\text{-}51)$$

It is assumed that there are no heat losses. The current I_0 in a single $\frac{1}{2}$-wavelength reference antenna is given by (11-23). The gain in field intensity $G_f(\phi)[\text{A./H.W.}]$ as a function of ϕ in the horizontal plane with respect to a $\frac{1}{2}$-wavelength reference antenna is obtained by substituting (11-51) in (11-37) and taking the ratio of this result to (11-25). This yields

$$G_f(\phi)\left[\frac{\text{A.}}{\text{H.W.}}\right] = \sqrt{\frac{2R_{00}}{R_{11} - R_{12}}} \left| \sin\left(\frac{d_r \cos\phi}{2}\right) \right| \qquad (11\text{-}52)$$

For a spacing of $\frac{1}{2}$ wavelength (11-52) reduces to

$$G_f(\phi)\left[\frac{\text{A.}}{\text{H.W.}}\right] = 1.3 \left| \sin\left[(\pi/2) \cos\phi\right] \right| \qquad (11\text{-}53)$$

In the end-fire directions ($\phi = 0°$ and $180°$) the pattern factor becomes unity, and the gain is 1.3 or 2.3 db. This is the gain G_f (see Fig. 11-9)

The gain in field intensity $G_f(\theta)[\text{A./H.W.}]$ as a function of θ in the vertical plane (x-z plane of Fig. 11-7a) with respect to a $\frac{1}{2}$-wavelength reference antenna is found by substituting (11-51) in (11-40) and taking the ratio of this result to (11-31) obtaining

$$G_f(\theta)\left[\frac{\text{A.}}{\text{H.W.}}\right] = \sqrt{\frac{2R_{00}}{R_{11} - R_{12}}} \left| \sin\left(\frac{d_r \sin\theta}{2}\right) \right| \qquad (11\text{-}54)$$

which is of the same form as the gain expression (11-52) for the horizontal plane (note that maximum radiation is in a direction $\theta = 90°$, $\phi = 0°$).

The gain in field intensity G_f of the array over an isotropic source with the same power input is $1.3 \times \sqrt{1.64} = 1.66$ (or 4.4 db).

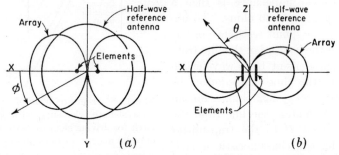

FIG. 11-9. Horizontal plane pattern (a) and vertical plane pattern (b) of end-fire array of two vertical $\frac{1}{2}$-wavelength elements with $\frac{1}{2}$-wavelength spacing. The patterns of a vertical $\frac{1}{2}$-wavelength reference antenna with the same power input are shown for comparison.

11-4. Array of Two Driven $\frac{1}{2}$-wavelength Elements. General Case with Equal Currents of Any Phase Relation.[1] In the preceding sections two special cases of an array of two $\frac{1}{2}$-wavelength driven elements have been treated. In one case the currents in the elements are in phase (phase difference $= 0°$), and in the other the currents are in opposite phase (phase difference $= 180°$). In this section the more general case is considered where the phase difference may have any value. As in the preceding cases the two $\frac{1}{2}$-wavelength elements are arranged side by side with a spacing d and are driven with currents of equal magnitude.

For the general phase case the radiation-field pattern in the horizontal plane (x-y plane of Fig. 11-7a) is from (4-20) given by

$$E(\phi) = 2kI_1 \cos\frac{\psi}{2} \qquad (11\text{-}55)$$

[1] For a more detailed discussion of this case and also of the most general case where the current amplitudes are unequal, see G. H. Brown, Directional Antennas, *Proc. I.R.E.*, **25**, 78–145, January, 1937.

where ψ is the total phase difference between the fields from element 1 and element 2 at a large distance in the direction ϕ (see Fig. 11-10). Thus,

$$\psi = d_r \cos \phi + \delta \qquad (11\text{-}56)$$

where δ = the phase difference of the currents in the elements

A positive sign in (11-56) indicates that the current in element 2 of Fig. 11-10 is advanced in phase by an angle δ with respect to the current in element 1. That is

$$I_2 = I_1 \,\underline{/\delta}$$

or $\qquad I_1 = I_2 \,\underline{/-\delta} \qquad (11\text{-}57)$

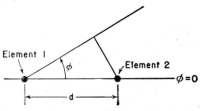

FIG. 11-10. Array of two side-by-side elements normal to plane of page.

The voltages applied at each element are

$$V_1 = I_1 Z_{11} + I_2 Z_{12} = I_1(Z_{11} + Z_{12} \,\underline{/\delta}) \qquad (11\text{-}58)$$

and

$$V_2 = I_2 Z_{22} + I_1 Z_{12} = I_2(Z_{22} + Z_{12} \,\underline{/-\delta}) \qquad (11\text{-}59)$$

The driving-point impedances of the elements are then

$$Z_1 = \frac{V_1}{I_1} = Z_{11} + Z_{12} \,\underline{/\delta} \qquad (11\text{-}60)$$

and

$$Z_2 = \frac{V_2}{I_2} = Z_{22} + Z_{12} \,\underline{/-\delta} \qquad (11\text{-}61)$$

The real part of the driving-point resistances are

$$R_1 = R_{11} + |Z_{12}| \cos(\tau + \delta) \qquad (11\text{-}62)$$

and

$$R_2 = R_{22} + |Z_{12}| \cos(\tau - \delta) \qquad (11\text{-}63)$$

where τ = the phase angle of the mutual impedance Z_{12} (that is, $\tau = \arctan X_{12}/R_{12}$ where $Z_{12} = R_{12} + jX_{12}$)

Therefore, the power W_1 in element 1 is

$$W_1 = |I_1|^2 R_1 = |I_1|^2 [R_{11} + |Z_{12}| \cos(\tau + \delta)] \qquad (11\text{-}64)$$

and the power W_2 in element 2 is

$$W_2 = |I_2|^2 [R_{22} + |Z_{12}| \cos(\tau - \delta)] \qquad (11\text{-}65)$$

Since $R_{11} = R_{22}$, the total power W is

$$\begin{aligned} W = W_1 + W_2 &= |I_1|^2 \{2R_{11} + |Z_{12}| [\cos(\tau + \delta) + \cos(\tau - \delta)]\} \\ &= 2|I_1|^2 (R_{11} + |Z_{12}| \cos \tau \cos \delta) \\ &= 2|I_1|^2 (R_{11} + R_{12} \cos \delta) \qquad (11\text{-}66) \end{aligned}$$

It follows that the gain in field intensity as a function of ϕ in the horizontal plane[1] of the array over a single $\frac{1}{2}$-wavelength element with the same power input is

$$G_f(\phi)\left[\frac{\text{A.}}{\text{H.W.}}\right] = \sqrt{\frac{2R_{11}}{R_{11} + R_{12}\cos\delta}} \left| \cos\left(\frac{d_r\cos\phi + \delta}{2}\right) \right| \quad (11\text{-}67)$$

A polar plot of (11-67) with respect to the azimuth angle ϕ gives the radiation-field pattern of the array in the horizontal plane, the ratio of the

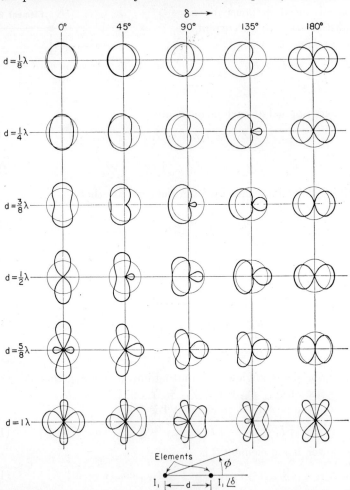

FIG. 11-11. Horizontal-plane field patterns of two vertical elements as a function of the phase difference δ and spacing d. (*After G. H. Brown.*) Both elements are the same length and have currents of equal magnitude. The circles indicate the field intensity of a single reference element of the same length with the same power input.

[1] This is the plane of the page in Fig. 11-10.

magnitude of the radius vector to a unit radius indicating the gain over a reference $\frac{1}{2}$-wavelength antenna. Brown[1] has calculated such patterns as a function of phase difference δ and spacing d_r. Examples of these are shown in Fig. 11-11.

The radiation-field pattern in the vertical plane containing the elements (in the plane of the page of Fig. 11-12) is

$$E(\theta) = 2kI_1 \cos\left(\frac{d_r \sin\theta + \delta}{2}\right) \frac{\cos\left[(\pi/2)\cos\theta\right]}{\sin\theta} \qquad (11\text{-}68)$$

Thus, the pattern in the vertical plane has the shape of the patterns of Fig. 11-11 multiplied by the pattern of a single $\frac{1}{2}$-wavelength antenna. The gain in the vertical plane over a vertical $\frac{1}{2}$-wavelength reference antenna with the same power input is then

$$G_f(\theta)\left[\frac{A.}{H.W.}\right] = \sqrt{\frac{2R_{11}}{R_{11} + R_{12}\cos\delta}} \left| \cos\left(\frac{d_r \sin\theta + \delta}{2}\right) \right| \qquad (11\text{-}69)$$

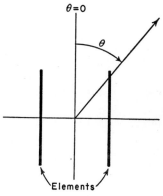

FIG. 11-12. Relation of polar angle θ in the plane of the elements.

It is often convenient to refer the gain to an isotropic source with the same power input. Since the gain of a $\frac{1}{2}$-wavelength antenna over an isotropic source is 1.64, the gain in field intensity as a function of θ in the vertical plane of a vertical $\frac{1}{2}$-wavelength antenna in free space over an isotropic source is

$$G_f(\theta)\left[\frac{H.W.}{iso.}\right]$$

$$= \sqrt{1.64} \left| \frac{\cos\left[(\pi/2)\cos\theta\right]}{\sin\theta} \right| \qquad (11\text{-}70)$$

The gain in field intensity in the vertical plane of the array over the isotropic source is then the product of (11-69) and (11-70) or

$$G_f(\theta)\left[\frac{A.}{iso.}\right] = G_f(\theta)\left[\frac{A.}{H.W.}\right] \times G_f(\theta)\left[\frac{H.W.}{iso.}\right]$$

$$= \sqrt{\frac{3.28R_{11}}{R_{11} + R_{12}\cos\delta}} \left| \cos\left(\frac{d_r \sin\theta + \delta}{2}\right) \frac{\cos\left[(\pi/2)\cos\theta\right]}{\sin\theta} \right| \qquad (11\text{-}71)$$

11-5. Closely Spaced Elements and Radiating Efficiency.[2] The end-fire array of two side-by-side, out-of-phase $\frac{1}{2}$-wavelength elements discussed in Sec. 11-3 produces substantial gains even when the spacing is decreased

[1] G. H. Brown, Directional Antennas, *Proc. I.R.E.*, **25**, 78–145, January, 1937.

[2] J. D. Kraus, Antenna Arrays with Closely Spaced Elements, *Proc. I.R.E.*, **28**, 76–84, February, 1940.

J. D. Kraus, The Corner Reflector Antenna, *Proc. I.R.E.*, **28**, 513–519, November, 1940.

to small values. As indicated by the $R_L = 0$ curve in the gain-vs.-spacing graph of Fig. 11-13a, the gain approaches 3.9 db at small spacings. At $\frac{1}{2}$ wavelength spacing the gain is 2.3 db. This curve is calculated from (11-52) for $\phi = 0°$ or (11-54) for $\theta = 90°$. As the spacing d approaches

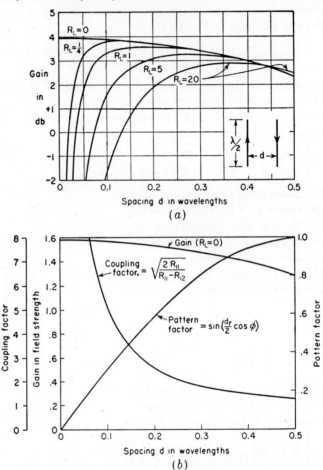

FIG. 11-13. (a) Gain of end-fire array of two out-of-phase $\frac{1}{2}$-wavelength elements (flat-top beam antenna) with respect to a $\frac{1}{2}$-wavelength reference antenna as a function of the spacing for five values of the loss resistance R_L. (b) Gain curve for $R_L = 0$ with variation of its component factors, the coupling factor and the pattern factor, for $\phi = 0$.

zero, the coupling factor becomes infinite, but at the same time the pattern factor approaches zero. The product of the two or gain stays finite, leveling off at a value of about 3.9 db for small spacings as illustrated by Fig. 11-13b. The fact that increased gain is associated with small spacings makes this arrangement attractive for many applications. End-fire arrays of this type with a spacing between elements of $\frac{1}{4}$ wavelength or less may be called "flat-top beam" antennas,[1] since the array is commonly operated with both elements horizontal as illustrated in Fig. 11-14, and in this position it resembles in appearance a top-loaded or flat-top antenna.

Thus far it has been assumed that there are no heat losses in the antenna system. In many antennas such losses are small and can be neglected. However, in the flat-top antenna such losses may have considerable effect on the gain. Therefore, the question of losses and of radiating efficiency will be treated in this section in connection with a discussion of arrays of two closely spaced, out-of-phase elements. The term "closely-spaced" will be taken to mean that the elements are spaced $\frac{1}{4}$ wavelength or less.

A transmitting antenna is a device

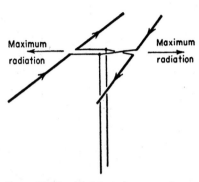

FIG. 11-14. Flat-top beam antenna with closely spaced elements carrying equal out-of-phase currents.

for radiating radio-frequency power. Let the *radiating efficiency* be defined as the ratio of the power radiated to the power input of the antenna. The real power delivered to the antenna that is not radiated is dissipated in the *loss resistance* and appears chiefly in the form of heat in the antenna conductor, in the insulators supporting the antenna, etc. An antenna with a total terminal resistance R_{1T} may be considered to have a terminal resistance R_1, which is all radiation resistance, and an equivalent terminal loss resistance R_{1L} such that

$$R_{1T} = R_1 + R_{1L} \qquad (11\text{-}72)$$

It follows that,

$$\text{Radiating efficiency, } \% = \frac{R_1}{R_1 + R_{1L}} \times 100 \qquad (11\text{-}73)$$

Since many types of high-frequency antennas have radiation resistances that are large compared to any loss resistance, the efficiencies are high. In an array with closely spaced, out-of-phase elements, however, the radiation resistance may be relatively small and the antenna current very large as illustrated by Fig. 11-15. Hence, a considerable reduction in radiating efficiency may result from the presence of any loss resistance. The radiating efficiency may also be small for low-frequency antennas which are very short compared to the wavelength. Although the effect of loss resistance will be discussed specifically for an array of two closely

[1] J. D. Kraus, Antenna Arrays with Closely Spaced Elements, *Proc. I.R.E.*, **28**, 76–84, February, 1940.

spaced $\frac{1}{2}$-wavelength elements, the method is general and may be applied to any type of antenna.

Let the equivalent loss resistance at the terminals of each element be R_{1L}. The elements are center-fed and are arranged side by side with a

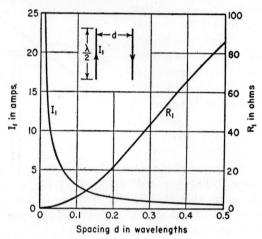

FIG. 11-15. Current I_1 and radiation resistance R_1 in each element of a flat-top beam antenna as a function of the spacing. The current is calculated for a constant input power of 100 watts to the array.

spacing d. The total terminal resistance R_{1T} is as given by (11-72). The terminal radiation resistance R_1 is given by

$$R_1 = R_{11} - R_{12} \qquad (11\text{-}74)$$

Substituting (11-74) in (11-72) the total terminal resistance for each element is then

$$R_{1T} = R_{11} + R_{1L} - R_{12} \qquad (11\text{-}75)$$

If a power W is supplied to the two-element array, the current I_1 in each element is

$$I_1 = \sqrt{\frac{W}{2(R_{11} + R_{1L} - R_{12})}} \qquad (11\text{-}76)$$

The total terminal resistance R_{0T} of a single, center-fed $\frac{1}{2}$-wavelength reference antenna is

$$R_{0T} = R_{00} + R_{0L} \qquad (11\text{-}77)$$

where R_{00} is the self-resistance and R_{0L} the loss resistance of the reference antenna

The current I_0 at the terminals of the reference antenna is then

$$I_0 = \sqrt{\frac{W}{R_{00} + R_{0L}}} \qquad (11\text{-}78)$$

With the array elements vertical, the gain in field intensity as a function of ϕ in the horizontal plane (x-y plane in Fig. 11-7a) is obtained by substituting (11-76) in (11-37), (11-78) in (11-24) and taking the ratio which gives

$$G_f(\phi)\left[\frac{\text{A.}}{\text{H.W.}}\right] = \sqrt{\frac{2(R_{00} + R_{0L})}{R_{11} + R_{1L} - R_{12}}}\left|\sin\left(\frac{d_r \cos \phi}{2}\right)\right| \qquad (11\text{-}79)$$

This expression reduces to (11-52) if the loss resistances are zero ($R_{0L} = R_{1L} = 0$).

In a similar way the gain in field intensity as a function of θ in the vertical plane (x-z plane in Fig. 11-7a) is

$$G_f(\theta)\left[\frac{\text{A.}}{\text{H.W.}}\right] = \sqrt{\frac{2(R_{00} + R_{0L})}{R_{11} + R_{1L} - R_{12}}}\left|\sin\left(\frac{d_r \sin \theta}{2}\right)\right| \qquad (11\text{-}80)$$

This reduces to (11-54) if the loss resistances are zero.

The effect of loss resistance on the gain of a closely spaced array of two out-of-phase $\frac{1}{2}$-wavelength elements over a $\frac{1}{2}$-wavelength reference antenna is illustrated by the curves in Fig. 11-13a. The gain presented is actually the maximum gain which occurs in the directions of maximum radiation from the array ($\phi = 0°$ and $180°$; $\theta = 90°$). The top curve, which was mentioned earlier, is for zero loss resistance ($R_{0L} = R_{1L} = 0$). The lower curves are for four different values of assumed loss resistance: $\frac{1}{4}$, 1, 5, and 20 ohms. The assumption is made that the loss resistance R_{1L} of each element of the array is the same as the loss resistance R_{0L} of the reference $\frac{1}{2}$-wavelength antenna (that is $R_{1L} = R_{0L}$). It is apparent from the curves that a loss resistance of only 1 ohm seriously limits the gain at spacings of less than $\frac{1}{10}$ wavelength, and larger loss resistances cause reductions in gain at considerably greater spacings. If the loss resistance is taken to be 1 ohm (a not unlikely value for a typical high-frequency antenna), the gain is almost constant (within 0.1 db) for spacings between $\frac{1}{8}$ and $\frac{1}{4}$ wavelength. Smaller spacings result in reduced gain because of decreased efficiency while larger spacings also give reduced gain, not because of decreased efficiency, but because of the decrease in the coupling factor. A spacing of $\frac{1}{8}$ wavelength has the advantage that the physical size of the antenna is less. However, resonance is sharper for this spacing than for wider spacings. Hence, a spacing of $\frac{1}{4}$ wavelength is to be preferred if a wide band width is desired. In some situations an intermediate or compromise spacing is indicated.

The Q of an antenna, like the Q of any resonant circuit, is proportional to the ratio of the energy stored to the energy lost (in heat or radiation) per cycle. For a constant power input to the closely spaced array the Q is nearly proportional to the square of the current I in each element. Referring to Fig. 11-15, it is apparent that the current for $\frac{1}{8}$ wavelength spacing is about twice the value for $\frac{1}{4}$ wavelength spacing. Hence the Q for $\frac{1}{8}$ wavelength spacing is about four times the Q for $\frac{1}{4}$ wavelength spacing. A large Q indicates a large amount of stored energy near the antenna in proportion to the energy radiated per cycle. This also means that the antenna acts like a sharply tuned circuit. Since the band width (if it is narrow) is inversely proportional to the Q, a spacing of $\frac{1}{4}$ wavelength provides about four times the band width obtained with $\frac{1}{8}$ wavelength spacing. Although the efficiency of an array with closely spaced, out-of-phase elements might be increased, for example, by using a large diameter conductor for each element, any substantial increase in band width requires an increase in the spacing between the elements. This increase also raises the radiating efficiency.

The flat-top beam or closely spaced antenna array discussed above in this section consists of two side-by-side, out-of-phase $\frac{1}{2}$-wavelength elements as indicated in Fig. 11-14 and in Fig. 11-16a. Five other examples of flat-top beam antennas are shown in Fig. 11-16 with arrows located at

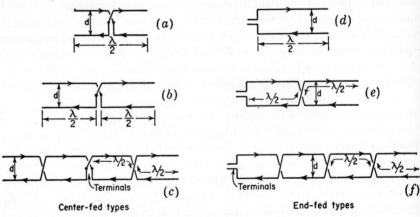

FIG. 11-16.   Six types of flat-top beam antennas.

current maxima indicating the instantaneous current directions. The type at Fig. 11-16b has an additional collinear $\frac{1}{2}$-wavelength section, the two sections being energized from the center. A four section center-fed array is illustrated in Fig. 11-16c. The additional sections yield a higher gain by virtue of the sharper beam in the plane of the elements. The antennas of Figs. 11-16d, e, and f are end-fed types corresponding to the center-fed arrays in the left-hand group. The spacing d is usually between $\frac{1}{8}$ and $\frac{1}{4}$ wavelength.

11-6. Array of n Driven Elements. The field pattern of an array of many elements can often be obtained by an application of the principle of pattern multiplication. As an example, consider the volume array of

Fig. 11-17 consisting of sixteen $\frac{1}{2}$-wavelength elements with equal currents. In the y direction the spacing between elements is d, in the x direction the spacing is a, and in the z direction the spacing is h. Let the y direction array and z direction arrays be broadside types and the x direction array an end-fire type such that the maximum radiation of the entire volume array is in the positive x direction. Let $d = h = \lambda/2$ and $a = \lambda/4$. Consider that the currents in all elements are equal in magnitude and that the currents in the front eight elements are in phase but retarded by 90° with respect to the currents in the rear eight elements. By the principle

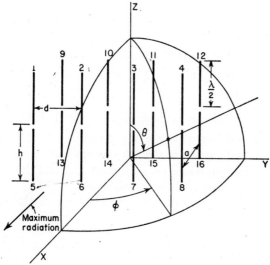

FIG. 11-17.   Array of 16 $\frac{1}{2}$-wavelength elements.

of pattern multiplication the pattern of the array is given by the pattern of a single element multiplied by the pattern of a volume array of point sources, where the point sources have the same space distribution as the elements. In general, the field pattern $E(\theta, \phi)$ of a volume array as a function of θ and ϕ is

$$E(\theta, \phi) = E_e(\theta, \phi)\, E_x(\theta, \phi)\, E_y(\theta, \phi)\, E_z(\theta, \phi) \qquad (11\text{-}81)$$

where $E_e(\theta, \phi)$ = pattern of single element

$E_x(\theta, \phi)$ = pattern of linear array of point sources in x direction

$E_y(\theta, \phi)$ = pattern of linear array of point sources in y direction

$E_z(\theta, \phi)$ = pattern of linear array of point sources in z direction

The product of the last three terms in (11-81) is the pattern of a volume array of point sources [see Eq. (4-77)]. If, for instance, we wish to obtain the pattern of the entire array $E(\phi)$ as a function of ϕ in the x-y plane ($\theta = 90°$), we introduce the appropriate pattern expression in this plane for each component array in (11-81). For the example being considered the normalized pattern becomes

$$E(\phi) = \frac{\sin (2\pi \cos \phi)}{4 \sin [(\pi/2) \cos \phi]} \cos \left[\frac{\pi}{4} (1 - \cos \phi) \right] \tag{11-82}$$

Only the $E_y(\phi)$ broadside pattern and the $E_x(\phi)$ end-fire pattern contribute to the array pattern in the x-y plane, since in this plane the $E_e(\phi)$ pattern of a single element and the $E_z(\phi)$ broadside pattern are unity.

The impedance relations for an array of any number n of identical elements are derived by an extension of the analysis used in the special cases in the preceding sections.[1] Thus, for n driven elements we have

$$\left. \begin{aligned} V_1 &= I_1 Z_{11} + I_2 Z_{12} + I_3 Z_{13} + \cdots + I_n Z_{1n} \\ V_2 &= I_1 Z_{21} + I_2 Z_{22} + I_3 Z_{23} + \cdots + I_n Z_{2n} \\ V_3 &= I_1 Z_{31} + I_2 Z_{32} + I_3 Z_{33} + \cdots + I_n Z_{3n} \\ &\quad \cdot \quad \cdot \quad \cdot \quad \cdot \quad \cdot \quad \cdot \quad \cdot \quad \cdot \quad \cdot \quad \cdot \\ V_n &= I_1 Z_{n1} + I_2 Z_{n2} + I_3 Z_{n3} + \cdots + I_n Z_{nn} \end{aligned} \right\} \tag{11-83}$$

where V_n = terminal voltage of the nth element
I_n = terminal current of the nth element
Z_{1n} = mutual impedance between element 1 and the nth element
Z_{nn} = self-impedance of the nth element

The driving-point or terminal impedance of one of the elements, say element 1, is then

$$Z_1 = \frac{V_1}{I_1} = Z_{11} + \frac{I_2}{I_1} Z_{12} + \frac{I_3}{I_1} Z_{13} + \cdots + \frac{I_n}{I_1} Z_{1n} \tag{11-84}$$

If the currents in the elements and the self and mutual impedances are known, the driving-point impedance Z_1 can be evaluated.

The voltage gain of an array of n elements over a single element can be determined in the same manner as outlined for the special cases considered in the previous sections. For instance, the gain in field intensity as a function of ϕ in the x-y plane ($\theta = 90°$) for the array of Fig. 11-17 with respect to a single vertical $\frac{1}{2}$-wavelength element with the same power input is

$$G_f(\phi) \left[\frac{A.}{H.W.} \right]$$
$$= \sqrt{\frac{R_{11} + R_{1L}}{R_{11} + R_{1L} + R_{13} + R_{15} + R_{17} + \frac{3}{2}(R_{12} + R_{16}) + \frac{1}{2}(R_{14} + R_{18})}}$$
$$\cdot \frac{\sin (2\pi \cos \phi)}{\sin [(\pi/2) \cos \phi]} \cos \left[\frac{\pi}{4} (1 - \cos \phi) \right] \tag{11-85}$$

[1] See for example, P. S. Carter, Circuit Relations in Radiating Systems and Applications to Antenna Problems, *Proc. I.R.E.*, **20**, 1007, June, 1932.

where R_{11} = self-resistance of one element

$\quad\quad R_{1L}$ = loss resistance of one element

$\quad\quad R_{12}$ = mutual resistance between element 1 and element 2

$\quad\quad R_{13}$ = mutual resistance between element 1 and element 3, etc.

The numbering of the elements is as indicated in Fig. 11-17. It is assumed that $d = h = \lambda/2$ and $a = \lambda/4$ and that the current magnitudes are equal, the currents in the front eight elements being all in the same phase but retarded 90° with respect to the currents in the rear eight elements.

11-7. Horizontal Antennas Above a Plane Ground. In the previous discussions it has been assumed that the antenna or array is in free space, that is, infinitely remote from the ground. Although the fields near elevated microwave antennas may closely approximate this idealized situation, the fields of most antennas are affected by the presence of the ground. The change in the pattern from its free-space shape is of primary importance. The impedance relations may also be different than when the array is in free space, especially if the array is very close to the ground. In this section the effect of the ground on horizontal antennas is discussed. In Sec. 11-8 the effect of the ground is analyzed for vertical antennas. A number of special cases are treated in each section, these being limited to single elements or to simple arrays of several elements.

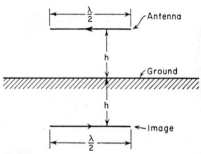

FIG. 11-18. $\frac{1}{2}$-wavelength antenna at height h above ground with image at equal distance below ground.

11-7a. Horizontal $\frac{1}{2}$-wavelength Antenna Above Ground. Consider the horizontal $\frac{1}{2}$-wavelength antenna shown in Fig. 11-18 at a height h above a plane ground of infinite extent. Owing to the presence of the ground, the field at a distant point P is the resultant of a direct wave and a wave reflected from the ground as in Fig. 11-19. Assuming that the ground is perfectly conducting, the tangential component of the electric field must vanish at its surface. To fulfill this boundary condition, the reflected wave must suffer a phase reversal of 180° at the point of reflection.

To obtain the field at a distant point P, it is convenient to transform the problem by the "method of images." In this method the ground is replaced by an image of the antenna situated a distance h below the ground plane. By taking the current in the image equal in magnitude but reversed in phase by 180° with respect to the antenna current, the condition of zero tangential electric field is met at all points along a plane everywhere equidistant from the antenna and the image. This is the plane of the ground which the image replaces. In this way, the problem of a horizontal antenna above a perfectly conducting ground[1] of infinite extent can be transformed into the problem already treated in Sec. 11-3 of a so-called end-fire array. One point of difference is that in developing the gain expression it is assumed that if a power W is delivered to the antenna, an equal power is also supplied to the image. Hence, a total power $2W$ is furnished to the "end-fire array" consisting of the antenna and its image.

Owing to the presence of the ground, the driving-point impedance of the

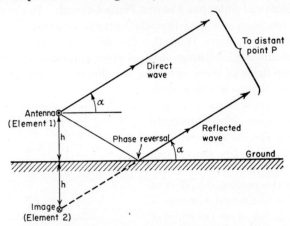

FIG. 11-19. Antenna above ground with image showing direct and reflected waves.

antenna is, in general, different than its free-space value. Thus, the applied voltage at the antenna terminals is

$$V_1 = I_1 Z_{11} + I_2 Z_m \qquad (11\text{-}86a)$$

where I_1 = the antenna current

I_2 = the image current

Z_{11} = the self-impedance of the antenna

Z_m = the mutual impedance of the antenna and its image at a distance of $2h$

Since $I_2 = -I_1$, the driving- or feed-point impedance of the antenna is

$$Z_1 = \frac{V_1}{I_1} = Z_{11} - Z_m \qquad (11\text{-}86b)$$

The real part of (11-86b) or driving-point radiation resistance is

$$R_1 = R_{11} - R_m \qquad (11\text{-}86c)$$

The variation of this resistance at the center of the $\frac{1}{2}$-wavelength antenna is shown in Fig. 11-20 as a function of the antenna height h above the

---

[1] It is also possible to apply the method of images to the case of a ground of infinite extent but of finite conductivity σ and of dielectric constant ϵ by properly adjusting the relative magnitude and phase of the image current with respect to the antenna current.

ground. As the height becomes very large, the effect of the image on the resistance decreases, the radiation resistance approaching its free-space value.

Since the antenna and image have currents of equal magnitude but opposite phase, there is zero radiation in the horizontal plane, that is, in the direction for which the elevation angle α is zero (see Fig. 11-19). If the height h is $\frac{1}{4}$ wavelength or less, the maximum radiation is always in the vertical direction ($\alpha = 90°$). For larger heights the maximum radiation is, in general, at some elevation angle between 0° and 90°.

It is convenient to compare the horizontal $\frac{1}{2}$-wavelength antenna at a

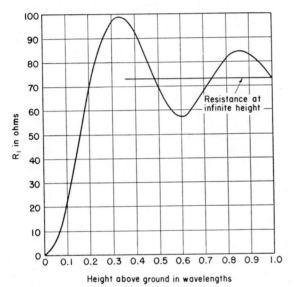

FIG. 11-20.   Driving- or feed-point resistance R_1 at the center of a horizontal $\frac{1}{2}$-wavelength antenna as a function of its height above a perfectly conducting ground.

height h above ground with respect to a $\frac{1}{2}$-wavelength antenna in free space with the same power input. At a large distance the gain in field intensity of the "Half-Wavelength antenna Above Ground" (H.W.A.G.) with respect to the "Half-Wavelength antenna in Free Space" (H.W.F.S.) is given by

$$G_f(\alpha)\left[\frac{\text{H.W.A.G}}{\text{H.W.F.S}}\right] = \sqrt{\frac{R_{11} + R_{1L}}{R_{11} + R_{1L} - R_m}}\ |2\sin(h_r \sin \alpha)| \qquad (11\text{-}87)$$

where $h_r = (2\pi/\lambda)h$
  R_{11} = self-resistance of $\frac{1}{2}$-wavelength antenna
  R_{1L} = loss resistance of $\frac{1}{2}$-wavelength antenna
  R_m = mutual resistance of $\frac{1}{2}$-wavelength antenna and its image at a distance of $2h$

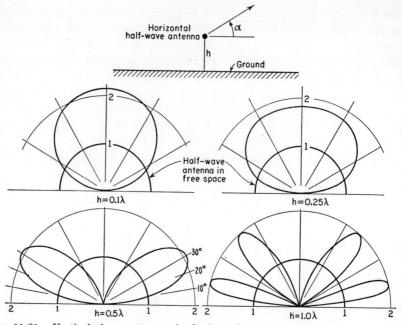

FIG. 11-21. Vertical-plane patterns of a horizontal $\frac{1}{2}$-wavelength antenna at various heights h above a perfectly conducting ground as calculated from (11-87) for $R_{1L} = 0$.

Equation (11-87) gives the gain in the vertical plane normal to the antenna as a function of α (see Fig. 11-21).

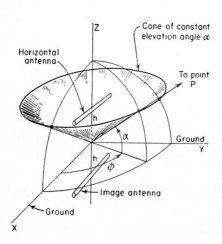

FIG. 11-22. Horizontal antenna at height h above ground (x-y plane) showing azimuth angle ϕ and elevation angle α for a distant point P.

The vertical-plane patterns of a horizontal $\frac{1}{2}$-wavelength antenna are shown in Fig. 11-21 for heights $h = 0.1, 0.25, 0.5,$ and 1.0 wavelength. The circular pattern is for a $\frac{1}{2}$-wavelength antenna in free space (that is, with the ground removed) with the same power input. It is assumed that loss resistances are zero.

It is also of interest to calculate the field pattern as a function of the azimuth angle ϕ for a constant elevation angle α. The radius vector to the distant point P then sweeps out a cone as suggested in Fig. 11-22. To find this field pattern, let us first consider the field pattern of a horizontal antenna in free space as in Fig. 11-23. The x-y plane is horizontal.

The field intensity at a large distance in the direction α, ϕ is then given by the length OA between the origin and the point of intersection of a cone of elevation angle α and the surface of the three-dimensional doughnut field pattern of the antenna as suggested in Fig. 11-23. This length is

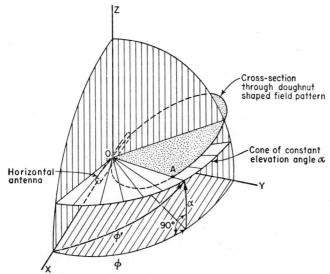

FIG. 11-23. Geometrical construction for finding the field intensity at a constant elevation angle α.

obtained from the field-pattern formula of the antenna in free space by expressing the polar angle ϕ' from the antenna axis in terms of α and ϕ. For the spherical right triangle in Fig. 11-23 we have

$$\cos \phi' = \cos \phi \cos \alpha \tag{11-88a}$$

or

$$\sin \phi' = \sqrt{1 - \cos^2 \phi \cos^2 \alpha} \tag{11-88b}$$

Substituting these relations in the pattern formula, we get the field intensity in the direction α, ϕ. For example, by substituting (11-88a) and (11-88b) into (5-84), noting that ϕ' in (11-88a) and (11-88b) equals θ in (5-84), we obtain for the field of a $\frac{1}{2}$-wavelength horizontal antenna

$$E(\alpha, \phi) = \frac{\cos \left[(\pi/2) \cos \phi \cos \alpha \right]}{\sqrt{1 - \cos^2 \phi \cos^2 \alpha}} \tag{11-89}$$

Then the relative field pattern of the horizontal $\frac{1}{2}$-wavelength antenna in free space as a function of ϕ at a fixed elevation angle α_0 is given by

$$E(\phi) = \frac{\cos \left[(\pi/2) \cos \phi \cos \alpha_0 \right]}{\sqrt{1 - \cos^2 \phi \cos^2 \alpha_0}} \tag{11-90}$$

To obtain the field pattern of the antenna when situated at a height h above a perfectly conducting ground, we multiply the above free-space relations by the pattern of two isotropic point sources of equal amplitude but opposite phase. The sources are separated by a distance $2h$ along the z axis. From (4-10) the pattern of the isotropic sources becomes in the present case

$$E_{iso.} = \sin (h_r \sin \alpha) \qquad (11\text{-}91)$$

where h_r is the height of the antenna above ground in radians, that is,

$$h_r = \frac{2\pi h}{\lambda}$$

This pattern is independent of the azimuth angle ϕ. Multiplying the free-space field pattern of any horizontal antenna by (11-91) yields the field pattern for the antenna above a perfectly conducting ground. Thus, for a horizontal $\frac{1}{2}$-wavelength antenna above a perfectly conducting ground the three-dimensional field pattern as a function of both α and ϕ is obtained by multiplying (11-89) and (11-91) which gives

$$E = \frac{\cos \left[(\pi/2) \cos \phi \cos \alpha \right]}{\sqrt{1 - \cos^2 \phi \cos^2 \alpha}} \sin (h_r \sin \alpha) \qquad (11\text{-}92)$$

where h_r = the height of the antenna above ground in radians

As an example, the field patterns as a function of the azimuth angle ϕ at elevation angles $\alpha = 10°$, $20°$, and $30°$ are presented in Fig. 11-24 as

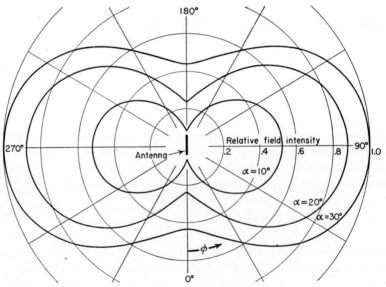

FIG. 11-24.   Azimuthal field patterns of horizontal $\frac{1}{2}$-wavelength antenna $\frac{1}{2}$ wavelength bove ground at elevation angles $\alpha = 10°$, $20°$, and $30°$.

calculated from (11-92) for a horizontal $\frac{1}{2}$-wavelength antenna at a height of $\frac{1}{2}$ wavelength ($h_r = \pi$) above a perfectly conducting ground of infinite extent.   The relative magnitudes of these patterns at $\phi = 90°$ or $270°$ are
seen to correspond to the field intensi-
ties at $\alpha = 10°, 20°$, and $30°$ in the vertical-plane pattern of Fig. 11-21 for
$h = 0.5\lambda$.   It should be noted that the
field is horizontally polarized at $\phi = 90°$
or $270°$ and is vertically polarized at
$\phi = 0°$ and $\phi = 180°$.   At intermediate
azimuth angles the field is linearly polarized at a slant angle.

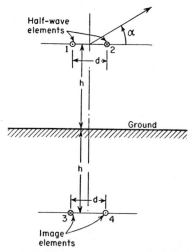

11-7b. *Flat-top Beam Antenna Above
Ground.*   In this section the case of
two horizontal, closely spaced, out-of-
phase $\frac{1}{2}$-wavelength elements or flat-
top beam antenna above a perfectly
conducting ground is discussed.   Referring to Fig. 11-25, let the $\frac{1}{2}$-wave-
length elements be at a height h above
the ground and separated by a distance
d.   The gain in field intensity of this

Fig. 11-25.   Flat-top beam antenna
above ground.

antenna relative to a $\frac{1}{2}$-wavelength antenna in free space with the same power input is given by[1]

$$G_f(\alpha)\left[\frac{\text{A.A.G.}}{\text{H.W.F.S.}}\right]^* = \sqrt{\frac{R_{11} + R_{1L}}{2(R_{11} + R_{1L} + R_{14} - R_{12} - R_{13})}}$$

$$\left| \left[1 - 1 \underline{/(d_r \cos \alpha)} - 1 \underline{/(2h_r \sin \alpha)} + 1 \underline{/(d_r \cos \alpha + 2h_r \sin \alpha)}\right] \right| \quad (11\text{-}93)$$

where d_r = spacing of elements in radians = $2\pi d/\lambda$
    h_r = height of element above ground in radians = $2\pi h/\lambda$
    R_{11} = self-resistance of a single element
    R_{1L} = loss resistance of a single element
    R_{12} = mutual resistance of elements 1 and 2
    R_{13} = mutual resistance of elements 1 and 3, etc.
where the elements are numbered as in Fig. 11-25.   The gain in (11-93) is expressed as a function of α in the vertical plane normal to the elements.

Polar plots calculated by (11-93) for the gain in field intensity of a flat-top beam antenna consisting of two $\frac{1}{2}$-wavelength elements spaced

[1] J. D. Kraus, Antenna Arrays with Closely Spaced Elements, *Proc. I.R.E.*, **28**, 76–84, February, 1940.

* The symbols in the brackets are by way of explanation that the gain in field intensity is for the "Array Above Ground with respect to a Half-Wavelength (antenna in) Free-Space."

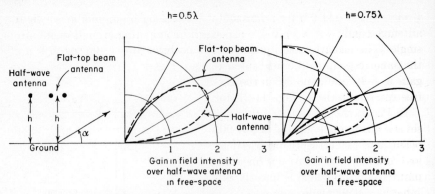

FIG. 11-26. Vertical-plane patterns (solid curves) of two-element flat-top beam antenna with $\frac{1}{8}$ wavelength spacing at heights of $\frac{1}{2}$ and $\frac{3}{4}$ wavelength above ground. The patterns are plotted relative to a $\frac{1}{2}$-wavelength antenna in free space with the same power input. The vertical plane patterns of a single $\frac{1}{2}$-wavelength antenna at the same heights above ground and with the same power input are shown for comparison by the dashed curves. The left-hand quadrants of the vertical planes are omitted.

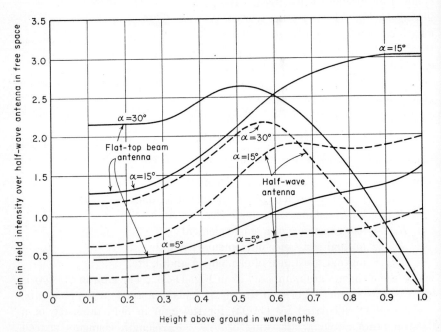

FIG. 11-27. Gain in field intensity of two-element flat-top beam antenna with $\frac{1}{8}$ wavelength spacing (solid curves) and of a single $\frac{1}{2}$-wavelength antenna (dashed curves) as a function of the height above a perfectly conducting ground. Gains are relative to a single $\frac{1}{2}$-wavelength antenna in free space with the same power input. Curves are given for elevation angles $\alpha = 5°$, $15°$, and $30°$.

$\frac{1}{8}$ wavelength apart are presented by the solid curves in Fig. 11-26 for antenna heights of $\frac{1}{2}$ and $\frac{3}{4}$ wavelength above ground. Patterns of a single $\frac{1}{2}$-wavelength antenna at the same heights above ground and with the same power input are shown for comparison (dashed curves). The gain in field intensity is expressed relative to a $\frac{1}{2}$-wavelength antenna in free space with the same power input.

In Fig. 11-27 the gain is given as a function of height above ground for several elevation angles. Curves are shown for both a two-element flat-top beam and a single horizontal $\frac{1}{2}$-wavelength antenna. It is assumed that loss resistances are zero. If for example, the effective elevation angle at a particular time on a certain short-wave circuit (transmission via iono-spheric reflections) is 30°, we note from Fig. 11-27 that the optimum

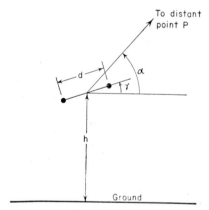

Fig. 11-28.   Tilted flat-top beam antenna.

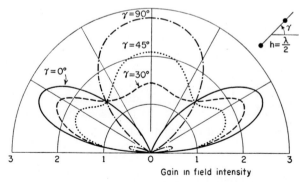

Fig. 11-29. Vertical-plane patterns for horizontal two-element flat-top beam antenna with $\frac{1}{8}$ wavelength spacing at an average height of $\frac{1}{2}$ wavelength above ground for tilt angles $\gamma = 0°$, 30°, 45°, and 90°. Patterns give gain in field intensity over a single $\frac{1}{2}$-wavelength antenna in free space with the same power input.

height for a two-element flat-top beam is 0.5 wavelength. For a single ½-wavelength antenna the optimum height is about 0.57 wavelength.

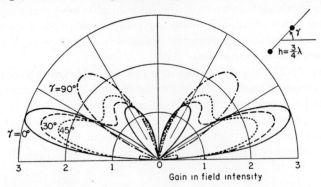

Gain in field intensity

FIG. 11-30. Same as for Fig. 11-29 but with array elements at average height of ¾ wavelength above ground.

It is interesting to consider the effect of tilting the plane of the flat-top beam elements by an angle γ as in Fig. 11-28. Results calculated by an extension of the above analysis are illustrated in Figs. 11-29 and 11-30 for two-element arrays at average heights of ½ and ¾ above a perfectly conducting ground.[1] Patterns are shown for tilt angles $\gamma = 0°, 30°, 45°$ and 90°. In all cases the effect of the tilt is to increase the field intensity at large elevation angles and to decrease it at small angles.

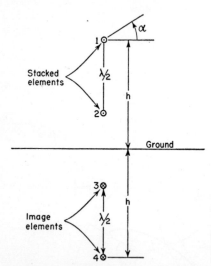

FIG. 11-31. Array of stacked horizontal ½-wavelength elements.

11-7c. Stacked Horizontal ½-Wavelength Antennas Above Ground. Consider the case of two horizontal ½-wavelength elements stacked in a vertical plane above a perfectly conducting ground of infinite extent. The elements have equal in-phase currents. The arrangement of the elements and their images is shown in Fig. 11-31. The height of the upper element above ground is h. Let the spacing between elements be ½ wavelength so that the height of the lower element above ground is $h - \lambda/2$.

[1] J. D. Kraus, Characteristics of Antennas with Closely Spaced Elements, *Radio*, 9–19, February, 1939.

The gain in field intensity of this array over a single $\frac{1}{2}$-wavelength antenna in free space with the same power input is

$$G_f(\alpha)\left[\frac{\text{A.A.G.}}{\text{H.W.F.S.}}\right] = \sqrt{\frac{R_{00} + R_{0L}}{2(R_{11} + R_{1L} + R_{12} - R_{13}) - R_{23} - R_{14}}}$$
$$\cdot\, 2\, |\, \{\sin\,(h_r\,\sin\,\alpha) + \sin\,[(h_r - \pi)\,\sin\,\alpha]\}\, | \quad (11\text{-}94)$$

where R_{12} is the mutual resistance between elements 1 and 2, R_{13} the mutual resistance between elements 1 and 3, etc. The elements are numbered as in Fig. 11-31. This expression gives the gain as a function of h and of the elevation angle α in the vertical plane normal to the plane of the elements. As an example, the gain in field intensity for two stacked in-phase horizontal $\frac{1}{2}$-wavelength elements over a free-space $\frac{1}{2}$-wavelength antenna with the same power input is presented in Fig. 11-32 as a function of the height h above ground, for an elevation angle $\alpha = 20°$. The gains at

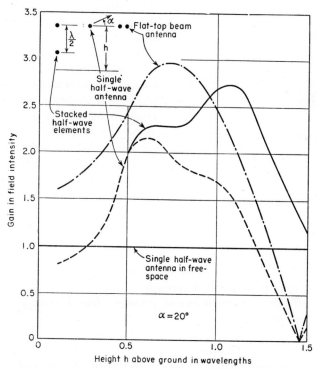

Fig. 11-32. Gain in field intensity of array of two stacked horizontal $\frac{1}{2}$-wavelength elements as a function of the height of the upper element for an elevation angle of 20°. The elements are stacked $\frac{1}{2}$ wavelength apart. The gain is relative to a single $\frac{1}{2}$-wavelength antenna in free space with the same power input. Gains of a two-element flat-top beam antenna and single $\frac{1}{2}$-wavelength antenna as a function of the height above ground are also shown for comparison at the same elevation angle.

$\alpha = 20°$ for a two-element flat-top beam antenna and a single horizontal $\frac{1}{2}$-wavelength antenna are also shown as a function of height for comparison.

In practice it is common to compare a directional array such as we have been discussing to a horizontal $\frac{1}{2}$-wavelength antenna with the same power input and at the same height above ground (or at the average height of the array). Thus, the gain as a function of α in the vertical plane for a horizontal flat-top beam antenna at a height h above ground with respect to a single $\frac{1}{2}$-wavelength reference antenna at the same height is found by taking the ratio of Eq. (11-93) to Eq. (11-87).

11-8. Vertical Antennas Above a Plane Ground.

Consider a vertical stub antenna of length l above a plane horizontal ground of infinite conductivity as in Fig. 11-33. By the method of images the ground may be replaced by an image antenna of length l with sinusoidal current distribution and instantaneous current direction as indicated. The problem of the stub antenna above ground then reduces to the problem already treated in Chap. 5 of a linear center-fed antenna with symmetrical current distribution. The electric field intensity as a function of the elevation angle α and distance r may be derived from (5-81) obtaining

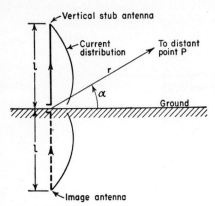

FIG. 11-33. Vertical stub antenna above a ground plane.

$$E(\alpha, r) = \frac{60}{r} \sqrt{\frac{W}{R_{11} + R_{1L}}} \frac{\cos (l_r \sin \alpha) - \cos l_r}{\cos \alpha} \qquad (11\text{-}95)$$

where $l_r = \beta l = (2\pi/\lambda)l$

R_{11} = self-resistance of a vertical stub antenna of length l referred to the point of current maximum

R_{1L} = effective loss resistance of antenna referred to same point

W = power input

The field intensity $E(\alpha, r)$ is in volts per meter if r is in meters, W in watts, and R_{11} and R_{1L} in ohms.

Values of the self-resistance referred to the current loop of a vertical stub antenna above a perfectly conducting ground have been given by Brown[1] and by Labus.[2] These values are presented as a function of

---

[1] G. H. Brown, A Critical Study of the Characteristics of Broadcast Antennas as Affected by Antenna Current Distribution, *Proc. I.R.E.*, **24**, 48–81, January, 1936.

[2] J. Labus, Rechnerische Ermittlung der Impedanz von Antennen, *Hochfrequenztechnik und Electroakustik*, **41**, 17–23, January, 1933.

antenna length in Fig. 11-34. Using these values of self-resistance, or radiation resistance, the field intensity of a vertical stub antenna of any length l and power input W can be calculated by (11-95) at any elevation angle α and distance r. Thus, the field intensity by (11-95) along the ground ($\alpha = 0$) for a $\frac{1}{4}$-wavelength vertical antenna ($l_r = \pi/2$) with a power input of 1 watt ($W = 1$) at a distance of 1 mile ($r = 1{,}609$ meters) is

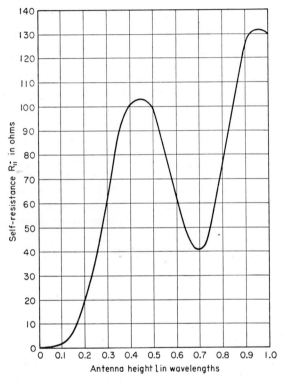

Fig. 11-34. Radiation resistance at the current loop of a thin vertical antenna as a function of the height l of the antenna. (*After Brown and Labus.*)

6.5 millivolts/meter. The value of R_{11} for a $\frac{1}{4}$-wavelength stub antenna is 36.5 ohms, and R_{1L} is assumed to be zero.

Vertical stub antennas, singly or in directional arrays, are very widely used for broadcasting. In this application the field intensity along the ground ($\alpha = 0$) is of particular interest. It is also customary to compare field intensities at some standard distance, say 1 mile, and for some standard input such as 1 kilowatt. For this case (11-95) reduces to

$$E = \frac{1.18(1 - \cos l_r)}{\sqrt{R_{11} + R_{1L}}} \qquad \text{volts/meter} \qquad (11\text{-}96)$$

where E is the field intensity along the ground at a distance of 1 mile for a power input of 1 kilowatt. The variation of E as given by (11-95) is presented in Fig. 11-35 as a function of antenna length.[1,2] A length of about 0.64 λ yields the greatest field intensity along the ground but as pointed out by Brown[1] the large high-angle radiation for this length reduces the nonfading range at broadcast frequencies (500 to 1,500 kc) as compared for example with an antenna about ½ wavelength long. The nonfading range is largest for an antenna height of 0.528λ. The vertical-plane patterns calculated by (11-95) as a function of the elevation angle α for vertical antennas of various heights are presented in Fig. 11-36.[1,2] It is assumed that the loss resistance $R_{1L} = 0$, that is, the entire input to the antenna is radiated. The small amount of high-angle radiation, which is an important factor in reducing fading, is apparent for the $l = 0.528$ λ antenna as compared to other lengths.

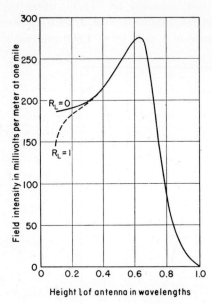

Height L of antenna in wavelengths

Fig. 11-35. Field intensity at the ground (zero elevation angle) at a distance of 1 mile from a vertical antenna with 1 kilowatt input as a function of its height l. Perfectly conducting ground is assumed. The solid curve is for an assumed loss resistance $R_L = 0$ and the dashed curve for $R_L = 1$ ohm.

The analysis of arrays of several vertical stub antennas can be reduced in a similar fashion to arrays of symmetrical center-fed antennas. Many of these have been treated in previous sections. In this case it is often convenient to compare the pattern and refer the gain to a single vertical stub antenna with the same power input. The situation of a symmetrical center-fed vertical antenna with its lower end some distance above the ground can also be treated by the method of images. In this case the antenna is reduced to a collinear array.

For the case of a linear array of vertical elements of equal height and of the same current distribution, the pattern $E(\phi)$ as a function of the azimuth angle ϕ at a constant elevation angle α is given by

$$E(\phi) = E_{\text{iso}}.(\phi') \times E_1 \qquad (11\text{-}97a)$$

[1] See G. H. Brown, A Critical Study of the Characteristics of Broadcast Antennas as Affected by Antenna Current Distribution, *Proc. I.R.E.*, **25**, 78–145, January, 1937.

[2] C. E. Smith, "Directional Antennas," Cleveland Institute of Radio Electronics, Cleveland, Ohio, 1946.

where $E_{iso.}(\phi')$ = relative pattern of array of isotropic point sources used
to replace elements

E_1 = relative field intensity of a single vertical element at the elevation angle α

The angle ϕ' in the pattern formula of the array of isotropic sources is the

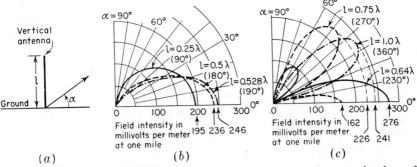

Fig. 11-36. Vertical-plane field patterns of vertical antennas for several values of antenna height l. The field intensity is expressed in millivolts per meter at a distance of 1 mile for 1 kilowatt input. Perfectly conducting ground and zero loss resistance are assumed.

angle with respect to the array axis or x axis in Fig. 11-37a. Before inserting this formula into (11-97a), it is necessary to express ϕ' in terms of

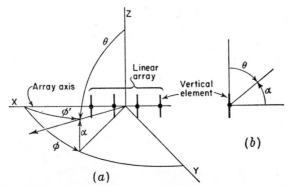

Fig. 11-37. Geometrical construction for finding field intensity of a linear array of vertical elements at a constant elevation angle α.

the azimuth angle ϕ and elevation angle α (Fig. 11-37a). This is done by the substitutions

$$\cos \phi' = \cos \phi \cos \alpha \qquad (11\text{-}97b)$$

and

$$\sin \phi' = \sqrt{1 - \cos^2 \phi \cos^2 \alpha} \qquad (11\text{-}97c)$$

If the relative field intensity formula E_1 of a single vertical element is given in terms of the polar angle θ, the elevation angle α is introduced by means of the substitution $\theta = 90° - \alpha$, since, as indicated in Fig. 11-37b, θ and α are complementary angles.

11-9. Arrays with Parasitic Elements. In the above sections it has been assumed that all the array elements are driven, that is, all are supplied with power by means of a transmission line. Directional arrays can also be constructed with the aid of elements in which currents are induced by the fields of a driven element. Such elements have no transmission-line connection to the transmitter and are usually referred to as "parasitic elements."

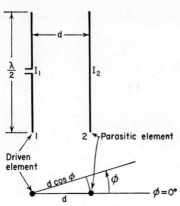

FIG. 11-38. Array with one driven element and one parasitic element.

Let us consider the case of an array in free space consisting of one driven $\frac{1}{2}$-wavelength element (element 1) and one parasitic element (element 2) as in Fig. 11-38. The procedure follows that used by Brown.[1] Suppose that both elements are vertical so that the azimuth angle ϕ is as indicated. The circuit relations for the elements are

$$V_1 = I_1 Z_{11} + I_2 Z_{12} \tag{11-98a}$$

$$0 = I_2 Z_{22} + I_1 Z_{12} \tag{11-98b}$$

From (11-98a) the current in element 2 is

$$I_2 = -I_1 \frac{Z_{12}}{Z_{22}} = -I_1 \frac{|Z_{12}| \angle \tau_m}{|Z_{22}| \angle \tau_2} = -I_1 \left| \frac{Z_{12}}{Z_{22}} \right| \angle \tau_m - \tau_2 \tag{11-99a}$$

or

$$I_2 = I_1 \left| \frac{Z_{12}}{Z_{22}} \right| \angle \xi \tag{11-99b}$$

where $\xi = \pi + \tau_m - \tau_2$, in which

$$\tau_m = \arctan \frac{X_{12}}{R_{12}}$$

$$\tau_2 = \arctan \frac{X_{22}}{R_{22}}$$

where $R_{12} + jX_{12} = Z_{12}$ = mutual impedance of elements 1 and 2

$R_{22} + jX_{22} = Z_{22}$ = self-impedance of the parasitic element

The electric field intensity at a large distance from the array as a function of ϕ is

[1] G. H. Brown, Directional Antennas, *Proc. I.R.E.*, **25**, 78–145, January, 1937.

$$E(\phi) = k(I_1 + I_2 \angle -d_r \cos \phi) \qquad (11\text{-}100)$$

where $d_r = \beta d = \dfrac{2\pi}{\lambda} d$

Substituting (11-99b) for I_2 in (11-100)

$$E(\phi) = kI_1\left(1 + \left|\frac{Z_{12}}{Z_{22}}\right| \angle \xi - d_r \cos \phi\right) \qquad (11\text{-}101)$$

Solving (11-98a) and (11-98b) for the driving-point impedance Z_1 of the driven element, we get

$$Z_1 = Z_{11} - \frac{Z_{12}^2}{Z_{22}} = Z_{11} - \frac{|Z_{12}^2| \angle 2\tau_m}{|Z_{22}| \angle \tau_2} \qquad (11\text{-}102)$$

The real part of Z_1 is

$$R_1 = R_{11} - \left|\frac{Z_{12}^2}{Z_{22}}\right| \cos(2\tau_m - \tau_2) \qquad (11\text{-}103)$$

Adding a term for the effective loss resistance if any is present, we have

$$R_1 = R_{11} + R_{1L} - \left|\frac{Z_{12}^2}{Z_{22}}\right| \cos(2\tau_m - \tau_2) \qquad (11\text{-}104)$$

For a power input W to the driven element

$$I_1 = \sqrt{\frac{W}{R_1}} = \sqrt{\frac{W}{R_{11} + R_{1L} - |Z_{12}^2/Z_{22}| \cos(2\tau_m - \tau_2)}} \qquad (11\text{-}105)$$

and substituting (11-105) for I_1 in (11-101) yields the electric field intensity at a large distance from the array as a function of ϕ. Thus,

$$E(\phi) = k\sqrt{\frac{W}{R_{11} + R_{1L} - |Z_{12}^2/Z_{22}| \cos(2\tau_m - \tau_2)}}$$
$$\cdot \left[1 + \left|\frac{Z_{12}}{Z_{22}}\right| \angle \xi - d_r \cos \phi\right] \qquad (11\text{-}106)$$

For a power input W to a single vertical $\frac{1}{2}$-wavelength element the electric field intensity at the same distance is

$$E_{\text{H.W.}}(\phi) = kI_0 = k\sqrt{\frac{W}{R_{00} + R_{0L}}} \qquad (11\text{-}107)$$

where R_{00} = self-resistance of single $\frac{1}{2}$-wavelength element

R_{0L} = loss resistance of single $\frac{1}{2}$-wavelength element

The gain in field intensity (as a function of ϕ) of the array with respect to a single $\frac{1}{2}$-wavelength antenna with the same power input is the ratio of (11-106) to (11-107). Since $R_{00} = R_{11}$ and letting $R_{0L} = R_{1L}$, we have

$$G_f(\phi)\left[\frac{\text{A.}}{\text{H.W.}}\right] = \sqrt{\frac{R_{11} + R_{1L}}{R_{11} + R_{1L} - |Z_{12}^2/Z_{22}| \cos(2\tau_m - \tau_2)}}$$
$$\cdot \left(1 + \left|\frac{Z_{12}}{Z_{22}}\right| \angle \xi - d_r \cos \phi\right) \qquad (11\text{-}108)$$

If Z_{22} is made very large by detuning the parasitic element (that is, by making X_{22} large), Eq. (11-108) reduces to unity, that is to say, the field of the array becomes the same as the single $\frac{1}{2}$-wavelength comparison antenna.

By means of a relation equivalent to (11-108), Brown[1] has analyzed the array with a single parasitic element for various values of parasitic element reactance (X_{22}) and was the first to point out that spacings of less than $\frac{1}{4}$ wavelength were desirable.

The magnitude of the current in the parasitic element and its phase relation to the current in the driven element depends on its tuning. The parasitic element may have a fixed length of $\frac{1}{2}$ wavelength, the tuning being accomplished by inserting a lumped reactance in series with the antenna at its center point. Alternatively the parasitic element may be continuous and the tuning accomplished by adjusting the length. This method is often simpler in practice but is more difficult of analysis. By changing the tuning of the parasitic element, it can act as a reflector sending the maximum radiation in the $\phi = 180°$ direction (Fig. 11-38) or as a director sending the maximum radiation in the $\phi = 0°$ direction.

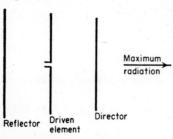

FIG. 11-39.   Three-element array.

Antenna arrays may also be constructed with more than one parasitic element. A common arrangement uses one driven element and two parasitic elements and is usually referred to as a three-element array. An array of this type is shown in Fig. 11-39, one parasitic element acting as a reflector and the other as a director. The analysis for the three-element array is more complex than for the two-element type treated above. Experimentally measured field patterns of a horizontal three-element array situated 1 wavelength above a square horizontal ground plane about 13 wavelengths on a side are presented in Fig. 11-40. The element lengths and spacings are as indicated. The gain at $\alpha = 15°$ for this array at a height of 1 wavelength is about 5 db with respect to a single $\frac{1}{2}$-wavelength dipole antenna at the same height.[2] The vertical plane pattern is shown in Fig. 11-40a. It is interesting to note that because of the finite size of the ground plane there is radiation at negative elevation angles. This phenomenon is characteristic of antennas with finite ground planes, the radiation at negative angles being largely the result of currents on the

[1] G. H. Brown, Directional Antennas, *Proc. I.R.E.*, **25**, 78–145, January, 1937.

[2] Note that it is necessary to specify both the height and elevation angle at which the comparison is made. In comparing one antenna with another, the gain as a function of elevation angle at a given height or as a function of height at a given elevation angle may, in general, range from zero to infinity.

edges of the ground planes or beneath it.   The azimuthal patterns at
elevation angles $\alpha = 10°$, $15°$, and $20°$ are shown in Fig. 11-40b.   A parasitic
array of this type with closely spaced elements has a small driving-point
radiation resistance and a relatively narrow band width.

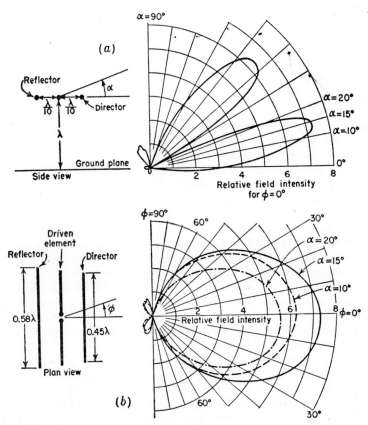

Fɪɢ. 11-40.   Measured vertical plane pattern (a) and horizontal plane patterns (b)
at three elevation angles for a three-element array located 1 wavelength above a large
ground plane.   (*Patterns by D. C. Cleckner, Antenna Laboratory, The Ohio State University.*)

Arrays may be constructed with larger numbers of parasitic elements
although customarily with larger spacings between elements.   For example,
Yagi[1] has built arrays with a number of parasitic director elements arranged in a row in front of the driven element.   He also used one or more
parasitic reflector elements with such arrays.

[1] H. Yagi, Beam Transmission of Ultra-short Waves, *Proc. I.R.E.*, **16**, 715–740,
June, 1928.

PROBLEMS

11-1. *a.* Calculate and plot the gain of a broadside array of two side-by-side $\frac{1}{2}$-wavelength elements in free space as a function of the spacing d for values of d from 0 to 2 wavelengths. Express the gain with respect to a single $\frac{1}{2}$-wavelength element. Assume all elements are 100 per cent efficient.

b. What spacing results in the largest gain?

c. Calculate and plot the radiation-field patterns for $\frac{1}{2}$ wavelength spacing. Show also the patterns of the $\frac{1}{2}$ wavelength reference antenna to the proper relative scale.

11-2. A two-element end-fire array in free space consists of two vertical side-by-side $\frac{1}{2}$-wavelength elements with equal out-of-phase currents. At what angles in the horizontal plane is the gain equal to unity?

a. When the spacing is $\frac{1}{2}$ wavelength?

b. When the spacing is $\frac{1}{4}$ wavelength?

11-3. Calculate and plot the field and phase patterns of the far field for an array of two vertical side-by-side $\frac{1}{2}$-wavelength elements in free space with $\frac{1}{4}$ wavelength spacing when the elements are

a. in phase and

b. 180° out of phase.

For the in-phase case show the patterns in both the y-z or vertical plane and x-y or horizontal plane of Fig. 11-2a. For the out-of-phase case show the patterns in both the x-z or vertical plane and x-y or horizontal plane of Fig. 11-7a.

11-4. Calculate the vertical and horizontal plane free-space field patterns of a flat-top beam antenna consisting of two horizontal out-of-phase $\frac{1}{2}$-wavelength elements spaced $\frac{1}{8}$ wavelength. Assume a loss resistance of 1 ohm and show the relative patterns of a $\frac{1}{2}$-wavelength reference antenna with the same power input.

11-5. Confirm Eqs. (11-85) and (11-93).

11-6. *a.* Consider two $\frac{1}{2}$-wavelength side-by-side vertical elements spaced a distance d with currents related by $I_2 = aI_1 \underline{/\delta}$. Develop the gain expression in a plane parallel to the elements and the gain expression in a plane normal to the elements, taking a vertical $\frac{1}{2}$-wavelength element with the same power input as reference $(0 \leq a \leq 1)$. Check that these reduce to (11-69) and (11-67) when $a = 1$.

b. Plot the field patterns in both planes, and show also the field pattern of the reference antenna in proper relative proportion for the case where $d = \lambda/4$, $a = \frac{1}{2}$, and $\delta = 120°$.

11-7. *a.* Calculate the driving-point impedance at the center of each element of an in-phase broadside array of six side-by-side $\frac{1}{2}$-wavelength elements spaced $\frac{1}{2}$ wavelength apart. The currents have a Dolph-Tchebyscheff distribution such that the minor lobes have $\frac{1}{5}$ the field intensity of the major lobe.

b. Design a feed system for the array.

11-8. *a.* Develop Eq. (11-94).

b. Calculate and plot from (11-94) the gain in field intensity for an array of two in-phase horizontal $\frac{1}{2}$-wavelength elements stacked $\frac{1}{2}$ wavelength apart (as in Fig. 11-31) over a $\frac{1}{2}$-wavelength antenna in free space with the same power input as a function of h up to $h = 1.5\lambda$ for an elevation angle $\alpha = 10°$. Also calculate and plot for comparison on the same graph the gains at $\alpha = 10°$ for a two-element horizontal flat-top beam antenna and for a single horizontal $\frac{1}{2}$-wavelength antenna as a function of the height above ground from $h = 0$ to $h = 1.5\lambda$. Note difference of these curves and those for $\alpha = 20°$ in Fig. 11-32.

11-9. A broadcast-station antenna array consists of two vertical $\frac{1}{4}$-wavelength owers spaced $\frac{1}{4}$ wavelength apart. The currents are equal in magnitude and in phase quadrature. Assume a perfectly conducting ground and zero loss resistance. Calculate and plot the azimuthal field pattern in millivolts (rms) per meter at 1 mile with 1 kilowatt input for vertical elevation angles $\alpha = 0°, 20°, 40°, 60°$, and $80°$. The towers are series fed at the base. Assume that the towers are infinitesimally hin.

11-10. Calculate and plot the relative field pattern in the vertical plane through he axis of the two-tower broadcast array fulfilling the requirements of Prob. 19, Chap. 4, if the towers are $\frac{1}{4}$-wavelength high and are series fed at the base. Assume hat the towers are infinitesimally thin and that the ground is perfectly conducting.

11-11. Calculate and plot the relative field pattern in the vertical plane through he axis of the three-tower broadcast array fulfilling the requirements of Prob. 20, Chap. 4, if the towers are $\frac{3}{8}$ wavelength high and are series fed at the base. Assume hat the towers are infinitesimally thin and that the ground is perfectly conducting.

11-12. Design a broadcast-station antenna array of two vertical base-fed towers $\frac{1}{4}$-wavelength high and spaced $\frac{3}{8}$ wavelength which produces a broad maximum of ield intensity to the north in the horizontal plane and a null at an elevation angle $\alpha = 30°$ and azimuth angle $\phi = 135°$ measured ccw from north. Assume that the owers are infinitesimally thin, that the ground is perfectly conducting, and that the base currents of the two towers are equal. Specify the orientation and phasing of he towers. Calculate and plot the azimuthal field pattern at $\alpha = 0°$ and $\alpha = 30°$ and also the pattern in the vertical plane through $\phi = 135°$. Suggested procedure: Solve (11-97b) for ϕ' at the null. Then set ϕ in the pattern factor in (11-67) equal o ϕ' and solve for the value of δ which makes the pattern factor zero. The relative ield intensity at any angle (ϕ, α) is then given by (11-68) where $\sin\theta = \cos\phi' = \cos\alpha\cos\phi$ in the first pattern factor and $\theta = 90° - \alpha$ in the second pattern factor.

11-13. Design a broadcast-station array of two vertical base-fed towers $\frac{1}{4}$-wavelength high that produces a broad maximum of field intensity to the north in the horizontal plane and a null at all vertical angles to the west. Assume that the owers are infinitesimally thin and that the ground is perfectly conducting. Specify he spacing, orientation, and phasing of the towers. Calculate and plot the azimuthal relative field patterns at elevation angles of $\alpha = 0°, 30°$, and $60°$.

11-14. Two, thin center-fed $\frac{1}{2}$-wavelength antennas are driven in phase opposition. Assume that the current distributions are sinusoidal. If the antennas are parallel and spaced 0.2 wavelength,

    a. Calculate the mutual impedance of the antennas.

    b. Calculate the gain of the array in free space over one of the antennas alone.

CHAPTER 12

REFLECTOR-TYPE ANTENNAS

12-1. Introduction. Reflectors are widely used to modify the radiation pattern of a radiating element. For example, the backward radiation from an antenna may be eliminated with a plane sheet reflector. In the more general case, a beam of predetermined characteristics may be produced by means of a large, suitably shaped, and illuminated reflector surface. The characteristics of antennas with sheet reflectors or their equivalent are considered in this chapter.

A number of reflector types are illustrated in Fig. 12-1. The arrangement in Fig. 12-1a has a large, flat sheet reflector near a linear dipole antenna to reduce the backward radiation (to the left in the figure). With small spacings between antenna and sheet this arrangement also yields a substantial gain in the forward radiation. This case has been discussed in Sec. 11-7a with the ground acting as the flat sheet reflector. The desirable properties of the sheet reflector may be largely preserved with the reflector reduced in size as in Fig. 12-1b and even in the limiting case of Fig. 12-1c. Here the sheet has degenerated into a thin reflector element. Whereas the properties of the large sheet are relatively insensitive to small frequency changes, the thin reflector element may be highly sensitive to frequency. The case of a $\frac{1}{2}$-wavelength antenna with parasitic reflector element was treated in Sec. 11-9.

With two flat sheets intersecting at an angle or corner as in Fig. 12-1d, a sharper radiation pattern can be obtained. This arrangement, called a *corner-reflector antenna*, is most practical where apertures of 1 or 2 wavelengths are of convenient size. A corner reflector without an exciting antenna can be used as a passive reflector or target for radar waves. In this application the aperture may be many wavelengths, and the corner angle is always 90°. Reflectors with this angle have the property that an incident wave is reflected back toward its source as in Fig. 12-1e.

When it is convenient to build antennas with apertures of many wavelengths, parabolic reflectors can be used to provide highly directional antennas. A parabolic reflector antenna is shown in Fig. 12-1f. The parabola reflects the waves originating from a source at the focus into a parallel beam. Many other shapes of reflectors can be employed for special applications. For instance, with an antenna at one focus, the ellipse reflector (Fig. 12-1g) produces a diverging beam with all reflected waves passing through the second focus of the ellipse. Examples of reflectors of other shapes are the hyperbolic[1] and the circular reflectors[2] shown in Figs. 12-1h and i.

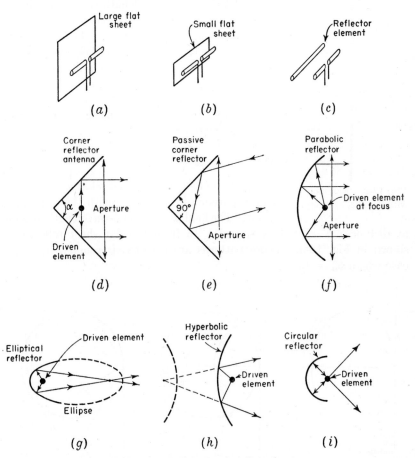

Fig. 12-1. Reflectors of various shapes.

The plane sheet reflector, the corner reflector, and the parabolic reflector are discussed in more detail in the following sections.

12-2. Plane Sheet Reflector. The problem of an antenna at a distance S from a perfectly conducting plane sheet reflector of infinite extent is

[1] Chap. 6 by G. Stavis and A. Dorne, "Very High Frequency Techniques," Radio Research Laboratory Staff, McGraw-Hill Book Company, Inc., New York, 1947.

[2] J. Ashmead and A. B. Pippard, The Use of Spherical Reflectors as Microwave Scanning Aerials, *J.I.E.E.* (London), **93**, Part IIIA, No. 4, 627–632, 1946.

readily handled by the method of images.[1] In this method the reflector is replaced by an image of the antenna at a distance $2S$ from the antenna as in Fig. 12-2. This situation is identical with the one considered in Sec. 11-7, for a horizontal antenna above ground. If the antenna is a $\frac{1}{2}$-wavelength dipole this in turn reduces to the problem of the two-element flat-top beam antenna discussed in Sec. 11-5. Assuming zero reflector losses, the gain in field intensity of a $\frac{1}{2}$-wavelength dipole antenna at a distance S from an infinite plane reflector is from (11-79),

$$G_f(\phi) = 2\sqrt{\frac{R_{11} + R_L}{R_{11} + R_L - R_{12}}} \,|\sin(S_r \cos\phi)| \quad (12\text{-}1)$$

where $S_r = 2\pi \dfrac{S}{\lambda}$

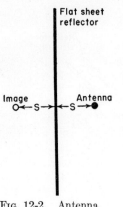

FIG. 12-2. Antenna with flat sheet reflector.

The gain in (12-1) is expressed relative to a $\frac{1}{2}$-wavelength antenna in free space with the same power input. The field patterns of $\frac{1}{2}$-wavelength antennas at distances $S = \lambda/4$, $\lambda/8$, and $\lambda/16$ from the flat sheet reflector are shown in Fig. 12-3. These patterns are calculated from (12-1) for the case where $R_L = 0$.

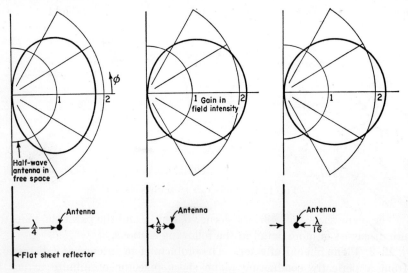

FIG. 12-3. Patterns of $\frac{1}{2}$-wavelength antenna at spacings of $\frac{1}{4}$, $\frac{1}{8}$, and $\frac{1}{16}$ wavelengths from infinite flat sheet reflector. Patterns give gain in field intensity over $\frac{1}{2}$-wavelength antenna in free space with same power input.

[1] See, for example, G. H. Brown, Directional Antennas, *Proc. I.R.E.*, **25**, 122, January, 1937.

The gain as a function of the spacing S is presented in Fig. 12-4 for assumed antenna loss resistances $R_L = 0$, 1, and 5 ohms. These curves

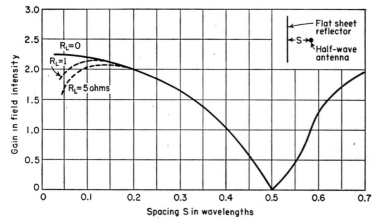

FIG. 12-4. Gain in field intensity of $\frac{1}{2}$-wavelength dipole antenna at distance S from flat sheet reflector. Gain is relative to $\frac{1}{2}$-wavelength dipole antenna in free space with the same power input. Gain is in direction $\phi = 0$ and is shown for an assumed loss resistance $R_L = 0$, 1, and 5 ohms.

are calculated from (12-1) for $\phi = 0$. It is apparent that very small spacings can be used effectively provided that losses are negligible. How-

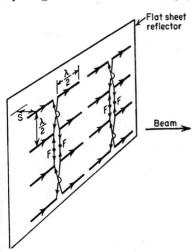

FIG. 12-5. Array of $\frac{1}{2}$-wavelength elements with flat sheet reflector (billboard or mattress antenna).

ever, the band width is narrow for small spacings as discussed in Sec. 11-5. With wide spacings the gain is less, but the band width is larger. Assuming an antenna loss resistance of 1 ohm, a spacing of 0.125 λ yields the maximum gain. For $S = 0.25$ λ, the gain is about 1.3 db less.

A large flat sheet reflector can convert a bidirectional antenna array into a unidirectional system. An example is shown in Fig. 12-5. Here a broadside array of 16 in-phase $\frac{1}{2}$-wavelength elements spaced $\frac{1}{2}$ wavelength apart is backed up by a large sheet reflector so that a unidirectional beam is produced. The feed system for the array is indicated, equal in-phase voltages being applied at the two pairs of terminals F-F. If the edges of the sheet extend some distance beyond the array, the assumption that the ground plane is infinite in extent is a good first approximation. The choice of the spacing S between the array and the sheet usually involves a compromise between gain and band width. If a spacing of $\frac{1}{8}$ wavelength is used, the radiation resistance of the elements of a large array remains about the same as with no reflector present.[1] This spacing also has the advantage over wider spacings of reduced inter-action between elements. On the other hand, a spacing such as $\frac{1}{4}$ wave-length provides a greater band width, and the precise value of S is less critical in its effect on the element impedance.

12-3. Corner-reflector Antenna.[2]

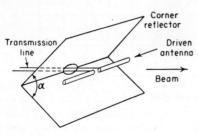

FIG. 12-6.   Corner-reflector antenna.

Two flat reflecting sheets intersecting at an angle or corner as in Fig. 12-6 form an effective directional antenna. When the corner angle $\alpha = 90°$, the sheets intersect at right angles form-ing a square corner reflector. Corner angles both greater or less than 90° can be used although there are prac-tical disadvantages to angles much less than 90°. A corner reflector with $\alpha = 180°$ is equivalent to a flat sheet reflector and may be considered as a limiting case of the corner reflector. This case has been treated in Sec. 12-2.

Assuming perfectly conducting reflecting sheets of infinite extent, the method of images can be applied to analyze the corner-reflector antenna for angles $\alpha = 180°/n$, where n is any positive integer. This method of handling corners is well-known in electrostatics.[3] Corner angles of 180° (flat sheet), 90°, 60°, etc. can be treated in this way. Corner reflectors of intermediate angle can not be determined by this method but can be interpolated approximately from the others.

In the analysis of the 90° corner reflector there are three image elements 2, 3, and 4 located as shown in Fig. 12-7a. The driven antenna 1 and the three images have currents of equal magnitude. The phase of the currents in 1 and 4 is the same. The phase of the currents in 2 and 3 is the same but 180° out of phase with respect to the currents in 1 and 4. All elements are assumed to be $\frac{1}{2}$ wavelength long.

At the point P at a large distance D from the antenna, the field intensity is

$$E(\phi) = 2kI_1 \, | \, [\cos\,(S_r\,\cos\,\phi) - \cos\,(S_r\,\sin\,\phi)] \, | \qquad (12\text{-}2)$$

[1] H. A. Wheeler, The Radiation Resistance of an Antenna in an Infinite Array or Waveguide, *Proc. I.R.E.*, **36**, 478–487, April, 1948.

[2] J. D. Kraus, The Corner Reflector Antenna, *Proc. I.R.E.*, **28**, 513–519, November, 1940.

[3] See, for example, Sir James Jeans, "Mathematical Theory of Electricity and Mag-netism," Cambridge University Press, London, 5th ed., p. 188.

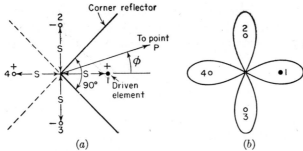

FIG. 12-7. Square corner reflector with images used in analysis (a) and four-lobed pattern of driven element and images (b).

where I_1 = current in each element

S_r = spacing of each element from the corner in radians

 = $2\pi(S/\lambda)$

k = constant involving the distance D, etc.

The emf V_1 at the terminals at the center of the driven element is

$$V_1 = I_1 Z_{11} + I_1 R_{1L} + I_1 Z_{14} - 2I_1 Z_{12} \tag{12-3}$$

where Z_{11} = self-impedance of driven element

R_{1L} = equivalent loss resistance of driven element

Z_{12} = mutual impedance of elements 1 and 2

Z_{14} = mutual impedance of elements 1 and 4

Similar expressions can be written for the emfs at the terminals of each of the images. Then if W is the power delivered to the driven element (power to each image element is also W), we have from symmetry that

$$I_1 = \sqrt{\frac{W}{R_{11} + R_{1L} + R_{14} - 2R_{12}}} \tag{12-4}$$

Substituting (12-4) in (12-2) yields

$$E(\phi) = 2k\sqrt{\frac{W}{R_{11} + R_{1L} + R_{14} - 2R_{12}}}$$
$$\cdot \mid [\cos(S_r \cos\phi) - \cos(S_r \sin\phi)] \mid \tag{12-5}$$

The field intensity at the point P at a distance D from the driven $\frac{1}{2}$-wavelength element with the reflector removed is

$$E_{\text{H.W.}}(\phi) = k\sqrt{\frac{W}{R_{11} + R_{1L}}} \tag{12-6}$$

where k = the same constant as in (12-2) and (12-5)

This is the relation for field intensity of a $\frac{1}{2}$-wavelength dipole antenna in free space with a power input W and provides a convenient reference for the corner-reflector antenna. Thus, dividing (12-5) by (12-6), we obtain the gain in field intensity of a square corner reflector antenna over a single $\frac{1}{2}$-wavelength antenna in free space with the same power input, or

$$G_f(\phi) = \frac{E(\phi)}{E_{\mathrm{H.w.}}(\phi)} = 2\sqrt{\frac{R_{11} + R_{1L}}{R_{11} + R_{1L} + R_{14} - 2R_{12}}}$$
$$\cdot \mid [\cos{(S_r \cos{\phi})} - \cos{(S_r \sin{\phi})}] \mid \quad (12\text{-}7)$$

where the expression in brackets is the pattern factor and the expression included under the radical sign is the coupling factor. The pattern shape is a function of both the angle ϕ and the antenna-to-corner spacing S. The pattern calculated by (12-7) has four lobes as shown in Fig. 12-7b. However, only one of the lobes is real.

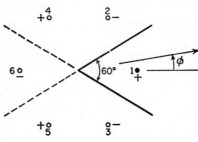

FIG. 12-8. 60° corner reflector with images used in analysis.

Expressions for the gain in field intensity of corner reflectors with corner angles of 60°, 45°, etc. can be obtained in a similar manner. For the 60° corner the analysis requires a total of six elements, one actual antenna and five images as in Fig. 12-8. Gain-pattern expressions for corner reflectors of 90° and 60° are listed in Table 12-1. The expression for a 180° "corner" or flat sheet is also included.

TABLE 12-1
GAIN-PATTERN FORMULAS FOR CORNER-REFLECTOR ANTENNAS

Corner angle	Number of elements in analysis	Gain in field intensity over $\frac{1}{2}$-wavelength antenna in free space with same power input
180°	2	$2\sqrt{\dfrac{R_{11} + R_{1L}}{R_{11} + R_{1L} - R_{12}}}\ \sin{(S_r \cos{\phi})}$
90°	4	$2\sqrt{\dfrac{R_{11} + R_{1L}}{R_{11} + R_{1L} + R_{14} - 2R_{12}}}$ $\mid [\cos{(S_r \cos{\phi})} - \cos{(S_r \sin{\phi})}] \mid$
60°	6	$2\sqrt{\dfrac{R_{11} + R_{1L}}{R_{11} + R_{1L} + 2R_{14} - 2R_{12} - R_{16}}}$ $\mid \{\sin{(S_r \cos{\phi})} - \sin{[S_r \cos{(60° - \phi)}]} - \sin{[S_r \cos{(60° + \phi)}]}\} \mid$

In the formulas of Table 12-1 it is assumed that the reflector sheets are perfectly conducting and of infinite extent. Curves of gain vs. spacing calculated from these relations are presented in Fig. 12-9. The gain given is in the direction $\phi = 0$. Two curves are shown for each corner angle. The solid curve in each case is computed for zero losses ($R_{1L} = 0$), while the dashed curve is for an assumed loss resistance $R_{1L} = 1$ ohm. It is apparent that for efficient operation too small a spacing should be avoided.

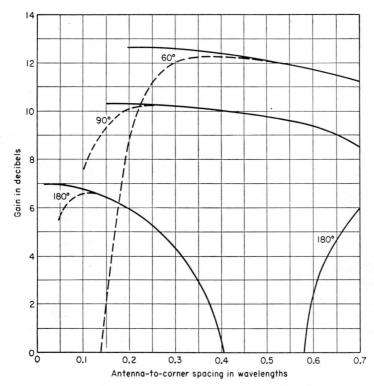

Fig. 12-9. Gain of corner reflector antennas over a $\frac{1}{2}$-wavelength antenna in free space with the same power input as a function of the antenna-to-corner spacing. Gain is in the direction $\phi = 0$ and is shown for zero loss resistance (solid curves) and for an assumed loss resistance of 1 ohm ($R_{1L} = 1$ ohm) (dashed curves).

A small spacing is also objectionable because of narrow band width. On the other hand, too large a spacing results in less gain.

The calculated pattern of a 90° corner reflector with antenna-to-corner spacing $S = 0.5\ \lambda$ is shown in Fig. 12-10a. The gain is nearly 10 db over a reference $\frac{1}{2}$-wavelength antenna. This pattern is typical if the spacing S is not too large. If S exceeds a certain value, a multilobed pattern may be obtained. For example, a square-corner reflector with $S = 1.0\ \lambda$ has a two-lobed pattern as in Fig. 12-10b. If the spacing is increased to 1.5, the pattern shown in Fig. 12-10c is obtained with major lobe in the $\phi = 0$ direction but with minor lobes present. This pattern may be considered as belonging to a higher order radiation mode of the antenna. The gain over a single $\frac{1}{2}$-wavelength dipole antenna is 12.7 db.

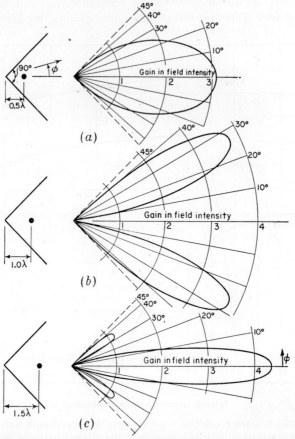

FIG. 12-10. Calculated patterns of square corner-reflector antennas with antenna-to-corner spacings of 0.5 wavelength (a), 1.0 wavelength (b), and 1.5 wavelengths (c). Patterns give gain relative to $\frac{1}{2}$-wavelength antenna in free space with same power input.

Restricting patterns to the lower order radiation mode (no minor lobes), it is generally desirable that S lie between the following limits:

α	S
90°	0.25–0.7 λ
180° (flat sheet)	0.1–0.3 λ

The terminal resistance R_T of the driven antenna is obtained by dividing (12-3) by I_1 and taking the real parts of the impedances. Thus,

$$R_T = R_{11} + R_{1L} + R_{14} - 2R_{12} \qquad (12\text{-}8)$$

If $R_{1L} = 0$, the terminal resistance is all radiation resistance. The variation of the terminal radiation resistance of the driven element is presented

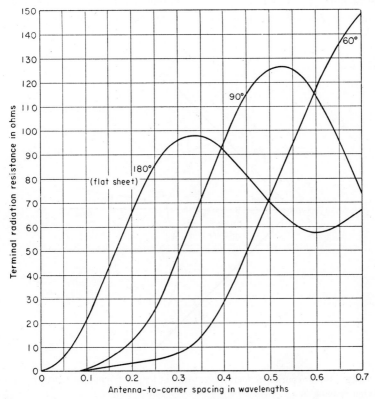

FIG. 12-11.   Terminal radiation resistance of driven $\frac{1}{2}$-wavelength antenna as a function of the antenna-to-corner spacing for corner reflectors of three corner angles.

in Fig. 12-11 as a function of the spacing S for corner angles $\alpha = 180°$, $90°$, and $60°$.

In the above analysis it is assumed that the reflectors are perfectly conducting and of infinite extent, with the exception that the gains with a finitely conducting reflector may be approximated with a proper choice of R_{1L}. The analysis provides a good first approximation to the gain-pattern characteristics of actual corner reflectors with finite sides provided that the sides are not too small. Neglecting edge effects, a suitable value for the length of sides may be arrived at by the following line of reasoning.

An essential region of the reflector is that near the point at which a wave from the driven antenna is reflected parallel to the axis. For example, this is the point A of the square corner reflector of Fig. 12-12. This point is at a distance of $1.41S$ from the corner C, where S is the antenna-to-corner spacing. If the reflector ends at the point B at a distance $L = 2S$ from the corner, as in Fig. 12-12, the reflector extends approximately $0.6S$ beyond A. With the reflector ending at B, it is to be noted that the only waves reflected from infinite sides, but not from finite sides, are

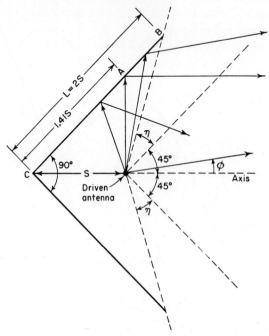

FIG. 12-12. Square corner reflector with sides of length L equal to twice the antenna-to-corner spacing S.

those radiated in the sectors η. Furthermore, these waves are reflected with infinite sides into a direction that is at a considerable angle ϕ with respect to the axis. Hence, the absence of the reflector beyond B should not have a large effect. It should also have relatively little effect on the driving-point impedance. The most noticeable effect with finite sides is that the measured pattern is appreciably broader than that calculated for infinite sides and a null does not occur at $\phi = 45°$ but at a somewhat larger angle. If this is not objectionable, a side length of twice the antenna-to-corner spacing ($L = 2S$) is a practical minimum value for square corner reflectors.

Although the gain of a corner reflector with infinite sides can be increased by reducing the corner angle, it does not follow that the gain of a corner reflector with finite sides of fixed length will increase as the corner angle is decreased.   To maintain a given efficiency with a smaller corner angle requires that S be increased.   Also on a 60° reflector, for example, the point at which a wave is reflected parallel to the axis is at a distance of $1.73S$ from the corner as compared to $1.41S$ for the square corner type. Hence, to realize the increase in gain requires that the length of the reflector sides be much larger than for a square corner reflector designed for the same frequency.   Usually this is a practical disadvantage in view of the relatively small increase to be expected in gain.

To reduce the wind resistance offered by a solid reflector, a grid of

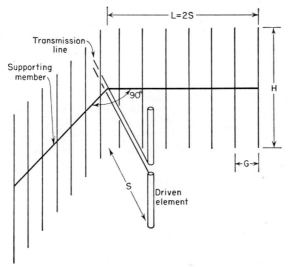

Fig. 12-13.   Grid-type reflector.

parallel wires or conductors can be used as in Fig. 12-13.   The supporting member joining the mid-points of the reflector conductors may be either a conductor or an insulator.   In general the spacing G between reflector conductors should be equal to or less than 0.1 λ.   With a $\frac{1}{2}$-wavelength driven element the length H of the reflector conductors should be equal to or greater than 0.6 λ.   If the length H is reduced to values of less than 0.6 λ, radiation to the sides and rear tends to increase and the gain decreases.   When H is decreased to as little as 0.3 λ, the strongest radiation is no longer forward and the "reflector" acts as a director.

Two square corner reflectors of practical dimensions are illustrated in Fig. 12-14.   The one at (a) with $S = 0.35$ λ and the side length $L = 0.7$ λ can be used where the physical size of the antenna must be a minimum. If physical size is not a restriction, the design of (b) may be used with the advantage of a greater band width.[1]

The square corner reflectors of Fig. 12-14 have apertures between 1 and 2 wavelengths. If an aperture of 1 wavelength is inconveniently large, a corner reflector of smaller side length and larger corner angle can be used. Carrying this procedure to the limit results in a closely spaced flat-sheet reflector ($\alpha = 180°$) as in Fig. 12-1b. If, on the other hand,

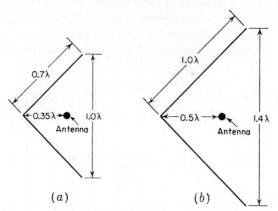

(a)   (b)

FIG. 12-14.   Dimensions for square corner-reflector antennas.

an aperture of more than 2 wavelengths is convenient, more directivity can be obtained for a given physical size of antenna with a parabolic reflector.

12-4. The Parabola.   General Properties.   Suppose that we have a point source and that we wish to produce a plane-wave front over a large aperture by means of a sheet reflector. Referring to Fig. 12-15a, it is then required that the distance from the source to the plane-wave front via path 1 and 2 be equal or[2]

$$2L = R(1 + \cos\theta) \tag{12-9}$$

and

$$R = \frac{2L}{1 + \cos\theta} \tag{12-10}$$

---

[1] The type of driven element is also a factor in determining the band width. Thus, a fat cylindrical element or a biconical element gives more band width than a thin driven element.

[2] This is an application of the principle of equality of path length to the special case where all paths are in the same medium. For the more general situation involving more than one medium see Chap. 14.

This is the equation for the required surface contour. It is the equation of a parabola with the focus at F.

Referring to Fig. 12-15b, the parabolic curve may be defined as follows. The distance from any point P on a parabolic curve to a fixed point F, called the *focus*, is equal to the perpendicular distance to a fixed line called the *directrix*. Thus, in Fig. 12-15b, $PF = PQ$. Referring now to Fig.

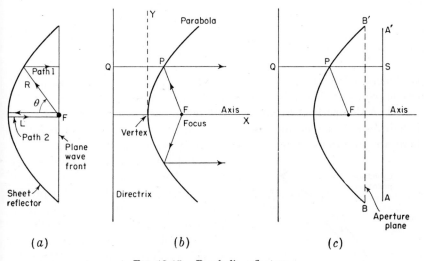

FIG. 12-15.   Parabolic reflectors.

12-15c, let AA' be a line normal to the axis at an arbitrary distance QS from the directrix. Since $PS = QS - PQ$ and $PF = PQ$, it follows that the distance from the focus to S is

$$PF + PS = PF + QS - PQ = QS \qquad (12\text{-}11)$$

Thus, a property of a parabolic reflector is that all waves from an isotropic source at the focus that are reflected from the parabola arrive at a line AA' with equal phase. The "image" of the focus is the directrix, and the reflected field along the line AA' appears as though it originated at the directrix as a plane wave. The plane BB' (Fig. 12-15c) at which a reflector is cut off is called the *aperture plane*.

A cylindrical parabola converts a cylindrical wave radiated by an in-phase line source at the focus, as in Fig. 12-16a, into a plane wave at the aperture. Or a paraboloid of revolution converts a spherical wave from an isotropic source at the focus as in Fig. 12-16b into a uniform plane wave at the aperture. Confining our attention to a single ray or wave path, the

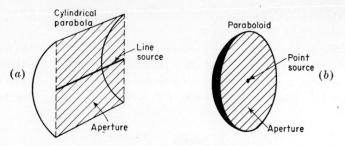

FIG. 12-16. Line source and cylindrical parabolic reflector (a) and point source and paraboloidal reflector (b).

paraboloid has the property of reflecting any ray from the focus into a direction parallel to the axis as suggested in Fig. 12-15b.

12-5. A Comparison Between the Parabolic and Corner Reflector. Although the corner reflector differs in principle from the parabolic reflector, there are situations in which the two may be nearly equivalent. This

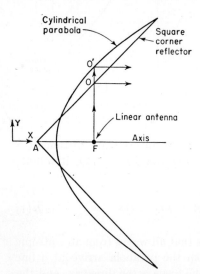

FIG. 12-17. Cylindrical parabolic reflector compared with square corner reflector.

may be illustrated with the aid of Fig. 12-17. Let a linear antenna be located at the focus F of a cylindrical parabolic reflector, and let this arrangement be compared with a square corner reflector of the same aperture and with an antenna-to-corner spacing AF. The parabolic and corner reflectors are superimposed for comparison in Fig. 12-17. A wave radiated in the positive y direction from F is reflected at 0 by the corner reflector and at $0'$ by the cylindrical parabolic reflector. Hence, this wave travels a shorter distance in the corner reflector by an amount $00'$. If $AF = 2\ \lambda$, the electrical length of $00'$ is about 180° so that a marked difference would be expected in the field patterns of the two reflectors. However, if $AF = 0.35\ \lambda$ the electrical length of $00'$ is only about 30°, and this would be expected to cause only a slight difference in the field patterns. It follows that if AF is small in terms of the wavelength the exact shape of the reflector is not of great importance. The practical advantage of the corner reflector is the simplicity and ease of construction of the flat sides.

12-6. The Paraboloidal Reflector.[1]   The surface generated by the revolution of a parabola around its axis is called a *paraboloid* or a *parabola of revolution*.   If an isotropic source is placed at the focus of a paraboloidal reflector as in Fig. 12-18.1a, the portion A of the source radiation that is

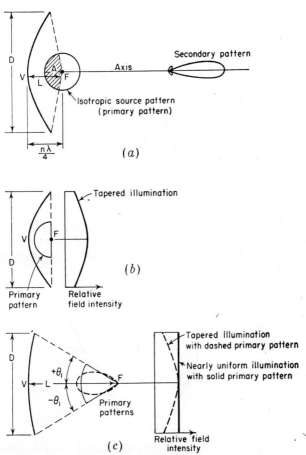

FIG. 12-18.1.   Parabolic reflectors of different focal lengths (L) and with sources of different patterns.

[1] "Microwave Antenna Theory and Design," edited by S. Silver, McGraw-Hill Book Company, Inc., New York, 1949.

H. T. Friis and W. D. Lewis, Radar Antennas, *Bell System Tech. J.*, **26**, 219–317, April, 1947.

C. C. Cutler, Parabolic Antenna Design for Microwaves, *Proc. I.R.E.*, **37**, 1284–1294, November, 1947.

J. C. Slater, "Microwave Transmission," McGraw-Hill Book Company, Inc., New York, 1942, pp. 272–276.

intercepted by the paraboloid is reflected as a plane wave of circular cross section provided that the reflector surface deviates from a true parabolic surface by no more than a small fraction of a wavelength.

If the distance L between the focus and vertex of the paraboloid is an even number of $\frac{1}{4}$ wavelengths, the direct radiation in the axial direction from the source will be in opposite phase and will tend to cancel the central region of the reflected wave. However, if

$$L = \frac{n\lambda}{4} \tag{12-12}$$

where $n = 1, 3, 5, \ldots$, the direct radiation in the axial direction from the source will be in the same phase and will tend to reinforce the central region of the reflected wave. Direct radiation from the source can be eliminated by means of a directional source or primary antenna[1] as in Fig. 12-18.1b and c.

A primary antenna with the idealized hemispherical pattern shown in Fig. 12-18.1b (solid curve) results in a wave of uniform phase over the reflector aperture. However, the amplitude is tapered as indicated. To obtain a more uniform aperture field distribution or illumination, it is necessary to make θ_1 small as suggested in Fig. 12-18.1c by increasing the focal length L while keeping the reflector diameter D constant.[2] If the

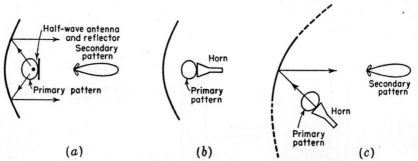

FIG. 12-18.2. Parabolic reflectors with various feed arrangements.

source pattern is uniform between the angles $\pm\theta_1$ as for the solid pattern, the aperture illumination is then nearly uniform. A typical pattern for a directional source as indicated by the dashed curve at (c) gives a more tapered aperture distribution as shown by the dashed line. The greater

[1] It is convenient to refer to the pattern of the source or primary antenna as the *primary pattern* and the pattern of the entire antenna as the *secondary pattern*.

[2] That is, by using a reflector system with a larger F number. The F number is the ratio of the focal distance L to the diameter D ($F = L/D$).

amount of taper with resultant reduction in edge illumination may be desirable in order to reduce the minor-lobe level, this being achieved, however, at some sacrifice in directivity.

The arrangement of Fig. 12-18.1b illustrates the case of a small ratio of focal distance L to aperture diameter D. The arrangement at (c) illustrates the case of a larger ratio. An extreme example of a parabolic reflector with large ratio of focal distance to aperture diameter is afforded by many astronomical telescopes of the reflecting type.

Suitable directional patterns may be obtained with various types of primary antennas. As examples, a $\frac{1}{2}$-wavelength antenna with a small ground plane is shown in Fig. 12-18.2a, and a small horn antenna in Fig. 12-18.2b.

The presence of the primary antenna in the path of the reflected wave, as in the above examples, has two principal disadvantages. These are, first, that waves reflected from the parabola back to the primary antenna produce interaction and mismatching.[1] Second, the primary antenna acts as an obstruction, blocking out the central portion of the aperture. To avoid both effects, only a portion of the paraboloid can be used and the primary antenna displaced as in Fig. 12-18.2c.

Let us next develop an expression for the field distribution across the aperture of a parabolic reflector. Since the development is simpler for a

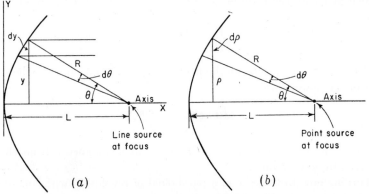

Fig. 12-19. Cross sections of cylindrical parabola (a) and of paraboloid of revolution (b).

cylindrical parabola, this case is treated first, as an introduction to the case for a paraboloid. Consider a cylindrical parabolic reflector with line source as in Fig. 12-19a. The line source is isotropic in a plane perpen-

---

[1] This may be greatly reduced by using a circularly polarized primary antenna, such as a helical beam antenna. If the primary antenna radiation is right circularly polarized, the wave reflected from the parabola is mostly left circularly polarized and the primary antenna is insensitive to this polarization.

dicular to its axis. For a unit distance in the z direction, Fig. 12-19a, the power W in a strip of width dy is

$$W = dy\, P_y \tag{12-13}$$

where P_y = the power density at y
But we have also that

$$W = d\theta\, U' \tag{12-14}$$

where U' = the power per unit angle per unit length in the z direction
Thus,

$$P_y\, dy = U'\, d\theta \tag{12-15}$$

and

$$\frac{P_y}{U'} = \frac{1}{(d/d\theta)(R\sin\theta)} \tag{12-16}$$

where

$$R = \frac{2L}{1 + \cos\theta} \tag{12-17}$$

This yields

$$P_y = \frac{1 + \cos\theta}{2L}\, U' \tag{12-18}$$

The ratio of the power density P_θ at θ to the power density P_0 at $\theta = 0$ is then given by the ratio of (12-18) when $\theta = \theta$ to (12-18) when $\theta = 0$, or

$$\frac{P_\theta}{P_0} = \frac{1 + \cos\theta}{2} \tag{12-19}$$

Hence, in the aperture plane the field-intensity ratio is equal to the square root of the power ratio or

$$\frac{E_\theta}{E_0} = \sqrt{\frac{1 + \cos\theta}{2}} \tag{12-20}$$

where E_θ/E_0 is the relative field intensity at a distance y from the axis as given by $y = R\sin\theta$.

Turning now to the case of a paraboloid of revolution with an isotropic point source as in Fig. 12-19b, the total power W through the annular section of radius ρ and width $d\rho$ is

$$W = 2\pi\rho\, d\rho\, P_\rho \tag{12-21}$$

where P_ρ = the power density at a distance ρ from the axis
This power must be equal to the power radiated by the isotropic source over the solid angle $2\pi\sin\theta\, d\theta$. Thus,

$$W = 2\pi\sin\theta\, d\theta\, U \tag{12-22}$$

where U = the radiation intensity (power per unit solid angle)
Then

$$\rho \, d\rho \, P_\rho = \sin \theta \, d\theta \, U \tag{12-23}$$

or

$$\frac{P_\rho}{U} = \frac{\sin \theta}{\rho(d\rho/d\theta)} \tag{12-24}$$

where $\rho = R \sin \theta = \dfrac{2L \sin \theta}{1 + \cos \theta}$

This yields

$$P_\rho = \frac{(1 + \cos \theta)^2}{4L^2} U \tag{12-25}$$

The ratio of the power density P_θ at the angle θ to the power density P_0 at $\theta = 0$ is then

$$\frac{P_\theta}{P_0} = \frac{(1 + \cos \theta)^2}{4} \tag{12-26}$$

Hence, in the aperture plane the field-intensity ratio is equal to the square root of the power ratio or

$$\frac{E_\theta}{E_0} = \frac{1 + \cos \theta}{2} \tag{12-27}$$

where E_θ/E_0 is the relative field intensity at a radius ρ from the axis as given by $\rho = R \sin \theta$.

12-7. Patterns of Large Circular Apertures with Uniform Illumination. The radiation from a large paraboloid with uniformly illuminated aperture

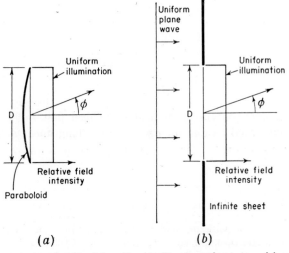

FIG. 12-20. Large paraboloid with uniformly illuminated aperture (a) and equivalent uniformly illuminated aperture of same diameter D in infinite flat sheet (b).

is equivalent to that from a circular aperture of the same diameter D in an infinite metal plate with a uniform plane wave incident on the plate as in Fig. 12-20. The radiation-field pattern for such a uniformly illuminated aperture can be calculated[1] by applying Huygens' principle in a similar way as done for a rectangular aperture in Chap. 4. The normalized field pattern $E(\phi)$ as a function of ϕ and D is

$$E(\phi) = \frac{2\lambda}{\pi D} \frac{J_1 \left[(\pi D/\lambda) \sin \phi \right]}{\sin \phi} \qquad (12\text{-}28)$$

where D = diameter of aperture
λ = free-space wavelength
ϕ = angle with respect to the normal to the aperture (Fig. 12-20)
J_1 = first-order Bessel function
The angle ϕ_0 to the first nulls of the radiation pattern are given by

$$\frac{\pi D}{\lambda} \sin \phi_0 = 3.83 \qquad (12\text{-}29)$$

since $J_1(x) = 0$ when $x = 3.83$. Thus,

$$\phi_0 = \arcsin \frac{3.83\lambda}{\pi D} = \arcsin \frac{1.22\lambda}{D} \qquad (12\text{-}30)$$

When ϕ_0 is very small (aperture large)

$$\phi_0 \simeq \frac{1.22}{D_\lambda} \text{ rad} = \frac{70}{D_\lambda} \text{ deg} \qquad (12\text{-}31)$$

where $D_\lambda = D/\lambda$ = diameter of aperture, wavelengths
The beam width between first nulls is twice this. Hence for large *circular apertures*, the beam width between first nulls is

$$\frac{140}{D_\lambda} \text{ deg} \qquad (12\text{-}32)$$

By way of comparison the beam width between first nulls for a large uniformly illuminated *rectangular aperture* or a long linear array is from (4-149)

$$\frac{115}{L_\lambda} \qquad (12\text{-}33)$$

where L_λ = length of aperture, wavelengths

---

[1] See, for example, J. C. Slater and N. H. Frank, "Introduction to Theoretical Physics," McGraw-Hill Book Company, Inc., New York, 1933, p. 325.

Also see "Microwave Antenna Theory and Design," edited by S. Silver, McGraw-Hill Book Company, Inc., New York, 1949, p. 194.

The beam width between half-power points for a large circular aperture is[1]

$$\frac{58}{D_\lambda} \tag{12-34}$$

These beam widths are summarized and compared with those for horn antennas in Table 13-1.

The directivity D of a large *uniformly illuminated* aperture is given by

$$D = 4\pi \frac{\text{area}}{\lambda^2} \tag{12-35}$$

For a *circular aperture*

$$D = 4\pi \frac{\pi D^2}{4\lambda^2} = 9.87 D_\lambda^2 \tag{12-36}$$

where D_λ = the diameter of the aperture in wavelengths
The power gain G of a circular aperture over a $\frac{1}{2}$-wavelength dipole antenna is

$$G = 6D_\lambda^2 \tag{12-37}$$

For example, an antenna with a uniformly illuminated circular aperture 10 wavelengths in diameter has a gain of 600 or nearly 28 db with respect to a $\frac{1}{2}$-wavelength dipole antenna.

For a *square aperture*, the directivity is

$$D = 4\pi \frac{L^2}{\lambda^2} = 12.6 L_\lambda^2 \tag{12-38}$$

and the power gain over a $\frac{1}{2}$-wavelength dipole is

$$G = 7.7 L_\lambda^2 \tag{12-39}$$

where L_λ = the length of a side
For example, an antenna with a square aperture 10 wavelengths on a side has a gain of 770 or nearly 29 db over a $\frac{1}{2}$-wavelength dipole.

The above directivity and gain relations are for uniformly illuminated apertures at least several wavelengths across. If the illumination is tapered, the directivity and gain are less.

The patterns for a square aperture 5 wavelengths on a side and for a circular aperture 5 wavelengths in diameter are compared in Fig. 12-21. In both cases the field is assumed to be uniform in both magnitude and phase across the aperture. The patterns are given as a function of ϕ in the x-y plane. The patterns in the x-z plane are identical to those in the x-y plane. Although the main-lobe beam width for the circular aperture

---

[1] "Microwave Antenna Theory and Design," edited by S. Silver, McGraw-Hill Book Company, Inc., New York, 1949, p. 194.

is greater than for the square aperture, the side-lobe level for the circular aperture is smaller. A similar effect could be produced with the square aperture by tapering the illumination.

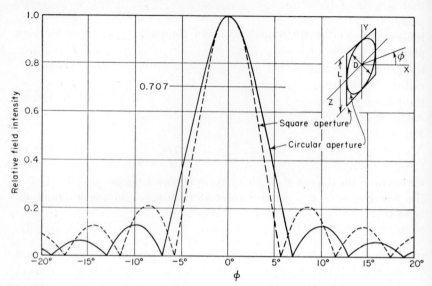

Fig. 12-21.   Relative radiation patterns of circular aperture of diameter $D = 10\,\lambda$ and of square aperture of side length $L = 10\,\lambda$.

12-8. The Cylindrical Parabolic Reflector. The cylindrical parabolic reflector is used with a line-source type of primary antenna. Two types are illustrated in Fig. 12-22. Both produce fan beams, that is, a field pattern that is wide in one plane and narrow in the other. The antenna

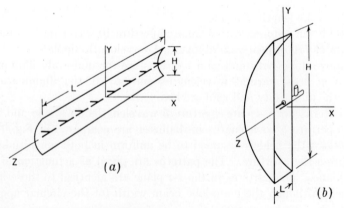

Fig. 12-22.   Parabolic reflector with linear array of eight in-phase $\frac{1}{2}$-wavelength antennas (a) and "pillbox" or "cheese" antenna (b).

in Fig. 12-22a has a line source of eight in-phase $\frac{1}{2}$-wavelength antennas and produces a beam that is narrow in the E plane (x-z plane) and wide in the H plane (x-y plane). The antenna in Fig. 12-22b produces a beam that is wide in the E plane (x-z plane) and narrow in the H plane (x-y plane). The primary antenna consists of a driven stub element with a reflector element. The driven element is fed by a coaxial line. The side plates act as a parallel plane wave guide. They guide the radiation from the primary antenna to the parabolic reflector. This type of antenna is called a "pillbox" or "cheese" antenna. If $L < \lambda/2$, propagation between the planes is restricted to the principal or TEM mode. In this case the source may be a stub antenna of length less than $\frac{1}{2}$ wavelength (as in Fig. 12-22b), or the source may be an open-ended wave guide or small horn. Neglecting edge effects, the patterns of the antennas of Fig. 12-22 are those of rectangular apertures of side dimensions L by H. If the illumination is substantially uniform over the aperture [θ small in Eq. (12-20)], the relations developed for rectangular apertures in Chap. 4 can be applied to calculate the patterns provided that the side length is large compared to the wavelength.

12-9. Aperture Distributions. The field pattern in the x-y plane from a line source of length L (Fig. 12-23a) is identical with the pattern in the x-y plane from a rectangular aperture of length L (Fig. 12-23b) provided that both have the same distribution in the y direction. The pattern of a circular aperture ($D = L$) with the same distribution will be different (wider beam width and smaller side lobes). However, the *relative* effect of a *change* in the taper of a distribution is the same in all cases.

A long linear array of discrete closely spaced sources has nearly the same pattern as a continuous array with the same amplitude and phase distribution, so that some of the conclusions reached in Chap. 4 can be extended to flat constant-phase broadside arrays or apertures in general. To summarize:

1. A uniform amplitude distribution yields the maximum directivity.[1]
2. Tapering the amplitude from a maximum at the center to a smaller value at the edges reduces the side-lobe level but results in a wider main lobe and less directivity.
3. A distribution with an inverse taper (amplitude depression at center)[2] results in a sharper main lobe but also in an increased side-lobe level and less directivity.

If the amplitude is decreased gradually to a small valve at the edges of

[1] See S. Silver, *op. cit.*, p. 177; see also T. T. Taylor, *Proc. I.R.E.*, **36**, 1135, September, 1948.

[2] This type of distribution might be inadvertently produced by the primary antenna blocking out the center of the aperture as discussed in Sec. 12-6.

the aperture, as in a binomial or Gauss error-curve type of distribution, the side-lobe level is effectively zero. However, the attendant decrease in directivity generally makes this kind of distribution unacceptable. For a predetermined side-lobe level the optimum distribution is of the Dolph-Tchebyscheff type. A number of other amplitude distributions are of some interest, for example, the triangular, cosine, and cosine squared types. These are conveniently analyzed by the Fourier transform method as described in the next section.

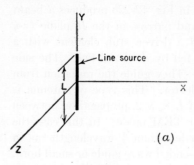

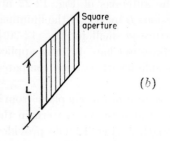

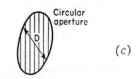

FIG. 12-23. Line source, square aperture, and circular aperture.

In the above discussion it is assumed that the phase is uniform over the aperture. However, if the primary antenna is displaced from the focus of the parabola, or if the phase pattern of the primary antenna is not constant, there will be a phase variation over the aperture. This is usually referred to as a *phase error.*[1] The effects of such phase errors are, in general, undesirable since increased side-lobe level and reduced directivity result. The level of the minima between lobes is also increased.

In some applications beams of special shape are desired that may require distributions having both amplitude and phase tapers. In general, a beam of any shape can be produced by the proper amplitude and phase distribution over an aperture.[2]

12-10. Fourier Transform Method. The Fourier transform method provides a convenient procedure for finding the field patterns of certain

[1] For a detailed discussion of both amplitude distributions and phase errors see "Microwave Antenna Theory and Design," edited by S. Silver, McGraw-Hill Book Company, Inc., New York, 1949; also H. T. Friis and W. D. Lewis, Radar Antennas, *Bell System Tech. J.*, **26**, 219–317, April, 1947.

[2] Chap. 13 by L. C. Van Atta and T. J. Keary, "Microwave Antenna Theory and Design," McGraw-Hill Book Company, Inc., New York, 1949, p. 465. Gives a general survey of beam-shaping techniques.

Chap. 6 by G. Stavis and A. Dorne, "Very High Frequency Techniques," McGraw-Hill Book Company, Inc., New York, 1947, p. 161. Gives a discussion of elliptical-parabolic reflectors.

aperture distributions. Specifically, the field pattern can be formulated as the Fourier transform of the aperture distribution.[1]

Consider a continuous linear in-phase source of length L or a rectangular aperture of height L as in Fig. 12-24. It is assumed that the amplitude distribution is known and that the phase distribution is uniform. It is further assumed that $L \gg \lambda$ so that the beam width of the main lobe (in x direction) is small. Then it may be shown that if the amplitude distribution is given by $F(y)$ the field pattern as a function of ϕ in the x-y plane is given by

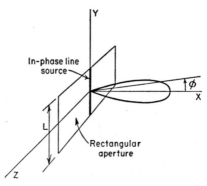

$$E(\phi) = \int_{-L/2}^{+L/2} F(y)\, e^{j\beta y \sin \phi}\, dy \quad (12\text{-}40)$$

where (12-40) is the Fourier transform of $F(y)$. The distribution function $F(y)$ is real if the phase is uniform over the aperture. Further, if the amplitude distribution is sym-

Fig. 12-24. Line source of height L and rectangular aperture of height L.

metrical about the center of the aperture (origin in Fig. 12-24), $F(y)$ is even and the pattern is given by the Fourier cosine transform of $F(y)$. For example, if the amplitude distribution is uniform, $F(y) = 1$ and the field pattern is

$$E(\phi) = \frac{2 \sin [(L_r \sin \phi)/2]}{\beta \sin \phi} \quad (12\text{-}41)$$

The normalized field pattern is

$$E(\phi) = \frac{2 \sin [(L_r \sin \phi)/2]}{L_r \sin \phi} \quad (12\text{-}42)$$

The field patterns for four types of amplitude distributions (see Ramsay[1]) are listed in Table 12-2.[2]

[1] J. F. Ramsay, Fourier Transforms in Aerial Theory, *Marconi Rev.*, **9**, 139, October–December, 1946.

R. C. Spencer, "Fourier Integral Methods of Pattern Analysis," M.I.T. Radiation Laboratory Rep. 762-1, January 21, 1946.

[2] For other distributions see "Microwave Antenna Theory and Design," edited by S. Silver, McGraw-Hill Book Company, Inc., New York, 1949; also R. C. Spencer, "Fourier Integral Methods of Pattern Analysis," M.I.T. Radiation Laboratory Rept. 762-1, January 21, 1946.

TABLE 12-2*

Type of distribution			Field pattern (normalized)
Name	Shape	Formula	
Uniform	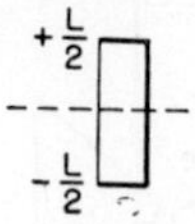	1	$\dfrac{\sin\,[(L_r\sin\phi)/2]}{[(L_r\sin\phi)/2]}$
Triangular	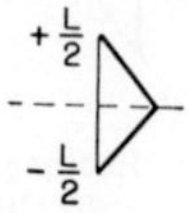	$1-\dfrac{2y}{L}$	$2\left[\dfrac{\sin\,[(L_r\sin\phi)/4]}{L_r\sin\phi}\right]^2$
Cosine	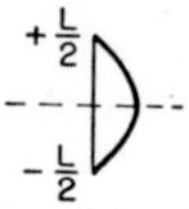	$\cos\dfrac{\pi y}{L}$	$\dfrac{(\pi/2)^2\,\cos\,[(L_r\sin\phi)/2]}{(\pi/2)^2-[(L_r\sin\phi)/2]^2}$
Cosine squared	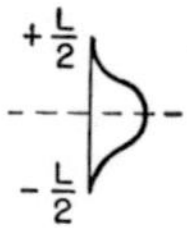	$\cos^2\dfrac{\pi y}{L}$	$\dfrac{\sin\,[(L_r\sin\phi)/2]}{L_r\sin\phi}\dfrac{2}{1-[(L_r\sin\phi)^2/4\pi^2]}$

*L_r = length of array or aperture in radians

     = $2\pi(L/\lambda)$

   ϕ = angle from the normal to the array or aperture (Fig. 12-24)

PROBLEMS

12-1. Calculate and plot the radiation pattern of a $\frac{1}{2}$-wavelength dipole antenna spaced 0.15 wavelength from an infinite flat sheet for assumed antenna loss resistances R_L = 0 and 10 ohms. Express the patterns in gain over a $\frac{1}{2}$-wavelength dipole antenna in free space with the same power input (and zero loss resistance).

12-2. A square-corner reflector has a driven $\frac{1}{2}$-wavelength dipole antenna spaced 0.5 wavelength from the corner. Assume perfectly conducting sheet reflectors of infinite extent (ideal reflector). Calculate and plot the radiation pattern in a plane at right angles to the driven element.

12-3. Calculate and plot the pattern of an ideal square-corner reflector with $\frac{1}{2}$-wavelength driven antenna spaced 0.5 wavelength from the corner but with the antenna displaced 20° from the bisector of the corner angle. The pattern to be calculated is in a plane perpendicular to the antenna and to the reflecting sides.

12-4. Calculate and plot the radiation patterns of a paraboloidal reflector with uniformly illuminated aperture when the diameter is 8 wavelengths and when the diameter is 16 wavelengths.

12-5. Calculate the radiation pattern of a cylindrical parabolic reflector of square aperture 16 wavelengths on a side when the illumination is uniform over the aperture and when the field intensity across the aperture follows a cosine variation with maximum intensity at the center and zero intensity at the edges. Compare the two cases by plotting the normalized curves on the same graph.

12-6. *a.* Calculate and plot the pattern of a 90° corner reflector with a thin center-fed $\frac{1}{2}$-wavelength driven antenna spaced 0.35 wavelength from the corner. Assume that the corner reflector is of infinite extent.

b. Calculate the radiation resistance of the driven antenna.

c. Calculate the gain of the antenna and corner reflector over the antenna alone. Assume that losses are negligible.

12-7. Assume that the corner reflector of Prob. 6 is removed and that in its place the three images used in the analysis are present physically resulting in a four-element driven array.

a. Calculate and plot the pattern of this array.

b. Calculate the radiation resistance at the center of one of the antennas.

c. Calculate the gain of the array over one of the antennas alone.

12-8. Four 90° corner-reflector antennas are arranged in line as a broadside array. The corner edges are parallel and side by side as in the figure. The spacing between corners is 1 wavelength. The driven antenna in each corner is a $\frac{1}{2}$-wavelength element spaced 0.4 wavelength from the corner. All antennas are energized in phase

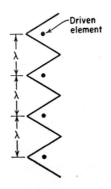

and have equal current amplitude. Assuming that the properties of each corner are the same as if its sides were of infinite extent, what is

a. the gain of the array over a single $\frac{1}{2}$-wavelength antenna?

b. the half-power beam width in the H plane?

12-9. Show that the variation of field across the aperture of a paraboloidal reflector with an isotropic source is proportional to $1/(1 + (\rho/2L)^2)$ where ρ is the radial distance from the axis of the paraboloid. Show that this relation is equivalent to $(1 + \cos \theta)/2$.

12-10. *a.* Show that the relative field pattern in the plane of the driven $\frac{1}{2}$-wavelength element of a square corner reflector is given by

$$E = [1 - \cos (S_r \sin \theta)] \frac{\cos (90° \cos \theta)}{\sin \theta}$$

where θ is the angle with respect to the element axis. Assume that the corner-reflector sheets are perfectly conducting and of infinite extent.

b. Calculate and plot the field pattern in the plane of the driven element for a spacing of $\frac{1}{2}$ wavelength to the corner. Compare with the pattern at right angles (Prob. 12-2).

CHAPTER 13

SLOT, HORN, AND COMPLEMENTARY ANTENNAS

13-1. Slot Antennas. The antenna shown in Fig. 13-1a, consisting of two resonant $\frac{1}{4}$-wavelength stubs connected to a two-wire transmission line, forms an inefficient radiator. The long wires are closely spaced ($w \ll \lambda$) and carry currents of opposite phase so that their fields tend to

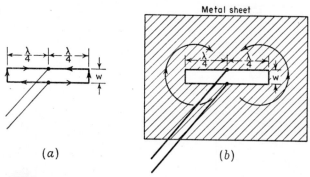

Fig. 13-1. Parallel connected $\frac{1}{4}$-wavelength stubs (a) and simple slot antenna (b).

cancel. The end wires carry currents in the same phase, but they are too short to radiate efficiently. Hence, enormous currents may be required to radiate appreciable amounts of power.

The antenna in Fig. 13-1b, on the other hand, is a very efficient radiator. In this arrangement a $\frac{1}{2}$-wavelength slot is cut in a flat metal sheet. Although the width of the slot is small ($w \ll \lambda$), the currents are not confined to the edges of the slot but spread out over the sheet. This is a simple type of slot antenna. Radiation occurs equally from both sides of the sheet. If the slot is horizontal, as shown, the radiation normal to the sheet is vertically polarized.

A slot antenna may be conveniently energized with a coaxial transmission line as in Fig. 13-2a. The outer conductor of the cable is bonded to the metal sheet. Since the terminal resistance at the center of a resonant $\frac{1}{2}$-wavelength slot in a large sheet is about 500 ohms and the characteristic impedance of coaxial transmission lines is usually much less, an off-center feed such as shown in Fig. 13-2b may be used to provide a better im-

353

pedance match. For a 50-ohm coaxial cable the distance s should be about $\frac{1}{20}$ wavelength. Slot antennas fed by a coaxial line in this manner are illustrated in Fig. 13-2c and d. The radiation normal to the sheet with the horizontal slot (Fig. 13-2c) is vertically polarized while radiation normal to the sheet with the vertical slot (Fig. 13-2d) is horizontally polarized. The slot may be $\frac{1}{2}$ wavelength long, as shown, or more.

A flat sheet with a $\frac{1}{2}$-wavelength slot radiates equally on both sides of the sheet. However, if the sheet is very large (ideally infinite) and boxed in as in Fig. 13-3a, radiation occurs only from one side. If the depth d

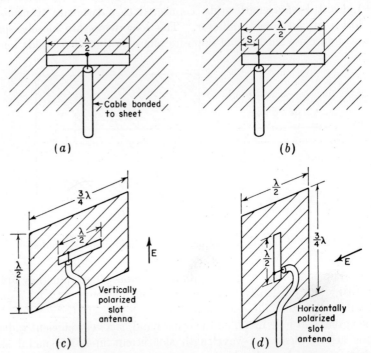

FIG. 13-2. Slot antennas fed by coaxial transmission lines.

of the box is appropriate ($d \sim \lambda/4$ for a thin slot), no appreciable shunt susceptance appears across the terminals. With such a zero susceptance box, the terminal impedance of the resonant $\frac{1}{2}$-wavelength slot is nonreactive and approximately twice its value without the box or about 1,000 ohms.

The boxed-in slot antenna might be applied even at relatively long wavelengths[1] by using the ground as the flat conducting sheet and exca-

[1] H. G. Booker, Slot Aerials and Their Relation to Complementary Wire Aerials, *J.I.E.E.* (London), **93**, Part IIIA, No. 4, 1946.

vating a trench $\frac{1}{2}$ wavelength long by $\frac{1}{4}$ wavelength deep as suggested in Fig. 13-3b. The absence of any structure above the ground level might make this type of antenna attractive, for example, in applications near airports. To improve the ground conductivity, the walls of the trench

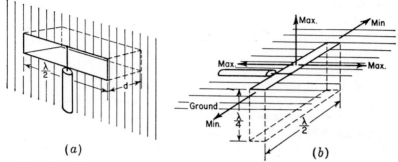

Fig. 13-3. Boxed-in slot antenna (a) and application to provide flush radiator (b).

and the ground surrounding the slot can be covered with copper sheet or screen. Radiation is maximum in all directions at right angles to the slot and is zero along the ground in the directions of the ends of the slot as

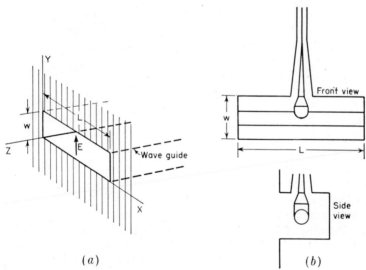

Fig. 13-4. Wave-guide fed slot (a) and T-fed slot (b).

suggested in Fig. 13-3b. The radiation along the ground is vertically polarized.

Radiation from only one side of a large flat sheet may also be achieved by a slot fed with a wave guide as in Fig. 13-4a. With transmission in the guide in the TE_{10} mode the direction of the electric field **E** is as shown. The width L of the guide must be more than $\frac{1}{2}$ wavelength to transmit energy, but it should be less than 1 wavelength to suppress higher order transmission modes.   With the slot horizontal, as shown, the radiation normal to the sheet is vertically polarized.   The slot opening constitutes an abrupt termination to the wave guide.   It has been found[1] that the resulting impedance mismatch is least over a wide frequency band if the ratio L/w is less than 3.

A compact wide-band method for feeding a boxed-in slot is illustrated in Fig. 13-4b.   In this T-fed arrangement[1] the bar compensates the impedance characteristics so as to provide a SWR on a 50-ohm feed line of less than 2 over a frequency range of nearly 2 to 1.   The ratio L/w of the length to width of the slot is about 3.

Dispensing with the flat sheet altogether, an array of slots may be cut

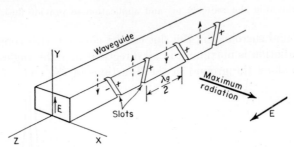

FIG. 13-5.   Broadside array of slots in wave guide.

in the wave guide as in Fig. 13-5 so as to produce a directional radiation pattern.[2]   With transmission in the guide in the TE_{10} mode, the instantaneous direction of the electric field **E** inside the guide is as indicated by the dashed arrows.   By cutting inclined slots as shown at intervals of $\lambda_g/2$ (where λ_g is the wavelength in the guide), the slots are energized in phase and produce a directional pattern with maximum radiation broadside to the guide.   If the guide is horizontal and **E** inside the guide is vertical, the radiated field is horizontally polarized as suggested in Fig. 13-5.

13-2. Patterns of Slot Antennas in Flat Sheets.   Consider the horizontal $\frac{1}{2}$-wavelength slot antenna of width w in a perfectly conducting flat sheet of infinite extent as in Fig. 13-6a.   The sheet is energized at the terminals FF.   It has been postulated by Booker that the radiation pattern of the slot is the same as that of the complementary horizontal $\frac{1}{2}$-wavelength dipole

[1] Chap. 7 by A. Dorne and D. Lazarus, "Very High Frequency Techniques," Radio Research Laboratory Staff, McGraw-Hill Book Company, Inc., New York, 1947.

[2] W. H. Watson, "The Physical Principles of Wave Guide Transmission and Antenna Systems," Oxford University Press, London, 1947.

consisting of a perfectly conducting flat strip of width w and energized at
the terminals FF as indicated in Fig. 13-6b but with two differences.
These are (1) that the electric and magnetic fields are interchanged and
(2) that the component of the electric field of the slot normal to the sheet

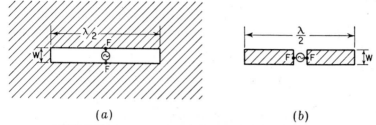

(a) (b)

FIG. 13-6. $\frac{1}{2}$-wavelength slot in infinite flat sheet (a) and complementary $\frac{1}{2}$-wavelength
dipole antenna (b).

is discontinuous from one side of the sheet to the other, the direction of
the field reversing.   The tangential component of the magnetic field is,
likewise, discontinuous.

The patterns of the $\frac{1}{2}$-wavelength slot and the complementary dipole are

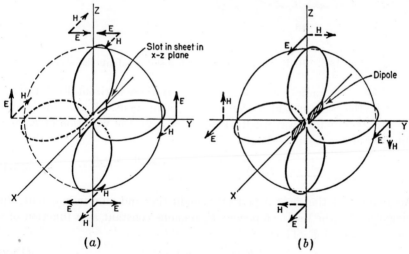

(a) (b)

FIG. 13-7.   Radiation field patterns of slot in infinite sheet (a) and of complementary
dipole antenna (b).

compared in Fig. 13-7.   The infinite flat sheet is coincident with the x-z
plane, and the long dimension of the slot is in the x direction (Fig. 13-7a).
The complementary dipole is coincident with the x axis (Fig. 13-7b).   The
radiation-field patterns have the same doughnut shape, as indicated, but

the directions of **E** and **H** are interchanged. The solid arrows indicate the direction of the electric field **E** and the dashed arrows the direction of the magnetic field **H**.

If the x-y plane in Fig. 13-7a is horizontal and the z axis vertical, the radiation everywhere in the x-y plane from the horizontal slot is vertically polarized. Turning the slot to a vertical position (coincident with the z axis) rotates the radiation pattern through 90° to the position shown in

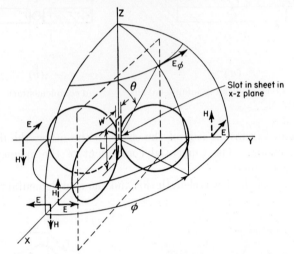

Fig. 13-8.   Radiation pattern of vertical slot in infinite flat sheet.

Fig. 13-8. The radiation in this case is everywhere horizontally polarized. That is, the electric field has only an E_ϕ component. If the slot is very thin $(w \ll \lambda)$ and $\frac{1}{2}$ wavelength long $(L = \lambda/2)$, the variation of E_ϕ as a function of θ is from (5-84) given by

$$E_\phi(\theta) = \frac{\cos\left[(\pi/2)\cos\theta\right]}{\sin\theta} \qquad (13\text{-}1)$$

Assuming that the sheet is perfectly conducting and infinite in extent, the magnitude of the field component E_ϕ remains constant as a function of ϕ for any value of θ. Thus,

$$E_\phi(\phi) = \text{constant} \qquad (13\text{-}2)$$

Consider now the situation where the slot is cut in a sheet of finite extent as suggested by the dashed lines in Fig. 13-8. This change produces relatively little effect on the $E_\phi(\theta)$ pattern given by (13-1). However, there must be a drastic change in the $E_\phi(\phi)$ pattern since in the x direction, for example, the fields radiated from the two sides of the sheet are equal in magnitude but opposite in phase so that they cancel. Hence, there is a null in all directions in the plane of the sheet. For a sheet of given length

L in the x direction the field pattern in the x-y plane might then be as indicated by the solid curve in Fig. 13-9a. The dashed curve is for an

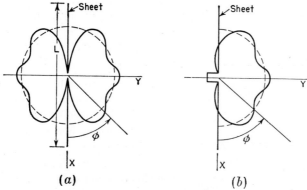

(a)   (b)

Fig. 13-9. Solid curves show patterns in x-y plane for slot in finite sheet of length L. Slot is open on both sides in (a) and closed on left side in (b). Dashed curves show pattern for infinite sheet. All patterns idealized.

infinite sheet ($L = \infty$). If one side of the slot is boxed in, there is radiation in the plane of the sheet as suggested by the pattern in Fig. 13-9b.[1] With a finite sheet the pattern usually exhibits a scalloped or undulating

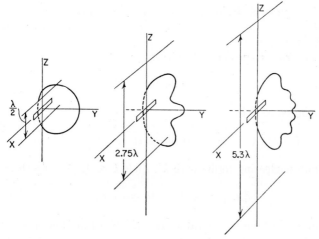

Fig. 13-10. Measured ϕ-plane patterns of $\frac{1}{2}$-wavelength boxed-in slot antennas in finite sheets of three lengths $L = 0.5$, 2.75, and 5.3 wavelengths. The width of the slots is 0.1 wavelength. (*After Dorne and Lazarus.*)

[1] According to H. G. Booker, Slot Aerials and Their Relation to Complementary Wire Aerials, *J.I.E.E.* (London), **93**, Part IIIA, No. 4, 1946, the energy density in the $\phi = 0°$ or 180° directions is $\frac{1}{2}$ that for an infinite sheet or the field intensity is 0.707 that for an infinite sheet.

characteristic as suggested in Fig. 13-9. As the length L of the sheet is increased, the pattern undulations become more numerous but the magnitude of the undulations decreases so that for a very large sheet the pattern conforms closely to a circular shape. Measured patterns[1] illustrating this effect are shown in Fig. 13-10 for three values of L. A method due to Alford for locating the angular positions of the maxima and minima is described by Dorne and Lazarus.[1] In this method the assumption is made that the far field is produced by three sources (see Fig. 13-11), one (1) at the slot of strength 1 sin ωt and two (2 and 3) at the edges of the sheet with a strength k sin ($\omega t - \delta$) where $k \ll 1$ and δ gives the phase difference of the edge sources with respect to the source (1) at the slot. At the point P at a large distance in the direction ϕ the relative field

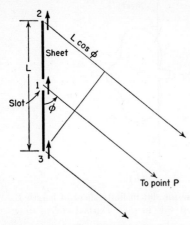

FIG. 13-11. Construction for locating maxima and minima of ϕ pattern for slot in a finite sheet.

intensity is then

$$E = \sin \omega t + k \sin (\omega t - \delta - \epsilon) + k \sin (\omega t - \delta + \epsilon) \qquad (13\text{-}3)$$

where $\epsilon = (\pi/\lambda) L \cos \phi$
By trigonometric expansion and rearrangement

$$E = (1 + 2k \cos \delta \cos \epsilon) \sin \omega t - (2k \sin \delta \cos \epsilon) \cos \omega t \qquad (13\text{-}4)$$

and the modulus of E is

$$|E| = \sqrt{(1 + 2k \cos \delta \cos \epsilon)^2 + (2k \sin \delta \cos \epsilon)^2} \qquad (13\text{-}5)$$

Squaring and neglecting terms with k^2, since $k \ll 1$, (13-5) reduces to

$$|E| = \sqrt{1 + 4k \cos \delta \cos \epsilon} \qquad (13\text{-}6)$$

The maximum and minimum values of $|E|$ as a function of ϵ occur when $\epsilon = n\pi$, so that

$$\epsilon = \frac{\pi}{\lambda} L \cos \phi = n\pi \qquad (13\text{-}7)$$

[1] Chap. 7, by A. Dorne and D. Lazarus, "Very High Frequency Techniques," Radio Research Laboratory Staff, McGraw-Hill Book Company, Inc., New York, 1947 (see Sec. 7-3).

where n is an integer.   Thus

$$\cos \phi = \frac{n\lambda}{L} \text{ and } \phi = \arccos \frac{n\lambda}{L} \qquad (13\text{-}8)$$

The values of ϕ for maxima and minima in the ϕ pattern are given by (13-8). These locations are independent of k and δ. If $\cos \delta$ is positive, then the maxima correspond to even values of n and the minima to odd value of n.

13-3. Babinet's Principle and Complementary Antennas. By means of Babinet's principle many of the problems of slot antennas can be reduced

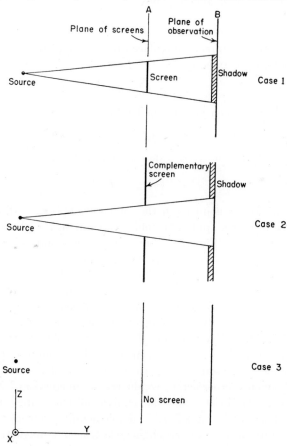

Fig. 13-12.   Optical illustration of Babinet's principle.

to situations involving complementary linear antennas for which solutions have already been obtained.   In optics Babinet's principle[1] may be stated as follows:

[1] See, for example, Max Born, "Optik," Verlag Julius Springer, Berlin, 1933, p. 155.

The field at any point behind a plane having a screen, if added to the field at the same point when the complementary screen is substituted, is equal to the field at the point when no screen is present.

The principle may be illustrated by considering an example with three cases. Let a source and two imaginary planes, plane of screens A, and plane of observation B, be arranged as in Fig. 13-12. As Case 1, let a perfectly absorbing screen be placed in plane A. Then in plane B there is a region of shadow as indicated. Let the field behind this screen be some function f_1 of x, y, and z. Thus,

$$F_s = f_1(x, y, z,) \qquad (13\text{-}9)$$

As Case 2 let the first screen be replaced by its complementary screen and the field behind it be given by

$$F_{cs} = f_2(x, y, z) \qquad (13\text{-}10)$$

As Case 3 with no screen present the field is

$$F_0 = f_3(x, y, z). \qquad (13\text{-}11)$$

Then, Babinet's principle asserts that at the same point x_1, y_1, z_1

$$F_s + F_{cs} = F_0 \qquad (13\text{-}12)$$

The source may be a point as in the above example or a distribution of sources. The principle applies not only to points in the plane of observation B as suggested in Fig. 13-12 but also to any point behind screen A. Although the principle is obvious enough for the simple shadow case above, it also applies where diffraction is considered.

Babinet's principle has been extended and generalized by Booker[1] to take into account the vector nature of the electromagnetic field. In this extension it is assumed that the screen is plane, perfectly conducting, and infinitesimally thin. Furthermore, if one screen is perfectly conducting ($\sigma = \infty$), the complementary screen must have infinite permeability ($\mu = \infty$). Thus, if one screen is a perfect conductor of electricity, the complementary screen is a perfector "conductor" of magnetism. No infinitely permeable material exists, but the equivalent effect may be obtained by making both the original and complementary screens of perfectly conducting material and interchanging electric and magnetic quantities everywhere. Although no perfect conductors of electricity exist, many metals, such as silver and copper, have so high a conductivity that we may assume the conductivity is infinite with a negligible error in most applications.

[1] H. G. Booker, Slot Aerials and Their Relation to Complementary Wire Aerials, *J.I.E.E.* (London), **93**, Part IIIA, No. 4, 1946.

As an illustration of Booker's extension of Babinet's principle, consider the cases in Fig. 13-13. The source in all cases is a dipole antenna. In Case 1 the dipole is horizontal, and the original screen is an infinite, perfectly conducting, plane, infinitesimally thin sheet with a vertical slot cut out as indicated. At a point P behind the screen the field is E_1. In Case 2 the original screen is replaced by the complementary screen con-

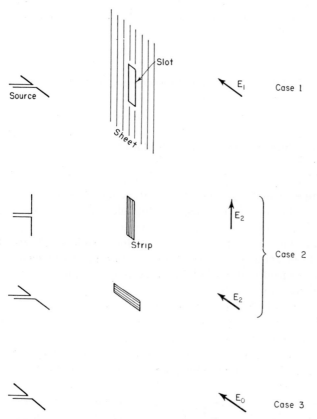

FIG. 13-13. Illustration of Babinet's principle applied to a slot in an infinite metal sheet and the complementary metal strip.

sisting of a perfectly conducting, plane, infinitesimally thin strip of the same dimensions as the slot in the original screen. In addition the dipole source is turned vertical so as to interchange **E** and **H**. At the same point P behind the screen the field is E_2. As an alternative situation for Case 2 the dipole source is horizontal, and the strip is also turned horizontal. Finally, in Case 3 no screen is present, and the field at point P is E_0. Then, by Babinet's principle

$$E_1 + E_2 = E_0 \qquad (13\text{-}13)$$

or

$$\frac{E_1}{E_0} + \frac{E_2}{E_0} = 1 \qquad (13\text{-}14)$$

Babinet's principle may also be applied to points in front of the screens. In the situation of Case 1 (Fig. 13-13) a large amount of energy may be transmitted through the slot so that the field E_1 may be about equal to the field E_0 with no intermediate screen (Case 3). In such a situation the complementary dipole acts like a reflector, and E_2 would be very small. The fact that a metal sheet with a $\frac{1}{2}$-wavelength slot, or, in general, an orifice of at least 1 wavelength perimeter, may transmit considerable energy, means that slots or orifices of this size should be assiduously avoided in sheet reflectors such as described in Chap. 12 when **E** is not parallel to the slot.

13-4. The Impedance of Complementary Screens. In this section Babinet's principle is applied with the aid of a transmission-line analogy to finding the relation between the surface impedance Z_1 of a screen and the surface impedance Z_2 of the complementary metal screen.[1]

Consider the infinite transmission line shown in Fig. 13-14a of characteristic impedance Z_0 or characteristic admittance $Y_0 = 1/Z_0$. Let a shunt admittance Y_1 be placed across the line. An incident wave traveling to the right of voltage V_i is partly reflected at Y_1 as a wave of voltage V_r and partly transmitted beyond Y_1 as a wave of voltage V_t. The voltages are measured across the line.

This situation is analogous to a plane wave of field intensity E_i incident normally on a plane screen of infinite extent with a surface admittance, or admittance per square, of Y_1. That is, the admittance measured between the opposite edges of any square section of the sheet as in Fig. 13-14c is Y_1. Neglecting the impedance of the leads the admittance

$$Y_1 = \frac{I}{V} \qquad \text{mhos (per square)} \qquad (13\text{-}15)$$

The value of Y is the same for *any square section* of the sheet. Thus, the section may be 1 cm square or 1 meter square. Hence, (13-15) has the dimensions of admittance rather than of admittance per length squared and is called a *surface admittance*, or *admittance per square*. The field intensities of the waves reflected and transmitted normally to the screen are E_r and E_t. Let the medium surrounding the screen be free space. It has a characteristic admittance Y_0 which is a pure conductance G_0. Thus,

[1] The treatment follows that given by H. G. Booker. See Slot Aerials and Their Relation to Complementary Wire Aerials, *J.I.E.E.* (London), **93**, Part IIIA, No. 4, 1946.

$$Y_0 = \frac{1}{Z_0} = \frac{1}{377} = G_0 \tag{13-16}$$

The ratio of the magnetic to the electric field intensity of any plane traveling wave in free space has this value. Hence,

$$Y_0 = \frac{H_i}{E_i} = -\frac{H_r}{E_r} = \frac{H_t}{E_t} \tag{13-17}$$

where H_i, H_r, and H_t are the magnetic field intensities of the incident, reflected, and transmitted waves, respectively.

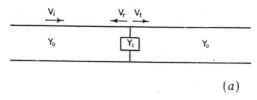

(a)

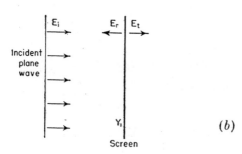

(b)

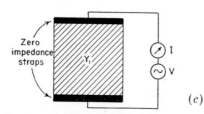

(c)

FIG. 13-14. Shunt admittance across transmission line (a) is analogous to infinite screen in path of plane wave (b). Method of measuring surface admittance of screen is suggested in (c).

The transmission coefficient for voltage τ_v of the transmission line[1] (Fig. 13-14a) is

$$\tau_v = \frac{V_t}{V_i} = \frac{2Y_0}{2Y_0 + Y_1} \tag{13-18}$$

[1] See, for example, S. A. Schelkunoff, "Electromagnetic Waves," D. Van Nostrand Company, Inc., New York, 1943, p. 212.

By analogy the transmission coefficient for the electric field (Fig. 13-14b) is

$$\tau_E = \frac{E_t}{E_i} = \frac{2Y_0}{2Y_0 + Y_1} \tag{13-19}$$

If now the original screen is replaced by its complementary screen with an admittance per square of Y_2, the new transmission coefficient is the ratio of the new transmitted field E_t' to the incident field. Thus,

$$\tau_E' = \frac{E_t'}{E_i} = \frac{2Y_0}{2Y_0 + Y_2} \tag{13-20}$$

Applying Babinet's principle, we have from (13-14) that

$$\frac{E_t}{E_i} + \frac{E_t'}{E_i} = 1 \tag{13-21}$$

or

$$\tau_E + \tau_E' = 1 \tag{13-22}$$

Therefore,

$$\frac{2Y_0}{2Y_0 + Y_1} + \frac{2Y_0}{2Y_0 + Y_2} = 1 \tag{13-23a}$$

and we obtain Booker's result that

$$Y_1 Y_2 = 4Y_0^2 \tag{13-23b}$$

Since $Y_1 = 1/Z_1$, $Y_2 = 1/Z_2$, and $Y_0 = 1/Z_0$,

$$Z_1 Z_2 = \frac{Z_0^2}{4} \quad \text{or} \quad \sqrt{Z_1 Z_2} = \frac{Z_0}{2} \tag{13-24a}$$

Thus, the geometric mean of the impedances of the two screens equals one-half the intrinsic impedance of the surrounding medium. Since, for free space, $Z_0 = 376.7$ ohms,

$$Z_1 = \frac{35,476}{Z_2} \quad \text{ohms} \tag{13-24b}$$

If screen 1 is an infinite grating of narrow parallel strips as in Fig. 13-15a, then the complementary screen (screen 2) is an infinite grating of narrow slots as shown in Fig. 13-15b. Suppose that a low-frequency plane wave is incident normally on screen 1 with the electric field parallel to the strips. Then the grating acts as a perfectly reflecting screen and zero field penetrates to the rear. Thus $Z_1 = 0$ and from (13-24b) $Z_2 = \infty$ so that the complementary screen of slots (screen 2) offers no impediment to the passage of the wave. If the frequency is increased sufficiently, screen 1 begins to transmit part of the incident wave. If at the frequency F_0

screen 1 has a surface impedance $Z_1 = j188$ ohms per square, the impedance Z_2 of screen 2 is $-j188$ ohms per square so that both screens transmit equally well. If screen 1 becomes more transparent (Z_1 larger) as the frequency is further increased, screen 2 will become more opaque (Z_2

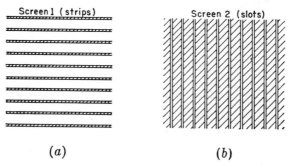

Screen 1 (strips)

Screen 2 (slots)

(a) (b)

Fig. 13-15.   Screen of parallel strips (a) and complementary screen of slots (b).

smaller). At any frequency the sum of the fields transmitted through screen 1 and through screen 2 is a constant and equal to the field without any screen present.

13-5. The Impedance of Slot Antennas. In this section a relation is developed for the impedance Z_s of a slot antenna in terms of the impedance Z_d of the complementary dipole antenna.[1] Knowing Z_d for the dipole, the impedance Z_s of the slot can then be determined.

Consider the slot antenna shown in Fig. 13-16a and the complementary dipole antenna shown in Fig. 13-16b. The terminals of each antenna are indicated by FF, and it is assumed that they are separated by an infinitesimal distance. It is assumed that the dipole and slot are cut from an infinitesimally thin, plane, perfectly conducting sheet.

Let a generator be connected to the terminals of the slot. The driving-point impedance Z_s at the terminals is the ratio of the terminal voltage V_s to the terminal current I_s. Let $\mathbf{E}_s$ and $\mathbf{H}_s$ be the electric and magnetic fields of the slot at any point P. Then the voltage V_s at the terminals FF of the slot is given by the line integral of $\mathbf{E}_s$ over the path C_1 (Fig. 13-16a) as C_1 approaches zero. Thus,

$$V_s = \lim_{C_1 \to 0} \int_{C_1} \mathbf{E}_s \cdot d\mathbf{l} \tag{13-25}$$

where $d\mathbf{l}$ = an infinitesimal vector element of length $\mathbf{l}$ along the contour or path C_1

[1] The treatment follows that given by H. G. Booker, Slot Aerials and Their Relation to Complementary Wire Aerials, *J.I.E.E.* (London), **93**, Part IIIA, No. 4, 1946 with minor embellishments suggested by V. H. Rumsey.

The current I_s at the terminals of the slot is

$$I_s = 2 \lim_{C_2 \to 0} \int_{C_2} \mathbf{H}_s \cdot d\mathbf{l} \tag{13-26}$$

The path C_2 is just outside the metal sheet and parallel to its surface. The factor 2 enters because only one-half the closed line integral is taken, the line integral over the other side of the sheet being equal by symmetry.

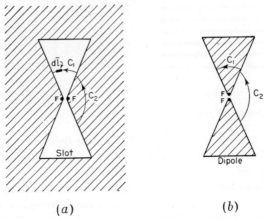

(a) (b)

Fig. 13-16.   Slot antenna and complementary dipole antenna.

Turning our attention to the complementary dipole antenna, let a generator be connected to the terminals of the dipole. The driving-point impedance Z_d at the terminals is the ratio of the terminal voltage V_d to the terminal current I_d. Let $\mathbf{E}_d$ and $\mathbf{H}_d$ be the electric and magnetic fields of the dipole at any point P. Then the voltage at the dipole terminals is

$$V_d = \lim_{C_2 \to 0} \int_{C_2} \mathbf{E}_d \cdot d\mathbf{l} \tag{13-27}$$

and the current is

$$I_d = 2 \lim_{C_1 \to 0} \int_{C_1} \mathbf{H}_d \cdot d\mathbf{l} \tag{13-28}$$

But

$$\lim_{C_2 \to 0} \int_{C_2} \mathbf{E}_d \cdot d\mathbf{l} = Z_0 \lim_{C_2 \to 0} \int_{C_2} \mathbf{H}_s \cdot d\mathbf{l} \tag{13-29}$$

and

$$\lim_{C_1 \to 0} \int_{C_1} \mathbf{H}_d \cdot d\mathbf{l} = \frac{1}{Z_0} \lim_{C_1 \to 0} \int_{C_1} \mathbf{E}_s \cdot d\mathbf{l} \tag{13-30}$$

where Z_0 is the intrinsic impedance of the surrounding medium. Substituting (13-27) and (13-26) in (13-29) yields

$$V_d = \frac{Z_0}{2} I_s \tag{13-31}$$

Substituting (13-28) and (13-25) in (13-30) gives

$$V_s = \frac{Z_0}{2} I_d \tag{13-32}$$

Multiplying (13-31) and (13-32) we have

$$\frac{V_s}{I_s} \frac{V_d}{I_d} = \frac{Z_0^2}{4} \tag{13-33}$$

or

$$Z_s Z_d = \frac{Z_0^2}{4} \quad \text{or} \quad Z_s = \frac{Z_0^2}{4Z_d} \tag{13-34}$$

Thus, we obtain Booker's result that the terminal impedance Z_s of a slot antenna is equal to $\frac{1}{4}$ of the square of the intrinsic impedance of the surrounding medium divided by the terminal impedance Z_d of the complementary dipole antenna. For free space $Z_0 = 376.7$ ohms, so

$$Z_s = \frac{Z_0^2}{4Z_d} = \frac{35,476}{Z_d} \quad \text{ohms}^1 \tag{13-35}$$

The impedance of the slot is proportional to the admittance of the dipole, or vice versa. Since, in general, Z_d may be complex, we may write

$$Z_s = \frac{35,476}{R_d + jX_d} = \frac{35,476}{R_d^2 + X_d^2} (R_d - jX_d) \tag{13-36}$$

where R_d and X_d are the resistive and reactive components of the dipole terminal impedance Z_d. Thus, if the dipole antenna is inductive, the slot is capacitative and vice versa. Lengthening a $\frac{1}{2}$-wavelength dipole makes it more inductive, but lengthening a $\frac{1}{2}$-wavelength slot makes it more capacitative.

Let us now consider some numerical examples proceeding from known dipole types to the complementary slot types. The impedance of an infinitesimally thin $\frac{1}{2}$-wavelength antenna ($L = 0.5\,\lambda$ and $L/D = \infty$) is $73 + j42.5$ ohms (see Chap. 10). Therefore, the terminal impedance of

---

[1] If the intrinsic impedance Z_0 of free space were unknown, (13-35) provides a means of determining it by measurements of the impedance Z_s of a slot antenna and the impedance Z_d of the complementary dipole antenna. The impedance Z_0 is twice the geometric means of Z_s and Z_d or

$$Z_0 = 2\sqrt{Z_s Z_d} \tag{13-37}$$

an infinitesimally thin $\frac{1}{2}$-wavelength slot antenna ($L = 0.5\ \lambda$ and $L/w = \infty$) is

$$Z_1 = \frac{35{,}476}{73 + j42.5} = 363 - j211 \text{ ohms}$$

See Fig. 13-17a.

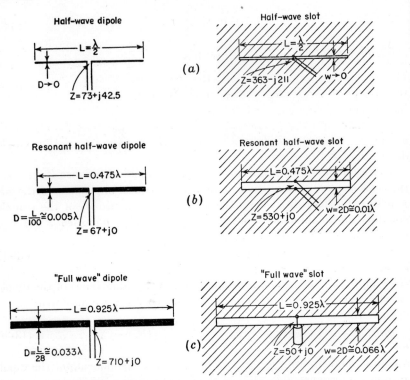

Fig. 13-17. Comparison of impedances of cylindrical dipole antennas with complementary slot antennas.

As another more practical example, a cylindrical antenna with a length-to-diameter ratio of 100 ($L/D = 100$) is resonant when the length is about 0.475 wavelength ($L = 0.475\ \lambda$). The terminal impedance is resistive and equal to about 67 ohms. The terminal resistance of the complementary slot antenna is then

$$Z_1 = \frac{35{,}476}{67} = 530 + j0 \text{ ohms}$$

See Fig. 13-17b.

The complementary slot has a length $L = 0.475 \lambda$, the same as for the dipole, but the width of the slot should be twice the diameter of the cylindrical dipole. As indicated in Sec. 9-7, a flat strip of width w is equivalent to a cylindrical conductor of diameter D provided that $w = 2D$. Thus, in this example, the width of the complementary slot is

$$w = 2D = \frac{2L}{100} = \frac{2 \times 0.475 \lambda}{100} \simeq 0.01 \lambda$$

As a third example, a cylindrical dipole with an L/D ratio of 28 and length of about 0.925 wavelength has a terminal resistance of about $710 + j0$ ohms. The terminal resistance of the complementary slot is then about $50 + j0$ ohms so that an impedance match will be provided to a 50-ohm coaxial line. See Fig. 13-17c.

If the slots in these examples are enclosed on one side of the sheet with a box of such size that zero susceptance is shunted across the slot terminals, due to the box, the impedances are doubled.

The band width or selectivity characteristics of a slot antenna are the same as for the complementary dipole. Thus, widening a slot (smaller L/w ratio) increases the band width of the slot antenna the same as increasing the thickness of a dipole antenna (smaller L/D ratio) increases its band width.

The above discussion of this section applies to slots in sheets of infinite extent. If the sheet is finite, the impedance values are substantially the same provided that the edge of the sheet is at least a wavelength from the slot. However, the measured slot impedance is sensitive to the nature of the terminal connections.

13-6. Horn Antennas. Several types of horn antennas are illustrated in Fig. 13-18. Those in the left column are rectangular horns. All are energized from rectangular wave guides. Those in the right column are circular types. To minimize reflections of the guided wave, the transition region or horn between the wave guide at the throat and free space at the aperture could be given a gradual exponential taper as in Figs. 13-18a or e. However, it is the general practice to make horns with straight flares as suggested by the other types in Fig. 13-18. The types in Fig. 13-18b and c are sectoral horns. They are rectangular types with a flare in only one dimension. Assuming that the rectangular wave guide is energized with a TE_{10} mode wave electric field ($\mathbf{E}$ in y direction), the horn in Fig. 13-18b is flared out in a plane perpendicular to $\mathbf{E}$. This is the plane of the magnetic field $\mathbf{H}$. Hence, this type of horn is called a sectoral horn flared in the H plane or simply *an H-plane sectoral horn*. The horn in Fig. 13-18c is flared out in the plane of the electric field $\mathbf{E}$, and, hence, it is called an *E-plane sectoral horn*. A rectangular horn with flare in both planes, as in Fig. 13-18d, is called a *pyramidal horn*. With a TE$_{10}$ wave in the wave guide the magnitude of the electric field is quite uniform in the y direction across the apertures of the horns of Figs. 13-18b, c and d but tapers to zero in the x direction across the apertures. This variation is suggested by the arrows at the apertures in Figs. 13-18b, c, and d. The

RECTANGULAR HORNS   CIRCULAR HORNS

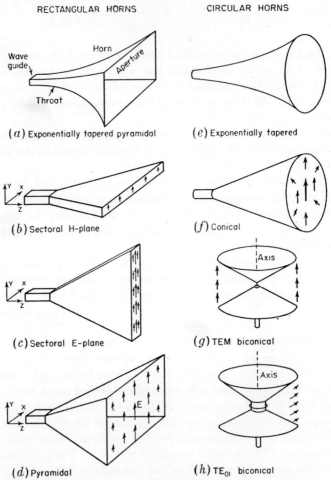

(a) Exponentially tapered pyramidal   *(e)* Exponentially tapered

(b) Sectoral H-plane   *(f)* Conical

(c) Sectoral E-plane   *(g)* TEM biconical

(d) Pyramidal   *(h)* TE$_{01}$ biconical

Fig. 13-18. Types of rectangular and circular horn antennas.

arrows indicate the direction of the electric field **E**, and their length gives an approximate indication of the magnitude of the field intensity. For small flare angles the field variation across the aperture of the rectangular horns is similar to the sinusoidal distribution of the TE$_{10}$ mode across the wave guide.

The horn shown in Fig. 13-18f is a *conical* type. When excited with a circular guide carrying a TE_{11} mode wave, the electric field distribution at the aperture is as shown by the arrows. The horns in Fig. 13-18g and h are *biconical* types. The one in Fig. 13-18g is excited in the TEM mode by a vertical radiator while the one in Fig. 13-18h is excited in the TE_{01} mode by a small horizontal loop antenna. These biconical horns are non-directional in the horizontal plane.

Neglecting edge effects, the radiation pattern of a horn antenna can be determined if the aperture dimensions and aperture field distribution are known. For a given aperture the directivity is maximum for a uniform distribution. Variations in the magnitude or phase of the field across the aperture decrease the directivity. Since the H-plane sectoral horn (Fig. 13-18b) has a field distribution over the x dimension which tapers to zero at the edge of the aperture, one would expect a pattern in the x-z plane relatively free of minor lobes as compared to the y-z plane pattern of an E-plane sectoral horn (Fig. 13-18c) for which the magnitude of $\mathbf{E}$ is quite constant over the y dimension of the aperture. This is borne out experimentally.

To obtain as uniform an aperture distribution as possible, a very long horn with a small flare angle is required. However, from the standpoint of practical convenience the horn should be as short as possible. An *optimum horn* is between these extremes and has the minimum beam width and side-lobe level for a given length.

Consider the longitudinal section through a horn antenna of Fig. 13-19.

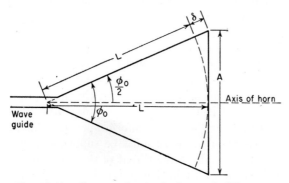

Fig. 13-19. Construction for finding path difference δ.

The axial length of the horn is L, the aperture is A, and the total flare angle is ϕ_0. The length δ is the difference in path length for a wave reaching the aperture at the axis and one reaching the aperture at the side of the horn. If δ is a sufficiently small fraction of a wavelength, the field is nearly uniform over the entire aperture. For a constant length L the directivity of the horn increases (beam width decreases) as the aperture A and flare angle ϕ_0 are increased. However, if A and ϕ_0 become so large that δ is equivalent to 180 electrical degrees, the field at the edge of the aperture is in phase opposition to the field at the axis. For all but very large flare angles the ratio $L/L + \delta$ is so nearly unity that the effect of the additional path length δ on the distribution of the field magnitude can be neglected. However, when $\delta = 180°$, the phase reversal at the edges of the aperture reduces the directivity (increases beam width). It follows that the maximum directivity occurs at the largest flare angle for which δ does not exceed a certain value (δ_0). Thus, the optimum horn dimensions can be related by

$$\delta_0 = \frac{L}{\cos(\phi_0/2)} - L \tag{13-38}$$

or

$$L = \frac{\delta_0 \cos(\phi_0/2)}{1 - \cos(\phi_0/2)} \tag{13-39}$$

or

$$\phi_0 = 2 \arccos \frac{L}{L + \delta_0} \tag{13-40}$$

It turns out that the value of δ_0 must usually be in the range of 0.1 to 0.4 free-space wavelength.[1] Suppose that for an optimum horn $\delta_0 = 0.25$ and that the axial length $L = 10\ \lambda$. Then from (13-40), $\phi_0 = 26°$. This flare angle then results in the maximum directivity for a 10-wavelength horn.

The path length, or δ effect, discussed above is an inherent limitation of all horn antennas of the conventional type.[2] The relations of (13-38), (13-39), and (13-40) can be applied to all the horns of Fig. 13-18, to determine the optimum dimensions. However, the appropriate value of δ_0 may differ as discussed in the following sections. Another limitation of horn antennas is that for the most uniform aperture illumination higher modes of transmission in the horn must be suppressed. It follows that the width of the wave guide at the throat of the horn must be between $\frac{1}{2}$ and 1 wavelength, or if the excitation system is symmetrical, so that even modes are not energized, the width must be between $\frac{1}{2}$ and $\frac{3}{2}$ wavelengths.

---

[1] At a given frequency the wavelength in the horn λ_h is always equal to or greater than the free-space wavelength λ. Since λ_h depends on the horn dimensions, it is more convenient to express δ_0 in free-space wavelengths λ.

[2] In the lens-compensated type of horn antenna (see Chap. 14) the velocity of the wave is increased near the edge of the horn with respect to the velocity at the axis in order to equalize the phase over the aperture.

13-7. The Rectangular Horn Antenna.[1] Provided that the aperture in both planes of a rectangular horn exceeds 1 wavelength, the pattern in one plane is substantially independent of the aperture in the other plane. Hence, in general, the H-plane pattern of an H-plane sectoral horn is the same as the H-plane pattern of a pyramidal horn with the same H-plane cross section. Likewise, the E-plane pattern of an E-plane sectoral horn is the same as the E-plane pattern of a pyramidal born with the same E-plane cross section. Referring to Fig. 13-20, the total flare angle in

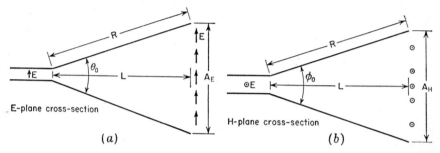

FIG. 13-20. E-plane and H-plane cross sections.

the E plane is θ_0 and the total flare angle in the H plane is ϕ_0. The axial length of the horn from throat to aperture is L, and the radial length is R. In Fig. 13-21a measured patterns[2] in the E plane and H plane are compared as a function of R. Both sets are for a flare angle of 20°. The E-plane patterns have minor lobes whereas the H-plane patterns have practically none. In Fig. 13-21b measured patterns[2] for horns 8 wavelengths long are compared as a function of flare angle. In the upper row E-plane patterns are given as a function of the E-plane flare angle θ_0, and in the lower row H-plane patterns are shown as a function of the

[1] W. L. Barrow and F. D. Lewis, The Sectoral Electromagnetic Horn, *Proc. I.R.E.*, **27**, 41–50, January, 1939.

W. L. Barrow and L. J. Chu, Theory of the Electromagnetic Horn, *Proc. I.R.E.*, **27**, 51–64, January, 1939.

L. J. Chu and W. L. Barrow, Electromagnetic Horn Design, *Trans. A.I.E.E.*, **58**, 333–337, July, 1939.

F. E. Terman, "Radio Engineers' Handbook," McGraw-Hill Book Company, Inc., New York, 1943, pp. 824–837. This reference includes a summary of design data on horns.

Chap. 10 by J. R. Risser, "Microwave Antenna Theory and Design," edited by S. Silver, McGraw-Hill Book Company, Inc., New York, 1949, pp. 349–365.

Chap. 6, by G. Stavis and A. Dorne, "Very High Frequency Techniques," by Radio Research Laboratory Staff, McGraw-Hill Book Company, Inc., New York, 1947.

[2] D. R. Rhodes, An Experimental Investigation of the Radiation Patterns of Electromagnetic Horn Antennas, *Proc. I.R.E.*, **36**, 1101–1105, September, 1948.

H-plane flare angle ϕ_0. For a flare angle $\theta_0 = 50°$ the *E*-plane pattern is split, whereas for $\phi_0 = 50°$ the *H*-plane pattern is not. This is because a given phase shift at the aperture in the *E*-plane horn has more effect on the pattern than the same phase shift in the *H*-plane horn. In the *H*-plane horn the field goes to zero at the edge of the aperture, so the phase near the edge is relatively less important. Accordingly, we should

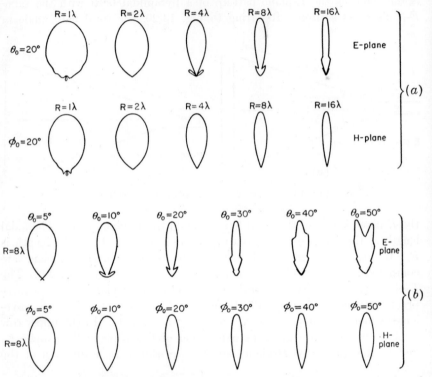

FIG. 13-21.   Measured *E*- and *H*-plane patterns of rectangular horns as a function of flare angle and horn length. (*After Rhodes.*)

expect the value of δ_0 for the optimum *H*-plane horn to be larger than for the optimum *E*-plane horn. This is illustrated in Fig. 13-22 discussed in the next paragraph.

From Rhodes's experimental patterns, optimum dimensions[1] were selected for both *E*- and *H*-plane flare as a function of flare angle and horn length *L*. These optimum dimensions are indicated by the solid lines in Fig. 13-22. The corresponding half-power beam widths and apertures in wavelengths are also indicated. The dashed curves show the calculated

[1] Minimum beam width as a function of θ_0 or ϕ_0 for a constant length *L*.

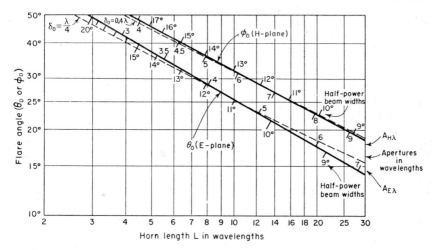

Fig. 13-22. Experimentally determined optimum dimensions for rectangular horn antennas. Solid curves give relation of flare angle θ_0 in E plane and flare angle ϕ_0 in H plane to horn length (see Fig. 13-20). The corresponding half-power beam widths and apertures in wavelengths are indicated along the curves. Dashed curves show calculated dimensions for $\delta_0 = 0.25\ \lambda$ and $0.4\ \lambda$.

dimensions for a path length $\delta_0 = 0.25\ \lambda$ and $\delta_0 = 0.4\ \lambda$. The value of $0.25\ \lambda$ gives a curve close to the experimental curve for E-plane flare, while the value of $0.4\ \lambda$ gives a curve close to the experimental one for H-plane flare over a considerable range of horn length. Thus, the tolerance in path length is greater for H-plane flare than for E-plane flare as indicated above.

To illustrate the use of Fig. 13-22, suppose that we wish to construct an optimum horn with a 14° half-power beam width in the H plane. From the upper solid curve in Fig. 13-22, the horn should have a flare angle $\phi_0 = 36°$ and a length $L = 7.8\lambda$. The corresponding H-plane aperture is $5\ \lambda$. If the maximum directivity is also desired in the E plane with this same horn ($L = 7.8\ \lambda$), we note from the lower solid curve that

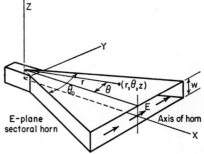

Fig. 13-23. Cylindrical coordinates for E-plane sectoral horn.

the flare angle θ_0 in the E plane should be 29° and that the half-power beam width to be expected in the E plane is 12°. The corresponding aperture E plane is about $4\ \lambda$. Thus, although the E-plane aperture is not so large as the H-plane aperture, the beam width is less (but minor lobes larger) because the E-plane aperture distribution is more uniform. For horn operation over a frequency band it is desirable to determine the optimum dimensions for the highest frequency to be used, since δ as measured in wavelengths is largest at this highest frequency.

The field in a sectoral horn may be determined by developing from Maxwell's equations a wave equation in cylindrical coordinates and then finding a solution appropriate to the boundary conditions at the walls of the horn. The horn is considered as a sectoral guide of infinite length. The general solutions for the fields in the horn have been given by Barrow and Chu.[1] For example, the fields inside the E-plane sectoral horn are given in terms of the cylindrical coordinates (r, θ, z) of Fig. 13-23 by

$$E_\theta = K_1 \cos\left(\frac{\pi z}{w}\right)[H_1^{(2)}(kr) + K_2 H_1^{(1)}(kr)] \tag{13-41}$$

$$H_r = \frac{j\pi K_1}{\mu\omega w} \sin\left(\frac{\pi z}{w}\right)[H_1^{(2)}(kr) + K_2 H_1^{(1)}(kr)] \tag{13-42}$$

$$H_z = \frac{j\beta K_1}{\mu\omega} \cos\left(\frac{\pi z}{w}\right)[H_0^{(2)}(kr) + K_2 H_0^{(1)}(kr)] \tag{13-43}$$

where K_1 = complex constant
K_2 = ratio of reflected to incident wave amplitudes at a point in the horn
$k = \sqrt{\beta^2 - (\pi/w)^2}$
w = height of horn
$\omega = 2\pi f$
$H_0^{(1)}$ = Hankel function of first kind and zero order
$H_0^{(2)}$ = Hankel function of second kind and zero order
$H_1^{(1)}$ = Hankel function of first kind and first order
$H_1^{(2)}$ = Hankel function of second kind and first order[2]

[1] See W. L. Barrow and L. J. Chu, Theory of the Electromagnetic Horn, *Proc. I.R.E.*, **27**, 51–64, January, 1939; also Chap. 10 by J. R. Risser, "Microwave Antenna Theory and Design," edited by S. Silver, McGraw-Hill Book Company, Inc., New York, 1949, pp. 349–365.

[2] $H_0^{(1)}(kr) = J_0(kr) + jN_0(kr)$
$H_0^{(2)}(kr) = J_0(kr) - jN_0(kr)$
$H_1^{(1)}(kr) = J_1(kr) + jN_1(kr)$
$H_1^{(2)}(kr) = J_1(kr) - jN_1(kr)$
where J represents a Bessel function and N a Neumann function.

Bessel and Neumann functions are somewhat analogous to sine and cosine functions. Similarly there is an analogy between Hankel functions and exponential functions. For example, compare

$$H_0^{(1)}(u) = J_0(u) + jN_0(u)$$

and

$$e^{ju} = \cos u + j \sin u$$

(Footnote continued on p. 379.)

Assuming field distributions across the horn aperture of the type given above, the radiation-field patterns of horns have been calculated by Barrow[1] and by Chu.[2] The method is similar to that discussed in Chap. 4 in which Huygens' principle is applied and the contributions to the far field integrated over the aperture. It is assumed that the aperture is at least several wavelengths. Edge effects are also neglected, that is, it is assumed that the field at the aperture is the same as though the sectoral guide extended to infinity. The actual field distribution differs from this because the abrupt termination of the sectoral guide at the aperture results in higher mode waves and also currents on the outside surface of the horn. Hence, extremely close agreement between calculated and measured patterns is not to be expected.

By calculating the radiation intensity in the direction of the horn axis and comparing this with the radiation intensity from an isotropic source radiating the same power, the directivity can be obtained for large sectoral horns. For example the directivity D for horns with only E-plane flare is given by Schelkunoff[3] as

$$D = \frac{64R}{\pi A_E} A_{H\lambda} \left[C^2\!\left(\frac{A_{E\lambda}}{\sqrt{2R_\lambda}}\right) + S^2\!\left(\frac{A_{E\lambda}}{\sqrt{2R_\lambda}}\right) \right] \qquad (13\text{-}44)$$

where R = radial side length of horn (in Fig. 13-19, $R = L + \delta$)

A_E = aperture of horn in E plane

$A_{E\lambda}$ = aperture of horn in E plane in free-space wavelengths

$A_{H\lambda}$ = aperture of horn in H plane in free-space wavelengths and where C and S indicate the Fresnel integrals. That is,

$$C(x) = \int_0^x \cos\frac{\pi n^2}{2}\, du \qquad (13\text{-}45)$$

and

$$S(x) = \int_0^x \sin\frac{\pi n^2}{2}\, du \qquad (13\text{-}46)$$

A cylindrical traveling wave may be represented by a Hankel function just as a plane traveling wave may be represented by an exponential function. Thus, in (13-41), (13-42), and (13-43) $H^{(2)}$ represents a cylindrical wave traveling in the $+r$ direction, and $H^{(1)}$ represents a cylindrical wave traveling in the $-r$ direction.

[1] W. L. Barrow and L. J. Chu, Theory of the Electromagnetic Horn, *Proc. I.R.E.*, **27**, 51–64, January, 1939; W. L. Barrow and F. M. Greene, Rectangular Hollow Pipe Radiators, *Proc. I.R.E.*, **26**, 1498–1519, December, 1938.

[2] L. J. Chu, Calculation of Radiation Properties of Hollow Pipes and Horns, *J. Applied Phys.*, **11**, 603–610, September, 1940.

[3] S. A. Schelkunoff, "Electromagnetic Waves," D. Van Nostrand Company, Inc., New York, 1943, pp. 360–365.

A simple approximate expression for the directivity of a horn antenna with large aperture may be written in terms of the maximum effective aperture. Thus, from (3-47)

$$D = \gamma 4\pi A_{E\lambda} A_{H\lambda} \qquad (13\text{-}47)$$

where $A_{E\lambda}$ = aperture in free-space wavelengths in E plane
$A_{H\lambda}$ = aperture in free-space wavelengths in H plane
γ = ratio of maximum effective aperture to physical aperture (see absorption ratio, Sec. 3-6).

For optimum horns a value of $\gamma \simeq 0.6$ is appropriate. Thus, (13-47) becomes

$$D \simeq 7.5 \, A_{E\lambda} A_{H\lambda} \qquad (13\text{-}48)$$

The power gain G of the horn over a $\frac{1}{2}$-wavelength dipole antenna is then

$$G \simeq 4.5 \, A_{E\lambda} A_{H\lambda} \qquad (13\text{-}49)$$

13-8. Beam-width Comparison. It is interesting to compare the beam width between first nulls and between half-power points for uniformly illuminated rectangular and circular apertures obtained in previous chapters with those for optimum rectangular horn antennas (sectoral or

TABLE 13-1*

Type of aperture	Beam width in degrees	
	Between first nulls	Between half-power points
Uniformly illuminated rectangular aperture or linear array	$\dfrac{115}{L_\lambda}$	$\dfrac{51}{L_\lambda}$
Uniformly illuminated circular aperture	$\dfrac{140}{D_\lambda}$	$\dfrac{58}{D_\lambda}$
Optimum E-plane rectangular horn	$\dfrac{115}{A_{E\lambda}}$	$\dfrac{56}{A_{E\lambda}}$
Optimum H-plane rectangular horn	$\dfrac{172}{A_{H\lambda}}$	$\dfrac{67}{A_{H\lambda}}$

* L_λ = length of rectangular aperture or linear array in free-space wavelengths
D_λ = diameter of circular aperture in free-space wavelengths
$A_{E\lambda}$ = aperture in E plane in free-space wavelengths
$A_{H\lambda}$ = aperture in H plane in free-space wavelengths

pyramidal). This is done in Table 13-1. In general, the relations apply to apertures that are at least several wavelengths. The beam widths between nulls for the horns are calculated, and the half-power beam widths are empirical.[1]

13-9. Circular Horn Antennas. The conical horn[2] (Fig. 13-18f) can be directly excited from a circular wave guide. 'Optimum dimensions can be determined from (13-38), (13-39), and (13-40) by taking $\delta_0 = 0.32\ \lambda$.

The biconical horns[3] of Fig. 13-18 have patterns that are nondirectional in the horizontal plane (axis of horns vertical). These horns may be regarded as modified pyramidal horns with a 360° flare angle in the horizontal plane. The optimum vertical-plane flare angle is about the same as for a sectoral horn of the same cross section excited in the same mode.

PROBLEMS

13-1. What is the terminal impedance of a slot antenna boxed in to radiate only in one half-space whose complementary dipole antenna has a driving point impedance of $Z = 100 + j0$ ohms. The box adds no shunt susceptance across the terminals.

13-2. What dimensions are required of a slot antenna in order that its terminal impedance be $75 + j0$ ohms. The slot is open on both sides. Use the empirical formula of Sec. 10-11 for the complementary dipole.

13-3. What is the approximate maximum power gain of an optimum horn antenna with a square aperture 10 wavelengths on a side?

13-4. *a.* Calculate and plot the E-plane pattern of the horn of Prob. 3, assuming uniform illumination over the aperture.

b. What is the half-power beamwidth and the angle between first nulls?

---

[1] Chap. 6, by G. Stavis and A. Dorne, "Very High Frequency Techniques," by Radio Research Laboratory Staff, McGraw-Hill Book Company, Inc., New York, 1947.

[2] G. C. Southworth and A. P. King, Metal Horns as Directive Receivers of Ultrashort Waves, *Proc. I.R.E.*, **27**, 95–102, February, 1939.

A. P. King, The Radiation Characteristics of Conical Horn Antennas, *Proc. I.R.E.*, **38**, 249–251, March, 1950. For optimum conical horns King gives half-power beam widths of $60/A_{E\lambda}$ in the E plane and $70/A_{H\lambda}$ in the H plane. These are about 6 per cent more than the values for a rectangular horn as given in Table 13-1.

[3] W. L. Barrow, L. J. Chu, and J. J. Jansen, Biconical Electromagnetic Horns, *Proc. I.R.E.*, **27**, 769–779, December, 1939.

CHAPTER 14

LENS, LONG WIRE, AND OTHER TYPES OF ANTENNAS

I N THIS chapter a considerable variety of antennas is considered. Some are combinations or modifications of types discussed in previous chapters, while others, such as the lens antennas treated in the first sections, are based on entirely different principles.

14-1. Lens Antennas. At centimeter wavelengths many optical devices can be applied. The parabolic reflector has already been considered (Chap. 12). The lens is another optical device which offers interesting possibilities.

Lens antennas may be divided into two distinct types: (1) those in which the electrical path length is increased by the lens medium and (2)

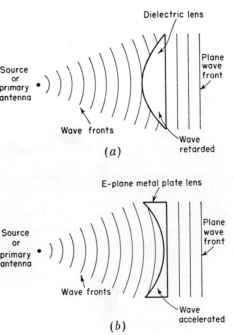

FIG. 14-1. Comparison of dielectric lens and *E*-plane metal-plate lens actions.

382

those in which the electrical path length is decreased by the lens medium. The first type is sometimes called a delay lens since the wave is retarded by the lens medium. Dielectric lenses and *H*-plane metal-plate lenses belong to this type. *E*-plane metal-plate lenses belong to the second type. The actions of a dielectric lens and an *E*-plane metal plate lens are compared in Fig. 14-1.

The dielectric antennas may be subdivided into two groups:

1. Lenses constructed of nonmetallic dielectrics, such as lucite or polystyrene
2. Lenses constructed of metallic or artificial dielectrics

These types are considered in the next two sections.

14-2. Nonmetallic Dielectric Lens Antennas.[1] This type is similar to the optical lens. It may be designed by the ray analysis methods of geometrical optics. As an example, let us determine the shape of the plano-convex lens of Fig. 14-1*a* for transforming the spherical wave front from an isotropic point source or primary antenna into a plane wave front.[2]

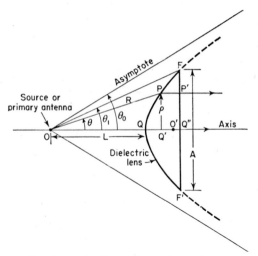

FIG. 14-2. Path lengths in dielectric lens.

The field over the plane surface can be made everywhere in phase by shaping the lens so that all paths from the source to the plane are of equal electrical length. This is the principle of equality of electrical (or optical) path length. Thus, in Fig. 14-2, the electrical length of the path *OPP'*

[1] A detailed discussion is given by J. R. Risser, Chap. 11, "Microwave Antenna Theory and Design," edited by S. Silver, McGraw-Hill Book Company, Inc., New York, 1949.
[2] A wave front is defined as a surface at all points of which the field is in the same phase.

must equal the electrical length of the path $OQQ'Q''$. Or more simply OP must equal OQ'. Let $OQ = L$ and $OP = R$, and let the medium surrounding the lens be air or vacuum. Then,

$$\frac{R}{\lambda_0} = \frac{L}{\lambda_0} + \frac{R \cos \theta - L}{\lambda_d} \tag{14-1}$$

where λ_0 = wavelength in free space (air or vacuum)
λ_d = wavelength in the lens
Multiplying (14-1) by λ_0

$$R = L + n(R \cos \theta - L) \tag{14-2}$$

where $n = \lambda_0/\lambda_d$ = index of refraction
In general,

$$n = \frac{\lambda_0}{\lambda_d} = \frac{f\lambda_0}{f\lambda_d} = \frac{v_0}{v_d} = \frac{\sqrt{\mu\epsilon}}{\sqrt{\mu_0\epsilon_0}} \tag{14-3}$$

where f = frequency
v_0 = velocity in free space
v_d = velocity in dielectric
μ = permeability of the dielectric medium
ϵ = dielectric constant of the dielectric medium
μ_0 = permeability of free space = $4\pi \times 10^{-7}$ henry/meter
ϵ_0 = dielectric constant of free space = 8.85×10^{-12} farad/meter

But

$$\mu = \mu_0\mu_r \tag{14-4}$$

and

$$\epsilon = \epsilon_0\epsilon_r \tag{14-5}$$

where $\mu_r = \dfrac{\mu}{\mu_0}$ = relative permeability of dielectric medium
$\epsilon_r = \dfrac{\epsilon}{\epsilon_0}$ = relative dielectric constant of dielectric medium
Thus, from (14-3)

$$n = \sqrt{\mu_r\epsilon_r} \tag{14-6}$$

For nonmagnetic materials μ_r is very nearly unity so that

$$n = \sqrt{\epsilon_r}$$

The index of refraction of dielectric substances is always greater than 1. For vacuum $\epsilon_r = 1$ by definition. For air at atmospheric pressure $\epsilon_r = 1.0006$, but in most applications it is sufficiently accurate to take $\epsilon_r = 1$

for air. The relative dielectric constant, index of refraction, and power factor for a number of lens materials are listed in Table 14-1 in order of increasing ϵ_r. Although the dielectric constant of materials may vary with frequency (ϵ_r for water is 81 at radio frequencies and about 1.8 at optical frequencies), the table values are appropriate at radio wavelengths

TABLE 14-1

Material	Relative dielectric constant ϵ_r	Index of refraction n	Power factor
Paraffin..............................	2.1	1.4	0.0003
Polyethylene..........................	2.2	1.5	0.0003
Lucite or plexiglass (methacrylic resin)....	2.6	1.6	0.01
Polystyrene...........................	2.5	1.6	0.0004
Flint glass...........................	7	2.5	0.004
Polyglas (TiO₂ or titanate fillers).........	4–16*	2–4	0.003
Rutile (TiO₂).........................	85–170†	9–13	0.0006

*Depends on composition.
†Depends on orientation of crystal with respect to field.

down to the order of 1 cm. The power factor also is a function of frequency. The values listed merely indicate the order of magnitude at radio frequencies.

Returning now to Eq. (14-2) and solving for R, we have

$$R = \frac{(n-1)L}{n \cos \theta - 1} \tag{14-7}$$

This equation gives the required shape of the lens. It is the equation of a hyperbola. The distance L is the focal length of the lens.[1] The asymptotes of the hyperbola are at an angle θ_0 with respect to the axis. The angle θ_0 may be determined from (14-7) by letting $R = \infty$. Thus,

$$\theta_0 = \arccos \frac{1}{n} \tag{14-8}$$

The point O is at one focus of the hyperbola. The other focus is at O'. For a point source at the focus the three-dimensional lens surface is a spherical hyperbola obtained by rotating the hyperbola on its axis. For an in-phase line source normal to the page (Fig. 14-2) as the primary antenna, the lens surface is a cylindrical hyperbola obtained by translating

[1] The F or f number of a lens is the ratio of the focal distance to the diameter A of the lens aperture. Thus, $F = L/A$.

the hyperbola parallel to the line source. The lens contours of Fig. 14-2 illustrate but one of many possible lens configurations.

Although Eq. (14-7) for the lens surface was derived without using Snell's laws of refraction,[1] these laws are satisfied by the lens boundary as given by (14-7).

The plane wave emerging from the right side of the lens produces a secondary pattern with maximum radiation in the direction of the axis. The shape of the secondary pattern is a function of both the aperture A and the type of illumination. This aperture-pattern relation has been discussed in previous chapters.

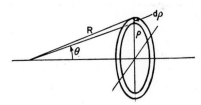

FIG. 14-3.   Annular zone.

For an isotropic point-source primary antenna and a given focal distance L, the field at the edge of the lens ($\theta = \theta_1$) is less than at the center ($\theta = 0$), the effects of reflections at the lens surfaces and losses in the lens material being neglected. The variation of field intensity in the aperture plane of the spherical lens can be determined by calculating the power per unit area passing through an annular section of the aperture as a function of the radius ρ.[2] Referring to Fig. 14-3, the total power W through the annular section of radius ρ and width $d\rho$ is given by

$$W = 2\pi\rho \, d\rho \, P_\rho \qquad\qquad (14\text{-}9)$$

where P_ρ = power density (power per unit area) at radius ρ
This power must be equal to that radiated by the isotropic source over the solid angle $2\pi \sin\theta \, d\theta$. Thus,

$$W = 2\pi \sin\theta \, d\theta \, U \qquad\qquad (14\text{-}10)$$

where U = radiation intensity of the isotropic source (power per unit solid angle)
Equating (14-9) and (14-10)

$$\rho \, d\rho \, P_\rho = \sin\theta \, d\theta \, U \qquad\qquad (14\text{-}11)$$

---

[1] Snell's laws of refraction are (1) that the incident ray, the refracted ray, and the normal to the surface lie in a plane and (2) that the ratio of the sine of the angle of incidence to the sine of the angle of refraction equals a constant for any two media. If the medium of the incident wave is air, the constant is the index of refraction n of the medium with the refracted ray. Thus, $\sin\alpha/\sin\beta = n$, where α is the angle between the incident ray in air and the normal to the surface and β is the angle between the refracted ray in the dielectric medium and the normal to the surface.

[2] J. R. Risser, Chap. 11, "Microwave Antenna Theory and Design," edited by S. Silver, McGraw-Hill Book Company, Inc., New York, 1949.

and

$$\frac{P_\rho}{U} = \frac{\sin \theta}{\rho(d\rho/d\theta)} \tag{14-12}$$

But $\rho = R \sin \theta$ and introducing the value of R from (14-7)

$$P_\rho = \frac{(n \cos \theta - 1)^3}{(n - 1)^2 (n - \cos \theta)L^2} U \tag{14-13}$$

The ratio of the power density P_θ at the angle θ to the power density P_0 at the axis ($\theta = 0$) is given by the ratio of (14-13) when $\theta = \theta$, to (14-13) when $\theta = 0$. Thus,

$$\frac{P_\theta}{P_0} = \frac{(n \cos \theta - 1)^3}{(n - 1)^2 (n - \cos \theta)} \tag{14-14}$$

In the aperture plane the field-intensity ratio is equal to the square root of (14-14), or[1]

$$\frac{E_\theta}{E_0} = \sqrt{\frac{P_\theta}{P_0}} = \frac{1}{n - 1} \sqrt{\frac{(n \cos \theta - 1)^3}{n - \cos \theta}} \tag{14-15a}$$

The ratio E_θ/E_0 is the relative field intensity at a radius ρ given by $\rho = R \sin \theta$. For $n = 1.5$,

$$\frac{E_\theta}{E_0} = 0.7 \text{ at } \theta = 20° $$

and

$$\frac{E_\theta}{E_0} = 0.14 \text{ at } \theta = 40° $$

Hence, for a nearly uniform aperture illumination an angle θ_1 to the edge of the lens even less than 20° is essential unless the pattern of the primary antenna is an inverted type, that is, one with less intensity in the axial direction ($\theta = 0$) than in directions off the axis. For a constant size of aperture a small value of θ_1 results in a large focal length L.

Instead of uniform aperture illumination, a tapered illumination may be desired in order to suppress minor lobes. Thus, in the above example

[1] Equation (14-15a) is for a spherical lens. Attenuation in the lens is neglected. For a cylindrical lens the field intensity ratio is

$$\frac{E_\theta}{E_0} = \frac{n \cos \theta - 1}{\sqrt{(n - 1)(n - \cos \theta)}} \tag{14-15b}$$

where E_θ/E_0 is the relative field intensity at a distance y from the axis given by $y = R \sin \theta$.

with $\theta_1 = 40°$, the field at the edge of the lens is 0.14 its value at the center. The disadvantage of this method of producing a taper is that the lens is bulky (Fig. 14-4a). An alternative arrangement, shown in Fig. 14-4b, has a lens of smaller θ_1 value with the desired taper obtained with a directional primary antenna at a larger focal distance (relative to the aperture). The lens in this case is less bulky, but the focal distance is larger (F number larger).

For compactness and mechanical lightness it would be desirable to com-

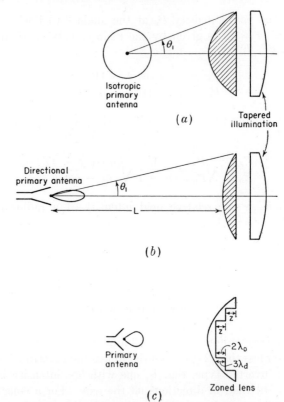

Isotropic
primary
antenna

Tapered
illumination

(a)

Directional
primary antenna

L

(b)

Primary
antenna

$2\lambda_0$

$3\lambda_d$

Zoned lens

(c)

FIG. 14-4.   Short-focus lens (a), long-focus lens (b), and zoned lens (c).

bine the short focal distance of the lens at (a) with the light weight of the lens at (b). This combination may be largely achieved with the short focal distance zoned lens of Fig. 14-4c. The weight of this lens is reduced by the removal of sections or zones, the geometry of the zones being such that the lens performance is substantially unaffected at the design frequency. Whereas the unzoned lens is not frequency sensitive, the zoned lens is and this may be a disadvantage. The thickness z of a zone step is such that the electrical length of z in the dielectric is an integral number of wavelengths longer (usually 1) than the electrical length of z in air. Thus, for a 1-wavelength difference

$$\frac{z}{\lambda_d} - \frac{z}{\lambda_0} = 1 \tag{14-16}$$

or

$$z = \frac{\lambda_0}{n - 1} \tag{14-17}$$

For a dielectric with index of refraction $n = 1.5$

$$z = 2\lambda_0$$

that is, each zone step is twice the free-space wavelength. Since $n = \lambda_0/\lambda_d$

$$z = 3\lambda_d$$

Thus, in this case, the electrical length of z in the dielectric is 3 wavelengths, while the electrical length of z in air is 2 wavelengths (see Fig. 14-4c).

In lens antennas the primary antenna does not interfere with the plane wave leaving the aperture as it does in a symmetrical parabolic reflector (Fig. 12-18.2b). However, the energy reflected from the lens surfaces may be sufficient to cause a mismatch of the primary antenna to its feed line

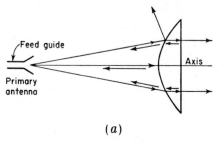

(a)

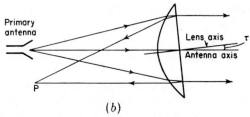

(b)

FIG. 14-5.   Reflected waves entering primary antenna (a) and refocused to one side of primary antenna (b).

or guide. In the lens of Fig. 14-5a reflections from the convex surface of the lens do not return to the source except from points at or near the axis. This is not serious. But the wave reflected internally from the plane lens surface is refocused at the primary antenna and may be disturbing. In this case, the wave is reflected at normal incidence, and the reflection coefficient is

$$\rho = \frac{Z_0 - Z}{Z_0 + Z} \qquad (14\text{-}18)$$

where Z_0 = intrinsic impedance of free space = $\sqrt{\mu_0/\epsilon_0}$

Z = intrinsic impedance of dielectric lens material = $\sqrt{\mu/\epsilon}$

Thus,

$$\rho = \frac{(Z_0/Z) - 1}{(Z_0/Z) + 1} = \frac{n - 1}{n + 1} \qquad (14\text{-}19)$$

where n = the index of refraction of the dielectric lens material

For $n = 1.5$, $\rho = 0.2$; while for $n = 4$, $\rho = 0.6$. Hence, for a small reflection a low index of refraction is desirable. The reflection can also be minimized by other methods. For example, a $\frac{1}{4}$-wavelength plate can be applied to the plane lens surface with the refractive index of the plate made equal to $\sqrt{n}$, where n is the refractive index of the lens proper.[1] Another method is to use a type of lens which does not have an equiphase surface. A third method is to tilt the lens slightly as indicated in Fig. 14-5b so that the reflected wave refocuses to one side of the primary antenna.

14-3. Artificial Dielectric Lens Antennas. Instead of using ordinary, nonmetallic dielectrics for the lens, Kock[2] has demonstrated that artificial or metallic dielectrics can be substituted, generally with a saving in weight. Whereas the ordinary dielectric consists of molecular particles of microscopic size, the artificial dielectric consists of discrete metal particles of macroscopic size. The size of the metal particles should be small compared to the design wavelength to avoid resonance effects. It is found that this requirement is satisfied if the maximum particle dimension (parallel to the electric field) is less than $\frac{1}{4}$ wavelength. A second requirement is that the spacing between the particles be less than a wavelength to avoid diffraction effects.

The particles may be metal spheres, discs, strips, or rods. For example,

---

[1] In general the refractive index of a $\frac{1}{4}$-wavelength matching plate between two media should be equal to the geometric mean of the indices of the two media. This is equivalent to saying that the intrinsic impedance Z_p of the plate material is made equal to the geometric mean of the intrinsic impedances Z_1 and Z_2 of the two media. Thus, $Z_p = \sqrt{Z_1 Z_2}$.

[2] W. E. Kock, Metallic Delay Lens, *Bell System Tech. J.*, **27**, 58–82, January, 1948.

a plano-convex lens constructed of metal spheres is illustrated in Fig. 14-6. The spheres are arranged in a three-dimensional array or lattice structure. Such an arrangement simulates the crystalline lattice of an ordinary dielectric substance but on a much larger scale. The radio waves from the source or primary antenna cause oscillating currents to flow on the spheres. The spheres are, thus, analogous to the oscillating molecular dipoles of an ordinary dielectric.

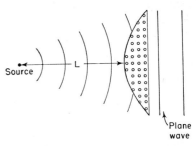

An artificial dielectric lens can be designed in the same manner as an ordinary dielectric lens (Sec. 14-2). To do this, it is necessary to know the effective index of refraction of the artificial dielectric. This can be measured experimentally with a slab of the material, or it can be calculated approximately by the following method of analysis.[1] Although metal discs or strips[2] are generally preferable to spheres because

FIG. 14-6. Artificial dielectric lens of metal spheres.

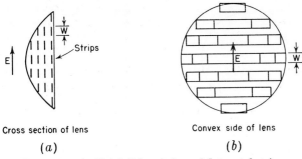

Cross section of lens

(a)

Convex side of lens

(b)

FIG. 14-7. Artificial dielectric lens of flat metal strips.

they are lighter in weight, the sphere is more readily analyzed, and the method will be illustrated for the case of the sphere.

Let an uncharged conducting sphere be placed in an electric field **E** as in Fig. 14-8a. The field induces positive and negative charges as indicated. At a distance the effect of these charges may be represented by point charges $+q$ and $-q$ separated by a distance l as in Fig. 14-8b. Such a configuration is an *electric dipole of dipole moment ql*. At a distance $r \gg l$ the potential due to the dipole is given by

$$V = \frac{ql \cos \theta}{4\pi\epsilon_0 r^2} \tag{14-20}$$

[1] W. E. Kock, Metallic Delay Lens, *Bell System Tech. J.*, **27**, 58–82, January, 1948.
[2] The strips may be continuous in a direction perpendicular to the electric field as indicated in Fig. 14-7.

The polarization **P** of the artificial dielectric is given by

$$\mathbf{P} = N q \mathbf{l} \tag{14-21}$$

where N = number of spheres per cubic meter
$\quad\;$ 1 = vector joining the charges q
The electric displacement **D**, the electric field intensity **E**, the polarization **P** are related by

$$\mathbf{D} = \epsilon\mathbf{E} = \epsilon_0\mathbf{E} + \mathbf{P} \tag{14-22}$$

where ϵ_0 = dielectric constant of free space
Thus, the effective dielectric constant ϵ of the artificial dielectric medium is

$$\epsilon = \epsilon_0 + \frac{\mathbf{P}}{\mathbf{E}} = \epsilon_0 + N\frac{q\mathbf{l}}{\mathbf{E}} \tag{14-23}$$

Hence, if the number of spheres per unit volume and the dipole moment per unit applied field are known, the effective dielectric constant can be

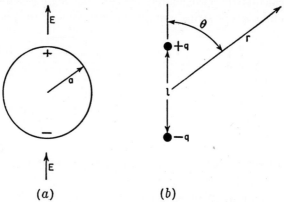

$$(a) \qquad\qquad\qquad (b)$$

Fig. 14-8.   Charged sphere and equivalent dipole.

determined.   Let us now determine the dipole moment per unit applied field.

We have $\mathbf{E} = -\nabla V$.   Then in a uniform field the potential

$$V = -\int_0^r E \cos\theta\,dr = -Er\cos\theta \tag{14-24}$$

where θ is the angle between the radius vector and the field (see Fig. 14-8b). The potential V_0 outside the sphere placed in an originally uniform field is the sum of (14-20) and (14-24) or

$$V_0 = -Er\cos\theta + \frac{ql\cos\theta}{4\pi\epsilon_0 r^2} \tag{14-25}$$

At the sphere (radius a) (14-25) becomes[1]

$$0 = -Ea \cos \theta + \frac{ql \cos \theta}{4\pi\epsilon_0 a^2}$$

and solving for ql/E we obtain

$$\frac{ql}{E} = 4\pi\epsilon_0 a^3 \qquad (14\text{-}26)$$

Introducing this value for the dipole moment per unit applied field in (14-23)

$$\epsilon = \epsilon_0 + 4\pi\epsilon_0 N a^3$$

or

$$\epsilon_r = 1 + 4\pi N a^3 \qquad (14\text{-}27)$$

where ϵ_r = effective relative dielectric constant of the artificial dielectric.

If the effective relative permeability of the artificial dielectric is unity, the index of refraction is given by the square root of (14-27). However, the lines of magnetic field of a radio wave are deformed around the sphere since high-frequency fields penetrate to only a very small distance in good conductors. The effective relative permeability of an artificial dielectric of conducting spheres is

$$\mu_r = 1 - 2\pi N a^3 \qquad (14\text{-}28)$$

TABLE 14-2*
ARTIFICIAL DIELECTRIC MATERIALS

Type of particle	Relative dielectric constant ϵ_r	Relative permeability μ_r	Index of refraction n
Sphere.........	$1 + 4\pi N a^3$	$1 - 2\pi N a^3$	$\sqrt{(1 + 4\pi N a^3)(1 - 2\pi N a^3)}$
Disc...........	$1 + 5.3 N a^3$	~ 1	$\sqrt{1 + 5.3 N a^3}$
Strip..........	$1 + 7.8 N' w^2$	~ 1	$\sqrt{1 + 7.8 N' w^2}$

*N = number of spheres or discs per cubic meter
a = radius of sphere or disc in meters
N' = number of strips per square meter in lens cross section (see Fig. 14-7a)
w = width of strips in meters (see Fig. 14-7)

[1] The potential of the sphere is zero since there is as much positive as negative charge on its surface.

The effective index of refraction of the artificial dielectric of conducting spheres is then given by

$$n = \sqrt{\epsilon_r \mu_r} = \sqrt{(1 + 4\pi N a^3)(1 - 2\pi N a^3)} \qquad (14\text{-}29)$$

Equation (14-29) gives a smaller n than obtained by the square root of (14-27) alone. According to (14-29) the index of refraction of an artificial dielectric of conducting spheres can be calculated if the radius a of the sphere (in meters) and the number N of spheres per cubic meter are known. The relative permeability of disc or strip-type artificial dielectrics is more nearly unity so that one can take $\sqrt{\epsilon_r}$ as their index of refraction. Theoretical values of ϵ_r, μ_r, and n for artificial dielectrics made of conducting spheres, discs, and strips are listed in Table 14-2.[1] According to Kock the table values are reliable only for $\epsilon_r \leq 1.5$, and only approximate for larger ϵ_r. For $\epsilon_r > 1.5$, N becomes sufficiently large that the particles interact because of their close spacing. This effect is neglected by the formulas.

14-4. E-plane Metal-plate Lens Antennas.[2] Whereas the ordinary and artificial dielectric lens depend for their action on a retardation of the wave in the lens, the E-plane metal-plate type of lens depends for its

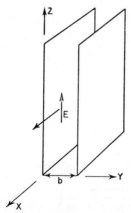

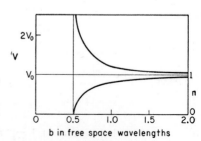

FIG. 14-9. Wave between plates in E-plane type of metal-plate lens.

FIG. 14-10. Velocity v of wave between parallel plates and equivalent index of refraction n as a function of spacing b between plates.

action on an *acceleration* of the wave by the lens. In this type of lens the metal plates are parallel to the E plane (or plane of the electric field). Referring to Fig. 14-9, the velocity v of propagation of a TE_{10} wave ($\mathbf{E}$ as

[1] From W. E. Kock, Metallic Delay Lens, *Bell System Tech. J.*, **27**, 58–82, January, 1948.

[2] W. E. Kock, Metal Lens Antenna, *Proc. I.R.E.*, **34**, 828–836, November, 1946.

indicated) in the x direction between two parallel conducting plates of large extent is given by[1]

$$v = \frac{v_0}{\sqrt{1 - \left(\frac{\lambda}{2b}\right)^2}}$$ (14-30)

where v_0 = velocity in free space
λ = wavelength in free space
b = spacing of plates or sheets

The plates act as a guide, transmitting the wave for values of $b \geq \lambda/2$. The spacing $b = \lambda/2$ is the critical spacing since for smaller values of b the guide is opaque and the wave is not transmitted. The variation of the velocity for a fixed wavelength as a function of the plate spacing b is illustrated in Fig. 14-10. The velocity of the wave between the plates is always greater than the free-space velocity v_0. It approaches infinity as b approaches 0.5λ, and it approaches v_0 as b becomes infinite.

The equivalent index of refraction of a medium constructed of many such parallel plates with a spacing b is

$$n = \frac{v_0}{v} = \sqrt{1 - \left(\frac{\lambda}{2b}\right)^2}$$ (14-31)

The index is always *less* than 1 as shown in Fig. 14-10.

The acceleration of waves between plates has been applied[2] in a metal-plate lens for focusing radio waves. For instance, a metal lens equivalent to the plano-convex dielectric lens of Fig. 14-1a or Fig. 14-2 is a plano-concave type as illustrated in Fig. 14-11. The plates are cut from flat

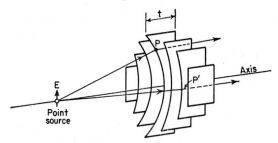

Fig. 14-11.   *E*-plane type of metal-plate lens.

sheets, the thickness t at any point being such as to transform the spherical wave from the source into a plane wave on the plane side of the lens. The electric field is parallel to the plates.

[1] L. J. Chu and W. L. Barrow, Electromagnetic Waves in Hollow Metal Tubes of Rectangular Cross Section, *Proc. I.R.E.*, **26**, 1520–1555, December, 1938.

[2] W. E. Kock, Metal Lens Antennas, *Proc. I.R.E.*, **34**, 828–836, November, 1946.

The lens plate on the axis of the lens in Fig. 14-11 is shown in Fig. 14-12. The shape of the plate can be determined by the principle of equality of electrical path length. Thus, in Fig. 14-12 OPP' must be equal to OQQ' in electrical length. Or

$$\frac{L}{\lambda} = \frac{R}{\lambda} + \frac{L - R \cos \theta}{\lambda_g} \qquad (14\text{-}32)$$

where λ = wavelength in free space
$\quad\;\; \lambda_g$ = wavelength in lens
Then

$$R = \frac{(1 - n)L}{1 - n \cos \theta} \qquad (14\text{-}33)$$

This relation is identical with (14-7). However, to keep both numerator and denominator positive (since $n < 1$ in the present case), the numerator and denominator of (14-7) have been multiplied by minus 1. With $n < 1$,

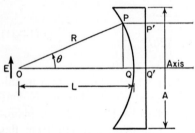

FIG. 14-12. Geometry for E-plane type of metal-plate lens.

(14-33) is the equation of an ellipse. The three-dimensional concave surface of the lens in Fig. 14-11 would be generated by rotating the contour for the center plate, as given by (14-33), on the axis. If the primary antenna were a line source perpendicular to the page in Fig. 14-12, all the plates would be identical and the lens surface would be in the form of an elliptical cylinder.

Waves entering the lens of Fig. 14-11 at the point P obey Snell's laws of refraction. However, this is not necessarily the case for waves entering at P' where the metal plates constrain the wave to travel between them. E-plane metal-plate lenses may be

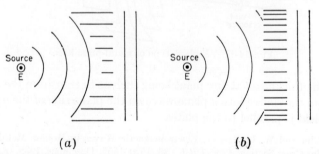

(a)   (b)

FIG. 14-13. Cross sections of constrained types of E-plane metal-plate lenses.

constructed that have only such constrained refraction. Two types are illustrated in cross section in Fig. 14-13. Both have a line source normal to the page. The electric field **E** is parallel to the source. All lens cross sections perpendicular to the line sources are the same as the ones shown in the figure. In the lens at (a) the spacing between plates is uniform, but the width varies from plate to plate. In the lens at (b) all plates have the same width, but the spacing varies.

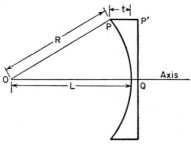

FIG. 14-14. Geometry for band-width considerations.

A disadvantage of the E-plane metal-plate lens as compared to the dielectric type is that it is frequency-sensitive, that is, the lens has a relatively small band width. To determine the band width,[1] consider the geometry of Fig. 14-14. At the design frequency f

$$\frac{L}{\lambda} = \frac{R}{\lambda} + \frac{t}{\lambda_g} \qquad (14\text{-}34)$$

or

$$L = R + nt \qquad (14\text{-}35)$$

where n = index of refraction at the design frequency f
At some other frequency f'

$$L + \delta = R + n't \qquad (14\text{-}36)$$

where δ = the difference in electrical path length of OQ and OPP'
  n' = index of refraction at the frequency f'
Subtracting (14-35) from (14-36)

$$\delta = \Delta n\, t \qquad (14\text{-}37)$$

where $\Delta n = n' - n$
But for a small wavelength difference $\Delta\lambda$,

$$\Delta n = \frac{\partial n}{\partial \lambda}\, \Delta\lambda \qquad (14\text{-}38)$$

Introducing n from (14-31) into (14-38), differentiating, and substituting this value of Δn in (14-37) yields

$$\delta = \frac{n^2 - 1}{n}\, \frac{\Delta\lambda_0}{\lambda_0}\, t \qquad (14\text{-}39)$$

[1] J. R. Risser, Chap. 11, "Microwave Antenna Theory and Design," edited by S. Silver, McGraw-Hill Book Company, Inc., New York, 1949.

or

$$\left| \frac{\Delta\lambda_0}{\lambda_0} \right| = \frac{n\delta}{(1 - n^2)t} \tag{14-40}$$

The total band width B is twice (14-40) so

$$B = \frac{2n\delta}{(1 - n^2)t} = \frac{2n}{1 - n^2} \frac{\delta_\lambda}{t_\lambda} \tag{14-41}$$

where δ_λ = maximum tolerable path difference in free-space wavelengths
t_λ = thickness of lens plate at edge of lens in free-space wavelengths
If we arbitrarily take $\delta = 0.25 \lambda$,

$$B = \frac{50n}{(1 - n^2)t} \% \tag{14-42}$$

For $n = 0.5$ and $t = 6 \lambda$, the band width

$$B = 5.5\%$$

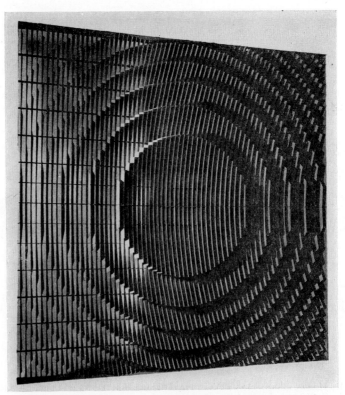

FIG. 14-15.   Zoned type of E-plane metal-plate lens with a square aperture 40 wavelengths on a side.   (*Courtesy W. E. Kock, Bell Telephone Laboratories.*)

Thus, the usable frequency band for this antenna is 5.5 per cent of the design frequency.[1] Although zoning a dielectric lens introduces frequency sensitivity, the effect of zoning an E-plane metal-plate lens is to decrease the frequency sensitivity. Hence, zoning is desirable with E-plane metal-plate lens, both to save weight and to increase the band width. An E-plane metal-plate lens 40 wavelengths square with nine zones is illustrated in Fig. 14-15. The radiation-field patterns of this lens, fed with a short primary horn antenna, are shown in Fig. 14-16.

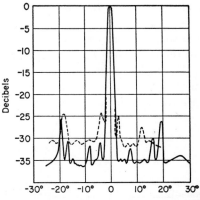

FIG. 14-16. E-plane pattern (solid) and H-plane pattern (dashed) of 40-wavelength square zoned E-plane lens of Fig. 14-15. (*After W. E. Kock.*)

The band width of a zoned E-plane metal-plate lens is given approximately by

$$B = \frac{50n}{1 + Kn} \% \qquad (14\text{-}43)$$

where n = index of refraction at the design frequency

K = number of zones. The zone on the axis of the lens is counted as the first zone.

A zoned lens comparable to the unzoned lens of $n = 0.5$, $t = 6\,\lambda$, and $B = 5.5$ per cent, has $n = 0.5$ and $K = 3$ since with $n = 0.5$, $K \sim t_\lambda/2$. The band width B of this zoned lens is 10 per cent, or nearly double the band width of the unzoned lens.

The maximum absorption ratio γ to be expected of large lens antennas is about 0.6 so that the directivity and gain are about the same as for optimum horns of the same size aperture [see (13-48) and (13-49)].

Referring to Fig. 14-17a, the thickness z of a zone step is given by

$$\frac{z}{\lambda} - \frac{z}{\lambda_g} = 1$$

or

$$z = \frac{\lambda}{1 - n} \qquad (14\text{-}44)$$

---

[1] $\dfrac{2\Delta\lambda}{\lambda} = \dfrac{\lambda_2 - \lambda_1}{\lambda} = \dfrac{(1/f_2) - (1/f_1)}{(1/f)} = \dfrac{f(f_1 - f_2)}{f_1\,f_2} \simeq \dfrac{f_1 - f_2}{f} = \dfrac{2\Delta f}{f}$

where λ = design wavelength
  f = design frequency
  λ_1 = short wavelength limit of band
  λ_2 = long wavelength limit of band
  f_1 = high-frequency limit of band
  f_2 = low-frequency limit of band

The equation for the contour of the zoned lens is the same as (14-33) for the unzoned lens except that L is replaced by L_k where

$$L_k = L + \frac{(K-1)\lambda}{1-n} = L + (K-1)z \qquad (14\text{-}45)$$

For the first zone (on the axis) $L_k = L$. For the second zone $L_k = L + z$, for the third zone $L_k = L + 2z$, etc.

To shield against stray radiation from the source side of a lens, a metallic enclosure may be used as in Fig. 14-17b. This enclosure forms an electromagnetic horn of wide flare angle with a lens at the aperture. With-

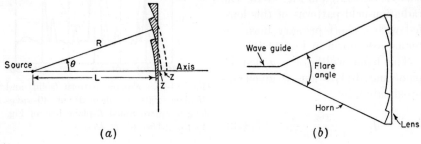

(a) (b)

FIG. 14-17. (a) Zoned lens plate. (b) Horn with lens.

out the lens an optimum horn of the same aperture would be much longer (smaller flare angle). The fact that the lens permits a much shorter structure for the same size aperture is, perhaps, the principal advantage of a lens or lens-horn combination over a simple horn antenna.

14-5. Tolerances on Lens Antennas.[1]   Let the maximum allowable variation δ in electrical path length be arbitrarily set at $\frac{1}{8}$ wavelength $(\delta = \lambda/8)$.[2] In a dielectric lens, differences in the path length may be caused by deviations in thickness from the ideal contour and by variations in the index of refraction. Then assigning an allowable variation of $\lambda/16$ to each cause, we have as the *thickness tolerance* that

$$\frac{\Delta t}{\lambda_d} - \frac{\Delta t}{\lambda} = \frac{1}{16}$$

or

$$\Delta t = \frac{\lambda}{16(n-1)}$$

or

$$\Delta t = \pm\frac{\lambda}{32(n-1)} = \pm\frac{0.03\,\lambda}{n-1} \qquad (14\text{-}46)$$

---

[1] J. R. Risser, Chap. 11, "Microwave Antenna Theory and Design," edited by S. Silver, McGraw-Hill Book Company, Inc., New York, 1949.

[2] The maximum allowable deviation from the mean is then $\pm 1/16$ wavelength.

For $n = 1.5$

$$\Delta t = \pm 0.06\lambda$$

For the *tolerance on n*

$$\Delta n \; t = \frac{\lambda}{16}$$

or

$$\Delta n = \pm \frac{0.03}{t_\lambda} \tag{14-47}$$

where t_λ = thickness of lens in free-space wavelengths
Dividing (14-47) by n

$$\frac{\Delta n}{n} = \pm \frac{3}{n t_\lambda} \% \tag{14-48}$$

If $n = 1.5$ and $t = 4\,\lambda$, $\Delta n/n = \pm \frac{1}{2}\%$.

In an E-plane metal-plate lens the path length may be affected by both the thickness of the lens and by the spacing b between lens plates. Taking $\delta = \lambda/8$ as for the dielectric lens and assigning $\lambda/16$ to each cause, we have as the *thickness tolerance* that

$$t = \frac{\lambda}{16(1 - n)} = \pm \frac{0.03\,\lambda}{1 - n} \tag{14-49a}$$

For the *tolerance on the spacing b between plates* we have

$$\frac{\Delta b}{b} = \pm \frac{3n}{(1 - n^2)t_\lambda} \% \tag{14-49b}$$

It is interesting to compare these tolerances with the surface contour requirement of a parabolic reflector. A displacement Δx normal to the surface of the reflector at the vertex (that is, a displacement in the axial direction) results in a change in wave path of $2\,\Delta x$. Taking $\delta = \lambda/8$, as for the lens antennas, the tolerance Δx on normal surface displacements of the reflector surface is given by

$$\Delta x = \pm \frac{\lambda}{32} = \pm 0.03\,\lambda \tag{14-50}$$

This is a severe requirement for a large reflector and small wavelength, since it means that the surface contour should be maintained to $\pm\,0.03\,\lambda$ with respect to the vertex and focus as reference points. This places a severe limitation on the allowable warping or twisting of the reflector. In contrast to this, the thickness tolerance on a lens refers only to the thickness dimension. It does not imply that the lens contour be maintained to this accuracy. With a lens, a relatively large amount of warping or twisting can be tolerated, and this is an important advantage of this type of antenna. Furthermore, the lens axis can be tilted a considerable angle τ with respect to the axis through the primary antenna and center of the lens (see Fig. 14-5b) without serious effects.[1]

TABLE 14-3

TOLERANCES ON LENS AND REFLECTOR ANTENNAS

Type of antenna	Type of tolerance	Amount of tolerance
Parabolic reflector	Surface contour	$\pm 0.03\,\lambda$
Dielectric lens* (unzoned)	Thickness	$\pm \dfrac{0.03\,\lambda}{n-1}$
	Index of refraction	$\pm \dfrac{3}{nt_\lambda}\,\%$
Dielectric lens* (zoned)	Thickness	$\pm 3\%$
	Index of refraction	$\pm \dfrac{3(n-1)}{n}\,\%$
E-plane metal-plate lens† (unzoned)	Thickness	$\pm \dfrac{0.03\,\lambda}{1-n}$
	Plate spacing	$\pm \dfrac{3n}{(1-n^2)t_\lambda}\,\%$
E-plane metal-plate lens† (zoned)	Thickness	$\pm 3\%$
	Plate spacing	$\pm \dfrac{3n}{1+n}\,\%$

n = index of refraction
t = lens thickness
t_λ = lens thickness in free-space wavelengths
* $n > 1$.
† $n < 1$.

The above-mentioned tolerances are summarized in Table 14-3. Tolerances for zoned lenses are also listed. These are derived from the unzoned lens tolerances by taking the dielectric lens thickness as nearly equal to

[1] But little difference in radiation-field patterns of an E-plane metal-plate lens antenna is revealed for a tilt angle τ as large as 30° according to patterns presented by Friis and Lewis. See H. T. Friis and W. D. Lewis, Radar Antennas, *Bell System Tech. J.*, **26**, 270, April, 1947.

$\lambda/n - 1$ and the metal-plate lens thickness as nearly equal to $\lambda/1 - n$. If the index tolerance of the lens antenna is zero, then the allowable tolerance on the thickness is doubled, or vice versa. Likewise, if the plate-spacing tolerance of the E-plane metal-plate lens antenna is zero, the thickness tolerance is doubled or vice versa. All tolerances in the table are based on a maximum allowable deviation in path length (from all causes) of $\pm\lambda/16$ from a mean value (total variation $\delta = \lambda/8$). For a larger allowable deviation in path length the tolerances are proportionately greater. For example, if the total variation $\delta = \lambda/4$, the tolerances are doubled.

14-6. *H*-plane Metal-plate Lens Antennas.[1]   A wave entering a stack of metal plates oriented parallel to the H plane (perpendicular to the E

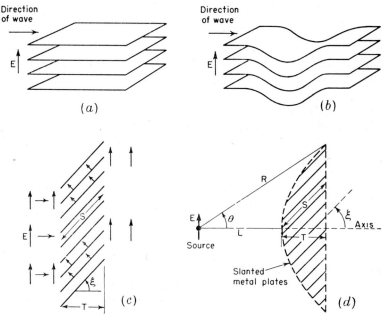

FIG. 14-18.   (*a*) H-plane stack of flat metal plates.   (*b*) H-plane stack with increased path length.   (*c*) Slanted H-plane plates.   (*d*) H-plane metal-plate lens using slanted plate construction.

plane) as in Fig. 14-18*a* is affected but little in its velocity. However, the wave is constrained to pass between the plates so that, once inside, the path length can be increased if the plates are deformed, as suggested in Fig. 14-18*b*. An increase in path length can also be produced by slanting the plates as at (*c*). The increase of path length is $S - T$. Using the

---

[1] W. E. Kock, Path Length Microwave Lenses, *Proc. I.R.E.*, **37**, 852–855, August, 1949.

slant plate method of increasing the path length, an H-plane metal-plate lens can be designed by applying the principle of equality of electrical path length. This type of lens is called an H-plane type since the plates are parallel to the magnetic field (perpendicular to the E plane).

Referring to Fig. 14-18d, the condition for equality of electrical path length requires that

$$R = L + \frac{R \cos \theta - L}{\cos \xi} \qquad (14\text{-}51a)$$

or

$$R = \frac{(n - 1)L}{n \cos \theta - 1} \qquad (14\text{-}51b)$$

where $n = 1/\cos \xi$ = effective index of refraction of the slant plate lens medium

In this case the index of refraction is equal to or greater than 1 so that (14-51b) is identical with (14-7) for a dielectric lens. The index n depends only on the plate slant angle ξ and is not a function of the frequency as in the E-plane type of metal-plate lens. The most critical dimension is the path length S in the lens. This may be affected by a change in T or in ξ. Assuming a maximum allowable variation $\delta = \lambda/8$ in electrical path length, the tolerance in S is given by

$$\Delta S = \pm 0.06 \, \lambda$$

A disadvantage of the H-plane metal-plate lens is that this type of construction tends to produce unsymmetrical aperture illumination in the E plane.

14-7. Polyrod Antennas. A dielectric rod or wire can act as a guide for electromagnetic waves.[1] The guiding action, however, is imperfect since considerable power may escape through the wall of the rod and be radiated. This tendency to radiate is turned to advantage in the *polyrod antenna,*[2] so-called because the dielectric rod is usually made of polystyrene. A 6-wavelength-long polyrod antenna is shown in cross section in Fig. 14-19a. The rod is fed by a short section of cylindrical wave guide which, in turn,

---

[1] D. Hondros and P. Debye, Elektromagnetische Wellen an dielektrischen Drahten, *Ann. Physik,* **32**, 465–476, 1910.

S. A. Schelkunoff, "Electromagnetic Waves," D. Van Nostrand Company, Inc., New York, 1943, pp. 425–428.

R. M. Whitmer, Fields in Non-metallic Guides, *Proc. I.R.E.,* **36**, 1105–1109, September, 1948.

[2] G. E. Mueller and W. A. Tyrrell, Polyrod Antennas, *Bell System Tech. J.,* **26**, 837–851, October, 1947.

is energized by a coaxial transmission line. This type of polyrod acts as an end-fire antenna.[1]

The phase velocity of wave propagation in the rod and also the ratio of the power guided outside the rod to the power guided inside are both functions of the rod diameter D in wavelengths and the dielectric constant[2] of the rod material.[3] For polystyrene rods with $D < \lambda/4$, the rod possesses

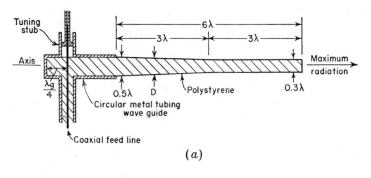

FIG. 14-19.   (a) Cylindrical polystyrene antenna 6 wavelengths long in cross section. (b) Radiation pattern. (After Mueller and Tyrrell.)

little guiding effect on the wave, and only a small fraction of the power is confined to the inside of the rod. The phase velocity in the rod is also close to that in the surrounding medium (free space). For diameters of the order of a wavelength, however, most of the power is confined to the rod, and the phase velocity in the rod is nearly the same as in an unbounded medium of polystyrene. The appropriate rod diameter D_λ in free-space wavelengths is given approximately by

$$D_\lambda = \frac{0.6}{\sqrt{\epsilon_r - 1}} \qquad (14\text{-}52a)$$

In practice, polystyrene rod diameters in the range 0.5 λ to 0.3 λ are used.[4]

---

[1] An end-fire polyrod antenna may be regarded as a degenerate form of lens antenna with an effective lens cross section of the order of a wavelength. See Gilbert Wilkes, Wavelength Lens, *Proc. I.R.E.*, **36**, 206–212, February, 1948.

[2] The relative dielectric constant $\epsilon_r = 2.5$ for polystyrene. See Table 14-1.

[3] G. E. Mueller and W. A. Tyrrell, Polyrod Antennas, *Bell System Tech. J.*, **26**, 837–851, October, 1947.

[4] To transmit the lowest (TE$_{11}$) mode in a circular wave guide, the diameter D of the guide must be at least 0.58 $\lambda/\sqrt{\epsilon_r}$ where λ is the free-space wavelength and ϵ_r is the

The rod may be uniform or to reduce minor lobes can be tapered as in Fig. 14-19a. This polyrod is tapered halfway and uniform in cross section the remainder of its length. The diameter D is 0.5 λ at the butt end and 0.3 λ at the far end. The radiation-field pattern for this polyrod as given by Mueller and Tyrrell is shown in Fig. 14-19b. The gain over an isotropic source is about 16 db.

To a first approximation the radiation pattern of a polyrod antenna excited uniformly along its length may be calculated by assuming that it is a continuous array of isotropic point sources with a phase shift of about 360 $(1 + 1/2L_\lambda)$ deg/wavelength of antenna, where L_λ is the total length of the antenna in wavelengths.[1] The relative field pattern as a function of the angle θ from the axis is then given from (4-139) by

$$E(\theta) = \frac{\sin (\psi'/2)}{\psi'/2} \quad (14\text{-}52b)$$

where $\psi' = 2\pi L_\lambda \cos \theta - 2\pi L_\lambda\left(1 + \frac{1}{2L_\lambda}\right) = 2\pi\left[L_\lambda(\cos \theta - 1) - \frac{1}{2}\right]$

The radiation field could be calculated exactly by applying Schelkunoff's equivalence principle, provided the fields on the surface were known.[2] By this principle the fields at the rod surfaces are replaced by equivalent electric and fictitious magnetic current sheets, and the radiation field is calculated from these currents. However, the fields are not known on the polyrod but an approximate calculation may be made by assuming a field distribution.[3]

The directivity D of a polyrod antenna is given approximately by[4]

$$D \simeq 8L_\lambda \quad (14\text{-}53)$$

and the half-power beam width B by

$$B \simeq \frac{60}{\sqrt{L_\lambda}} \quad (14\text{-}54)$$

where L_λ = length of polyrod in free-space wavelengths

Polyrod antennas may also be of square or rectangular cross section.

relative dielectric constant of the guide. Thus, for a rod of polystyrene ($\epsilon_r = 2.5$) fed from a circular wave guide as in Fig. 14-19a, the guide diameter must be at least 0.37 λ to allow transmission in the metal tube.

[1] This is the Hansen and Woodyard condition for maximum directivity of an end-fire array. See Sec. 4-6.

[2] S. A. Schelkunoff, Equivalence Theorems in Electromagnetics, *Bell System Tech. J.*, **15**, 92–112, 1936.

[3] R. B. Watson and C. W. Horton, The Radiation Patterns of Dielectric Rods— Experiment and Theory, *J. Applied Phys.*, **19**, 661–670, July, 1948.

[4] G. E. Mueller and W. A. Tyrrell, Polyrod Antennas, *Bell System Tech. J.*, **26**, 837–851, October, 1947.

Another possibility is to use a dielectric sleeve of circular or square cross section, the interior of the sleeve being air-filled. In this case the appropriate diameter of the sleeve may be of the order of 1 wavelength.

14-8. Long Wire Antennas.

In the next sections antennas of quite a different type are considered briefly. These are long wire antennas. Their principal application is found in the wavelength range of 1 to 50 meters.

14-9. V Antennas.[1]

By assuming a sinusoidal current distribution, the pattern of a long thin wire antenna can be calculated as described in Chap. 5. A typical pattern is shown in Fig. 14-20a for a wire 2 wavelengths long. The main lobes are at an angle $\beta = 36°$ with respect to the wire. By arranging two such wires in a V with an included angle $\gamma = 72°$ as in Fig. 14-20b, a bidirectional pattern can be obtained. This pattern is the sum of the patterns of the individual wires or legs. Although an included angle $\gamma = 2\beta$ results in the alignment of the major lobes at zero elevation angle (wires horizontal) and in free space, it is necessary to make γ somewhat less than 2β in order to obtain alignment at elevation angles greater than zero.[2] This is because the space pattern of a single wire is conical, being obtained by revolving the pattern of Fig. 14-20a, for example, with the wire acting as the axis.

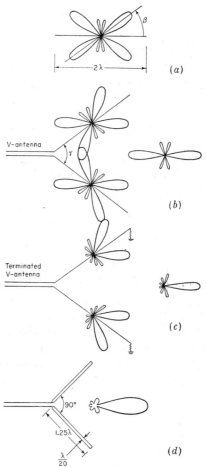

Fig. 14-20. (a) Calculated pattern of 2-wavelength wire with standing wave. (b) V antenna of two such wires. (c) Terminated V antenna with legs 2 wavelengths long. (d) V antenna of cylindrical conductors 1 wavelength long with measured pattern.

[1]P. S. Carter, C. W. Hansell, and N. E. Lindenblad, Development of Directive Transmitting Antennas by R.C.A. Communications, Inc., *Proc. I.R.E.*, **19**, 1773–1842, October, 1931.

P. S. Carter, Circuit Relations in Radiating Systems and Applications to Antenna Problems, *Proc. I.R.E.*, **20**, 1004–1041, June, 1932.

[2]"The A.R.R.L. Antenna Book," American Radio Relay League, Inc., West Hartford, Conn., 1949, p. 174. Gives design charts.

If the legs of the thin wire V antenna are terminated in their characteristic impedance, as in Fig. 14-20c, so that the wires carry only an outgoing traveling wave, the back radiation is greatly reduced. The patterns of the individual wires can be calculated, assuming a single traveling wave as done in Chap. 5.

A similar effect may be produced without terminations by the use of V conductors of considerable thickness. The reflected wave on such a conductor may be small compared to the outgoing wave, and a condition approaching that of a single traveling (outgoing) wave may result. For example, a V antenna consisting of two cylindrical conductors 1.25 wavelengths long and $\frac{1}{20}$ wavelength diameter with an included angle $\beta = 90°$ has the highly unidirectional pattern[1] of Fig. 14-20d.

14-10. Rhombic Antennas.[2]   A rhombic antenna may be regarded as a double-V type. The wires at the end remote from the feed end are in close

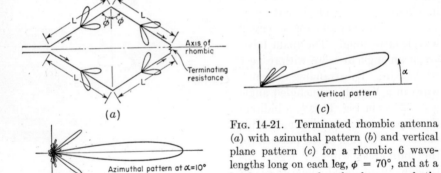

(a)

(b)   Azimuthal pattern at α=10°

(c)   Vertical pattern

FIG. 14-21. Terminated rhombic antenna (a) with azimuthal pattern (b) and vertical plane pattern (c) for a rhombic 6 wavelengths long on each leg, $\phi = 70°$, and at a height of 1.1 wavelengths above a perfectly conducting ground. (*After A. E. Harper.*)

proximity, as in Fig. 14-21a. A termination resistance, usually 600 to 800 ohms, can be conveniently connected at this location so that there is substantially a single outgoing traveling wave on the wires. The length of each leg is L, and one-half the included side angle is ϕ. The calculated

[1]Chap. 4 by A. Dorne, "Very High Frequency Techniques," Radio Research Laboratory Staff, McGraw-Hill Book Company, Inc., New York, 1947, p. 115.

[2]E. Bruce, Development in Short-wave Directive Antennas, *Proc. I.R.E.*, **19**, 1406–1433, August, 1931.

E. Bruce, A. C. Beck, and L. R. Lowry, Horizontal Rhombic Antennas, *Proc. I.R.E.*, **23**, 24–46, January, 1935.

A. E. Harper, "Rhombic Antenna Design," D. Van Nostrand Company, Inc., New York, 1941.

Donald Foster, Radiation from Rhombic Antennas, *Proc. I.R.E.*, **25**, 1327–1353, October, 1937.

patterns[1] of a terminated rhombic with legs 6 wavelengths long are shown in Fig. 14-21*b* and *c*. The rhombic is assumed to be 1.1 wavelengths above a perfectly conducting ground, and $\phi = 70°$.

In designing a rhombic antenna, the angle ϕ, the leg length, and the height above ground may be so chosen that (1) the maximum of the main lobe coincides with the desired elevation angle α (*alignment design*), or (2) so the maximum relative field intensity E for a constant antenna current is obtained at the desired elevation angle α (*maximum E design*).[2] If the height above ground is less than that required for these designs, alignment may be obtained by increasing the leg length. If the height is maintained but the leg length is reduced, alignment may be obtained by changing the angle ϕ. Or as a third possibility, if both the height and the leg length are reduced, the angle ϕ can be changed to produce alignment. Any of these three modifications results in a so-called *compromise design*[2] having reduced gain. If moderate departures from optimum performance are acceptable, a rhombic antenna can be operated without adjustment over a frequency band of the order of 2 to 1.

The pattern of a rhombic antenna may be calculated as the sum of the patterns of four tilted wires each with a single outgoing traveling wave. The effect of a perfectly conducting ground may be introduced by the method of images. For a horizontal rhombic of perfectly conducting wire above a perfectly conducting plane ground, Bruce, Beck, and Lowry[2] give the relative field intensity E in the vertical plane coincident with the rhombic axis* as a function of α, ϕ, L_λ, and H_λ as

$$E = \frac{(\cos \phi)[\sin (H_r \sin \alpha)][\sin (\psi L_r)]^2}{\psi} \tag{14-55}$$

where α = elevation angle with respect to ground
  ϕ = half included side angle of rhombic antenna
  $H_\lambda = H/\lambda$ = height of rhombic antenna above ground
  $L_\lambda = L/\lambda$ = leg length
  $H_r = 2\pi H_\lambda = 2\pi(H/\lambda)$
  $L_r = 2\pi L_\lambda = 2\pi L/\lambda$
  $\psi = (1 - \sin \phi \cos \alpha)/2$
A constant antenna current is assumed, and mutual coupling is neglected.

[1] From A. E. Harper, "Rhombic Antenna Design," D. Van Nostrand Company, Inc., New York, 1941.

[2] E. Bruce, A. C. Beck, and L. R. Lowry, Horizontal Rhombic Antennas, *Proc. I.R.E.*, **23**, 24–26, January, 1935.

* The radiation in this plane is horizontally polarized. However, in other planes the polarization is not, in general, horizontal.

Following the procedure of Bruce, Beck, and Lowry, the various designs may be determined as follows. For the maximum E condition, E is maximized with respect to H_λ, that is, we make

$$\frac{\partial E}{\partial H_\lambda} = 0 \qquad (14\text{-}56)$$

which yields

$$\cos (2\pi H_\lambda \sin \alpha) = 0$$

which is satisfied when

$$2\pi H_\lambda \sin \alpha = n \frac{\pi}{2}$$

where $n = 1, 3, 5, \ldots$
For the lowest practical height, $n = 1$. Therefore,

$$H_\lambda = \frac{1}{4 \sin \alpha} \qquad (14\text{-}57)$$

Equation (14-57) gives the height H_λ for the antenna. To find the leg length, E is maximized with respect to L_λ, obtaining

$$L_\lambda = \frac{1}{2(1 - \sin \phi \cos \alpha)} \qquad (14\text{-}58)$$

Finally, by maximizing E with respect to ϕ and introducing the condition of (14-58)

$$\phi = 90° - \alpha \qquad (14\text{-}59)$$

Substituting (14-59) back into (14-58) yields

$$L_\lambda = \frac{1}{2 \sin^2 \alpha} \qquad (14\text{-}60a)$$

Equations (14-57), (14-59), and (14-60a) then give the height in wavelengths H_λ, the half-side angle ϕ, and the leg length in wavelengths L_λ, for *maximum E* at the desired elevation angle α. This is for a constant antenna current. It does not follow that the field intensity at the desired elevation angle is a maximum for a given power input to the antenna. However, it is probably very close to this condition. It is also of interest that for the maximum E condition the maximum point of the main lobe of radiation is not, in general, aligned with the desired elevation angle.

In the *alignment design* the maximum point of the main lobe of radiation is aligned with the desired elevation angle α. For this condition, E at α

TABLE 14-4

DESIGN FORMULAS FOR TERMINATED RHOMBIC ANTENNAS*

Type of rhombic antenna	Formulas
Maximum E at elevation angle α	$H_\lambda = \dfrac{1}{4 \sin \alpha}$ $\phi = 90° - \alpha$ $L_\lambda = \dfrac{0.5}{\sin^2 \alpha}$
Alignment of major lobe with elevation angle α	$H_\lambda = \dfrac{1}{4 \sin \alpha}$ $\phi = 90° - \alpha$ $L_\lambda = \dfrac{0.371}{\sin^2 \alpha}$
Reduced height H' Compromise design for alignment at elevation angle α	$\phi = 90° - \alpha$ $L_\lambda = \dfrac{\tan\,[(L_r/2)\,\sin^2 \alpha]}{\sin \alpha} \left[\dfrac{1}{2\pi \sin \alpha} - \dfrac{H'_\lambda}{\tan\,(H'_r \sin \alpha)} \right]$ where $H'_\lambda = \dfrac{H'}{\lambda}$ and $H'_r = 2\pi \dfrac{H'}{\lambda}$
Reduced length L' Compromise design for alignment at elevation angle α	$H_\lambda = \dfrac{1}{4 \sin \alpha}$ $\phi = \arcsin \left[\dfrac{L'_\lambda - 0.371}{L'_\lambda \cos \alpha} \right]$ where $L'_\lambda = L'/\lambda$
Reduced height H' and length L' Compromise design for alignment at elevation angle α	Solve this equation for ϕ: $\dfrac{H'_\lambda}{\sin \phi \tan \alpha \tan\,(H'_r \sin \alpha)} = \dfrac{1}{4\pi\psi} - \dfrac{L'_\lambda}{\tan\,(\psi L'_r)}$ where $\psi = \dfrac{1 - \sin \phi \cos \alpha}{2}$ and $L'_r = 2\pi \dfrac{L'}{\lambda}$

*After E. Bruce, A. C. Beck, and L. R. Lowry, Horizontal Rhombic Antennas *Proc. I.R.E.*, **23**, 24–26, January, 1935.

is slightly less than for the maximum E condition. Alignment is accomplished by maximizing E with respect to α and introducing the condition of (14-57). This gives

$$L_\lambda = \frac{0.371}{1 - \sin \phi \, \cos \alpha} \qquad (14\text{-}60b)$$

Substituting (14-60b) in (14-55) and maximizing the resulting relation for the field with respect to ϕ gives

$$\phi = 90° - \alpha \qquad (14\text{-}61)$$

as before. Finally substituting (14-61) in (14-60b) we obtain

$$L_\lambda = \frac{0.371}{\sin^2 \alpha} \qquad (14\text{-}62)$$

Equations (14-57), (14-61), and (14-62) then give H_λ, ϕ, and L_λ for *alignment* of the maximum point of the main lobe of radiation with the desired elevation angle α. Only the length is different in the alignment design, being $0.371/0.5 = 0.74$ of the value for the maximum E design.

The above design relations are summarized in Table 14-4 together with design formulas for three kinds of compromise designs.

An end-to-end receiving array of a number of rhombics may be so connected as to provide an electrically controllable vertical plane pattern which can be adjusted to coincide with the optimum elevation angle of downcoming waves. This Multiple Unit Steerable Antenna,[1] or Musa, constitutes the present-day ultimate for long-distance short-wave reception of horizontally polarized downcoming waves.

14-11. Beverage or Wave Antenna.[2] The electric field of a wave traveling along a perfectly conducting surface is perpendicular to the surface as in Fig. 14-22a. However, if the surface is an imperfect conductor, such as the earth's surface or ground, the electric-field lines have a forward tilt near the surface as in Fig. 14-22b. Hence, the field at the surface has a vertical component E_y and a horizontal component E_x.* The component E_x is associated with that part of the wave that enters the surface and is dissipated as heat. The E_y component continues to travel along the surface.

---

[1] H. T. Friis and C. B. Feldman, A Multiple Unit Steerable Antenna for Short-wave Reception, *Proc. I.R.E.*, **25**, 841–917, July, 1937.

[2] H. H. Beverage, C. W. Rice, and E. W. Kellogg, The Wave Antenna, a New Type of Highly Directive Antenna, *Trans. A.I.E.E.*, **42**, 215, 1923.

* Actually the wave exhibits elliptical cross-field, that is, the electric vector describes an ellipse whose plane is parallel to the direction of propagation. However, the axial ratio of this ellipse is usually very large, and the field may be regarded as being linear. For a discussion of cross-field see Chap. 9 by A. Alford, J. D. Kraus, and E. C. Barkofsky, "Very High Frequency Techniques," Radio Research Laboratory Staff, McGraw-Hill Book Company, Inc., New York, 1947, p. 200.

The fact that a horizontal component E_x exists is applied in the Beverage or wave type of antenna for receiving vertically polarized waves. This antenna consists of a long horizontal wire terminated in its characteristic impedance at the end toward the transmitting station as in Fig. 14-22c. The ground acts as the imperfect conductor. The emfs induced along the antenna by the E_x component, as the wave travels toward the receiver, all add up in the same phase at the receiver. Energy from a wave arriving from the opposite direction is largely absorbed in the termination. Hence,

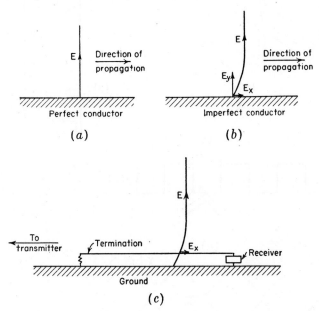

FIG. 14-22.   (a) Wave front over a perfect conductor.   (b) Wave front over imperfect conductor.   (c) Beverage or wave antenna.

the antenna exhibits a directional pattern in the horizontal plane with maximum response in the direction of the termination (to left in Fig. 14-22c). The Beverage antenna finds application in the low and medium frequency range.

14-12. Curtain Arrays.   In short-wave communications the curtain type of array finds many applications. As an example, a curtain type is illustrated in Fig. 14-23a that consists of an array of $\frac{1}{2}$-wavelength dipoles with a similar curtain at a distance of about $\lambda/4$ acting as a reflector.[1] If the array is large in terms of wavelengths, the reflector curtain is nearly equivalent to a large sheet reflector.

[1] H. Brückmann, "Antennen, ihre Theorie und Technik," S. Hirzel, Leipzig, 1939, p. 300.

Several other examples of curtain arrays are the Bruce type of Fig. 14-23b, the Sterba type[1] of Fig. 14-23c, and the Chireix-Mesny type[2] of Fig. 14-23d. The arrows are located at or near current maxima and

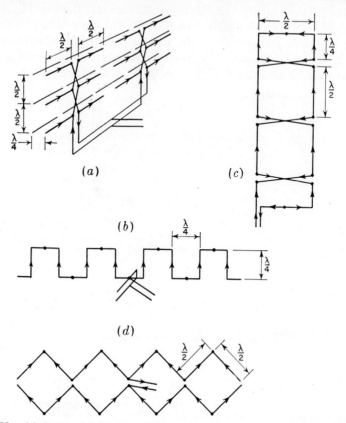

(a)

(c)

(b)

(d)

FIG. 14-23. (a) Array of $\frac{1}{2}$-wavelength dipoles with reflectors, (b) symmetrical Bruce antenna, (c) Sterba curtain array, and (d) Chireix-Mesny array. Arrows indicate instantaneous current directions, and dots indicate current minimum points.

indicate the instantaneous current direction. The small dots indicate the locations of current minima.

14-13. Location and Method of Feeding Antennas. It is interesting to note the effect which the method and location of feeding has on the characteristics of an antenna. As illustrations, let us consider the following cases.

[1] E. J. Sterba, Theoretical and Practical Aspects of Directional Transmitting Systems, *Proc. I.R.E.*, **19**, 1184–1215, July, 1931.

[2] H. Chireix, French System of Directional Aerials for Transmission on Short Waves, *Exp. Wireless and Wireless Eng.*, **6**, 235, May, 1929.

14-24) and also places the stub antenna at d-c ground potential. This is desirable to protect the transmission line from lightning surges.

With reference to solid sheet ground-plane antennas, it should be noted that the radiation pattern of a vertical $\frac{1}{4}$-wavelength stub on a *finite* ground sheet differs appreciably from the pattern with an infinite sheet. This is illustrated by Fig. 14-30. The solid curve is the calculated pattern with a ground sheet of infinite extent. The dashed curve is for a sheet several wavelengths in diameter and the dotted curve for a sheet of the order of 1 wavelength in diameter. With finite solid sheet ground planes the maximum radiation is generally not in the direction of the ground plane but at an angle α above it. In order that maximum radiation be in the horizontal plane, the ground plane may be modified as in Figs. 14-29b or (c). The maximum radiation from

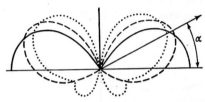

Fig. 14-30. Vertical-plane patterns of $\frac{1}{4}$-wavelength stub antenna on infinite ground plane (solid), and on finite ground planes several wavelengths in diameter (dashed) and about 1 wavelength in diameter (dotted).

the discone antenna is nearly horizontal (normal to axis) over a considerable band width.[1]

By top loading a vertical stub antenna, it may be modified through the

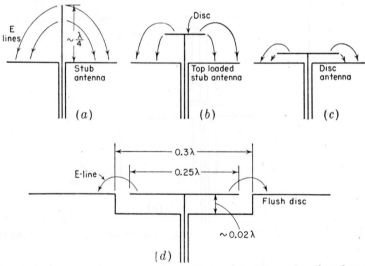

Fig. 14-31. Evolution of flush disc antenna from vertical $\frac{1}{4}$-wavelength stub antenna.

[1] A. G. Kandoian, Three New Antenna Types and Their Applications, *Proc. I.R.E.*, **34**, 70W–75W, February, 1946.

successive stages of Fig. 14-31 to the form in Fig. 14-31*d*. This antenna consists of a circular disc with an annular slot between it and the ground plane. The ground plane is depressed below the disc forming a shallow cavity.[1,2] The radiation pattern of the antenna at (*d*) is quite similar to the pattern for the vertical stub at (*a*).[2]

14-17. Sleeve Antennas. Carrying the ground-plane modification of Fig. 14-29*b*, a step further results in the vertical ½-wavelength sleeve antenna of Fig. 14-32*a*. Here the ground plane has degenerated into a

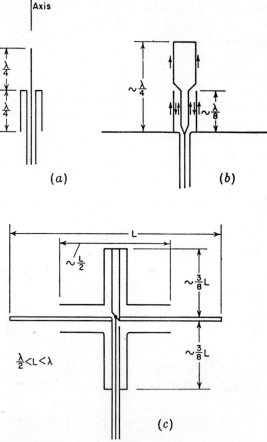

FIG. 14-32.   (*a*) ½-wavelength sleeve antenna, (*b*) sleeve antenna above ground plane, and (*c*) balanced sleeve antenna.

[1] A. A. Pistolkors, Theory of Circular Diffraction Antenna, *Proc. I.R.E.*, **36**, 56–60, January, 1948.

[2] D. R. Rhodes, Flush-mounted Antenna for Mobile Application, *Electronics*, **22**, 115–117, March, 1949.

sleeve or cylinder $\frac{1}{4}$ wavelength long.   Maximum radiation is normal to the axis of this antenna.

Another variety of sleeve antenna is illustrated in Fig. 14-32b.[1]   The antenna is similar to a stub antenna with ground plane but with the feed point moved to approximately the center of the stub.   This is accomplished by enclosing the lower end of the stub in a cylindrical sleeve.   By varying the characteristic impedance of this $\frac{1}{8}$-wavelength-long section, some control is afforded over the impedance presented to the coaxial line at the ground plane.

A balanced sleeve dipole antenna corresponding to the sleeve stub type of Fig. 14-32b is illustrated in Fig. 14-32c.   It is shown with a coaxial line feed and balance-to-unbalance transformer or balun.[1]   This antenna may be operated over a frequency range of about 2 to 1 such that L is in the range from about $\frac{1}{2}$ to 1 wavelength.

14-18. Slotted Cylinder Antennas.[2]   A slotted sheet antenna is shown in Fig. 14-33a.   By bending the sheet into a U-shape as in (b) and finally

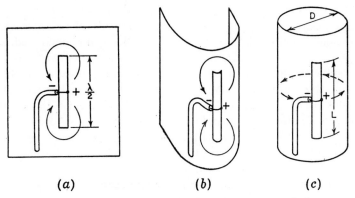

(a)   (b)   (c)

FIG. 14-33.   Evolution of slotted cylinder from slotted sheet.

into a cylinder as in (c), we arrive at a slotted cylinder antenna.   The impedance of the path around the circumference of the cylinder may be

---

[1] Chap. 5 by E. L. Bock, J. A. Nelson, and A. Dorne, "Very High Frequency Techniques," Radio Research Laboratory Staff, McGraw-Hill Book Company, Inc., New York, 1947.

[2] George Sinclair, The Patterns of Slotted Cylinder Antennas, *Proc. I.R.E.*, **36**, 1487–1492, December, 1948.

A. Alford, Long Slot Antennas, *Proc. Natl. Electronics Conf.*, 1946, p. 143.

E. C. Jordan and W. E. Miller, Slotted Cylinder Antennas, *Electronics*, **20**, 90–93, February, 1947.

A. Alford, Antenna for F-M Station WGHF, *Communications*, **26**, 22, February, 1946.

sufficiently low so that most of the current tends to flow in horizontal loops around the cylinder as suggested. If the diameter D of the cylinder is a sufficiently small fraction of a wavelength, say, less than $\frac{1}{8}$ wavelength, the vertical slotted cylinder radiates a horizontally polarized field with a pattern in the horizontal plane which is nearly circular.[1] As a diameter

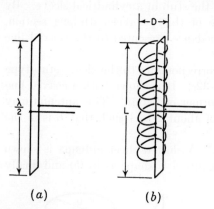

of the cylinder is increased, the pattern in the horizontal plane tends to become more unidirectional with the maximum radiation from the side of the cylinder with the slot. For resonance the length L of the slot is greater than $\frac{1}{2}$ wavelength. This may be explained as follows. Referring to Fig. 14-34a, the two-wire transmission line is resonant when it is $\frac{1}{2}$ wavelength long. However, if this line is loaded with a series of loops of diameter D as at (b), the phase velocity of wave transmission on the line can be increased, so that the resonant frequency is raised.

(a) (b)

FIG. 14-34. Slotted cylinder as a loop loaded transmission line.

With a sufficient number of shunt loops the arrangement of (b) becomes equivalent to a slotted cylinder of diameter D. Typical slotted cylinder dimensions are $D = 0.125\,\lambda$, $L = 0.75\,\lambda$, and the slot width about $0.02\,\lambda$.

This type of antenna has found considerable application for broadcasting a horizontally polarized wave with an omnidirectional or circular pattern in the horizontal plane. Vertical plane directivity may be increased by using a long cylinder with stacked, that is, collinear, slots.

14-19. Turnstile Antennas.[2] Consider two crossed infinitesimal dipoles energized with currents of equal magnitude but in phase quadrature. This arrangement, shown in plan view in Fig. 14-35a, produces a circular pattern in the θ plane since the field pattern E as a function of θ and time is given by

$$E = \sin\theta\cos\omega t + \cos\theta\sin\omega t \qquad (14\text{-}66)$$

which reduces to

$$E = \sin(\theta + \omega t) \qquad (14\text{-}67)$$

At any value of θ the maximum amplitude of E is unity at some instant during each cycle. Hence, the rms field pattern is circular as shown by

[1] George Sinclair, The Patterns of Slotted Cylinder Antennas, *Proc. I.R.E.*, **36**, 1487–1492, December, 1948.

[2] G. H. Brown, The Turnstile Antenna, *Electronics*, **9**, 15, April, 1936.

the circle in Fig. 14-35*b*. At any instant of time the pattern is a figure of eight of the same shape as for a single infinitesimal dipole. An instantaneous pattern is shown in Fig. 14-35*b* for $\omega t = 135°$. As a function of time this pattern rotates, completing 1 revolution per cycle. In the case being considered in Fig. 14-35, the pattern rotates clockwise. Thus, the phase of the field as a function of θ is given by $\theta + \omega t =$ constant, and if the constant is zero by

$$\omega t = -\theta \qquad (14\text{-}68)$$

If the field is a maximum in the direction $\theta = 0$ at a given instant, then according to (14-68) the field is a maximum in the $\theta = -45°$ direction $\frac{1}{8}$ period later.

The above discussion concerns the field in the θ plane (plane of the crossed dipoles). The field in the axial direction (normal to the crossed-infinitesimal dipoles) has a constant magnitude given by

$$|E| = \sqrt{\cos^2 \omega t + \sin^2 \omega t} = 1 \qquad (14\text{-}69)$$

Thus, the field normal to the infinitesimal dipoles is circularly polarized.[1] In the case being considered in Fig. 14-35 the field rotates in a clockwise direction.

Replacing the infinitesimal dipoles by $\frac{1}{2}$-wavelength dipoles results in a practical type of antenna with approximately the same pattern characteristics. This kind of antenna is called a *turnstile antenna*.[2] Since the pattern of a $\frac{1}{2}$-wavelength element is slightly sharper than for an infinitesimal dipole, the θ-plane pattern of the turnstile with $\frac{1}{2}$-wavelength elements is not quite circular but departs from a circle by about ± 5 per cent. The relative pattern is shown in Fig. 14-35*c*. The relative field as a function of θ and time is expressed by

$$E = \frac{\cos (90° \cos \theta)}{\sin \theta} \cos \omega t + \frac{\cos (90° \sin \theta)}{\cos \theta} \sin \omega t \qquad (14\text{-}70)$$

Although the θ-plane pattern with $\frac{1}{2}$-wavelength elements differs from the pattern with infinitesimal dipoles, the radiation is circularly polarized in the axial direction from the $\frac{1}{2}$-wavelength elements provided that the currents are equal in magnitude and in phase quadrature.

A turnstile antenna may be conveniently mounted on a vertical mast. The mast is coincident with the axis of the turnstile. To increase the vertical plane directivity, several turnstile units can be stacked at about $\frac{1}{2}$-wavelength intervals as in Fig. 14-35*d*. The arrangement at *(d)* is called

[1] See Secs. 14-10 to 14-17, for a more detailed discussion of circular polarization.
[2] G. H. Brown, The Turnstile Antenna, *Electronics*, **9**, 15, April, 1936.

a "four-bay" turnstile. It requires two bays to obtain a field intensity approximately equal to the maximum field from a single $\frac{1}{2}$-wavelength dipole with the same power input.

In order that the currents on the $\frac{1}{2}$-wavelength dipoles be in phase quadrature, the dipoles may be connected to separate nonresonant lines of

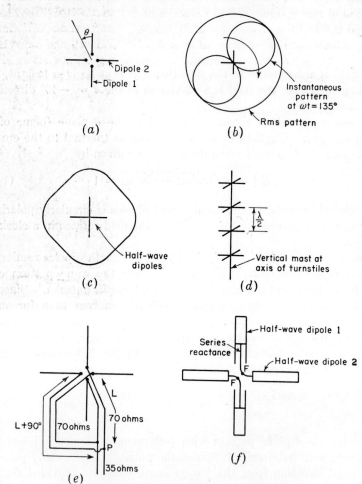

Fig. 14-35. Turnstile antenna arrangements.

unequal length. Suppose, for example, that the terminal impedance of each dipole in a single-bay turnstile antenna is $70 + j0$ ohms. Then by connecting 70-ohm lines (dual coaxial type), as in the schematic diagram of Fig. 14-35e, with the length of one line 90 electrical degrees longer than the other, the dipoles will be driven with currents of equal magnitude and in phase quadrature. By connecting a 35-ohm line between the junction point P of the two 70-ohm lines and the transmitter, the entire transmission-line system is matched.

Another method of obtaining quadrature currents is by introducing reactance in series with one of the dipoles.[1] Suppose, for example, that the length and diameter of the dipoles in Fig. 14-35f result in a terminal impedance of $70 - j70$ ohms. By introducing a series reactance (inductive) of $+j70$ ohms at each terminal of dipole 1 as in Fig. 14-35f, the terminal impedance of this dipole becomes $70 + j70$ ohms. With the two dipoles connected in parallel, the currents are

$$I_1 = \frac{V}{70 + j70}$$

and
$$I_2 = \frac{V}{70 - j70} \quad (14\text{-}71)$$

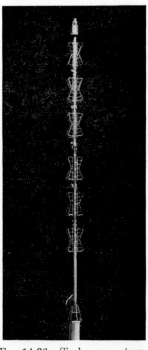

where V = impressed emf
I_1 = current at terminals of dipole 1
I_2 = current at terminals of dipole 2

Thus,

$$I_1 = \frac{V}{99} \angle{-45°}$$

and
$$I_2 = \frac{V}{99} \angle{+45°} \quad (14\text{-}72)$$

FIG. 14-36. Six-bay superturnstile antenna. (*Courtesy Radio Corporation of America.*)

so that I_1 and I_2 are equal in magnitude, but I_2 leads I_1 by 90°. The two impedances in parallel yield

$$Z = \frac{1}{Y} = \frac{1}{[1/(70 + j70)] + [1/(70 - j70)]} = 70 + j0 \quad \text{ohms} \quad (14\text{-}73)$$

so that a 70-ohm (dual coaxial) line will be properly matched when connected to the terminals FF.

In order to obtain a very low SWR over a considerable band width, the turnstile described above has been modified to the form shown in the photograph of Fig. 14-36. In this arrangement, called a "superturnstile," the simple dipole elements are replaced by flat sheets or their equivalent.[2]

[1] G. H. Brown and J. Epstein, A Pretuned Turnstile Antenna, *Electronics*, **18**, 102–107, June, 1945.

[2] R. W. Masters, The Super-turnstile Antenna, *Broadcast News*, 42, January, 1946.

Each "dipole" is equivalent to a slotted sheet about 0.7 λ by 0.5 λ as in Fig. 14-37a. The terminals are at FF. As in the slotted cylinder antenna, the length of the slot for resonance is more than $\frac{1}{2}$ wavelength (about 0.7 λ). The dipole can be mounted on a mast as in Fig. 14-37b. To reduce wind resistance, the solid sheet is replaced by a grid of conductors. Typical dimensions for the center frequency of operation are shown. This arrangement gives a SWR of about 1.1 or less over about a 30 per cent band width, which makes it convenient as a mast-mounted television transmitting antenna for frequencies as low as about 50 Mc. Unlike the simple turnstile there is relatively little radiation in the axial

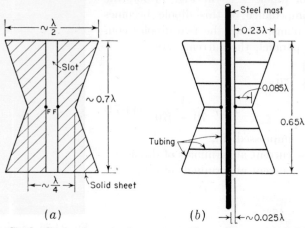

FIG. 14-37. Single dipole element of superturnstile antenna. (a) Solid sheet construction, (b) tubing construction showing method of mounting on mast.

direction (along the mast), and only one bay is required to obtain a field intensity approximately equal to the maximum field from a single $\frac{1}{2}$-wavelength dipole with the same power input. For decreased beam width in the vertical plane the superturnstile bays are stacked at intervals of about 1 wavelength between centers.

14-20. Other Omnidirectional Antennas. The radiation patterns of slotted cylinder and the turnstile antennas are nearly circular in the horizontal plane. Such antennas are sometimes referred to as omnidirectional types, it being understood that "omnidirectional" refers only to the horizontal plane.

As shown in Chap. 6, a circular loop with a uniform current radiates a maximum in the plane of the loop provided that the diameter D is less than about 0.58 wavelength. The pattern is doughnut shaped with a null in the axial direction as suggested by the vertical plane cross section in Fig. 14-38a.

One method of simulating the uniform loop is illustrated in Fig. 14-38b. Here four smaller loops are connected in parallel across a coaxial line. This arrangement is called a "cloverleaf" antenna.[1] Another method is shown in Fig. 14-38c, three folded dipoles being connected in parallel

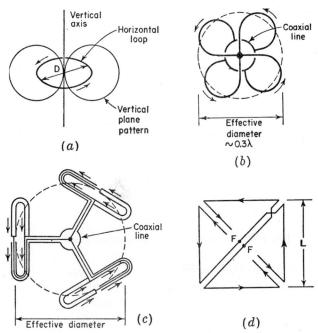

FIG. 14-38.   Circular loop antenna (a) and approximately equivalent arrangements of "clover-leaf" type (b), "triangular-loop" type (c), and square loop, or Alford type (d).

across a coaxial line.[2]   A third method utilizing a square loop is illustrated in Fig. 14-38d.[3]   The terminals are at *FF*.   The side length *L* may be of the order of $\frac{1}{4}$ wavelength.   A single equivalent loop or bay of any of these types produces approximately the same field intensity as the maximum field from a single $\frac{1}{2}$-wavelength dipole with the same power input. For increased directivity in the vertical plane, several loops may be stacked, forming a multibay arrangement.

14-21. Circularly Polarized Antennas.   Circularly polarized radiation may be produced with various antennas.   The axial mode helical antenna

---

[1] P. H. Smith, Cloverleaf Antenna for FM Broadcasting, *Proc. I.R.E.*, **35**, 1556–1563, December, 1947.

[2] A. G. Kandoian and R. A. Felsenheld, Triangular High-band TV Loop Antenna System, *Communications*, **29**, 16–18, August, 1949.

[3] A. Alford and A. G. Kandoian, Ultra-high Frequency Loop Antennas, *Trans. A.I.E.E.*, **59**, 843–848, 1940.

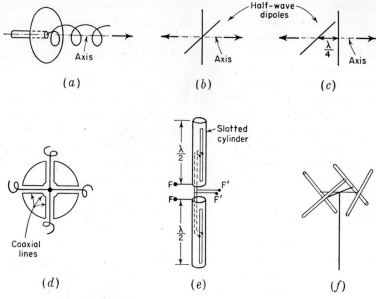

FIG. 14-39.   Antenna types for circular polarization.

(Fig. 14-39a) is a simple, effective type of antenna for generating circular polarization. The helix is discussed in Chap. 7. Circular polarization may also be produced in the axial direction from a pair of crossed $\frac{1}{2}$-wavelength dipoles with equal currents in phase quadrature (Fig. 14-39b). This was mentioned in connection with the turnstile antenna. If radiation in one axial direction is right circularly polarized, it is left circularly polarized in the opposite axial direction.

A third type of circularly polarized antenna consists of two in-phase crossed dipoles separated in space by $\frac{1}{4}$ wavelength as in Fig. 14-39c. With this arrangement the type of circular polarization is the same in both axial directions.

Any of these three arrangements can serve as a primary antenna that illuminates a parabolic reflector. Or they can be placed within a circular wave guide so as to generate a circularly polarized TE_{11} mode wave. By flaring the guide out into a conical horn, a circularly polarized beam can be produced.

Another technique by which a circularly polarized beam may be obtained with a parabolic reflector of large focal length with respect to the diameter is with the aid of a metal grid or grating of parallel wires spaced $\frac{1}{8}$ wavelength from the reflector and oriented at 45° with respect to the plane of polarization of the wave from the primary antenna. The primary antenna in this case is linearly polarized.

Three arrangements for producing an omnidirectional pattern of circularly polarized radiation are illustrated by Figs. 14-39d, (e), and (f). At (e) four short axial mode helices of the same type are disposed around a metal cylinder with axis vertical and fed in phase from a central coaxial line.[1] In the system at (e) vertically polarized omnidirectional radiation is obtained from two vertical $\frac{1}{2}$-wavelength cylinders when fed at FF and horizontally polarized omnidirectional radiation is obtained from the slots fed at $F'F'$. By adjusting the power and phasing to the two sets of terminals so that the vertically polarized and horizontally polarized fields are equal in magnitude and in phase quadrature, a circularly polarized omnidirectional pattern is produced.[2] At (f) four in-phase $\frac{1}{2}$-wavelength dipoles are mounted around the circumference of an imaginary circle about $\frac{1}{3}$ wavelength in diameter.[3] Each dipole is inclined to the horizontal plane as suggested in the figure.

In general, any linearly polarized wave can be transformed to an elliptically or circularly polarized wave, or vice versa, by means of a wave polarizer.[4] For example, assume that a linearly polarized wave is traveling in the negative z direction and that the plane of polarization is at a 45° angle with respect to the positive x axis (Fig. 14-40). Suppose that this wave is incident on a large grating of many dielectric slabs of depth L with air spaces between. A

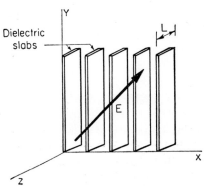

Fig. 14-40. Wave polarizer.

section of this grating is shown in Fig. 14-40. The slab spacing (in x direction) is assumed to be a small part of a wavelength.

The incident electric field **E** can be resolved into two components, one parallel to the x axis (E_x) and the other parallel to the y axis (E_y). That is, $\mathbf{E} = \mathbf{i}E_x + \mathbf{j}E_y$. The x component (E_x) will be relatively unaffected by the slabs. However, E_y will be retarded (velocity reduced). If the depth L of the slabs is just sufficient to retard E_y by 90° in time phase behind E_x, the wave emerging from the back side of the slabs will be cir-

[1] J. D. Kraus, Helical Beam Antenna for Wide-band Applications, *Proc. I.R.E.*, **36**, 1236–1242, October, 1948.

[2] C. E. Smith and R. A. Fouty, Circular Polarization in F-M Broadcasting, *Electronics*, **21**, 103–107, September, 1948.

[3] G. H. Brown and O. M. Woodward, Jr., Circularly-polarized Omnidirectional Antenna, *RCA Rev.*, **8**, 259–269, June, 1947.

[4] F. Braun, "Elektrische Schwingungen und drahtlose Telegraphie," *Jahrbuch der drahtlosen Telegraphie und Telephonie*, Vol. 4, No. 1, 1910, p. 17.

cularly polarized if $|E_x| = |E_y|$. Viewing the approaching wave from a point on the negative z axis, the **E** vector rotates clockwise.

If the depth of the slabs is increased to $2L$, the wave emerging from the back side will again be linearly polarized since E_x and E_y are in opposite phase, but **E** is at a negative angle of 45° with respect to the positive x axis. Increasing the slab depth to $3L$ makes the emerging wave circularly polarized but this time with a counterclockwise rotation direction for **E** (as viewed from a point on the negative z axis). Finally, if the slab depth is increased to $4L$, the emerging wave is linearly polarized at a slant angle of 45° the same as the incident wave. The dielectric grating in this example behaves similar to the atomic planes of a uniaxial crystal, such as calcite or rutile, to the propagation of light. For such crystals the velocity of propagation of light, linearly polarized parallel to the optic axis, is different than the velocity for light, linearly polarized perpendicular to the optic axis.

14-22. Receiving vs. Transmitting Considerations. According to the principle of reciprocity the field pattern of an antenna is the same for reception as for transmission. However, it does not always follow that because a particular antenna is desirable for a given transmitting application it is also desirable for reception. In transmission the main objective is usually to obtain the largest field intensity possible at the point or points of reception. To this end, high efficiency and gain are desirable. In reception, on the other hand, the primary requirement is usually a large signal-to-noise ratio. Thus, although high efficiency and also gain may be desirable, they are important only insofar as they improve the signal-to-noise ratio. As an example, a receiving antenna with the pattern of Fig. 14-41a may be preferable to a higher gain antenna with

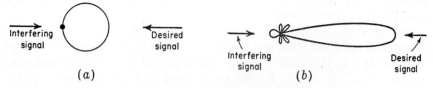

FIG. 14-41.   Patterns for discussion on receiving antennas.

the more directional pattern of Fig. 14-41b, if there is an interfering signal or noise arriving from the back direction as indicated. Although the gain of the antenna with the pattern at (a) is less, it may provide a much higher signal-to-noise ratio since its pattern has a null directed toward the source of the noise or interference.

However, by way of contrast suppose that circuit noise in the receiver is the limiting factor. Then high antenna gain and efficiency would be important in order to raise the signal-to-noise ratio.

There is a special class of receiving antennas that finds application in direction finding. The directional characteristic of the antenna is employed to determine the direction of arrival of the radio wave. If the signal-to-noise ratio is high, a null in the field pattern may be used to find the direction of arrival.[1] With a low signal-to-noise ratio, however, the maximum of the main lobe may provide a more satisfactory indication.[2]

14-23. Band-width Considerations. The useful band width of an antenna depends, in general, on both its pattern and impedance characteristics. In thin dipole antennas the band width is usually determined by the impedance variation since the pattern changes less rapidly.[3] However, with very thick cylindrical antennas or biconical antennas of considerable cone angle, the impedance characteristics may be satisfactory over so wide a band width that the pattern variation determines one or both of the frequency limits. The pattern may also determine the useful band width of horn antennas, metal-plate lens antennas, or zoned lens antennas.

If the acceptable band width for pattern exceeds that for impedance, the band width can be arbitrarily specified by the frequency limits F_1 and F_2 at which the SWR on the transmission line exceeds an acceptable value. What is acceptable varies widely depending on the application. In some cases the SWR must be close to unity. In others it may be as high as 10 to 1 or higher. The frequency band width can be specified as the ratio of $F_2 - F_1$ to F_0 or in per cent as

$$\frac{F_2 - F_1}{F_0} \times 100$$

where F_0 = the center or design frequency

The band width due to the impedance can also be specified (if the band width is small) in terms of its reciprocal or Q at F_0 where

$$Q = 2\pi \frac{\text{total energy stored by antenna}}{\text{energy dissipated or radiated per cycle}}$$

In some instances an attempt is made to obtain as much gain as possible from an antenna of given physical size[4] or conversely to obtain a given

[1] R. Keen, "Wireless Direction Finding," Iliffe and Sons, Ltd., London, 1938.
D. S. Bond, "Radio Direction Finders," McGraw-Hill Book Company, Inc., New York, 1944.
[2] Chap. 9, A. Alford, J. D. Kraus, and E. C. Barkofsky, "Very High Frequency Techniques," Radio Research Laboratory Staff, McGraw-Hill Book Company, Inc., New York, 1947.
[3] A dipole $\frac{1}{2}$ wavelength long has a half-power beam width of 78°. If the frequency is reduced so that the dipole length approaches an infinitesimal fraction of a wavelength, the beam width only increases from 78° to 90°, while if the frequency is doubled so that the dipole is 1 wavelength long the beam width decreases from 78° to about 47°.
[4] That is, a high gain-to-size ratio.

gain with as small an antenna as possible. Such attempts generally reduce the band width of the antenna and also decrease its radiating efficiency. This effect was discussed in Chap. 11 where it was pointed out that a spacing of less than about $\frac{1}{10}$ wavelength between parallel out-of-phase $\frac{1}{2}$-wavelength elements is usually impractical because of reduced band width and efficiency. The rapidity with which the band width and efficiency fall off if the gain-to-size ratio is increased too far has been emphasized by Chu[1] and by Taylor.[2] The limitations imposed are particularly severe for arrays that are large in terms of the wavelength, and it may be concluded that it is impractical to attempt any appreciable increase in directivity with a large broadside array or aperture of fixed size over that given with a uniform aperture distribution.

14-24. Matching Arrangements. Impedance matching between a transmission line and antenna may be accomplished in various ways.[3] As illustrations, several methods for matching a transmission line to a simple $\frac{1}{2}$-wavelength dipole will be considered. Suppose that the antenna is a cylindrical dipole with a length diameter ratio of 60 ($L/D = 60$) and that the measured terminal impedances at 5 frequencies are as follows:

Frequency	Antenna length	Terminal impedance
$1.15F_0$	$L = 0.53\ \lambda$	$110 + j90$
$1.07F_0$	$L = 0.49\ \lambda$	$80 + j40$
$F_0 =$ center frequency	$L = 0.46\ \lambda$	$65 + j0$
$0.93F_0$	$L = 0.43\ \lambda$	$52 - j40$
$0.85F_0$	$L = 0.39\ \lambda$	$40 - j100$

The center frequency F_0 corresponds to the resonant frequency of the antenna. At this frequency the terminal impedance is $65 + j0$ ohms.

The most direct arrangement for obtaining an impedance match is to feed the dipole with a dual coaxial transmission line of 65 ohms characteristic impedance as in Fig. 14-42a. The variation of the antenna impedance referred to 65 ohms is shown by the solid curve in the Smith chart[4] of

[1] L. J. Chu, Physical Limitations of Omni-directional Antennas, *J. Applied Phys.*, **19**, 1163–1175, December, 1948.

[2] T. T. Taylor, A Discussion of the Maximum Directivity of an Antenna, *Proc. I.R.E.*, **36**, 1135, September, 1948.

[3] Only arrangements with transmission-line elements will be described. These are convenient at high frequencies. However, at low or medium frequencies the length of the required transmission-line sections may be inconveniently large so that it is the usual practice to use matching circuits with lumped elements. Radio-frequency transformers, π, T, and L sections are employed in this application. See, for example, W. L. Everitt, "Communication Engineering," McGraw-Hill Book Company, Inc., New York, 1937, Chap. 8.

[4] P. H. Smith, An Improved Transmission Line Calculator, *Electronics*, **17**, 130, January, 1944.

Fig. 14-43. The normalized impedances plotted on the chart are obtained by dividing the antenna terminal impedances by 65. The SWR on the 65-ohm line as a function of frequency and antenna length is presented by the solid curve in Fig. 14-44.

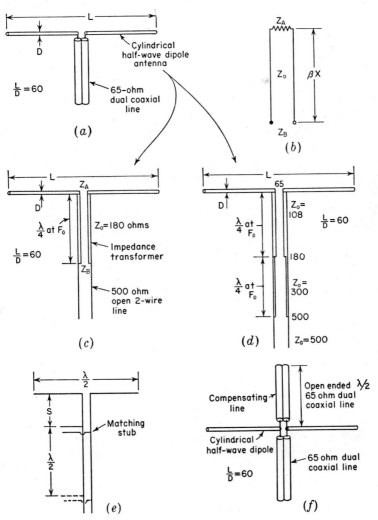

Fig. 14-42. Matching arrangements for cylindrical ½-wavelength dipole antenna.

The dipole antenna may also be energized with a two-wire open type of transmission line. Since the characteristic impedance of convenient sizes of open two-wire line is in the range of 200 to 600 ohms, an impedance transformer is required between the line and the antenna. A suitable

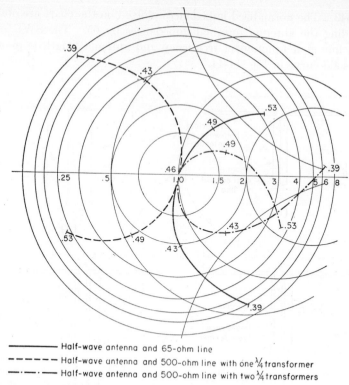

——————— Half-wave antenna and 65-ohm line
— — — — — Half-wave antenna and 500-ohm line with one ¼ transformer
—·—·—·— Half-wave antenna and 500-ohm line with two ¼ transformers

FIG. 14-43. Normalized impedance variation for cylindrical $\frac{1}{2}$-wavelength dipole antenna ($L/D = 60$) fed directly by 65-ohm line (solid), by a 500-ohm line with one $\frac{1}{4}$-wavelength transformer (dashed), and by a 500-ohm line with two $\frac{1}{4}$-wavelength transformers in series (dash-dot).

transformer design may be deduced as follows. Referring to Fig. 14-42b, the impedance Z_B at the terminals of a lossless transmission line terminated in an impedance Z_A is

$$Z_B = \frac{Z_A + jZ_0 \tan \beta x}{Z_0 + jZ_A \tan \beta x} \qquad (14\text{-}74)$$

where $\beta x = (2\pi/\lambda)x$ = length of line, radians
Z_0 = characteristic impedance of the transmission line (since the line is assumed to be lossless, Z_0 is a pure resistance)
Equation (14-74) may be reexpressed as

$$Z_B = Z_0 \frac{(Z_A/\tan \beta x) + jZ_0}{(Z_0/\tan \beta x) + jZ_A} \qquad (14\text{-}75)$$

When the line is $\frac{1}{4}$ wavelength long ($\beta x = 90°$), (14-75) reduces to

$$Z_B = \frac{Z_0^2}{Z_A}$$

or

$$Z_0^2 = Z_A Z_B \qquad (14\text{-}76)$$

or

$$Z_0 = \sqrt{Z_A Z_B} \qquad (14\text{-}77)$$

If Z_A is the antenna terminal impedance and Z_B is the characteristic impedance of the transmission line we wish to use, the two can be matched with a $\frac{1}{4}$-wavelength section having a characteristic impedance Z_0 given by (14-77). The arrangement is shown in Fig. 14-42c. At the center frequency, $Z_A = 65$. Supposing that the characteristic impedance of the line we wish to use is 500 ohms ($Z_B = 500$), we have from (14-77) that the characteristic impedance of the $\frac{1}{4}$-wavelength section should be $Z_0 = 180$ ohms.

This type of transformer gives a perfect match (zero reflection coefficient) at only the center frequency. At a higher frequency the antenna impedance is different, and the line length is also greater than $\frac{1}{4}$ wavelength. The resultant impedance variation with frequency on the 500-ohm line for the $L/D = 60$-dipole antenna and 180-ohm transformer ($\lambda/4$ at F_0) is shown by the dashed curve in Fig. 14-43, and the SWR (standing-wave ratio) on the 500-ohm line is indicated by the dashed curve in Fig. 14-44. It is apparent that this arrangement is more frequency-sensitive than the arrangement with the dual coaxial 65-ohm line.

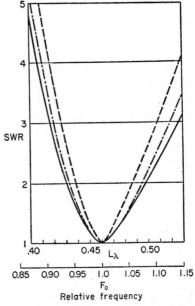

FIG. 14-44. SWR as a function of antenna length L in wavelengths and as a function of the frequency (the resonant frequency F_0 is taken as unity). The SWR curves are for the same three cases of Fig. 14-43.

Instead of making the transformation from the 500-ohm line to the antenna in a single step with a single-section transformer, two sections may be connected in series as in Fig. 14-42d. Each is $\frac{1}{4}$ wavelength long at the center frequency F_0. At F_0 the first section ($Z_0 = 108$) transforms the antenna resistance of 65 ohms to 180 ohms. The second section $(Z_0 = 300)$ transforms this to 500 ohms. The antenna and line are perfectly matched at only the center frequency, as before. However, this two-section arrangement is less frequency-sensitive than the single section. The normalized impedance variation with the two-section transformer is indicated by the dash-dot curve in Fig. 14-43, and the SWR on the 500-ohm line is shown by the dash-dot dotted curve in Fig. 14-44.

If the number of sections in the transformer is increased further, it should be possible to approach closer to the frequency sensitivity with the direct connected 65-ohm line.[1] As the number of sections is increased indefinitely, we approach in the limit a transmission line tapered gradually in characteristic impedance over a distance of many wavelengths.[2] At one end the line has a characteristic impedance equal to the antenna resistance (65 ohms in the example) and at the other end has a characteristic impedance equal to that of the transmission line we wish to use (500 ohms in the example).

Another more frequency-sensitive method of matching a 500-ohm line to a $\frac{1}{2}$-wavelength dipole is with a stub[3] as shown in Fig. 14-42e. The line between the stub and the transmitter may be nonresonant or perfectly matched to the antenna at one frequency with the stub as shown. The stub may also be placed $\frac{1}{2}$ wavelength farther from the antenna as shown by the dashed lines.[4] In this case, however, the resonant line between the stub and antenna is longer, and this arrangement is more frequency-sensitive than with the stub closer to the antenna. In general, it is de-

---

[1] The logarithms of the impedance ratios may be made to correspond to a set of binomial coefficients. (See J. C. Slater, "Microwave Transmission," McGraw-Hill Book Company, Inc., New York, 1942, p. 60.) Thus, the logarithms of the impedance ratios for two-, three-, and four-section transformers would be as follows:

two-sections: 1, 2, 1
three-sections: 1, 3, 3, 1
four-sections: 1, 4, 6, 4, 1

In the two-section transformer of Fig. 14-42d these ratios are followed since

$$\log \frac{108}{65} : \log \frac{300}{108} : \log \frac{500}{300} \simeq 1:2:1$$

[2] C. R. Burrows, The Exponential Transmission Line, *Bell System Tech. J.*, **17**, 555–573, October, 1938.

H. A. Wheeler, Transmission Lines with Exponential Taper, *Proc. I.R.E.*, **27**, 65–71, January, 1939.

[3] F. E. Terman, "Radio Engineers' Handbook," McGraw-Hill Book Company, Inc., New York, 1943, pp. 187–191. Gives design charts for open stub, closed stub, and reentrant matching arrangements.

[4] In general, the distance of the stub from the antenna can be increased by $n\lambda/2$ where n is an integer.

sirable to place matching or compensating networks as close to the antenna as possible if frequency sensitivity is to be a minimum.

With the single stub as in Fig. 14-42e both the length of the stub and its distance S from the antenna are adjustable. The stub may be open or short-circuited at the end remote from the line, the stub length being $\frac{1}{4}$ wavelength different for the two cases. To adapt this arrangement to a coaxial line requires that a line stretcher be inserted between the stub and the antenna. An alternative arrangement is a double stub tuner which has two stubs at fixed distances from the antenna but with the lengths of both stubs adjustable.[1]

The frequency sensitivity[2] of a dipole antenna may be made less than for the $L/D = 60$ dipole direct-connected to a 65-ohm line, as above, in several ways. A larger diameter dipole can be used (smaller L/D ratio) since, as shown in Chap. 9, the impedance variation with frequency is inherently less for thick dipoles as compared to thin dipoles. The thick dipole is desirable for very wide-band applications. If such a dipole is inconvenient, the impedance variation can often be reduced over a moderate band width by means of a compensating network. For example, the frequency sensitivity of the $L/D = 60$ dipole with direct-connected 65-ohm line can be reduced over a considerable band width by connecting a compensating line in parallel with the antenna terminals as in Fig. 14-42f. If this line or stub has an electrical length of $\frac{1}{2}$ wavelength at the center frequency and has a 65-ohm characteristic impedance, the same as the transmission line, the variation of normalized antenna terminal impedance with frequency, as referred to 65 ohms, is shown by the dash-dot curve in Fig. 14-45a. The variation without compensation (antenna of Fig. 14-42a) is given by the solid curve (same curve as in Fig. 14-43). The SWR on a 65-ohm line are compared in Fig. 14-45b for the antenna without compensation (solid curve) and with the compensating stub (dash-dot curve). The frequency sensitivity of the compensated arrangement is appreciably less over the frequency range shown. For instance, the band width for SWR ≤ 2 is about 14 per cent for the uncompensated dipole but is about 18 per cent for the compensated dipole.

The action of the parallel-connected compensating line or stub is as follows. At the center frequency F_0 it is 180° in length. Since it is open

---

[1]These arrangements are discussed in many texts on transmission lines. See, for example,

R. W. P. King, H. R. Mimno, and A. H. Wing, "Transmission Lines, Antennas, and Wave Guides," McGraw-Hill Book Company, Inc., New York, 1945, Chap. 1.

E. W. Kimbark, "Electrical Transmission of Power and Signals," John Wiley and Sons, Inc., New York, 1949, Chap. 13.

[2]Frequency sensitivity as used here refers only to impedance. The pattern of an antenna also varies with frequency.

ended, it places an infinite impedance across the antenna terminals and has no effect. At a frequency slightly above F_0 the line becomes capacitative. Hence, it places a positive susceptance in parallel with the antenna admittance which at this frequency has a negative susceptance.[1] Admit-

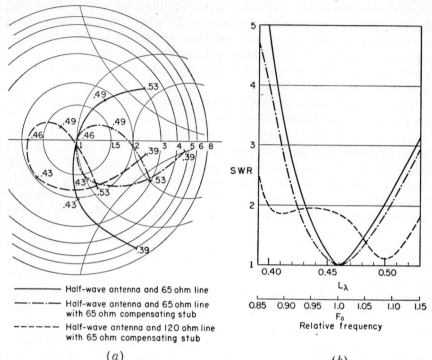

——————— Half-wave antenna and 65 ohm line

———·———·— Half-wave antenna and 65 ohm line
with 65 ohm compensating stub

— — — — Half-wave antenna and 120 ohm line
with 65 ohm compensating stub

(a)   *(b)*

FIG. 14-45.   Normalized impedance *(a)* and SWR *(b)* for cylindrical $\frac{1}{2}$-wavelength dipole ($L/D = 60$) fed directly with 65-ohm line as in Fig. 14-42a (solid curves); with 65-ohm line and 65-ohm $\frac{1}{2}$-wavelength compensating stub as in Fig 14-42f (dash-dot curves); and with a 120-ohm line and 65-ohm $\frac{1}{2}$-wavelength compensating stub (dashed curves).

tances in parallel are additive so this tends to reduce the total susceptance at the antenna terminals, and, therefore, the SWR on the line. At a frequency slightly below F_0 the result is similar, but in this case the stub is inductive and the antenna has capacitive reactance.

The above matching arrangements provide for a perfect impedance

———————————

[1] The antenna impedance at this frequency has a positive reactance. Hence,

$$Y = \frac{1}{Z} = \frac{1}{R + jX} = G - jB$$

where G is the conductance component and B the susceptance component of the admittance Y.

match (SWR = 1) at the resonant frequency of the antenna. Sometimes a perfect impedance match is not required at any frequency, and it is sufficient to make the SWR less than a certain value over as wide a frequency band as possible. For example, the SWR for the ½-wavelength dipole (L/D = 60) may be made less than 2 over nearly the entire frequency band under consideration if the antenna with 65-ohm compensating stub is fed with a 120-ohm line instead of a 65-ohm line. The impedance and SWR curves for this case are shown by the dashed lines in Figs. 14-45a and b.

Although the above discussion deals specifically with matching arrangements between a ½-wavelength dipole and a two-conductor transmission

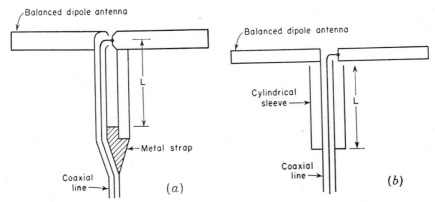

Fig. 14-46. Methods of feeding a balanced antenna with a single coaxial line.

line, the principles are general and can be applied to other types of antennas and to coaxial lines.

Antenna impedance characteristics may also be compensated by series reactances or by combinations of series and parallel reactances.[1] Many of the techniques of impedance compensation are discussed with examples by J. A. Nelson and G. Stavis.[2]

It is often convenient to use a single coaxial cable to feed a balanced antenna. This may be accomplished with the aid of a balance-to-unbalance transformer or balun.[2] One type of balun suitable for operation over a

[1] F. D. Bennett, P. D. Coleman, and A. S. Meier, The Design of Broadband Aircraft-antenna Systems, *Proc. I.R.E.*, **33**, 671–700, October, 1945.

H. J. Rowland, The Series Reactance in Coaxial Lines, *Proc. I.R.E.*, **36**, 65–69, January, 1948.

J. R. Whinnery, H. W. Jamieson, and T. E. Robbins, Coaxial-line Discontinuities, *Proc. I.R.E.*, **32**, 695–709, November, 1944.

[2] Chap. 3, "Very High Frequency Techniques," Radio Research Laboratory Staff, McGraw-Hill Book Company, Inc., New York, 1947, pp. 53–92.

wide frequency band is illustrated in Fig. 14-32c. Another more compact type is shown in Fig. 14-46a. The gap spacing at the center of the dipole is made small to minimize unbalance. The length L may be about $\frac{1}{4}$ wavelength at the center frequency with operation over a frequency range of 2 to 1 or more. With this arrangement a reactive impedance $Z = jZ_0$ $\tan \beta L$ appears in parallel with the antenna impedance at the gap, Z_0 being the characteristic impedance of the two-conductor line of length L. Yet another form of balun is shown in Fig. 14-46b. This form provides a balanced transformation only when L is $\frac{1}{4}$ wavelength and, accordingly, is suitable only for operation over a few per cent band width.

PROBLEMS

14-1. *a.* Design a plano-convex dielectric lens for 5,000 Mc with a diameter of 10 wavelengths. The lens material is to be paraffin, and the F number is to be unity. Draw the lens cross section.

b. What type of primary antenna pattern is required to produce a uniform aperture distribution?

14-2. Design an artificial dielectric with a dielectric constant of 1.4 for use at 3,000 Mc when the artificial dielectric consists of

a. copper spheres

b. copper discs

c. copper strips

14-3. Design an unzoned plano-concave E-plane type of metal-plate lens of the unconstrained type with an aperture 20 wavelengths square for use with a 3,000-Mc line source 20 wavelengths long. The source is to be 20 wavelengths from the lens ($f/1$ lens). Make the index of refraction 0.6.

a. What should the spacing between the plates be?

b. Draw the shape of the lens, and give dimensions.

c. What is the band width of the lens if the maximum tolerable path difference is $\frac{1}{4}$ wavelength?

14-4. Give the answers to parts *b* and *c* of Prob. 3 if the lens is a zoned type.

14-5. Design a maximum E type rhombic antenna for an elevation angle $\alpha = 17.5°$.

14-6. Design an alignment type rhombic antenna for an elevation angle $\alpha = 17.5°$.

14-7. Design a compromise type of rhombic antenna for an elevation angle $\alpha = 17.5°$ but at a height above ground of 0.5 wavelength.

14-8. Design a compromise type of rhombic antenna for an elevation angle $\alpha = 17.5°$ but with a leg length of 3 wavelengths.

14-9. Design a compromise type of rhombic antenna for an elevation angle $\alpha = 17.5°$ but at a height above ground of 0.5 wavelength and a leg length of 3 wavelengths.

14-10. Calculate the relative vertical plane patterns in the axial direction for the rhombics of Probs. 5, 6, 7, 8, and 9.   Compare the patterns with the main lobes adjusted to the same maximum value.

14-11. Derive (14-55) for the relative field intensity of a horizontal rhombic antenna above a perfectly conducting ground.

14-12. Verify (14-57), (14-61), and (14-62) for the alignment design rhombic antenna.

14-13. Calculate the SWR on a 65-ohm line connected to the $L/D = 60$ dipole of Sec. 14-24 over a 30 per cent band width if an open-ended line of 40 ohms characteristic impedance is connected in parallel with the antenna terminals.   The line is 180° long at the center frequency F_0.

14-14. Prove (14-15b).

14-15. *a.* What is the terminal impedance of a ground plane mounted stub antenna fed with a 50-ohm air-filled coaxial line if the SWR on the line is 2.5 and the first voltage minimum is 0.17 wavelength from the terminals?

   b. Design a transformer so that the SWR = 1.

14-16. Calculate and plot the far-field pattern in the plane of a loop antenna consisting of four $\frac{1}{2}$-wavelength center-fed dipoles with sinusoidal current distribution arranged to form a square $\frac{1}{2}$ wavelength on a side.   The dipoles are all in phase around the square.

14-17. Calculate and plot the far-field pattern in the plane of a loop antenna consisting of three $\frac{1}{2}$-wavelength center-fed dipoles with sinusoidal current distribution arranged to form a triangle $\frac{1}{2}$ wavelength on a side.   The dipoles are all in phase around the triangle.

CHAPTER 15

ANTENNA MEASUREMENTS

15-1. Introduction. Most of the discussion in the preceding chapters deals with methods of analyzing and calculating antenna characteristics. In this chapter methods and techniques are discussed for experimental measurements on antennas. There are sections on the measurement of pattern, gain, current distribution, impedance and polarization. The discussion on polarization occupies several sections and includes an analysis of elliptically polarized waves. According to the reciprocity relation, the same pattern will be measured whether the antenna is transmitting or receiving. The same is true of certain other characteristics, so that it will be convenient in some cases to regard the antenna as a radiator and in other cases as a receiver.

15-2. Patterns. The far- or radiation-field pattern of an antenna is one of its most important characteristics. The field pattern is actually a three-

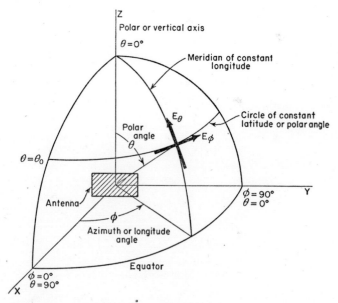

Fig. 15-1. Antenna and coordinates for pattern measurements.

dimensional or space pattern, and its complete description requires field intensity measurements in all directions in space.

A space pattern may be measured according to the following procedure. Let the antenna under test be situated at the origin with the x-y plane horizontal and the z axis vertical as in Fig. 15-1. Then on an imaginary sphere of large radius with the origin at the center, patterns of the θ and ϕ components of the electric field (E_θ and E_ϕ) are measured along latitude circles (that is, circles of constant latitude or polar angle, θ). These patterns are measured as a function of the longitude or azimuth angle ϕ.[1] Measuring such patterns at 10° intervals in latitude from $\theta = 0°$ to $\theta = 180°$ requires a total of 36 patterns, 18 for E_ϕ, and 18 for E_θ. At the poles the measurements reduce to polarization patterns at a point. For more detail, smaller increments are taken in the angle θ. It also may

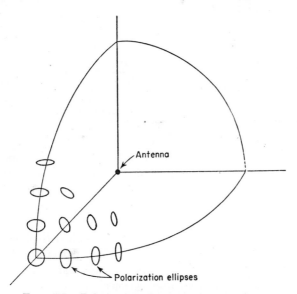

FIG. 15-2.   Polarization ellipses on distant sphere.

be desirable to measure patterns for the field components at angles between the ϕ and θ directions. In fact, if the field from the antenna is, in general, elliptically polarized, it may be useful to measure polarization patterns for different directions and then to draw the corresponding polarization ellipses on a sphere as in Fig. 15-2. The subject of elliptically polarized waves and their measurement is discussed in more detail in a later section.

[1] The angle ϕ is the longitude angle of an imaginary sphere with the antenna at its center. It is also the azimuth angle since the x-y plane is taken to be horizontal.

Although comprehensive pattern surveys such as outlined above are sometimes necessary, it is frequently possible to obtain sufficient information with only a few patterns. For example, suppose that the antenna is a horizontally polarized type with its major lobe of radiation in the x direction as shown in Fig. 15-3a. In this figure the x-y plane is horizontal.

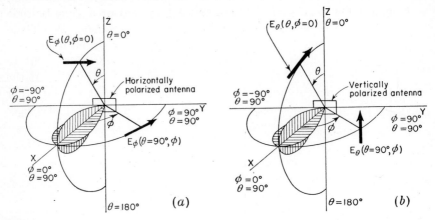

FIG. 15-3. Vertical and horizontal plane patterns for horizontally polarized antenna (a) and vertically polarized antenna (b).

Then two patterns may be sufficient. In one, the ϕ component of the electric field (horizontal) is measured as a function of ϕ in the x-y plane ($\theta = 90°$). This pattern is the so-called E-plane pattern and may be designated $E_\phi(\theta = 90°, \phi)$ as indicated in Fig. 15-3a. In the other pattern the ϕ component of the field is measured as a function of θ in the x-z plane (plane of meridian for $\phi = 0°$). This is the so-called H-plane pattern and may be designated $E_\phi(\theta, \phi = 0°)$. Since these patterns bisect the major lobe of radiation in two mutually perpendicular planes, they may provide sufficient information for many applications.

If the antenna is a vertically polarized type with its major lobe of radiation in the x direction, the patterns are measured as a function of ϕ and θ in the same planes as for the horizontally polarized antenna except that measurements are made of the θ component of the field. Thus, the patterns measured are the $E_\theta(\theta = 90°, \phi)$ and the $E_\theta(\theta, \phi = 0°)$ patterns as suggested in Fig. 15-3b.

Although the dominant radiation from an antenna may be horizontally polarized, some of the minor lobes may be vertically polarized. To observe such cross-polarization in both the vertical (x-z) plane and horizontal (x-y) planes requires the measurement of all four patterns mentioned above. To summarize, these are:

$E_\phi(\theta = 90°, \phi)$ = pattern of ϕ component of electric field as a function of ϕ in x-y plane $(\theta = 90°)$

$E_\phi(\theta, \phi = 0°)$ = pattern of ϕ component as a function of θ in x-z plane $(\phi = 0°)$

$E_\theta(\theta = 90°, \phi)$ = pattern of θ component as a function of ϕ in x-y plane $(\theta = 90°)$

$E_\theta(\theta, \phi = 0°)$ = pattern of θ component as a function of θ in the x-z plane $(\phi = 0°)$

In the case of a circularly or elliptically polarized antenna, the measurements might consist of these four patterns or, for measurements in only one plane, of two patterns, one for each field component (E_θ and E_ϕ).

Field patterns are commonly plotted in terms of relative or absolute field intensity. They may also be conveniently presented as a decibel ratio with the maximum field intensity as the zero or reference level. This type of presentation is particularly valuable with high-gain antennas when accurate information as to the level of minor lobes is needed. See, for example, Fig. 14-16.

15-3. Pattern Measurement Arrangements. In pattern measurements it is usually convenient to operate the antenna under test as a receiver, placing it under suitable illumination by a transmitting antenna as illustrated in Fig. 15-4. The transmitting antenna is fixed in position, and the

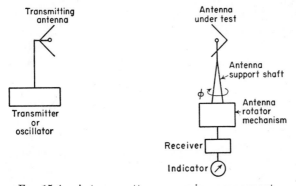

FIG. 15-4. Antenna pattern measuring arrangement.

antenna under test is rotated on a vertical axis by the antenna support shaft. Assuming that both antennas are linearly polarized, the $E_\phi(\theta = 90°, \phi)$ pattern is measured by rotating the antenna support shaft with both antennas horizontal as in Fig. 15-4. To measure the $E_\phi(\theta, \phi = 0)$ pattern, the antenna support shaft is rotated with both antennas vertical.

Indication may be on a direct reading meter calibrated in field intensity, or the meter may always be adjusted to a constant value by means of a calibrated attenuator. Where large numbers of patterns are taken, work is facilitated by an automatic pattern recorder such as shown in Fig. 15-5.

15-3a. *Distance Requirement.* For an accurate far-field or Fraunhofer pattern of an antenna a first requirement is that the measurements be made at a sufficiently large distance.[1] Suppose that the antenna to be

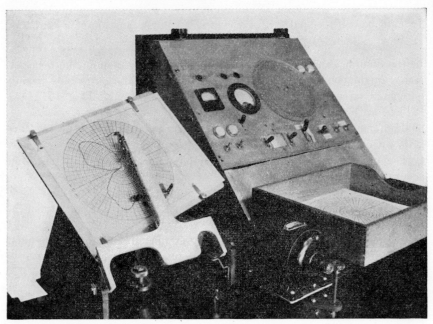

FIG. 15-5. Automatic antenna pattern recorder. The pattern is drawn by a pen on polar coordinate paper. Control equipment is at the right. (*Antenna Laboratory, The Ohio State University.*)

measured is a broadside array consisting of a number of in-phase linear elements as suggested in Fig. 15-6. The width or physical aperture of the array is a. At an infinite distance normal to the center of the array, the fields from all parts of the aperture will arrive in the same phase. How-

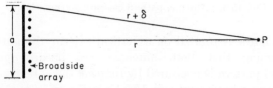

FIG. 15-6. Geometrical relations for distance requirement.

[1]If the distance is insufficient, the near field or Fresnel pattern is measured. In general, this pattern is a function of the distance at which it is measured.

ever, at any finite distance r, as in Fig. 15-6, the field from the edge of the array must travel a distance $r + \delta$ and, hence, is retarded in phase by $(360°/\lambda)\delta$ with respect to the field from the center of the array. If δ is a large enough fraction of a wavelength, the measured pattern will depart appreciably from the true far-field pattern. Referring to Fig. 15-6,

$$r^2 + 2r\delta + \delta^2 = r^2 + \frac{a^2}{4} \tag{15-1}$$

If $\delta \ll a$ and $\delta \ll r$

$$r \simeq \frac{a^2}{8\delta} \tag{15-2}$$

Thus, the minimum distance r depends on the maximum value of δ which can be tolerated. Some workers[1] recommend that δ be equal to or less than $\lambda/16$. Then

$$r \geq 2\frac{a^2}{\lambda} \tag{15-3}$$

In general the constant factor [equal to 2 in (15-3)] may be represented by k. Thus,

$$r \geq k\frac{a^2}{\lambda} \tag{15-4}$$

The phase difference for $\delta = \lambda/16$ is 22.5° since

$$\text{Phase difference} = \frac{360°}{\lambda}\,\delta$$

In some special cases phase differences of more than 22.5° can be tolerated and in other cases less. The table on p. 450 gives the constant factor k [Eq. (15-4)] for three values of tolerable phase difference equal to 10°, 22.5°, and 30°.

According to (15-4) the minimum distance of measurement is a function of *both* the antenna aperture a and the wavelength λ. In the case of antennas of large physical aperture and small wavelength, large distances may be required. For example, consider a 30,000-Mc broadside beam antenna with a physical aperture of 1 meter. Taking $k = 2$, we obtain for the minimum distance $r = 200$ meters.

15-3b. *Requirement of Uniform Field.* A second requirement for an accurate field pattern is that the transmitting antenna produce as nearly

---

[1] C. C. Cutler, A. P. King, and W. E. Kock, Microwave Antenna Measurements, *Proc. I.R.E.*, **35**, 1462–1471, December, 1947.

Maximum tolerable phase difference	δ	k^*
10°	$\dfrac{\lambda}{36}$	4.5
22.5°	$\dfrac{\lambda}{16}$	2
30°	$\dfrac{\lambda}{12}$	1.5

*To reduce the interaction of microwave antennas under test, it is recommended that k have a value at least equal to 2. See Chap. 15 by H. Krutter, "Microwave Antenna Theory and Design," edited by S. Silver, McGraw-Hill Book Company, Inc., New York, 1949, p. 592.

as possible a plane wave of uniform amplitude and phase over a region at least as great as that occupied by the antenna under test. Variations or gradients in the field could be caused by interference of the direct wave

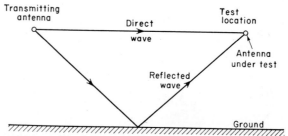

FIG. 15-7. Interference of direct and reflected waves may produce undesirable variations in the field at the test location.

with waves reflected from the ground as in Fig. 15-7 or from other objects. Reflections from walls or buildings can be avoided by selecting an open field or a flat roof as the measuring site.

The effect of the ground reflection may be minimized by using a directional transmitting antenna and placing both antennas on towers as in Fig. 15-8a or near the edges of adjacent buildings as in Fig. 15-8b. With such arrangements the amplitude of the reflected wave is reduced since the groundward radiation from the transmitting antenna is reduced and also since the path length of the reflected wave is appreciably greater than the path length of the direct wave. In a typical case the variation of the field intensity as a function of the height at the test location may be as indicated by the solid curve in Fig. 15-9. The transmitting antenna is directional and is at a fixed height h. There is a considerable region near the height h with a relatively uniform field. If the transmitting antenna

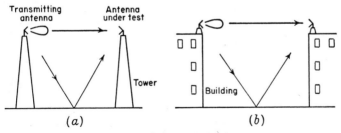

FIG. 15-8. Antenna test setups.

were nondirectional in the vertical plane, a much greater field variation would result at the test location as indicated by the dashed curve in Fig. 15-9.

Sometimes the distance requirement of (15-4) is so large that the required tower height may be impractical. In this case the test antenna

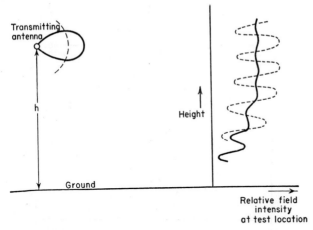

FIG. 15-9. Variation of field intensity with height at the test location with transmitting antenna relatively close.

can be situated in a region of maximum field intensity such as at the height h_1 or h_2 in Fig. 15-10. This arrangement has the limitation that the height of the test antenna must be adjusted for each change in frequency. This may be a considerable inconvenience when testing very wide-band antennas.

Other causes of a nonuniform field at the test location are an improperly directed transmitting antenna or one with too narrow a beam. In making pattern measurements, it is good practice to explore the entire volume to be occupied by the test antenna with a $\frac{1}{2}$-wavelength antenna at each frequency of operation while observing the received field intensity. A

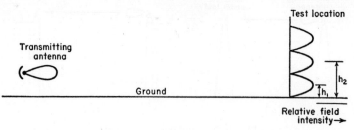

FIG. 15-10. Variations of field intensity with height at test location with transmitting antenna at large distance.

variation of more than $\frac{1}{4}$ db is sometimes taken as the maximum tolerable field variation.[1]

15-4. Phase Measurements. The preceding sections on pattern measurements deal only with the magnitude of the field intensity. To measure the phase variation of the field, an arrangement such as shown in Fig. 15-11

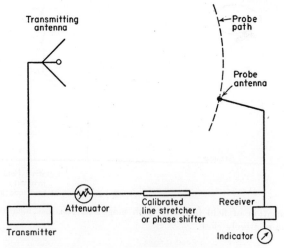

FIG. 15-11. Setup for phase measurements.

[1]See C. C. Cutler, A. P. King, and W. E. Kock, Microwave Antenna Measurements, *Proc. I.R.E.*, **35**, 1462–1471, December, 1947. This reference also discusses the use of fences to reduce ground reflection effects. See also Chaps. 2 and 10, "Very High Frequency Techniques," Radio Research Laboratory Staff, McGraw-Hill Book Company, Inc., New York, 1947.

can be used. The antenna under test is operated as a transmitting antenna. The output of a receiving antenna is combined with the signal conveyed by cable from the oscillator. The receiving antenna is then moved so as to maintain either a minimum or a maximum indication. The path traced out in this way is a line of constant phase. This method was mentioned earlier in Chap. 2.

In another type of measurement the receiving antenna is moved along a reference line. A calibrated line stretcher or phase shifter is then adjusted to maintain a maximum or minimum indication. The measured phase shift can then be plotted as a function of position along the reference line.[1]

15-5. Directivity. The directivity of an antenna can be determined from the measured field pattern. Thus, as defined in Chap. 2, the directivity of an antenna is

$$D = \frac{4\pi}{\iint f(\theta, \phi) \sin \theta \, d\theta \, d\phi} \tag{15-5}$$

where $f(\theta, \phi)$ = relative radiation intensity (power per square radian) as a function of the space angles θ and ϕ (see Fig. 15-1)

Since the radiation intensity is proportional to the square of the field intensity, the directivity expression (15-5) can be written as

$$D = \frac{4\pi}{\iint F^2(\theta, \phi) \sin \theta \, d\theta \, d\phi} \tag{15-6}$$

where $F(\theta, \phi)$ = relative field pattern, that is, the relative total field intensity as a function of θ and ϕ (see Appendix, Sec. 20).

The directivity is determined by the shape of the field pattern by graphical integration and is independent of antenna loss or mismatch.

15-6. Gain. The gain of an antenna over an isotropic source is defined in Chap. 3 as

$$G_0 = \alpha D \tag{15-7}$$

where G_0 = gain with respect to an isotropic source (G without a subscript indicates the gain with reference to some antenna other than an isotropic source)

D = directivity

α = effectiveness ratio ($0 \le \alpha \le 1$)

---

[1] C. C. Cutler, A. P. King, and W. E. Kock, Microwave Antenna Measurements *Proc. I.R.E.*, **35**, 1462–1471, December, 1947.

Chap. 15 by H. Krutter, "Microwave Antenna Theory and Design," edited by S., Silver, McGraw-Hill Book Company, Inc., New York, 1949, p. 543.

Harley Iams, Phase Plotter for Centimeter Waves, *RCA Rev.*, **8**, 270–275, June, 1947. Describes automatic device for plotting phase fronts near antennas.

The constant α takes into account the radiating efficiency of the antenna and the effects of any mismatch. If matching is proper, α is equal to the radiating efficiency k of the antenna. Since the radiating efficiency of many very high-frequency antennas is high (nearly 100 per cent or $k \sim 1$), we have $\alpha = k \simeq 1$, and the measured gain closely approximates the directivity D calculated by the method of Sec. 15-5. The gain of an actual antenna is always less than the directivity. Assuming perfect matching, any difference between the gain and directivity can be attributed to antenna losses.

15-6a. Gain by Comparison. Gain is always measured with respect to some reference antenna. Since an isotropic source is a hypothetical standard, it is common practice to make actual gain measurements with respect to a $\frac{1}{2}$-wavelength reference antenna. The gain G is then

$$G = \frac{W_1}{W_2} = \left(\frac{V_1}{V_2}\right)^2 \tag{15-8}$$

where W_1 = power received with antenna under test
 W_2 = power received with $\frac{1}{2}$-wavelength reference antenna
 V_1 = voltage received with antenna under test
 V_2 = voltage received with $\frac{1}{2}$-wavelength reference antenna
It is assumed that both antennas are properly matched. Making the additional assumption that the $\frac{1}{2}$-wavelength antenna is lossless, the gain G_0 over a lossless isotropic source is

$$G_0 = 1.64G \tag{15-9}$$

The comparison should be made with both antennas in a suitable location where the wave from a distant source is substantially plane and of constant amplitude. The requirements of Secs. 15-3a and 15-3b should be fulfilled.

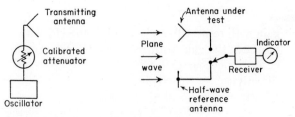

FIG. 15-12. Gain measurement by comparison.

Both antennas may be mounted side by side as in Fig. 15-12 and the comparison made by switching the receiver from one antenna to the other. The ratio V_1/V_2 is observed on an output indicator calibrated in relative voltage.   An alternative method is to adjust the power radiated by the transmitting antenna with a calibrated attenuator so that the received indication is the same for both antennas.   The ratio W_1/W_2 is then obtained from the attenuator settings.

Mounting both antennas side by side as in Fig. 15-12 but in too close proximity may vitiate the measurements because of coupling between the antennas.   To avoid such coupling, a direct substitution may be made with the idle antenna removed to some distance.   If the antennas are of unequal gain, it is more important that the high-gain antenna be thus removed.

If the gain of the antenna under test is large, it is often more convenient to use a reference antenna of higher gain than that of a $\frac{1}{2}$-wavelength element.   At microwave frequencies electromagnetic horns are frequently employed for this purpose.[1]

Short-wave directional antenna arrays, such as used in transoceanic communication, are situated at a fixed height above the ground.   The gain of such antennas is customarily referred to either a vertical or a horizontal $\frac{1}{2}$-wavelength antenna placed at a height equal to the average height of the array.   This gain comparison is at the elevation angle α of the downcoming wave.   If the directional antenna is a high-gain type and any mutual coupling exists between it and the $\frac{1}{2}$-wavelength antenna, the directional antenna can be rendered completely inoperative by lowering it to the ground or sectionalizing its elements when receiving with the $\frac{1}{2}$-wavelength antenna.

In the above discussion it has been assumed that the antennas are perfectly matched.   It is not always practical to provide such matching. This is particularly true with wide-band receiving antennas that are only approximately matched to the transmission line.   In general, another mismatch may occur between the transmission line and the receiver.   In such cases the measured gain is a function of the receiver input impedance and the length of the transmission line.[2]   To determine the range of fluctuation of gain of such wide band antennas with a given receiver as a function of the frequency and line length, the length of the line can be adjusted at each frequency to a length giving maximum gain and then to a length giving minimum gain.   The average of this maximum and minimum may be called the average gain.

15-6b. *Absolute Gain of Identical Antennas.*   The gain can also be meas-

---

[1] Chap. 15 by H. Krutter, "Microwave Antennas," edited by S. Silver, McGraw-Hill Book Company, Inc., New York, 1949, p. 543.

[2] Chap. 10 by Kraus, Clark, Barkofsky, and Stavis, "Very High Frequency Techniques," Radio Research Laboratory Staff, McGraw-Hill Book Company, Inc., New York, 1947, pp. 232 and 271.

ured by a so-called absolute method[1] in which two identical antennas are arranged in free space as in Fig. 15-13. One antenna acts as a transmitter

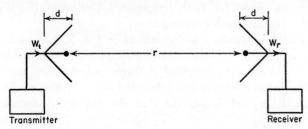

FIG. 15-13. Absolute gain measurements with two identical antennas.

and the other as a receiver. By the Friis transmission formula (Chap. 3)

$$\frac{W_r}{W_t} = \frac{A_{er}A_{et}}{\lambda^2 r^2} \tag{15-10}$$

where W_r = received power
W_t = transmitted power
A_{er} = effective aperture of receiving antenna
A_{et} = effective aperture of transmitting antenna
λ = wavelength
r = distance between antennas

The distance requirement of Sec. 15-3a should be fulfilled. If r is large compared to the depth d of the antenna, the precise points on the antennas between which r is measured will not be critical. Since

$$A_{er} = G_0 \frac{\lambda^2}{4\pi} \tag{15-11}$$

where G_0 = gain of antenna over an isotropic source
and since it is assumed that $A_{er} = A_{et}$, (15-10) becomes

$$\frac{W_r}{W_t} = \frac{G_0^2 \lambda^2}{(4\pi)^2 r^2} \tag{15-12}$$

and

$$G_0 = \frac{4\pi r}{\lambda} \sqrt{\frac{W_r}{W_t}} \tag{15-13}$$

Thus, by measuring the ratio of the received to transmitted power, the distance r, and the wavelength λ, the gain of either antenna can be determined. Although it may have been intended that the antennas be

[1]C. C. Cutler, A. P. King, and W. E. Kock, Microwave Antenna Measurements, *Proc. I.R.E.*, **35**, 1462–1471, December, 1947; also Chap. 15 by H. Krutter, "Microwave Antennas," edited by S. Silver, McGraw-Hill Book Company, Inc., New York, 1949, p. 543.